1711
John Scott
James & William Scott

John Scott &
Sons from 1802

1825
Scott
Sinclair & Co

1825
John Penn

1830

4
& Cunliff

7
lliott & Co

1837
Ditchburn & Mare

1840

1842
John Coutts & Co.

1846
CJ Mare & Co

1848
Closed

1850

1853
Robert Hickson & Co.

1850
Scott & Co
Cartsdyke
Yard

1851
Palmer
Brothers & Co
(Jarrow)

1851
Miller, Ravenhill & Co

2
der & Co

1858
Edward J Harland & Co.

1859
Greenock
Foundry Co

1857
Thames Iron Works &
Ship Building Co Ltd

1855-7
Vernon & Burn

1860

1861
Harland & Wolff.

1860
Wigham Richardson & Co.
Neptune Yard

4
hipyard

1865
**Palmer's
Shipbuilding
& Iron Co Ltd**

Various
changes
in title

3
ole partner

0

r & Co

1872
John Shaw & Co
Engine Works

1873
Coulson, Cooke & Co

1874
CS Swan & Co

1871
Wallsend Slipway

1879
acquired

1879
CS Swan & Hunter
(Wallsend yard)

1878
**Wallsend
Slipway &
Engineering
Co Ltd**

1883
Robert Steele's
Cartside Yard
acquired

1885
Queens Island Sb
& Eng Co Ltd

5

buidling
ng Co Ltd

1888
Harland & Wolff Ltd

1889
**John Penn
& Sons Ltd**

1895
CS Swan & Hunter Ltd

1897
Old Schlesinger
Davis site acquired

1890

1899
**Thames Iron Works
Shipbuilding & Engineering
Co Ltd**

1899
Wigham Richardson & Co Ltd.

1903
63%
shareholding
Continued as
Wallsend
Slipway &
Engineering
Co Ltd

1900

1904
**Scotts Shipbuilding
& Engineering Co Ltd**

**Swan, Hunter &
Wigham Richardson Ltd**

1911
R Stephenson's
Hebburn Yard acquired

1912
Yard closed

1910

THE
BATTLESHIP
BUILDERS

THE BATTLESHIP BUILDERS

Constructing and Arming British Capital Ships

IAN JOHNSTON & IAN BUXTON

Seaforth
PUBLISHING

First published in Great Britain in 2013 by
Seaforth Publishing
An imprint of Pen & Sword Books Ltd
47 Church Street, Barnsley
S Yorkshire S70 2AS

www.seaforthpublishing.com
Email info@seaforthpublishing.com

Reprinted 2014

British Library Cataloguing in Publication Data
A CIP data record for this book is available from the British Library

ISBN 978-1-84832-093-2

Typeset and designed by Stephen Dent
Printed and bound in China

CONTENTS

Acknowledgements

The authors would like to thank the following individuals and organisations for their support in writing this book.

For their expertise and checking draft chapters:
Brian Newman of the Marine Technology Special Collection at Newcastle University for his expertise in marine engineering, shipbuilding and cranes, Nathan Okun for his unrivalled knowledge on armour, John Brooks for fire control and ammunition, Tony Arnold for shipbuilders' finances and especially Vickers at Barrow, Simon Harley for naval personalities and Richard Osborne of the World Ship Society for use of the late D K Brown's photographs.

For guidance and access to key documents:
Jeremy Michell, Andrew Choong and Bob Todd at the plans and photographs department of the National Maritime Museum, the staff at Tyne & Wear Archives, the staff at Glasgow University Business Archives, Frank Bowles and the staff of the Manuscripts section at Cambridge University Library, Jenny Wraight and the staff of the Naval Library, Portsmouth, The National Archives, Wirral Archives, the Mitchell Library Glasgow, Newcastle Central Library, Sheffield Archives, Sheffield Central Library, Barrow Archives.

For assistance on specific points:
Paul Sweeney and Tommy Vaughn of BAE Systems; William Kane; Stephen Dent, John Jordan, Steve McLaughlin.

Abbreviations

ADM	Admiralty series files at The National Archives	KC	Krupp Cemented (armour)
AEW	Admiralty Experiment Works, Haslar	KCB	Knight Commander of the Bath
AFCT	Admiralty Fire Control Table	KNC	Krupp Non-Cemented (armour)
APC	armour piercing, capped (projectile)	lb	pound (weight)
ASI	Admiralty Supply Items	LP	low pressure (cylinder/turbine)
B&W	Babcock & Wilcox (boilers)	MD	Modified (Cordite)
BISCO	British Iron & Steel Corporation	MI	Metal Industries Ltd
BL	breech loading (gun)	MP	medium pressure (cylinder)
BTU	British Thermal Unit	NC	non-cemented (armour)
C	cemented (armour)	NCA	Naval Construction & Armaments Co Ltd
cal	calibres	NMM	National Maritime Museum
CO	Commanding Officer	NRS	Navy Records Society
COW	Coventry Ordnance Works	NSS	National Shipbuilders Security Ltd
CPC	common pointed, capped (projectile)	P	pedestal (mounting)
crh	calibres radius of head (projectile head shape)	pdr	pounder (gun)
DNC	Director of Naval Construction	QF	quick firing (gun)
DNO	Director of Naval Ordnance	R&D	Research & Development
efc	effective full charge (gun life)	RGF	Royal Gun Factory (Woolwich)
E-in-C	Engineer in Chief	RN	Royal Navy
EOC	Elswick Ordnance Company	RNTF	Royal Naval Torpedo Factory
ESC	English Steel Corporation	ROF	Royal Ordnance Factory
grt	gross registered tons (merchant ships)	rpg	rounds per gun
H & W	Harland & Wolff	rpm	revolutions per minute
HA	high angle	SC	Solventless Carbamite (Cordite)
HA/LA	high angle/low angle (dual purpose gun)	SEF	Shipbuilding Employers Federation
HE	high explosive (projectile)	shp	shaft horsepower (steam turbines)
hp	horsepower	SHWR	Swan Hunter & Wigham Richardson Ltd
HP	high pressure (cylinder/turbine)	STAAG	Stabilised Tachymetric Anti-Aircraft Gun
HT	high tensile (steel)	TIW	Thames Iron Works
ihp	indicated horsepower (steam reciprocating engines)	TNT	Tri-nitro-toluene (high explosive)
IWM	Imperial War Museum	V-A	Vickers-Armstrongs Ltd

PREFACE

THE BATTLESHIP WAS FOR LONG considered to be the ultimate weapon of war at sea until technological change rendered the type obsolete. Throughout a century of development, the British Admiralty was responsible for most of the major as well as incremental design iterations of the battleship, notably *Dreadnought* with her all big gun armament and turbine machinery. Britain also constructed more battleships than any other nation and was substantially more dependent on them than any other nation for the defence of the homeland and empire. Although several battleships have survived until the present day, most notably in the USA, not one example of a British battleship survived after 1960. Some compensation for this can be found in the voluminous library of books on the design and operational histories of battleships, an output which shows no sign of stopping. However, none of these books address in any detail the great industrial infrastructure required to build, power, arm and protect these ships. While some economic historians have addressed companies building battleships, such as Vickers and Armstrong, they have understandably concentrated on business aspects rather than manufacturing.

The point driving the production of this work is that the industries that produced these ships have all but disappeared and potentially a remarkable record of achievement with them. These industries employed hundreds of thousands of people in a myriad of concerns big and small in locations spread across the UK. Often household names, these firms were as essential to the defence of the realm as the battleships themselves.

The rapid de-industrialisation of Britain since the 1960s swept all before it and only a few of these industrial sites remain although now in different ownership. The dismantling of individual companies is often an ill-conceived process and many of these companies have sunk almost without trace, at least in the sense that the records describing their activities and achievements that have survived are scant, with very little for notable firms such as Thames Iron Works and Palmers. However, new information, as for example at the Vickers archives in Sheffield where accounting records revealed production as well as financial information, has come to light. Such records have enabled the full story to be told of the armour manufacturers and their profiteering before the First World War – but hidden at the time from the Admiralty.

Inevitably the hit and miss nature of surviving records has resulted in the amplification of some companies over others and this should not devalue the contribution made by companies whose archival legacy is threadbare. This also applies to the present-day understanding of the processes and skills that were required to design and build the large number of components that went into a battleship, most notably from the 1890s when the complex and then state-of-the-art gunnery, protective and propulsion systems evolved rapidly. From the standpoint of the second decade of the twenty-first century, one can but marvel at the scale of resources, organisation, engineering and skill, taken as commonplace in the industrial Britain of 100 years ago.

The authors have endeavoured to bring together as much information as is practically available for this book in recognition of past industrial achievements and the interest that still endures a century later.

Ian Buxton, Tynemouth
Ian Johnston, Glasgow

1: INTRODUCTION

DURING THE LAST HALF OF THE nineteenth century, a number of British industrial concerns involved in the construction of ships and the manufacture of armaments grew substantially in size, mainly through contracts from the British Admiralty and overseas governments. By the early 1900s, through a series of mergers and take-overs, these businesses had coalesced into a formidable naval construction industry comprised of vertically integrated companies employing tens of thousands in their shipyards, engine works, ordnance factories, steel works, armour mills, forges and foundries across the UK.

In 1904, the British fleet was undoubtedly the most powerful in the world, being greater than the combined fleets of the next two largest naval powers, France and Russia. In 1905 the Admiralty decided to proceed with the construction of the revolutionary battleship *Dreadnought*, a stratagem which effectively made their own and all other existing battle fleets obsolete. Much of this 'pre-dreadnought' fleet, as it was rather disparagingly termed, was of very recent construction. Indeed, the very last examples of the type, *Lord Nelson* and *Agamemnon*, were not completed until two years after *Dreadnought*. The eclipse of the pre-dreadnoughts, created at great cost to the country, nevertheless presented an opportunity for the new armaments combines and the Royal Dockyards to construct a new battle fleet.

In many respects there was no alternative to building this new fleet as the concept of a dreadnought type ship was obvious to other naval powers. The Admiralty pre-empted other naval powers and took the initiative to create a new battle fleet comprised exclusively of the dreadnought type battleship and its larger, faster but less heavily armoured variation, the battle-cruiser. *Dreadnought* represented a step change in the development of the battleship because of two main technical changes employed for the first time: a uniform main armament of ten 12in guns instead of the mixed calibre armament typical of contemporary battleships, and steam turbine propulsion machinery instead of reciprocating machinery, all of which conferred significantly greater tactical advantage in the design. These developments like many others associated with armament design and manufacture were pioneered by private industry.

At a different level, the decision to proceed with *Dreadnought* brought with it the risk that British battleship numbers might soon be matched by rival powers. Such risks were not hard to identify as the old order of established naval powers, Britain, France and Russia, was challenged by Germany, the USA and Japan, each of which had emerged at the end of the nineteenth century as industrialised powers with worldwide political ambitions. German naval intentions to build a major surface fleet declared before the construction of *Dreadnought* had begun, represented the most serious political and naval challenge.

Germany had grown rapidly in industrial and economic power since unification in 1871 and by 1900 had overtaken Britain in key industrial measures, such as steel production. Whilst previously British shipbuilders had constructed many merchant ships for German owners, now a large and technically advanced shipbuilding industry, coupled with a system of naval Dockyards and the Krupp armaments firm, had been created in Germany. This challenge had already been demonstrated in the mercantile marine by the construction of large, fast Atlantic liners which had, by 1902, pushed British ships into second position in terms of size and speed on the prized North Atlantic crossing. The architect of Germany's rise as a sea power was Admiral Alfred von Tirpitz whose ambitions mirrored the grandiose impe-

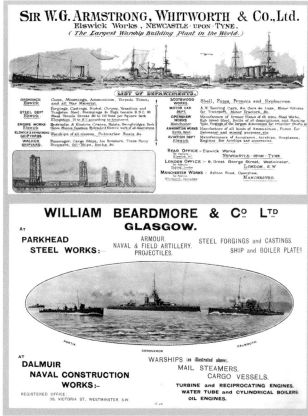

rial aspirations of Kaiser Wilhelm II. In 1897 the enactment of the first of Tirpitz's naval laws made it clear that Germany was determined to challenge British hegemony of the seas.

To make *Dreadnought*'s appearance on the world stage an unchallenged *fait accompli*, she was built in the record time of fourteen months at Portsmouth, drawing on the collective experience of that Dockyard, the armaments industry and turbine manufacturers to create this apparently effortless demonstration of British industrial expertise. A race had begun, later referred to as the Anglo-German naval race, which was as much to do with industrial capacity as it was with political aspiration and domination of the high seas.

The subsequent construction of the battle fleet in just ten years demonstrated the resourcefulness and capacity of British industry. Including *Hood*, laid down in 1916 but not completed until 1920, this totalled fifty-one ships, a remarkable total considering the great volume of merchant and other naval ships produced by the same yards in the same period. This achievement was made possible by the collective efforts of shipyards, engine works, armour and steel works, ordnance factories and a myriad of other manufacturers which drew

deeply from the heart of industrial Britain. The advertisements in any pre-First World War *Jane's Fighting Ships* bear witness to these now long gone businesses.

During this period, when the naval race was underway, industrial capacity was continually extended to meet the unprecedented demands placed upon it. Investment was made in new tools and plant by the companies and later by the Government in the form of munitions factories and finance during the war. By 1918, the scale of British capacity to construct warships stood at an all-time high and one that it would never reach again. At the same time, the need to construct battleships became less important as it was clear that Britain had a significant lead over German numbers.

The end of the war brought with it a wholly understandable but abrupt end to naval contracts. The political map was redrawn and the German fleet, interned at Scapa Flow, was soon to disappear in an act of self-immolation. There was to be no respite for the Admiralty however, as a new naval race between the USA and Japan demanded a response. Since the middle of the First World War, both the US and Japanese governments had backed major fleet construction programmes which by 1918 were

Above: The private firms that contributed towards the construction of the battle fleet were household names as well as major employers in districts throughout the UK. *(Author's collection)*

well established. Compelled by its strategic outlook and with the world's largest navy, the Admiralty was obliged to consider a new round of capital ship construction.

The rapid development of capital ships from *Dreadnought* to *Hood* resulted in ships of exceptional offensive and defensive capabilities on hulls of great length and displacement. Size alone brought an end to the Royal Dockyards' role in the construction of capital ships, no longer able to accommodate such large hulls. Henceforth, the requirement for capital ships would have to be met exclusively by private industry. The same constraints applied also to the private yards however, and those capable of constructing these very large warships were reduced to a handful. Contracts for the first of these ships, four G3 battlecruisers, were placed in 1921 and offered a lifeline to the armaments companies for whom times had become lean with survival threatened. Political intervention in the form of the 1921 Washington Treaty of Limitation prevented this new arms race from continuing and placed a ban on the construction of new capital ships for ten years, subsequently extended for another five. Despite the political and economic wisdom of this initiative, the cancellation of the G3s in February 1922 was a severe blow to a British armaments industry with a capacity now grossly in excess of demand.

In addition to halting new construction, the Washington Treaty required the reduction of fleets to agreed numbers which meant reducing the size of the British fleet to that of the US Navy. And so began the scrapping of much of the battle fleet on which so much effort, material and expenditure had so recently been spent. Only the most modern classes of battleship and battlecruiser were retained as shipbreaking yards extracted monetary values from ship material representing the merest fraction of original construction costs.

Inevitably, the industry that had produced the battle fleet was subject to a fate not dissimilar to that of the once nationally revered ships themselves. Despite attempts at diversification into peacetime production, plant lay idle or underutilised, while many companies haemorrhaged financially throughout the depressed years of the 1920s and early 1930s, forcing rationalisation and restructuring, notably the merger of Vickers and Armstrong at the end of 1927. This period saw the most significant contraction of British heavy industry in modern times and importantly the loss of skilled manpower to

other industries and emigration. Efforts were made to retain key technologies and core manufacturing capacity as strategic assets such as armament design and heavy armour manufacture for which there was little demand in the 1920s, by rationalisation and a trickle of orders for cruisers.

The armaments industry, which had become inextricably linked with the shipbuilding industry through vertical integration, was subject to accusations of fomenting wars and anti-competitive practices in pursuing self-interest at various periods during the history described here. This came to a head in 1935 with the appointment of a Royal Commission on the Private Manufacture of and Trading in Arms to examine such accusations. The Commission came to the realistic conclusion that private manufacture was necessary, and indeed the overwhelming need to re-arm the country in the face of rampant militarism abroad had, by the time the Commission reported in 1936, made it a somewhat moot issue in any case.

Re-armament in 1936 assisted in pulling industrial Britain out of recession. With few if any profits generated during the depressed years, little had been invested on industrial infrastructure, plant and machinery and thus Britain approached the Second World War with an armaments and shipbuilding industry little changed from 1918 in type of facility, albeit smaller in capacity. While the global strategic role of the Royal Navy had not changed, as a consequence of Washington, it was now equal first with the US Navy and battleships, although even then considered by some as an endangered species, were still the primary unit of offensive power. In 1936 after the eclipse of the limitation treaties, and the resumption of battleship building by the leading powers, the Admiralty moved as quickly as possible to place contracts for five units of the *King George V* class. These 35,000-ton ships which had been designed in accordance with Treaty conditions were followed in 1938 and 1939 by four larger *Lion* class battleships. However, the limited resources available to complete these ships meant that two of the *King George V* class were completed late while the *Lion* class, although ordered, could not be built at all because of limitations in main armament construction, other wartime priorities and a lack of shipyard labour. *Vanguard*, last of the British battleships, was made possible only because of the availability of existing but modernised 15in main armament mountings.

2: AN UPWARD TRAJECTORY, 1860 TO 1919

IT IS PERHAPS UNSURPRISING THAT the British shipbuilding industry was for over 100 years the world's largest, given Britain's position as the first developed industrial nation. The rising demand for manufactured products of all kinds, made accessible by the development of railways, stimulated trade and encouraged the rapid growth of industry across the UK. The creation, protection and maintenance of the British Empire and worldwide trade was made possible by the twin elements of seapower, the Royal Navy and merchant marine, and therein lay the foundation and success of the modern private shipbuilding industry from the mid-1800s onwards. This success was based on steam power as a prime mover and iron, later steel, as a constructional material. Prior to this, Britain was a leading builder of wooden ships and it was in this tradition that the Royal Navy's ships were constructed in a number of Royal Dockyards concentrated around the southern half of the country.

However, in the modern era of steam and iron, the Admiralty began to place orders with the new private shipyards which, driven by commercial considerations, were pioneering the latest methods of construction and propulsion in the highly competitive building of merchantmen. By contrast, the Royal Dockyards were steeped in traditional ways of working and much slower to react to change. This was most obviously the case with the ground-breaking, all-iron, steam-propelled warship *Warrior* which entered service in 1861. Her construction was in response to the French *Gloire*, the first seagoing armour-clad, which created great unease at the Admiralty when

they were made aware of her construction in 1858. The contracts for *Warrior* and her near sister-ship *Black Prince* were given to private yards skilled in iron construction and steam propulsion, as such sophisticated ships could not have been built by the Royal Dockyards in the time required, still building only in wood. In making such a swift and decisive response to the French ship, the Admiralty was making use of the already significant resources that private British industry offered.

As the private shipbuilding industry began to expand during the last half of the nineteenth century, more commercial shipyards were encouraged into warship construction, including exports, although the Royal Dockyards retained a major share; figures in early 1890s suggest about 60 per cent. During this period the battleship as a distinct warship type began to emerge through a series of design iterations where various new technologies, armament and protective systems were tried out. This process resulted in the fundamental characteristics that would define the battleship as the ultimate seaborne weapon of offence and the measure by which all navies would come to be assessed.

In 1884 concerns over the preparedness of the navy, its organisation and equipment, began a process of naval reform which reached its climax in 1889 with the passing of the Naval Defence Act. In addition to providing for a large increase in the size of the navy, the Act formalised the 'Two Power Standard' which required the navy to be maintained at a size equal to or greater than the combined strength of the next two largest navies, at that time

Above: The main centres of battleship production in the UK, giving some idea of the distances to be covered when transporting machinery, mountings and guns from the point of manufacture to the shipyards. While material such as steel plate and armour could be moved by rail, coasters were especially adapted to transport gun mountings from Barrow and Newcastle to shipyards and Dockyards. All material and manufactures had to be shipped to Belfast. Chatham and Pembroke are included for pre-dreadnought output and Rosyth for its role in completion work on First and Second World War battleships.

France and Russia. Although this had been the *de facto* ambition for many decades, it had not always been met. Enshrining the Two Power Standard in law effectively committed the Admiralty to a continued process of ship construction. The Act planned ten new battleships and sixty other warships costing £21.5 million, with £11.5 million or 53 per cent planned for the Royal Dockyards.[1] This was complemented by the Naval Works Act of 1895, which financed a large expansion of the Dockyards, including extensions at Portsmouth and Devonport.

A little over a decade after the formal adoption of the Two Power Standard, Germany, unified in 1871, emerged as a significant industrial power, determined to exert political influence worldwide and take what it regarded as its rightful place in the world, as had the British, French and other colonial powers before it. The key to achieving this was seapower and, conveniently, a handbook for how this should be done entitled *The Influence of Seapower Upon History* had been published in 1890 by Alfred Thayer Mahan, a captain in the US Navy. This study used the example of Britain and the Royal Navy in the creation of political influence and empire through seapower. Hitherto

the German Navy, or Prussian Navy until unification, had been small, concerned only with the protection of the relatively small coastline on the North and Baltic Seas. While there was debate about how the German Navy might be utilised to support the German Emperor, Kaiser Wilhelm II, in his foreign policy ambitions, it was with the appointment of Admiral Alfred von Tirpitz to the position of Naval Secretary in 1897 that a policy embracing these aims was formed. The essence of the Tirpitz plan was that the navy should be greatly expanded through the construction of a large fleet, the core of which would be battleships. This plan accorded well with the Kaiser's fascination for battleships and ambition for a battlefleet similar to that of the Royal Navy which, as Queen Victoria's grandson, he had seen and been greatly impressed with on many occasions.

To ensure implementation of the Tirpitz plan, it was passed into the Naval Laws, thereby circumventing the vagaries of an annual parliamentary vote, as was normally the case with the annual British Navy Estimates. In total, five laws were passed by the Reichstag between 1898 and 1912, the first of which envisaged a fleet that included sixteen battleships to be constructed over three years. On completion this would bring the German fleet to a size equivalent to that of France or Russia. The second naval law, passed in 1900, caused unease in Britain as it approved the doubling of the battlefleet to thirty-eight battleships over seventeen years making the German Navy second only to the British. Tirpitz recognised that to achieve German political aims, the British fleet must sooner or later be challenged, if not from a position of overwhelming strength then from one of comparative strength, in which an encounter was bound to cause significant losses in the British fleet thus eroding British seapower and influence.

The German challenge brought with it significant political ramifications in the form of international agreements designed to provide a bulwark against German intentions. The first was the signing of the Anglo-Japanese Alliance in 1902, renewed in 1905, which among other key points stipulated that an attack on one signatory obliged the one to come to the assistance of the other. In time this alliance enabled the British to transfer its Far Eastern Fleet to home waters to counter the German threat. The second was the signing of the Entente Cordiale in 1904, settling many areas of disagreement with Britain's traditional enemy,

France. To this declaration was added the Anglo-Russian Convention, signed in 1907, forming the Triple Entente, the countries that would face the Central Powers, Germany and Austro-Hungary, in the First World War. But Britain recognised that a formal Two Power Standard was no longer affordable, especially as that would now include the United States, although not seen as a threat, so in 1909 changed it to a 60 per cent superiority over the next largest fleet, i.e. Germany.[2]

All of the above events did much to raise awareness of the crucial role that the Royal Navy performed in defending the nation and Empire and underlined the context in which the shipbuilding industry was seen as a vital national resource. As a result of the 1889 Naval Defence Act, primarily intended to counter the growth of the French and Russian fleets, and the Spencer Programme of 1894 of £21.26 million with seven new battleships, the Admiralty had begun a major fleet expansion programme which resulted in thirty-one battleships being launched during the 1890s alone. After 1900, with the threat implicit in the German Naval Laws, a further twenty battleships were launched before the great succession of dreadnought types began in 1906. To achieve

this level of output the Admiralty relied not only on the Royal Dockyards but ever more on private industry. To that extent the Admiralty encouraged the growth of the private shipyards, rewarding additions to plant and capacity with orders. Such orders were prestigious and generally, but not always, profitable, and carried with them that patriotic chauvinism with which the companies were happy to be identified in defence of the nation. The substantial commitment to new ships in the 1889 Act and 1894 Programme, compared with the normal trickle of annual orders, had persuaded many compa-

Above: Like Vickers and Cammells, John Brown was drawn into naval construction as an extension of their forging and armour plate business. This drawing shows the extent of the Atlas Works in Sheffield as they were in 1903. Further extension was made before and during the First World War. *(Author's collection)*

Left: A substantial overseas market existed for British shipbuilders more than happy to construct battleships at lucrative prices for minor navies and emerging navies such as the Japanese. Here the Japanese pre-dreadnought *Katori* is launched at Vickers Sons & Maxim's Barrow shipyard on 4 July 1905, the drag chains about to tighten. *(Author's collection)*

Above: The *King Edward VII* class battleship *Commonwealth* running trials in 1905. By this time, at fifty-two units, Britain had twice as many pre-dreadnought battleships as any of the other major powers. *(Author's collection)*

nies to make major investments in their production facilities in the 1890s. Throughout this period, the private shipbuilding industry had developed a thriving business building warships for governments worldwide. This worked to the benefit of the Admiralty as the differing tactical requirements of foreign governments encouraged new and sometimes better design solutions than those required by the Admiralty, thus allowing greater design expertise to be developed by the shipyards, as well as spreading overhead costs – see also Chapter 10.

In step with the events of the 1890s, the companies that would form the core of future armaments production in Britain began a process of amalgamation and linkages to form the great armaments complexes that would bear the brunt of war production in both World Wars. Companies such as Armstrong Whitworth, Vickers Sons & Maxim, John Brown, Beardmore and Cammell Laird, entered the pantheon of British industrial giants, as major producers and employers as well as household names.

There was one final and enormously significant twist in the development of the battleship which would deliver an order bonanza to the new armament companies. In 1904, Britain had a massive modern battlefleet of over fifty battleships, created at great cost, which meant that industry could expect new construction to be

modest in extent based on replacing the oldest units. However, in the same year, the Admiralty dared to overturn the *status quo* by establishing a Committee on Designs to investigate the construction of a radically new design of battleship and cruiser. Central to these types was the introduction of a uniform main armament of 12in guns in contrast to the then standard mixed-calibre armament. It was also proposed that the propulsion of these ships would be equally radical, utilising new steam turbine technology in place of reciprocating machinery. The 'cruiser', it was envisaged, would be a completely new type, later known as the battlecruiser, where battleship main armament would be placed on a lightly armoured cruiser hull of great length to provide high speed. The idea for an all big gun battleship was not entirely new and other navies, notably the US Navy, were already well advanced in designing such ships. The result of these deliberations by the Committee on Designs was the battleship *Dreadnought* and the three armoured cruisers of the *Invincible* class, all ordered in the 1905–06 Programme.[3]

Often presented as a revolution in battleship design, this development undoubtedly represented a significant leap forward in the evolution of the battleship and rendered the existing battleship fleet obsolete, which were henceforth called pre-dreadnoughts. Moreover, there was a high risk that building these ships would

precipitate an arms race by compelling other navies to build ships of this type. At this time the number of pre-dreadnought battleships built by the three largest navies was Britain fifty-two, the USA twenty-six, Germany twenty-four and France nineteen. The Russian fleet was all but annihilated by the Japanese at the Battle of Tsushima in 1905, while the latter's fleet was growing rapidly but still much smaller than the three largest. Whatever the political and military implications, there can be little doubt that the introduction of *Dreadnought* was interpreted as a very lucrative commercial opportunity by the armaments companies who would be required to build the battlefleet all over again.

Dreadnought did introduce a new era of construction for the fleets of the world and none more so than for a Britain and Germany already sensitised to future conflict and for whom the foundations for an arms race had been laid. To get ahead of the competition, the Admiralty built *Dreadnought* at Portsmouth in secrecy and at great speed. She was presented to the world as a *fait accompli* in December 1906 and thereby accelerated the Anglo-German naval race, a boom in battleship building that would last for the next ten years. By the time the German Imperial Navy had commissioned its first six dreadnought battleships and battle-cruisers in 1909/10, the Royal Navy had completed ten.

When the need for such vessels was most urgent, the Admiralty was able to rely on a vast industry which it had carefully nurtured over preceding years. As before, the Royal Dockyards played a major role in the construction of battleships, although production was now concentrated at just two, Portsmouth and Devonport, both of which had been recently extended and modernised. During the first decade of the century major investment by the private firms had brought several large new shipbuilding facilities into existence such as Beardmore at Dalmuir, Cammell Laird at Tranmere Bay and Armstrong at Walker Naval Yard, as well as considerable new investment at existing yards such as at Vickers, John Brown and Fairfield. During the same period new armour plant was laid down in Manchester and Glasgow, while the Coventry Ordnance Works was established to compete for a share in the construction of heavy naval guns and mountings currently the exclusive domain of Armstrong and Vickers.

Central to the operation of this vast network of manufacturing capacity was the Admiralty which, through the Director of Naval Construction's (DNC) department aided by the Engineer-in-Chief, the Director of Naval Ordnance (DNO) and Director of Contracts, drove the process of ship design, tendering, allocation of contracts, as well as supervision at the shipyards, engine works, armour mills,

Right: The *Orion* class battleship *Monarch* nearing completion at Elswick on 26 July 1911. The turntable and working chamber of her twin 13.5in X mounting, the last to be fitted, is being lowered into position over the barbette by the 150-ton hydraulic crane, at near its maximum capacity. All five mountings and their guns weighing 2800 tons were installed in only five days. The tripod foremast with the fighting top has been hinged downwards to permit passage under the Redheugh, King Edward and High Level bridges at Newcastle. The large gun mounting shops behind are No 24 (right), 7 (centre), 6 (left). *(Author's collection)*

ordnance factories and a myriad of other equipment suppliers. By this means the ships that formed the Grand Fleet of 1914–18 were constructed. Between 1906 and the end of the First World War, fifty-four capital ships were laid down in British yards, of which three were cancelled and one completed in 1920. In the same period, thirty-five were laid down in Germany of which twenty-seven were completed. British fears that they would be out-built by Germany were groundless given the capacity of the British armament industries, the priority that Germany gave to its army and, of course, the political will to finance their construction by successive Governments determined to remain rulers of the waves. At this time, Britain's financial position was relatively healthy from tax revenues and the ability to borrow money, unlike some of its rivals.

BUILDING PROGRAMME YEARS

The political, military and financial imperatives of the day determined how many battleships would be built in each financial year. The last phase of battleship construction produced the *Queen Elizabeth* and *Royal Sovereign* classes, destined to be the longest-serving of all the modern British battleships. In both classes a greater number of ships were intended than actually built. Originally there were to have been six *Queen Elizabeth*s but one, to have been named *Agincourt*, was cancelled in 1914 and the name subsequently allocated to the Turkish battleship *Sultan Osman I* under construction at Armstrong's yard when that ship was taken over by the Royal Navy. Eight *Royal Sovereign* class vessels were originally planned; however, as discussed below, two of them, *Renown* and *Repulse*, were cancelled late in 1914 and the names given to two battlecruisers while a third, *Resistance*, was cancelled outright in 1914.

This highly concentrated period of capital ship construction, lasting a little over ten years, accelerated the development of battleship design at an astonishing rate. Where pre-dreadnought battleships had remained at between 14,000 to 18,000 displacement tons for the last ten years of their development, under the impetus of the Anglo-German naval race, dreadnought battleships in the same time scale increased displacement by 50 per cent. Battlecruisers doubled in displacement.

BATTLESHIPS AND BATTLECRUISERS ORDERED UNDER NAVY ESTIMATES PROGRAMME YEARS

1893–4	*Majestic, Magnificent*
1894–5	*Prince George, Victorious, Mars, Jupiter, Caesar, Hannibal, Illustrious*
1896–7	*Canopus, Ocean, Goliath, Glory, Albion*
1897–8	*Vengeance, Formidable, Implacable, Irresistible*
1898–9	*Bulwark, London, Venerable, Duncan, Russell, Exmouth, Cornwallis*
1899–1900	*Albemarle, Montagu*
1900–01	*Queen, Prince of Wales*
1901–02	*King Edward VII, Commonwealth, Dominion*
1902–03	*Hindustan, New Zealand*
1903–04	*Britannia, Africa, Hibernia* [*Triumph, Swiftsure*]
1904–05	*Lord Nelson, Agamemnon*
1905–06	*Dreadnought, Invincible, Indomitable, Inflexible*
1906–07	*Bellerophon, Temeraire, Superb*
1907–08	*St Vincent, Collingwood, Vanguard*
1908–09	*Neptune, Indefatigable*
1909–10	*Hercules, Colossus, Orion, Lion, Monarch, Thunderer, Conqueror, Princess Royal,* [*Australia, New Zealand*]
1910–11	*King George V, Centurion, Audacious, Ajax, Queen Mary*
1911–12	*Iron Duke, Marlborough, Benbow, Emperor of India, Tiger*
1912–13	*Queen Elizabeth, Warspite, Barham, Valiant,* [*Malaya*]
1913–14	*Royal Sovereign, Royal Oak, Revenge, Resolution, Ramillies*
1914–15	*Renown, Repulse* (both as battleships), *Agincourt, Resistance* (both cancelled). (*Erin, Agincourt, Canada*)
1915–16	*Renown, Repulse* (both as battlecruisers), *Courageous, Glorious, Furious.*
1916–17	*Hood, Anson, Howe, Rodney* (last three cancelled)

Ships in brackets were paid for by other governments or taken over and paid for by the UK government.
Ship construction dates are given on p.133.

Battleships Built by Private Yards and Royal Naval Dockyards 1860–1904

These charts show numbers of battleships completed by yard over the period 1860–1904, i.e. from *Warrior* until the advent of the dreadnought.

Private Shipyards

At the beginning of this period the private yards on the Thames are most numerous yet by the end of the century, only one of these yards was still in business. This was largely because shipbuilding on the Thames was increasingly displaced by competition from the shipbuilding centres emerging in the north, especially on the Clyde and the North East coast. These centres enjoyed numerous advantages, especially plentiful, cheaper labour and materials as well as better access to steel supply and a multitude of ancillary industries that had grown up around these new areas of production. A good example of the redistribution of naval shipbuilding in Britain was made over the years 1905/7 when Yarrow & Co, builders of destroyers and torpedo boats, moved their works at Poplar on the Thames to Scotstoun on the Clyde to be part of the shipbuilding industry there.

British Battleship Construction 1860 - 1904 (Iron and steel)
Private Yards

Company	Location	1860-64	1865-69	1870-74	1875-79	1880-84	1885-89	1890-94	1895-99	1900-04
Armstrong (Elswick)	Tyne							1		
Fairfield	Clyde									1
Laird Brothers	Mersey		2	1				2	1	2
Thames Iron Works	Thames	2			1		1	1		3
Palmer	Tyne	1		2				1		1
Napier	Clyde	2	2							
Thomson - Clydebank - John Brown	Clyde							1	1	
Vickers	Barrow									1
Westwood & Baillie	Thames	2								
Millwall Iron Works	Thames		1							
									Total	**33**

The names most readily associated with battleship construction in the twentieth century such as Armstrong, Beardmore, Brown and Vickers appear late in the period because, with the exception of Armstrong, they were new entrants in the field of naval construction having recently expanded from their core business of steelmaking.

Royal Dockyards

The main trend marking the performance of the Royal Dockyards over this period was the decline of Chatham and Pembroke at the turn of the century despite a consistently high output. The eclipse of these yards as battleship builders was almost certainly because investment required to construct vessels of increasing size then under consideration was concentrated at Portsmouth and Devonport. After the last battleship to be launched at Pembroke, *Hannibal* (1896) of the *Majestic* class, the yard continued to build smaller classes of warship and survived until 1926 when it was closed being surplus to requirements. Chatham launched its last battleship, *Africa*, in 1905 with larger vessels precluded from construction there because of site restrictions. Chatham nevthe-

British Battleship Construction 1860 - 1904 (Iron and steel)
Royal Dockyards

Dockyard	1860-64	1865-69	1870-74	1875-79	1880-84	1885-89	1890-94	1895-99	1900-04
Chatham	1	3	2	3	1	2	2	3	5
Devonport									5
Pembroke			2	1	3	2	3	2	
Portsmouth			1	1	1	1	3	4	2
								Total	**53**

less continued in an important role building submarines until 1984 when it was closed. Deptford and Woolwich Dockyards were early casualties closing in 1869, building only in wood. Devonport, with little or no contribution throughout much of this period, emerges strongly from 1895 onwards to become the main Admiralty construction site along with Portsmouth.

Overseas Construction

The overwhelming trend in the construction of battleships for overseas governments during the 1860–1904 timeframe, was the early domination of this market by British builders, especially those on the Thames, owing to their mastery of steam and iron construction. However, as other nations industrialised, they too developed shipbuilding industries where, over time, they began to build naval vessels for their own governments. Some of these countries, such as France, Germany and the USA then began to compete against British yards for overseas orders. The loss of markets over this period was also mirrored in merchant ship construction where British yards, although collectively still by far the largest ship-

Overseas Battleship Construction by British Firms 1860 - 1904 (Iron and steel)

Company	Location	1860-64	1865-69	1870-74	1875-79	1880-84	1885-89	1890-94	1895-99	1900-04
Armstrong (Elswick)	Tyne								1 Japan	1 Japan 1 Chile*
Millwall Iron Works	Thames			1 Italy						
Thames Iron Works	Thames	1 Russia 1 Turkey	1 Spain 1 Germany	1 Turkey					1 Japan	1 Japan
Napier	Clyde	2 Turkey								
Samuda Brothers	Thames		1 Germany	2 Germany	1 Brazil	1 Brazil	1 Brazil			
Thomson - Clydebank - John Brown	Clyde	1 Denmark								1 Japan
Vickers	Barrow									1 Japan 1 Chile*
*To RN on completion									**Total**	**23**
									Grand Total	**109**

builders in the world, gradually lost overseas market share to competing countries.

Table excludes wooden hulled ships, coast defence vessels, cruisers, frigates and monitors.

Battleships delivered almost twice the weight of broadside through increases in main armament calibre from 12in to 15in while the power of propelling machinery increased from 23,000 to

Right: The prestige associated with naval construction is reflected through money spent on stone carvings and the Italianate design of the portico at Beardmore's new shipyard offices in Dalmuir. *(Author's collection)*

Below: The battle-cruiser *Queen Mary* fitting out at Palmers' yard at Jarrow on 18 March 1913. Her four twin 13.5in turrets have just been installed by Elswick, while her forward boilers appear to have steam up. She left in May for drydocking at Devonport. *(NMM)*

75,000 shp in the case of battleships and from 41,000 to a staggering 144,000 shp in the case of battlecruisers. All of this was delivered at great cost to the country but the evidence suggests this was done with the bulk of the population in support and who, moreover, took enormous pride in the Royal Navy as defender of the nation.

However, during this period of intense construction, the 'battleship industry' revealed a less than savoury side to its activities, accused of anti-competitiveness, of making excessive profits out of a nation soon to be at war and of fanning the flames of jingoism at home and abroad in the service of shareholders. Procurement operated on a regulated basis where the Navy's governing body, the Board of Admiralty, presented an annual budget (the Navy Estimates) to Parliament each March for approval. This budget covered the costs of the naval establishment, a major part of which was the requirement for new vessels. Then as now, Parliament took a balanced view of competing demands on the public purse, allocating funds accordingly. Through its own Dockyards, the Admiralty had a fair estimate of the cost of ship construction and could use this information to

gauge the competitiveness of private tenders. However, in other areas of production such as armour manufacture, the Admiralty had few means of comparing prices, so the opportunity for manufacturers to charge excessive prices existed, as is discussed in Chapter 9.

The system of tendering for hulls and machinery used by the Admiralty ensured that excessive profits could not be made, as there were around a dozen bidders and in most cases the lowest tender won the contract. However, this did not prevent collusion between some companies and the forming of cartels or rings to fix prices, such as was the case in armour manufacture. The five armour manufacturers, Armstrong, Vickers, John Brown, Beardmore and Cammell Laird, all had Krupp licences and agreed a collective price in negotiation with the Admiralty. The surviving financial records show that these companies grossly inflated the price for armour in the years before the First World War, in the knowledge that the Admiralty had virtually no means of establishing the true cost of manufacture. This issue was brought into focus and public attention when an enquiry took place in a House of Commons Select Committee in 1913, as discussed more fully in Appendix 2.

Once the war had started, the time-consuming process of tendering was dispensed with and contracts were placed directly by the Admiralty wherever suitable capacity existed. This method was facilitated by the introduction of the Munitions of War Act in July 1915, which declared all factories associated with war work as 'Controlled Establishments', thus providing a higher level of scrutiny to the Government, including direction of labour. Beginning with the Finance Acts of 1915, the Government introduced an Excess Profits Duty, backdated to the start of the war, intended to stop businesses enriching themselves from the vastly increased volume of Government contracts. The tax on excess profits above pre-war levels was set at 50 per cent at the start of the war and was subsequently raised to 60 per cent and from 1917 onwards to 80 per cent.

False alarm bells were rung on one notable occasion to stimulate orders in a furore about battleship contracts involving the Coventry Ordnance Works. As described on p.76, the Coventry Ordnance Works had been set up by John Brown, Cammell Laird and Fairfield to construct naval guns and mountings in an attempt to break the duopoly enjoyed by Armstrong and Vickers in this complex but lucrative manufacturing business. Naturally, the

Above: With war only days away, the Fleet Review and mobilisation of July 1914 was visible evidence that Britain had a large margin of superiority in battleship numbers over Germany. *(IWM Q220494)*

latter firms were highly resistant to this challenge and, moreover, had reached accommodation with one another regarding the distribution and pricing of contracts. In addition, they held a number of patents covering the design of these mechanically sophisticated mechanisms which they were reluctant to share with what they regarded as the unwelcome Coventry upstart.

Nevertheless, John Brown, Cammell Laird and Fairfield had laid out considerable sums in setting up new works and plant for this enterprise. From the outset, the trading position was woeful, resulting in losses year on year, requiring repeated subventions from the parent companies to the new business. In 1908, the press caught a whiff of concern that the German naval building programme was being greatly accelerated through the commissioning of new plant at Krupp's works in Essen. The managing director of the Coventry Ordnance Works, H H Mulliner, was the source of this information which implied that a greatly increased number of mountings and guns for German dreadnoughts could be built, resulting in Germany eclipsing Britain in battleship numbers. During 1908 this information was taken up by the Parliamentary opposition and the press and came to a head in the following year as the Naval Scare of 1909. The issue compromised the Liberal Government elected on a mandate of defence cuts in favour of social reforms. On 16 March, the First Lord of the Admiralty, Reginald McKenna, introduced the Navy Estimates in the House of Commons and, using Mulliner's information, made a strong case for increasing the number of dreadnoughts to be built. The Prime Minister,

H H Asquith, and others, including Winston Churchill, refuted the notion that Germany had embarked on an accelerated shipbuilding programme. Nevertheless, such was the sentiment in the country that it was decided that four dreadnoughts would be laid down in 1909 and that four additional or 'contingent' ships would follow if warranted by subsequent events in Germany. This compromise proved unpopular and the Government remained under continued pressure to build all eight ships. The campaign for more battleships was taken up by the press and characterised by the slogan 'We want eight, and we won't wait'. On 26 July, the Government relented and announced that the four 'contingent' dreadnoughts would be built. This issue prompted the Australian and New Zealand Governments to offer finance for the construction of two further ships, the battlecruisers *Australia* and *New Zealand*. Although Mulliner's information was found to be incorrect and he was replaced as managing director of the Coventry Ordnance Works later in 1909, the outcome was the first of a series of contracts for heavy gun mountings for the Works starting with the five 13.5in twin mountings for the *Orion* class battleship *Conqueror*.

As events would prove, British preparedness and capacity to build battleships outstripped that of Germany. However, during the last years of the naval race, two examples stand out that illustrate what could be achieved by a finely tuned procurement process and, conversely, how labour shortages and wartime priorities prevented the Admiralty from having all the ships it wanted.

The first concerns the construction of the

battlecruisers *Renown* and *Repulse* which had initially been ordered as battleships under the 1914–15 Programme. Under the direction of the newly re-appointed First Sea Lord, Admiral Fisher, this change was made in December 1914 and demanded that both ships were to be constructed in just fifteen months. For vessels of this size and complexity such a demand was without precedent, the best previously achieved being twenty-four months. Even the record construction in fourteen months of the much smaller *Dreadnought* had benefited from a considerable amount of steelwork preparation and her gun mountings were prioritised over and used material from earlier contracts. Although Fisher's demand on building time was grossly optimistic for such large ships, it did set up an example of superb cooperation and rapid shipbuilding. From the main Admiralty departments concerned, to the armour and gun mounting contractors and the shipbuilders, down to the manufacturers of the smallest item, the entire system was pressured to good effect. In 1915, with so many battleships recently built or building, all concerned in the procurement-construction pipeline knew exactly what to do and how it worked. Even though Fisher resigned in May 1915, it took his pugnacious style to iron out the last vestiges of inertia and deliver these ships in record time.

In contrast to the above, the last capital ship contracts of the First World War proved impossible to complete because the shipyards were short of labour, occupied as they were with work of a higher priority, including merchant ships after the serious losses to U-boats in 1917. Of the four ships of the 'Admiral' class ordered in April 1916, only one, *Hood*, was completed, although the other three survived on the stocks until 1919 in the hope of resumption. Their progress from keel laying in 1916 to suspension in 1917 and outright cancellation in 1919 explains much about a naval construction industry, large as it was, being unable to satisfy all of the demands placed upon it in time of war. That the three sister vessels lingered on the stocks so long highlights a change in Admiralty focus from war with Germany to a post-war world in which Britain would only have one post-Jutland capital ship, *Hood*, against the many new American and Japanese capital ships then under construction. No more battleships were ordered during the First World War, the last of the pre-war orders, *Ramillies* only being completed in 1917.

Below: A midships view of the Fairfield-built *Valiant* passing Clydebank shipyard in January 1916. Large numbers of people, crew and civilian workmen, have moved to the starboard side of the ship to look at ships in the fitting-out basin including the recently launched battlecruiser *Repulse*. (NRS)

THE THREE 'ADMIRALS'[4]

Approval to proceed with contracts for the four 'Admiral' class battlecruisers was given on 11 April 1916 when the First Lord met the Chancellor of the Exchequer to approve the new shipbuilding programme including the 'Admirals' or *Hood* class.[5] One each of the new ships went to John Brown, Cammell Laird and Fairfield. A fourth, to be placed with Armstrong Whitworth, was delayed for two months. In the letter sent to each of the yards on 19 April authorising construction, it was noted that work should: 'proceed at first only at such a rate as will employ a nucleus of men accustomed to heavy frame work, involving the least call on labour and material required by them for the war vessels being rapidly completed for the war and for merchant ships urgently required for carrying cargo.'

The emphasis on warships and merchant

An Example of Rapid Shipbuilding

Fisher had decided in December 1914 that the last two of the *Royal Sovereign* class battleships, on order at Palmers and Fairfield's shipyards, should be redesigned and completed as battlecruisers to take part in his 'Baltic Project'. It immediately became clear that Palmers largest berth was not long enough for the additional 174ft length of the battlecruiser so would have to be re-allocated. It did not take long for Fisher to find that a suitable berth was available at John Brown's Clydebank shipyard and thus the contract for the ship that became *Repulse* was switched there.[6]

To expedite construction Fisher delivered his customary shock to the system by summoning both shipyard managing directors, Thomas Bell and Alexander Gracie, to the Admiralty at the end of December to press the urgency with which these ships were to be built, emphasising this with an interesting turn of phrase: 'I am going to have these ships delivered on time and if you fail me your houses will be made a dunghill and you and your wives liquidated'. He added 'I expect to hear tomorrow that you have started preparations for these ships.'[7] For both shipbuilders and the Admiralty constructors alike it was a cold start with no design, no building drawings, no specifications and just a handful of preliminary calculations. Moreover, any material suitable for the battlecruiser gathered at Palmers had to be transferred to Clydebank and a whole range of contracts made to the order of Palmers similarly transferred to John Brown's name.

Everything that could be done to build the ships in the shortest possible time was investigated. The main armament mountings, now six in total rather than eight for the battleships, had been ordered but had not been started. As they took as long to build as the ship itself, mountings from other ships previously ordered, e.g. *Resolution* and *Ramillies*, were switched to the battlecruisers and newly ordered monitors. To save time designing new machinery, the arrangements for the battlecruiser *Tiger*, also built at Clydebank, were largely duplicated to make use of existing patterns and jigs while the engine and boiler room layout of the new ships would also be broadly similar to *Tiger*. The keels were laid on Fisher's birthday, 25 January 1915, although serious steelwork could not proceed beyond that for some weeks afterwards because of the lack of drawings. Work proceeded on the drawings at the DNC's department at great speed to enable the bottom sections of the hull to be erected but it was not until 12 April that enough drawings, specifications and calculations were completed, with formal Admiralty approval being given on the 22nd.

On 12 March Fisher wired John Brown: 'I hear you have nothing like the number of men on *Repulse* that are required to complete her by the desired date. I had hoped that you would let nothing whatever prevent your pushing her on with the utmost speed possible. Please reply'. When the company replied that labour directed to other naval contracts was partly to blame, this resulted in a determined effort by the Admiralty to concentrate as much labour on the two battlecruisers as possible. This included taking 500 men of the steel trades from *Ramillies* at Dalmuir and splitting them between the battlecruiser contracts at John Brown and Fairfield. This indicates that the Admiralty was already intervening in the direction of labour prior to the passing of the Munitions of War Act in which shipyards and other essential industries were declared Controlled Establishments, enabling the Admiralty to formally direct labour as it saw fit in the national interest.

Despite Fisher's resignation, work continued at great speed with *Repulse* and *Renown* completed in August and September 1916 respectively. While they were not built in the fifteen months demanded, at nineteen and twenty months it was a remarkably short time for ships of this size. Their rapid construction had demonstrated what could be achieved by the collective efforts of the Admiralty and industry, particularly when the process was driven as hard as it was in the initial stages by Fisher, and money was no object allowing a great deal of overtime to be worked. Both ships cost about 40 per cent more than *Tiger*. On 25 September 1916, their Lordships forwarded a letter to the DNC expressing and conveying to him and to the members of his staff concerned, 'their appreciation of the highly satisfactory and expeditious manner in which the work of designing, building and completing the *Repulse*, had been carried out'.[8]

ships already under construction reflected the most immediate demands of the war at sea and ensured a low priority for the *Hood*s. Nevertheless, in the normal manner of working, drawing office workload was shared between the three, later four, yards with expected completion dates for all four ships of 1918/19. The first significant delay affecting construction was the Battle of Jutland which showed fundamental weakness in the protection of British battlecruisers following the catastrophic loss of three.

As recasting the design would take many months, work continued at low priority while the order for the fourth ship of the class was placed with Armstrong Whitworth on 13 June with the machinery sub-contracted to Hawthorn Leslie. However, on the same day, the Admiralty wrote to John Brown to inform them that the low priority given to their ship, No 460, had been removed and that work 'should be fully proceeded with under ordinary conditions, no special steps being taken

however to work under accelerated conditions'. Why John Brown's ship was chosen is unclear as no keels had been laid – perhaps because *Repulse* was due to complete shortly. The principal effort so far affected only the drawing office, mould loft, and the advanced ordering of material. On 26 June, the Admiralty placed provisional orders for the 15in main armament for all four ships of the class:

Company	Sets	Condition
Vickers	1 (4 turrets)	Peace condition (*Hood*)
Vickers	1 "	Slow condition (probably *Howe*)
Armstrong	1 "	Slow condition (probably *Anson*)
Coventry OW	1 "	Slow condition. (probably *Rodney*)

Hood's main armament was accelerated to 'peace conditions', matching the pace of construction given to her hull and machinery.

Below: *Repulse* with two destroyers, probably *Romola* and *Rowena*, and the submarine *E35* in the fitting-out basin at Clydebank in August 1916. *Repulse* and her sister-ship *Renown* were built at great speed demonstrating what could be done by the DNC, shipbuilder and suppliers when it mattered. *(Author's collection courtesy of NRS)*

By 5 July 1916, the DNC's department had
produced the first of a series of proposed modifications to the protection of the new battlecruisers while on the 14th, the Ship Branch
announced that the new ships were to be
named after Admirals: *Anson* (Armstrong), *Hood*
(Brown), *Howe* (Cammell Laird) and *Rodney*
(Fairfield). With sufficient drawings prepared to
permit construction of the portions of the hull
unaffected by the armour scheme under revi-
sion, material began to flow from the shops to
the building slips. All four ships were laid down
within nine weeks of one another:

Hood	(Ship No 460)	1 September 1916
Howe	(Ship No 834)	16 October
Rodney	(Ship No 527)	9 October
Anson	(Ship No 909)	9 November

The situation at the beginning of November
noted by shipyard staff at Clydebank was that:

'sufficient information is gradually being
obtained from the Admiralty to enable more
material to be ordered for this vessel and to
employ a few more men on her construction,
but in view of the alterations in her design,
comparatively slow progress can only be made
until the beginning of next year'.[9]

The original design for a ship of 36,300 tons
as approved by the Board on 7 April 1916, had
by 13 September grown to a ship of 40,600
tons while a re-arrangement of their protection
scheme was approved on 2 October. However,
it was not until 20 August 1917 that the design
was finalised, and only then could the sheer and
structural section drawings be completed.

The new armour scheme was sufficiently
fixed to permit placing the first orders on 16
December 1916 for bulkhead and lower tier
barbette armour with Vickers' River Don
Works. On 10 February 1917 the Admiralty
decided to further accelerate *Hood* with the

19-8-16.

Left: 16 October 1916. The clock is showing 5.14, one minute before the working day is over and the gates will be opened by the gatemen. Tramcars would have been lined up on the main road not far from the yard to deal with this mass exodus. Young boys in the employ of local newsagents wait to sell evening newspapers to the men. During the First World War employment at the Dalmuir works peaked at over 13,000 people. *(Author's collection)*

proviso that merchant shipbuilding and anti-submarine vessel construction was not impeded. At this stage a completion date of November 1918 was theoretically possible. In the same month, progress on the new armour layout enabled contracts for the bulk of the remaining ship's heavy armour to be placed:

Company	Armour
John Brown	480lb (12in) belt armour lower tier starboard side. Total 1130 tons.
Vickers	Upper tiers of barbettes.
Cammell Laird	480lb lower tier belt armour port side. Total 1130 tons.
Beardmore	Middle and upper tiers of belt armour starboard side and belt forward and aft of the main belt. Total 946 tons.
Armstrong	Middle and upper tiers of belt armour port side and belt forward and aft of the main belt. Total 946 tons.

By the beginning of 1917, progress had been made on all four ships on the building slips with many thousands of tons worked into the hulls. However, on 9 March 1917 it was decided to suspend work on *Anson*, *Howe* and *Rodney*. The reason often quoted for this was that the construction of the *Mackensen* and *Ersatz Yorck* battlecruisers in Germany had been abandoned and that accordingly the need for the other three *Hood*s had been significantly reduced. This, however, was not strictly correct, as the German battlecruisers were not cancelled until the end of the War. Like their British counterparts, German shipbuilders suffered from labour shortages and had to prioritise competing wartime construction programmes. The unrestricted U-boat war required additional concentration on U-boat construction. Construction of the German battlecruisers continued although at a slower rate. *Mackensen* was launched on 21 April and *Graf Spee* on 15 September 1917 and by the end of December 1917, 10,850 and 11,590 tons of material had been worked into their hulls respectively.[10]

The reason for suspension was lack of skilled labour, allied to which was the pressure on ordnance factories, as the most likely bottleneck was the priority for army guns and ammunition. While the hulls of the three *Hood* class battlecruisers were suspended, revisions to the design continued while those for *Hood* were close to being fixed. Although from this point onward efforts were made to expedite *Hood*, her three sisters were not entirely ignored and, despite suspension, contracts for their auxiliary machinery were issued in March while evidence suggests that work on main machinery continued at a slow rate.[11]

To hasten construction of *Hood*, the

Controller, Rear-Admiral Frederick Tudor, wrote to all Admiralty departments on 17 March:

> In view of the fact that *Hood* is to be completed as quickly as possible, steps should be taken by the departments to ensure that full information is furnished to the contractors so as to enable work to proceed at full dispatch: it is also most necessary that no alterations in the gunnery, torpedo, electric etc. fittings should be intro-duced in this ship with consequent risk of delay.

The evidence of John Brown's manning returns however, suggests that no significant expansion in production occurred in February/March 1917 beyond a gradual incremental increase in labour allocated to this contract.

With pressure from the C-in-C Grand Fleet, now Admiral Sir David Beatty, to restart the three suspended ships, the Controller, now Rear-Admiral Lionel Halsey, considered that no action could be taken to hasten their construction and proposed that the only alter-native way of meeting the need was 'that most energetic action be taken to induce the Japanese to help us by letting us have some of the Kongo Class'.

On 15 October 1917 the First Sea Lord, Admiral John Jellicoe, wrote:

> In regard to the question of battlecruiser construction and expediting the completion of HOOD, the Naval Staff is unable to suggest any items in the shipbuilding programme which could be sacrificed for this purpose, unless it is possible to suspend work on the light cruisers RALEIGH and EFFINGHAM and to transfer the labour and men to the HOOD. The Commander-in-Chief, Grand Fleet, who discussed this matter with the Deputy First Sea Lord, expressed the view that the completion of the HOOD should be expedited, whatever the sacrifice.

The above gives some insight into the serious-ness of the situation. Transferring labour from *Raleigh* was a straightforward matter as the Beardmore shipyard was adjacent to John Brown's. However, *Effingham* was under construction at Portsmouth with the altogether more troublesome issue of relocating hundreds of Dockyard workers to Clydebank. In a meeting held between the Controller and the Deputy Controller of Dockyards and War Shipbuilding (Sir Thomas Bell) on 4 October

1917, the acute shortage of labour was discussed, with one suggestion briefly consid-ered being to recruit miners into the ship-building industry. This proposition had been seriously considered in a meeting on 28 September between the Controller and the Minister for National Service, Auckland Geddes (brother of Eric Geddes, First Lord of the Admiralty in 1917). It was recognised, however, that this would result in miners wanting to retain their existing wage levels, and thus being paid more than a plater's helper or even platers themselves 'resulting in serious demands for wage increases by the whole of the ironworkers in existing shipyards with consequent unrest and loss of production all over the Country.' With regard to *Hood* it was decided that:

> If it is decided that the position of HOOD was the same as that of steel and other raw mate-rials, acceleration is only possible at the expense of other shipbuilding. If it be decided that acceleration of the HOOD is of prime neces-sity, the preferable way of effecting this would be to delay the construction of the oilers, stan-dard ships and destroyers building in the same yard and thereby confine the disturbance of shipbuilding production to one yard.

Bell pointed out that both the DNC and DNO considered that *Hood* could be completed by December 1918 provided an early decision was made to accelerate her construction. On 25 October 1917, despite their best efforts to push *Hood* forward, the Board of Admiralty decided that it was not advisable to accelerate *Hood* given the effect this would have on the ship-building programme.

In April 1918, the War Cabinet decided that under the shipbuilding programme for 1919, work on *Howe* should proceed but that work on *Anson* should be deferred. This was ratified on 15 May when the Naval Expenditure Emergency Standing Committee stated that the Lords Commissioners of H M Treasury were pleased to sanction 'the continuation of work on HMS *Howe*, one of the three battle cruisers for which £10 million was sanctioned by the Treasury in 1 April 1916, instead of on HMS *Anson*'. There was no mention of *Rodney* at this stage. However, the Admiralty was pressing for two of the battlecruisers to be resumed at the normal rate, but the War Cabinet decided to defer a decision until the end of the year. In December, Fairfield was advised by the Admiralty that 'as regards *Rodney* it should be assumed, in making the future programme for the work in your yard, that this vessel will remain as at present, i.e. no expenditure for labour or material is to be incurred on her'.

At a meeting of the War Cabinet on 4 September, the issue of progressing two of the battlecruisers at the normal rate in addition to *Hood* was proposed but after discussion it was agreed a decision on this should wait until the end of the year. The Controller was of the view that this delay would not prevent these ships being completed in the first half of 1921. With the end of the First World War in November 1918, the urgency that surrounded *Hood's* completion evaporated. However, *Hood* and her three sisters did represent the latest British capital ships and viewed against the large warship building programmes being undertaken by the Japanese and US navies, the issue was of importance. At the Board of the Admiralty meeting of 26 December 1918, the three sister-ships were discussed within this broader political context as well as noting the implications for large warship construction at home if they were cancelled:

Question of completing *Anson*, *Howe* and *Rodney*.

It has been pointed out by Messrs Cammell Laird & Co in whose yard *Howe* is laid down, that the berth on which she has been commenced was specially equipped at a large cost and is the most important in their yard, that it is a serious matter for the berth to continue to stand idle now that ample labour is available, and that unless the work on *Howe* is proceeded with, compensation will be claimed until the berth is available for merchant shipbuilding.

The First Sea Lord informed the Board that the Chancellor of the Exchequer had intimated that it was assumed that the Admiralty would not proceed with new construction at the present time. He pointed out the difficulty in coming to any decision with regard to completing the three battle cruisers until more definite information is available as to the intentions of the United States of America in regard to their naval programme.

It was generally agreed that, but for the United States programme which had been foreshadowed, there would not be any strong argument for proceeding with the construction of these ships, and it was felt that in any case until the exact nature of any international arrangements that may be made at the Peace Conference are ascertained, it would be impos-

sible to obtain Cabinet approval to proceed with the construction of ships each of which will cost not less than £5,750,000. The view was expressed that in any event it might be better to take up the ships at once in order to set free the berths and so that, should it be necessary to lay down other ships of this Class, a fresh design embodying the results of recent experience might be adopted. On the other hand it was pointed out that this would leave a gap of practically five years in the construction of large ships. It was agreed that a memorandum should be forwarded to the War Cabinet setting forth the whole position in order to obtain a cabinet decision as to the policy to be adopted.

Right: Looking over the berths and platers' shed at the Fairfield shipyard during 1918. The suspended *Hood* class battlecruiser *Rodney*, to be broken up in the following year, is at left with a succession of vessels beyond. The liner *Ormonde*, serving as an Armed Merchant Cruiser, can be seen on the opposite side of the river. See drawing on page 121 showing vessels in the yard at this time. *(IWM Q18506)*

As late as February 1919, the contracts were still in the balance and on the seventh of that month the DNC wrote to Cammell Laird and Fairfield:

> I am commanded by My Lords Commissioners of the Admiralty to inform you that the question of proceeding with work on HMS *Howe*/ HMS *Rodney* has again been under consideration and it has been decided that all hull work including work on hull-subcontracts is to remain stopped for the present. It has also been decided that work on the main and auxiliary machinery and all work in connection with the main and auxiliary machinery for this ship is to be stopped for the present.

However, the fate of these ships was close to resolution as the Board meeting of 27 February made clear:

> …having regard to all the circumstances the Board agreed that the construction of HM ships *Anson*, *Howe* and *Rodney* should forthwith be cancelled and the slips set free for merchant ship construction, and that in communicating this decision to the War Cabinet it should be made clear that the question of building additional battle cruisers will be reconsidered at the earliest possible moment after the terms of peace are finally settled; as unless further battle cruisers are built

in the near future we shall before long fall behind the United States Navy in ships of that class…

The 'Admirals' had begun life in the summer of 1916 as urgently required units to face expected German equivalents. Three years later, with the German threat gone, the Admiralty had refocused on the consequences of a post-war world where the Royal Navy would be at a considerable disadvantage to US and Japanese new construction. However, when the decision was finally taken in February 1919 to break the *Hood*s up on the slips, it was in the knowledge that far superior designs were under development and that future construction was in any case likely to be the subject of a peace conference and calls for disarmament.[12]

Final invoices were submitted by the three shipbuilders for a price covering work done together with a cancellation fee. Fairfield submitted the sum of £321,978 for *Rodney*, covering work on hull and machinery, that being their outlay including profit. However, the Admiralty's Dockyard Expense Account for 1919–20 lists a total figure of £614,852 for this ship which probably accounts for work done on armour and armament in addition to the shipyard's costs. The Dockyard Expense Accounts list expenditure of £315,732 on *Anson* and £470,521 on *Howe*, the latter about 8 per cent of expected final cost.

3: RETRENCHMENT AND REVIVAL, 1920 TO 1945[1]

POST-WAR PLANS AND THE WASHINGTON CONFERENCE

In early 1918, in anticipation of a successful conclusion to the war, the Government advised the shipbuilding industry that the present level of warship contracts would come to an end and that they would thereafter have to rely substantially on merchant tonnage.

The cancellation of the three *Hood* class battlecruisers in 1919 ended the immediate prospect for manufacturing heavy armour and gun mountings and placed the armaments industry on the edge of a precipice. Having steadily built up capacity to handle unprecedented capital ship construction, it now seemed certain that there was no alternative to closing or 'moth-balling' much of this recently acquired capacity.

However, if armaments production was understandably about to collapse, such was the optimism that the end of the war engendered, that for shipbuilders at least, it was thought that a prolonged period replacing the ships lost to enemy action during the U-boat campaign was in prospect. So certain were they of this that some major shipbuilders, such as Beardmore and Fairfield, invested in additional capacity, adding new berths and steel working shops to their existing organisations.

The switch from war to peace production was structural in nature and had to be accomplished in a very short space of time as the orders for ordnance, warships and tanks etc, came to an end. It was thought that some of the heavy plant associated with armaments production could be utilised in the construction of civilian transport-related products such as loco-motives, and as a consequence Armstrong Whitworth, Vickers and Beardmore established locomotive departments. One captain of industry, Sir William Beardmore, summarised the challenge facing the armaments industry in the following manner:

> It was as though in 1914 when the war commenced, we had to create nationally a huge wheel. We had to set it in motion, gradually getting up the speed for a considerable time, and by this huge store of energy overcome the munitions shortage. Since the Armistice, we have had to take the energy out of the wheel and gradually reverse its direction of motion. That you will agree is no easy thing to do – to reverse a wheel of such gigantic proportions as we were running during the war. We now have a big task in front of us, and I think history will relegate to us for the manner in which we have reversed this wheel and turned it into peace products.[2]

Other companies wasted no time in divesting themselves of what was now excess capacity. The pursuit of naval contracts which had brought John Brown, Cammell Laird and Fairfield into alliance no longer applied and they moved quickly, at the end of 1918, to divest themselves of the Coventry Ordnance Works which had struggled throughout its short life, which with the exception of the war years had been a serious drain on resources. A new firm, the English Electric Co Ltd, established in December 1918 by John Brown to manufacture electric motors and transformers, took over the Coventry works. However, the

Above: The conse-
quences for Japan and
the USA following the
signing of the
Washington Treaty was
the commitment to
dispose of battleships
and battlecruisers then
under construction.
Here the incomplete
battleship *Tosa* is being
moved from her builders
at Nagasaki, Mitsubishi,
in August 1922. She was
sunk as a target in 1925.
(Author's collection)

Scotstoun gun mounting branch did not fit easily into this arrangement and was sold separately to Harland & Wolff in 1920 who used the works to manufacture marine diesel engine components. Other alliances borne out of the Anglo-German naval race broke down at the same time: Cammell Laird and Fairfield disposed of their joint shareholdings in one another to concentrate on core activities.

However, all hope of a future capital ship building programme had not receded. In fact, while the First World War raged in Europe, the first steps in a new naval race had already been taken by the United States and Japan who were looking afresh at their wider interests in the Pacific region. In the United States, a naval expansion Bill was passed in 1916 under which terms a battlefleet comprising ten battleships and six battlecruisers were to be built providing the United States with, in the words of President Wilson, 'incomparably the greatest navy in the world'. The Japanese response to what was perceived as a direct threat to their areas of influence in the Pacific, came in the form of the so-called 8-8 programme which envisaged a battlefleet equal to that of the US Navy comprising eight battleships and eight battlecruisers to be completed by 1928.

In the United States, between 1917 and 1921, four *Colorado* class battleships, *Colorado*, *Maryland*, *Washington* and *West Virginia*, six *Lexington* class battlecruisers and six *South Dakota* class battleships were laid down. The first two battleships of the 8-8 programme, *Nagato* and *Mutsu*, were laid down in 1917 and 1918. These were followed by two further battleships, *Tosa* and *Kaga*, both laid down in 1920 and four battlecruisers, *Amagi*, *Akagi*, *Atago* and *Takao*, laid down in 1920 and 1921.

At the end of the First World War, the Royal Navy, with the largest but ageing battlefleet in the world, had to reconcile the fact that the planned US and Japanese capital ships would inevitably be superior. *Hood*, the most modern British capital ship, did not fully embody the lessons of the recent war and there were no capital ships under construction or planned with the exception of the three *Hood*s, the design of which was still rooted in pre-Jutland thinking.

Rapid advances made during 1905–20 meant that the oldest ships armed with 12in and 13.5in guns were markedly inferior to the most recent 15in-gunned ships, while the new Japanese and American ships mounted 16in guns. Despite the exhausting and financially crippling war years, if the British Government was to remain in the forefront of the world's fleets, it had little option but to begin the process of planning a major capital shipbuilding programme of its own.

THE G3 BATTLECRUISERS

The Director of Naval Construction, Sir Eustace Tennyson d'Eyncourt, and his team of constructors began work bringing together a wealth of accumulated wartime operational experience as well as feedback from *Hood* which began trials early in 1920. Throughout 1920 and 1921, the DNC's department developed a large number of designs most of which made a radical break from previous design conventions. These designs were evaluated by the Admiralty and from this process a definitive battlecruiser, the G3 design, and battleship, the N3 design, emerged with the intention that four battlecruisers would be laid down in 1922 and four battleships in 1923. The G3 and N3 designs represented the pinnacle of British capital ship design in size, offensive power and protection and were unmatched until the later variations on the *Lion* class twenty years later.

See table at right for particulars of the G3 design as signed off by the DNC in February 1922.

The N3 battleship design mounted 9 x 18in guns on a similar displacement to the G3s but were not as long, reflecting the smaller machinery spaces for a slower speed of 23.5 knots. The N3s were never ordered and the final design was still in gestation at the time of the Washington Conference. With the G3 design complete, drawings were provided and a specification drawn up to enable the tendering process to begin.

Although Portsmouth and Devonport Dockyards would never build a capital ship again, partly because of physical restrictions on larger hulls, the DNC's department was alive to the issue resulting in the following reply written on 19 July 1919 by C L Hutson in response to a question posed by constructor E L Attwood:[3]

Mr Attwood,

With reference to your query as to the possibility of [building] a warship similar to HOOD at Portsmouth, Devonport or Chatham Yards, the plans have been examined and it is considered impractical to do so with the yards at present equipped for the following reasons.

Portsmouth

The Steam Basin at the head of the building slip does not allow of extension sufficient to take a ship of this length. It is considered that the construction of a ship in either Lock C or D would be objectionable, as it would only leave the other Lock for docking bulged ships; during which the only available entrance for large ships would be M opening from the Fountain Lake (tidal) and then only at light draughts and very small clearances.

Devonport & Chatham

There is room for the necessary extension of the present building slips, but the vessel after launching could not be taken into any of the basins for completion, and there are no docks of sufficient size.

Clearly the same factors applied to some of the private yards, the consequence of which was that Palmers, Scotts and Vickers were also out of

BASIC PARTICULARS OF THE G3 BATTLECRUISERS

Length on waterline:	850ft
Length overall:	862ft
Breadth:	106ft
Draught:	32.5ft
Displacement:	48,360 tons. In fighting condition (extra deep), displacement rose to 56,540 tons.
Main and secondary armament:	9 x 16in 45-calibre with 40° elevation in triple turrets; 16 x 6in 50-calibre with 40° elevation in twin turrets.
Protection:	14in belt armour over machinery and magazine spaces, 14in barbettes; 8in and 9in deck armour over magazines, 4in over machinery spaces.
Machinery:	160,000 shp for 32 knots.

the running unless they were prepared to spend large sums reorganising their yards.

While the G3 and N3 designs were carried forward, international consensus was being sought in Washington DC where a conference gathered on 12 November 1921 attended by the leading naval powers. The aims of the conference were numerous although, in the broadest sense, these were to prevent a new arms race which potentially would make Britain, the United States and Japan adversaries. Implicit in this thinking was that the recent Anglo-German naval race had at least contributed to raising the temperature in an increasingly volatile political environment. The growth of the US and Japanese navies in particular pointed to a future conflict in the Pacific, an area also of considerable importance to the British in the maintenance of Empire. At the same time, rivalry between Britain and the US was already manifest in US war planning scenarios against Britain, codenamed War Plan Orange.

Although the thought of a new arms race was clearly abhorrent to governments given recent events, nevertheless this scenario was considered should consensus fail to be reached on these issues. It is against this background that the following chronology charts the events leading to the ordering and subsequent cancellation of Britain's new capital ship programme.

August 1921. Provisional orders placed with Armstrong Whitworth and Vickers for the triple 16in main armament mountings and twin 6in mountings for the G3 battlecruisers. The 16in gun mountings were designed by Armstrong and the total requirement of twelve mountings plus three spares was split equally between the two firms. These complex and large mechanisms had to be ordered first to ensure they would be complete when the hulls were launched and ready for installation.

1 September. Invitations to tender sent to the following shipbuilders: Beardmore, Brown, Cammell Laird, Harland & Wolff, Vickers, Swan Hunter, Fairfield, Armstrong Whitworth. The shipbuilders were told that the tender should be based on materials and labour costs, that a fixed sum of £700,000 would cover establishment charges and profit and that a bonus for economical construction would be awarded. The bonus, a new tactic developed by the Admiralty to promote economy, was to be based on the average cost of all four ships on completion rather than the individual cost of each ship. Where the individual cost was below the average cost, the Admiralty agreed to apply a bonus of 30 per cent of the difference between the two prices. Completion of the ships was to be within thirty-six months after keel-laying. Contracts would be awarded only to employers who were members of the King's National Roll Scheme. This scheme was established in 1915 to ensure that disabled ex-servicemen were not excluded from the job market.

8 October. Completed tenders were submitted to the Admiralty and the internal review of each tender, prices, technical strategies to be adopted etc., began.

24 October 1921. Hull and machinery contracts were provisionally awarded to the lowest bidders, John Brown, Fairfield and Swan Hunter. The machinery for the Swan Hunter ship was awarded to Parsons Marine Steam Turbine.

Winning tenders.

John Brown	£3,879,000
Fairfield	£3,900,000
Swan Hunter	£3,977,175

31 October 1921. Notice given of drawing office work to be subdivided among the four contractors (the fourth had yet to be selected).

1 November. The fourth contract was awarded to Wm Beardmore & Co Ltd, at a tender price of £3,786,332 for the hull with machinery subcontracted to Vickers. All four ships were to be completed by 20 October 1924 (1 November for the Beardmore ship).

3 November. The Admiralty provided shipyards, starting with John Brown, with sufficient drawings including offsets to enable the hulls to be laid off.

11 November. A conference was held at the Admiralty attended by the shipbuilders and marine engineers to discuss engineering issues for the 160,000 shp turbine machinery installation.

12 November. Delegates from the leading naval powers gathered in Washington to begin negotiations intended to stop a new naval arms race developing.

14 November. The Admiralty provided shipbuilders with a list of the armour contractors for their ship in the table below.

16 November. The contracts for the ships were suspended until further notice pending the outcome of the Washington Conference.

22 November. Marine engineering personnel from the shipyards met the Engineer-in-Chief, Vice-Admiral Sir George Goodwin, to discuss machinery arrangements.

25 November. New machinery specifications issued.

By the end of November, several new designs for battlecruisers of 35,000 tons, mounting 9 x 15in with 112,000 shp for 30 knots light on twin shafts, had been developed by the DNC in the expectation that if the G3s were not acceptable to the Conference then smaller battlecruisers might be required, given likely tonnage restrictions.

6 December 1921. The Washington Conference concluded with an agreement that brought the existing naval construction plans of the major naval powers to an end. The Admiralty wrote to

ALLOCATION OF ARMOUR FOR G3 BATTLECRUISERS

Item	John Brown ship	Fairfield ship	Beardmore ship	Swan Hunter ship
500lb belt	Brown	Vickers	Beardmore	Vickers
480lb belt	Armstrong	Cammell	Beardmore	Cammell
Funnel protection	Brown	Brown	Vickers	Vickers
Upper deck	Brown	Armstrong	Beardmore	Cammell
Lower deck	Brown	Beardmore	Beardmore	Brown
200lb bulkhead	Vickers	Vickers	Vickers	Vickers
480lb bulkhead	Armstrong	Cammell	Vickers	Cammell
400lb bulkhead	Armstrong	Cammell	Vickers	Cammell
160lb bulkhead	Vickers	Vickers	Vickers	Vickers
'A' barbette	Vickers	Vickers	Vickers	Vickers
'B' barbette	Brown	Armstrong	Armstrong	Brown
'C' barbette	Cammell	Cammell	Cammell	Cammell

the shipbuilders stating that any expense incurred relative to the ship's machinery was to be confined to turbine design arrangements, boiler design, feed arrangements, condenser evacuating arrangements and turbine drive for circulating pumps. Details were not to be considered and no expense was to be incurred with sub-contractors.

9 December. A further instruction from the Admiralty asked that drawing office and experimental work be carried out by John Brown in the following areas:

1. Tests of electrically-welded deck plates.
2. Full-sized test of a double bottom tank to determine the suitability of framing and frame spacing.
3. Theoretical investigation into the strength of the main transverse and longitudinal bulkheads.
4. Design work in connection with special fittings such as hatchway covers and similar arrangements to protect openings in the thick armour deck including the making of samples of such fittings for tests.
5. Design of shaft brackets.

Fairfield was asked to continue with items 1 and 4 above and additionally to undertake the design of the stern post castings. Beardmore and Swan Hunter were asked to continue with item 1 only.

13 February 1922. The Controller, Rear-Admiral Frederick Field, held a conference to consider the cancellation of the four battle-cruisers given the draft conclusions of the Washington Conference agreed on 10 February. The report, produced on the following day and reproduced in part here, goes some way to explain the Admiralty perception of the post-Washington outlook for the private armaments sector.

The conference agreed that 1) Letters should be sent cancelling the four ships and that the Admiralty should be informed at once of expense incurred for work done. At the same time the firms might be informed confidentially that contracts for two new capital ships of revised design are being contemplated. 2) With regard to hulls and machinery of the two new ships, it was considered better to have an open competition and not limit this to firms who had obtained orders for the four cancelled

ships. However, the allocation of orders should take into account any economy that might be effected on compensation claims by giving an order to firms who had previously received an order for one of the four cancelled ships. 3) As regards armour it is desirable to place orders for the new ships with firms whom it will be necessary to keep in being during the ten years' naval holiday, assuming there will be an output of two capital ships per annum, when building again starts. Three firms would be required on this basis. The firms of Vickers and Armstrong who have gun and gun mounting plant as well as armour plant would have prominent claims for compensation, because the plant for armour overlaps the gun and gun mounting plant, and moreover if the firms are left out of consideration for armour the effect would be felt in increased prices for guns and gun mountings. These two firms are also specialists in gun shield armour and two firms are required for this work in the estimated output in view. On the other hand, Armstrong is regarded as being very expensive for armour; also their armour works are at Openshaw, and it was thought there might be some advantage in keeping the armour firms who are to be maintained, in the Sheffield district, where the majority of the workmen skilled in armour plate working live.

Heavy gun mountings require two firms to be kept in being to provide for the estimated output of 2 capital ships per annum. Guns require Woolwich and two firms to produce the requisite number in 3 years.

It was arranged that the departmental officers would go into the matter, consulting firms as necessary without committing the Admiralty, and making reports as to the best and most economical allocation of armour, gun mountings and guns for the two capital ships, and as to firms ultimately to be supported by subsidies taking into account all the factors touched upon above, namely the number of firms that will be required to be maintained as a result of the Washington Conference decisions, and the effect of various distributions of the orders as regards prices, subsidies and compensation claims. 4) After this question has been examined and decision given, it will be proper that Admiralty intentions should be intimated to firms whose plant will not need to be maintained any longer.

21 February 1922. The four shipbuilders were informed that it had definitely been decided that no further work was to be carried out on the hulls and machinery of the four battle-cruisers.

March 1922. Shipbuilders submitted expense claims. In the case of John Brown, this amounted to £32,000 covering all the work done by this firm on the G3 contract.

April 1922. Drawings supplied to shipbuilders were returned to the Admiralty.

The outcome of the Washington Conference was far-reaching in its effect.[4] A new and hugely expensive naval race had been averted and in its place agreed tonnage limits were imposed for those ships that were permitted to be built. Under these terms the British and United States navies were each allowed a battlefleet of 525,000 standard displacement tons and Japan 315,000 tons. Both France and Italy were limited to 175,000 tons. At a stroke, and for the first time in modern history, the Royal Navy was equalled in strength, as measured in capital ships, by a rival power, the USA.[5]

The tonnage ratio applied to capital ships was also applied to aircraft carriers where the Royal and US Navies were each allowed 135,000 tons, Japan 81,000 tons and France and Italy 60,000 tons. The Treaty was concerned with territorial issues in addition to warship numbers and size and sought to reach agreement on possessions and fortifications in the Pacific.

No battleships or battlecruisers would be built during the ten-year term of the Treaty with a few exceptions. In specific terms, battleships were limited in overall tonnage to 35,000 tons and main armament to guns of 16in calibre. Britain was allowed to retain twenty-two battleships and battlecruisers and construct two new battleships, eventually *Nelson* and *Rodney*, to maintain parity with the USA. Scrapping of the ships not included in the above was to be undertaken within eighteen months of the Treaty coming into force. This meant that seventeen capital ships of the British battlefleet would be cut up, many prematurely if twenty years is taken as the average lifespan of a warship (if the pre-dreadnoughts *Agamemnon* and *Commonwealth*[6] are included the number is nineteen). These were, with the age of the ship: *Dreadnought* 15, *Inflexible* 13, *Indomitable* 13, *Bellerophon* 12, *Superb* 12, *Temeraire* 12, *St Vincent* 11, *Neptune* 10, *Hercules* 10, *New Zealand* 9, *Lion* 9, *Conqueror* 9, *Monarch* 9, *Orion* 9, *Australia* 8, *Agincourt* 7 and *Erin* 7. On completion of *Nelson* and *Rodney*, which was expected in 1925, an additional four battleships were to be scrapped. These were, with the age they would be, *King George V* 13, *Ajax* 12, *Centurion* 12 and *Thunderer* 13.

Although the ships earmarked for scrapping were of limited fighting power and usefulness by the standards of 1922, there is nevertheless a great irony in their destruction under the scrapper's torch. The great financial burden so recently imposed on the nation by their construction, measured by direct cost, materials and manpower, yielded a very small return to the Exchequer in their subsequent conversion into 'pots, pans and razor blades'. In fact, only tiny amounts of steel ended up as such as the bulk of the steel recovered went to construction, railways, machinery, mining and shipbuilding. Whilst their construction was previously seen as vital components in national defence, their destruction was undertaken in the interests of international peace. The wholesale reduction in the size of the Royal Navy by disposal enabled the shipbreaking industry to expand significantly. In another irony, one of the most important shipbreakers, Thomas W Ward Ltd located a new shipbreaking yard at Inverkeithing on the Firth of Forth where just a few years previously Admiral Beatty and the elite Battlecruiser Squadron of the Grand Fleet had been based. So great was the requirement for shipbreaking that a number of battleships

Below: After the war the immediate fate of a large portion of the British battle fleet was the scrapper's torch, hastened by the Washington Treaty. There was more than a little irony in this given the headlong rush bordering on panic at times to build these ships in the first instance. Some were barely a dozen years old, like *Ajax* seen arriving at Rosyth on 14 December 1926 under tow from Portsmouth. She had been sold on 9 November to Alloa Shipbreaking Co Ltd (later Metal Industries) for £59,287. *(Newcastle University Marine Technology Special Collection)*

were sent to Holland and Germany for scrapping (see Appendix 3).

The Washington Treaty also provided a timetable of when new battleships could be constructed for elderly ships that were to be taken out of commission should a successor treaty not be signed in 1932. Had this been the case, the list of ships due for decommissioning thus allowing replacements to be laid down was:

1934 *Iron Duke, Marlborough, Emperor of India* and *Benbow*
1935 *Tiger, Queen Elizabeth, Warspite* and *Barham*
1936 *Malaya* and *Royal Sovereign*
1937 *Revenge* and *Resolution*
1938 *Royal Oak*
1939 *Valiant* and *Repulse*
1940 *Renown*
1941 *Ramillies* and *Hood*
1942 *Nelson* and *Rodney*

While the Treaty was a brilliant success in 'contributing to the maintenance of the general peace and to reduce the burdens of competition in armament[s]', at a domestic level it forced the reduction of the armaments industry to levels that the country was able to afford. This was a painful process, the effects of which were most immediate as a consequence of the cancellation of the G3s. It was estimated that they would have employed 25,000 people with a total order value of £30 million, much of

which would have been in wages. After Washington long-term prospects held little hope for capital ships beyond the two that the Royal Navy was permitted to build. There were no restrictions on the construction of other classes of warship as the Treaty covered capital ships only, meaning battleships, battlecruisers, and aircraft carriers. Consequently, the construction of 8in gunned 'Treaty' cruisers, which were not at that time subject to numerical limitation, became a prominent feature in the shipyards of the naval powers from the mid-1920s onwards.

NELSON AND RODNEY

While the Conference was in session, the smaller battleship designs that had been prepared assumed increasing importance as treaty-compliant. Of these designs, O3 was preferred and by the end of December 1921, the DNC had agreed the basic particulars that would result in *Nelson* and *Rodney*. Sometimes referred to as 'cut down' versions of the G3s, *Nelson* and *Rodney* were of course fully developed new designs incorporating the main armament of the G3s, with minor modifications, together with some of the main design characteristics of these ships. To carry the main armament and armour scheme on a 35,000-ton upper limit meant a hull length of just over 700ft and a modest speed of 23 knots.

As the new battleships were just capable of being built at either Portsmouth or Devonport, the Controller, Field, wrote on 1 August 1922

Below: *Nelson* was launched from Berth No. 2 at Walker Naval Yard on 3 September 1925. Typical Tyne tugs are in attendance to move her alongside the fitting-out quay. *(Newcastle University Marine Technology Special Collection)*

to the DNC that 'one of the main contentions put forward by the Admiralty against building one or both of the new capital ships in the Dockyards, is that the consequent delay in commencing construction cannot be accepted'. He requested that all measures necessary to enable tenders to be issued in time for orders to be placed not later than 1 January 1923 should be taken. The DNC replied that if no alterations were made to the design, the specifications and drawings would be ready for inviting tenders on 1 November. This date was subsequently brought forward to 16 October.

The main battleship builders were invited to tender and each shipyard sent a small team of draughtsmen to the Admiralty where they copied or were supplied with drawings and collected printed specifications concerning hull and machinery etc., to enable the cost estimators back at the respective shipyards to work out a cost, for management then to decide a price to quote. Tenders were submitted by 25 November 1922, whereupon the Admiralty deliberated on the relative merits of each. The recent award of contracts for the G3s had encouraged those yards that had been unsuccessful to cut their prices for the new battleships to the minimum. On 11 December 1922, provisional acceptance was given to the two lowest tenders, Armstrong Whitworth (*Nelson*) and Cammell Laird (*Rodney*). The hull and machinery prices submitted by the yards invited to tender were:

	£
Armstrong	1,479,000
Cammell Laird	1,563,000
Swan Hunter	1,616,000
Fairfield	1,650,000
Palmers	1,767,000
Brown	1,771,000
Beardmore	1,775,000
Vickers	1,858,000
Scotts	2,059,000

Where previously three Clyde yards and one Tyne yard had been awarded G3 contracts, in this competition none of these yards were successful. When questions about this were asked in the House of Commons, the Prime Minister, Andrew Bonar Law, suggested that the winning tenders had been put in at a loss while the others had not (see p.242 for losses made).

Although not on the scale of the G3 contracts and only a quarter of the total cost including armament and armour, the new battleships provided work for two shipyards, while in their letter to successful contractors, the Admiralty stressed that 'the Admiralty will be glad if you will arrange, subject to Admiralty approval, to distribute sub-contracts for large items such as machinery parts, forgings, castings etc. etc. as much as possible with a view to spreading employment over the country as evenly as possible, having regard, however, to the necessity of avoiding an increase of cost on such account'.

The gun mountings and shields for the new 16in 45 cal main armament for two of the G3s had provisionally been placed with Armstrong Whitworth in August 1921 and later cancelled. That summer the company had begun the modifications to their No. 24 gun mounting shop and its pits, as shown in the drawing on p.184, specifically for these ships. They were now used for *Nelson* and *Rodney*, although it was not until 11 December 1922, that Armstrong submitted their tender for the main armament for both ships totalling six mountings plus three spares. The 16in director firing gear and twelve new twin 6in mountings were manufactured by Vickers at Barrow. The contracts for side, deck and barbette armour together with various other steel castings and forgings were distributed across the principal steel firms: Armstrong at Openshaw, Beardmore at Parkhead and John Brown, Cammell Laird and Vickers all at Sheffield. Other steel castings were contracted out to Hadfield and Thomas Firth at Sheffield and the Steel Company of Scotland at Glasgow.

Under the terms of the Washington Naval Treaty, the battleships *King George V*, *Ajax*, *Centurion* and *Thunderer* were required to be rendered unfit for 'warlike service' no later than four years after laying the keels of *Nelson* and *Rodney* which meant the end of December 1926. The Admiralty stressed that *Nelson* and *Rodney* must be ready for service before 28 December 1926 otherwise the Fleet will be 'very seriously weakened in the interval between that date and the dates when *Nelson* and *Rodney* are ready to replace the four ships named'. The four ships were withdrawn from service in the last months of 1926 but *Nelson* and *Rodney* did not join the fleet until August 1927.

CONTRACTION

As recalled, at the beginning of the 1920s there was a sense that there would be a prolonged period of prosperity and that industries so long diverted into war production would thrive in peacetime production. The opposite would apply. In the shipbuilding industry work was plentiful throughout 1919 and into 1920. However, during the war, the cost of materials and labour had risen significantly and that plus a surplus of US mass-produced and German reparations merchant tonnage conspired to make shipowners cautious and shipbuilders increasingly anxious. By late 1920, a downturn in the global economy set in, prompting a period of economic stagnation that would last throughout most of the 1920s. The resulting low shipping freight rates not only discouraged shipowners from new ordering but also resulted in cancellations of existing contracts or requests for a slower rate of construction, for example, from Cunard.

Increasingly, the view that warship contracts would be replaced with merchant work began to look highly optimistic. The loss of warship work coupled to the trade depression resulted in an industry with capacity that no longer reflected demand. For its part the Admiralty endeavoured to place what orders it had, mostly cruisers and submarines, across the Dockyards and private shipyards in an attempt to hold this strategic resource together. In 1925, agreement was reached between the private firms over the sharing of Admiralty work. However, this measure on its own was not sufficient to stave off the inevitable. So acute had the problems within the armament industry become, that the Bank of England had to intervene and undertake a process of restructuring aimed at creating a financially viable industry shorn of loss-making divisions but which nevertheless preserved crucial defence industry assets.

The company causing most concern was the one that had led the way in previous decades as the model armaments contractor, Armstrong Whitworth. Since 1924, the company had been incurring serious losses. The prospect of this firm collapsing forced the issue and precipitated a reorganisation in which the company was taken over by Vickers, a financially stronger and more astutely led company. Over the course of 1927, it was agreed that the naval shipbuilding and armaments assets of both companies would be amalgamated and transferred to a new company, Vickers-Armstrongs Ltd. Thus the capacity to produce heavy gun mountings, the technologically most critical elements of a capital ship, were concentrated in one firm.

Next was the steel industry which had been greatly expanded to meet wartime needs. In the changed circumstances of the 1920s, this resulted in under-utilised plant and, moreover,

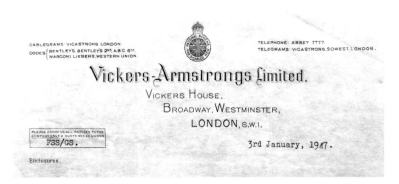

duplicated capacity from one steel company to the next. Shortly after the Vickers-Armstrongs merger, moves were made to amalgamate and restructure the steel interests of Vickers (Sheffield), Vickers-Armstrongs (Openshaw) and Cammell Laird. The outcome was the English Steel Corporation formed on 17 December 1928 with a share capital of just under £6 million. The armour plate and forging capacity of the constituent companies was included in this merger but gun mounting capacity was not. A wider association of interests was proposed to include the other major steelmakers with armament interests, Beardmore and John Brown. However, for a number of reasons including the creation of a monopoly in the armour industry, both Beardmore and John Brown remained independent of the English Steel Corporation.

The businesses of Thomas Firth and John Brown had been associated since 1902 with Firth's manufacture of projectiles complementing Brown's armaments interests. However, the need to pool their interests resulted in a formal merger in 1930 with Brown holding the controlling interest. The new firm was styled Thomas Firth & John Brown Ltd, or Firth-Brown for short, although John Brown & Co Ltd continued with their non-steelmaking business interests including the shipyard at Clydebank which was retained as a wholly-owned subsidiary.

While before the First World War, the armaments firms had sought vertical integration to take maximum advantage of the glut of orders now, in harder economic circumstances, these structures were, in some instances, deconstructed and restructured along horizontal lines. At the end of this process, armour plate capacity was concentrated in three firms, the English Steel Corporation with mills at River Don and Cyclops Works, Firth-Brown at Atlas Works and Beardmore at Parkhead. Gun mountings remained at Elswick and Barrow,

Above: An armaments giant emerges. The retrenchment of the armaments industry and the collapse of Armstrongs enabled restructuring of the industry to begin, part of which was the emergence in 1928 of a new armaments giant, Vickers-Armstrongs with Vickers firmly in control. *(Newcastle University Marine Technology Special Collection)*

both now part of Vickers-Armstrongs, although the former works of the Coventry Ordnance Works at Scotstoun, now owned by Harland & Wolff would have a role to play later in the Second World War, as discussed in Chapter 8. Heavy forging capacity existed with the big three, English Steel Corporation, Firth-Brown and Beardmore, as well as smaller companies.

A similar process of contraction if somewhat more draconian in nature was about to be applied to the shipbuilding industry which, like the steel industry, was in a parlous state. As early as 1925, the President of the Institution of Engineers and Shipbuilders in Scotland, A J Campbell, stated:

> Today there are about 96 shipyards in Britain. In 30 of these there is not a single keel laid. In 15 work in hand is rapidly nearing completion while the remainder are barely occupied beyond a quarter of their capacity. The situation is partly understood when it is realised that there are now 20% more berths in this country since before the war and that only 28% of these are occupied. The percentage of unemployed workmen is between 30 and 40%. In 1913 we built 60% of the world's output, while at present this figure has dropped to 46%.[7]

The crisis grew into a far deeper depression after the collapse of Wall Street in 1929, reducing further the transportation of goods by

Right: Although an advertisement for Beardmore ships placed in 1926, Backs to the Wall nevertheless captures something of the mood of the times in the midst of a depression and the imminent collapse of much of the armaments industry. The advert invokes Sir Douglas Haig in his famous 'Backs to the Wall' order to British troops in April 1918. For Beardmore, however, a better analogy would have been the defeats of 1916. *(Author's collection)*

BACKS TO THE WALL.

No one misunderstood Sir Douglas Haig in March, 1918, when he said every man's back was to the wall, and no one is under any delusion about British industry being in an analogous position to-day.

These are the occasions when men rise to achievements which seemed impossible. History is full of striking incidents when men have risen, even on their figurative dead selves to unparalleled heights of eminence.

Adversity is often a blessing.

The great shipbuilding industry of this country still holds its pre-eminent position. But it is being threatened on all sides. To-day, as never in the past, are British Shipbuilders fighting with their backs to the wall.

Despite the slump, great ships are being built. The Beardmore Shipyard contributes its share of shipbuilding masterpieces that reflects credit not only on the architects and builders, but on the British nation who have always set the pace for other nations to follow in this leading industry. Beardmores are proud, not only of their own, but of the reputation of Clyde shipbuilding, the records of which are not sullied nor likely to be.

Buy Beardmore Built Ships.

WILLIAM
BEARDMORE
AND COMPANY LIMITED

NAVAL CONSTRUCTION WORKS, DALMUIR, near GLASGOW.

sea and the demand for shipping. Conditions described as the worst in living memory were experienced across the industry, typical of which was the Vickers-Armstrongs' Naval Yard on the Tyne which was forced to close temporarily in August 1928. This yard was reopened in March 1930 when the contract for the passenger ship *Monarch of Bermuda* was won but closed again at the end of 1931 after its completion. At John Brown's Clydebank yard, only the order for Cunard's *Queen Mary* kept the works open. Even here however, the collapse of the bond market forced Cunard to suspend this contract in December 1931 and the shipyard was brought to a standstill. By the end of 1930, Cammell Laird's Tranmere yard was temporarily closed, with unemployment nationally in the shipbuilding industry accelerating beyond 100,000, a rate of 60 per cent by 1932.

In July 1929, statistics produced by a Committee of Lloyds Register stated that on average only 240 berths had been occupied out of 650 available over the last five years in Britain.

> …this question must be seriously faced in order to ensure that when a genuine revival of trade takes place, the industry is not robbed of its proper share of prosperity by reason of any excess of facilities beyond that which could be reasonably required to deal with any marked demand likely to arise… . At present it is almost impossible to build except at a loss. The only way in which matters can be improved within the shipbuilding industry as a whole is for those interested to come to some arrangement by which redundant yards could be got rid of. [8]

There were interested parties and in February 1930, National Shipbuilders Security Ltd (NSS) was formed by the main shipbuilding firms, partly funded by the Bank of England and chaired by Clyde shipbuilder Sir James Lithgow to 'assist the shipbuilding industry by the purchase of redundant and/or obsolete shipyards and dismantling and disposal of their contents and the re-sale of the sites under restrictions against further use for shipbuilding.' The restrictions were far reaching, preventing the re-use of sites declared redundant for shipbuilding purposes for forty years.[9]

For NSS the task of cutting down the capacity of the shipbuilding industry was relatively straightforward if controversial – there was no shortage of candidates. One of the first was Wm Beardmore & Co Ltd. The fortunes of this company, like the other armaments companies described above, were parlous. Greatly extended during the First World War and employing 40,000 at its height, the company had been unable to stem the tide of losses through diversification. By 1929 moves were made, funded by the Bank of England, to restructure this important but loss making company. The timing fitted well with NSS's agenda and in March 1930, Beardmore's 100-acre Naval Construction Works at Dalmuir, the largest shipyard on the Clyde, was acquired for £200,000 and preparations for permanent closure put in hand. The contents of the shipyard were auctioned over the following year and fixed structures such as the shipbuilding gantry demolished after just twenty-five years of operation. The engine works on the site continued to operate for a few more years. There was considerable opposition to this closure as the Beardmore yard was seen as one of the most up to date with one of the best launching sites on the Clyde. Many other yards followed, including some of the early Armstrong Whitworth yards on the Tyne. The closure that captured the national mood was that of Palmers, which was acquired by NSS in 1934. The closure and subsequent dismantling of this yard, characterised by pulling down the iconic steel cableways, resulted in a 70 per cent unemployment rate in Jarrow, later prompting the 'Jarrow Crusade' of 1936 when 200 unemployed men marched to Parliament in protest and to draw attention to the chronic unemployment and endemic poverty.[10]

While the shipbuilding industry was shorn of redundant yards, those remaining had little option but to hope for the better times. The Chairman of the Fairfield shipyard, Sir A M Kennedy, probably expressed the mood for much of the industry when he said at the company's AGM in November 1933:

> During recent years the Admiralty have done a good deal to assist the industry [and this] assistance would probably have been greater but for Government restrictions, which were, no doubt, considered expedient under the then prevailing circumstances. It is now realised however, that these restrictive measures have resulted in reducing our Navy to danger point and the expectation is that the naval programmes of the future will be enlarged. There is another consideration, however, which from the point of view of industrial efficiency

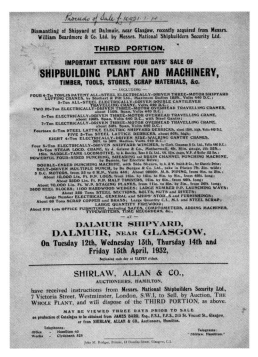

Left: 1932 and the physical removal of shipbuilding capacity begins. The auctioneer's catalogue for the sale of part of the plant and equipment at Beardmore's Dalmuir shipyard. Ninety-six pages long with 1751 lots, the total raised was just £10,921. 1s. 4d. At the time of its closure the shipyard had been in operation for just twenty-five years. *(Author's collection)*

and industrial development ought to weigh with our Government, and that is, that in periods of depression when merchant shipping is at a low ebb naval programmes should be anticipated in order to advance our technical skill and maintain skilled workmen in regular employment. This is, in my view, a matter of national importance. The future of our country and her retention of the high position she has always held in industry depends in a large degree on the skill of her craftsmen, and it must be recognised that increased knowledge and skill render invaluable aid in industrial development.[11]

A further factor affecting the industry as a consequence of the prolonged depression over the 1920s and 1930s, was the understandable lack of investment made in plant and facilities. With some yards closing for extended periods and others barely breaking even or drawing on reserves, capital expenditure was curtailed or deferred until better times. Thus the engine works and shipyards with which Britain went to war in 1939 used very much the same equipment and facilities that they had in 1914/18. In 1925, the warship builders did however set up a group within their trade association, the Shipbuilding Conference, to quote minimum prices for the few Admiralty orders such as destroyers, to avoid the ruinous competition of quoting loss making prices, formalised in 1934.

Whether or not the rationalisation of the shipbuilding that took place during the 1930s was a success or not is difficult to quantify as it was only under the stimulus of re-armament in the mid-1930s that the outlook for industry in Britain began to improve. However, there is little doubt that it helped more of the industry survive than would otherwise have happened. Furthermore, bankruptcies were reduced, as the yards were paid to close, causing less disruption. It was the reduction in competition that gave the other yards a better chance of survival. In the crises that would face the country from 1939 onwards, it was not so much the lack of shipbuilding facilities that would prove to be a serious issue but the lack of skilled labour. Forced to find work elsewhere, some men emigrated while many of those who stayed at home found other work, or moved away to such as the motor car industry in the Midlands and never returned to the shipyards.

The only work carried out on capital ships during this time was the modernisation of certain ships allowed under the terms of the Washington Treaty. With a normal life of twenty years, the oldest ships of the British battlefleet, the *Queen Elizabeth*s, and *Renown*s would have been due for replacement in the early 1930s. Like the other major naval powers, Britain exercised its right to modernise these units to varying degrees. For *Warspite*, *Valiant*, *Queen Elizabeth* and *Renown* this meant the complete removal of upperworks, boilers and machinery and the substitution of new bridge works, aircraft handling arrangements, secondary armament, thicker deck protection and new machinery as well as the upgrading of their main armament. Very little was done to

the *Royal Sovereign* class with *Hood*, *Repulse*, *Barham* and *Malaya* some way in between. This work was undertaken by the Royal Dockyards although as before, machinery, new weapon systems, armour and other major fittings were manufactured and supplied by the private firms.

No new battleships were built between the wars by anyone except the great powers, who had their own shipyards. Thus the export market in such vessels ceased to exist, although a few heavy guns were built for coast defence in places like Spain, for example. With the dearth of British government orders, Vickers-Armstrongs sought out any overseas orders for warships and ordnance. Their new managing director, Charles Craven, appointed in 1931, was tireless in pursuing such orders in an attempt to keep the company's core facilities employed. Anti-aircraft guns and ammunition were sold in the 1930s to Holland, Spain, Turkey, Japan, Siam, Argentina, and Peru. Torpedoes were a steady seller, if not in large numbers, to Holland, Portugal, Poland, Finland, Romania, Greece and China. In its first quarterly report of 1932 to the V-A Board, the subsidiary Whitehead Torpedo Co Ltd reported: 'On 6 January 1932, a very successful dropping trial of a 45cm Whitehead Weymouth torpedo from an aircraft was carried out in Weymouth Bay before all the foreign commissions. Cdr Y Yasuba of the Japanese Navy visited Weymouth to witness the trial.'[12]

LATER NAVAL CONFERENCES

The Washington Treaty was highly successful in limiting the construction of warships and rather than allow the momentum behind international agreement to be lost, a further series of naval disarmament conferences were convened to either modify the original Treaty or extend its remit after expiry. These efforts to control naval armaments are briefly summarised here.

Following Washington was the Geneva Naval Conference of 1927 which attempted to apply the criteria adopted at Washington in 1922 to cruisers and lesser warship types without further qualification to existing agreements concerning capital ships. The conference was unsuccessful and resulted in no agreement. In 1930, with the 1922 Treaty soon to expire, the five major powers, the UK, US, Japan, France and Italy, met in London to reach agreement on limits for cruiser tonnage, make a distinction between light and heavy cruisers and consider aspects of submarine warfare. At the same time

VICKERS–ARMSTRONGS OVERSEAS WARSHIP AND ARMAMENT ORDERS 1931–8

1931   Armament for five Portuguese destroyers, building at Yarrow and Lisbon.
1932   Training ship for Brazil (*Almirante Saldanha*) £316,000.
1932   Three submarines for Portugal (*Delfim, Espadarte, Golfinho*) £545,000.
1934   Two submarines for Estonia (*Kalev, Lembit*) £360,000.
1935   Directors and fire control systems for Spanish cruisers *Canarias* and *Baleares*, £198,000.
1935   Cruiser and armament for Argentina (*La Argentina*) £1.438 million.
1935   Armament for two sloops for Siam building in Japan (*Tachin, Meklong*).
1936   Three destroyers for Argentina (*Buenos Aires, Entre Rios, Corrientes*) £1.145 million.
1936   Armament for four destroyers for Argentina building by John Brown and Cammell Laird, £290,000.
1937   Two destroyers for Brazil (*Jurua/Harvester, Japarua/Hurricane*) £1.132 million.
1937   Armament for four destroyers for Brazil building by Thornycroft and White, £527,000.
1937   Ammunition for Argentine Navy £316,000.
1938   Two destroyers for Turkey (*Muavenet/Inconstant, Gayret/Ithuriel*).
1938   Four submarines for Turkey (*Oruc Reis/P.611, Murat Reis/P.612, Burak Reis/P.614, Uluc Ali Reis/P.615*).

it was agreed to uphold and extend the 1922 Treaty limitations applied to the construction of battleships which resulted in an extension to the so-called 'battleship building holiday' until the end of 1936. The Conference reached agreement in April and the London Treaty was ratified in October 1930.

In 1932, a second conference was convened at Geneva on the wider theme of general disarmament but had no bearing on capital ships which were in any case still under the terms of the Washington and London Treaties. In December 1935, the Second London Naval Disarmament Conference began, although the Government of Japan withdrew early in the proceedings through frustration with the western powers whom the Japanese considered disrespectful. This did not prevent agreement being reached by the remaining five powers across a wide range of ship types although it did set the scene for later abrogation of the Treaty. The construction of new capital ships was to be limited to remain at 35,000 tons standard displacement with main armament reduced to 14in guns. However, the Treaty mandated that should any of the signatories of the 1922 Washington Treaty fail to ratify the 1936 London Treaty by April 1937, main armament could be raised to 16in. Although the Second London Naval Treaty attempted to maintain limitation, it was ultimately subverted by Japanese failure to sign up to its conditions. This enabled the major powers to change from the planned 35,000-ton, 14in-gunned ships or, in the case of some countries less scrupulous than the British, to continue to build battleships in excess of 35,000 tons with 15in guns and above.

In 1935 a short-lived naval agreement was reached between Britain and Germany, recognising the latter's resurgence, which enabled the German Navy to expand to 35 per cent of that of the Royal Navy, in defiance of the Versailles Treaty of 1919. Widely seen as an act of appeasement, the agreement was abrogated by Germany in 1939. While the naval powers were still subject to Treaty restraints, this did not prevent the preparation of battleship designs to meet eventualities once Treaty conditions expired. As early as 1927, the DNC's department had worked on a series of sketch designs for battleships of various sizes should the 1922 Treaty fail to be extended in 1931.

In the late 1920s a sequence of events began when Germany laid down the first of three panzerschiffe, small but relatively fast armoured ships mounting 11in guns, sometimes called 'pocket battleships'. This prompted a French response in the two *Dunkerque* class battleships, which in turn provided the impetus for the two larger *Scharnhorst* type battleships. In 1934, Italy laid down the keels of two *Littorio* class battleships nominally of 35,000 tons and 15in guns prompting the French *Richelieu*s. This sequence of construction was permitted under Treaty provisions as these nations had not built up to their permitted strength although, in so doing, serious violations of tonnage restrictions were made. In 1934 Japan renounced all treaty obligations which enabled her to design ships without reference to external obligations.

By 1935 the most modern British battleships, *Nelson* and *Rodney*, were, at eight years old, nearly half-way through their lifespan while the unmodernised units of the battlefleet at twenty years old, were almost at the end of their useful life. Even modernised units would not be a match for the new fast battleships under construction or planned in Europe. Against these disturbing international developments, the Admiralty was perforce to respond, and a new round of capital ship construction was initiated immediately on the expiration of the Treaty.

THE LAST BATTLESHIPS

Once it was clear that war was inevitable Britain moved to make preparation for no fewer than ten battleships to be laid down over five years starting at the beginning of 1937. The first five would be restricted under original Treaty conditions to 35,000 tons standard displacement and 14in guns although the five later units would take advantage of the new upper limit of 45,000 tons and 16in guns. The armaments industries, now much reduced in scale from the 1918 peak, contemplated a resumption in orders for which new plant would have to be laid down. New armour plant in particular had to be provided for and in this respect the Admiralty made substantial contributions, e.g. over £1 million to the English Steel Corporation alone, to ensure that adequate capacity was provided – see Chapter 9.

The ordering sequence for these ships by year as originally envisaged by the Admiralty was:

1936   *King George V* and *Prince of Wales*. To be completed in 1940.
1937   *Anson, Beatty* and *Jellicoe* – later renamed *Duke of York, Howe* and *Anson*. To be completed in 1941.

1938 *Lion* and *Temeraire*. To be completed in 1942.
1939 *Conqueror* and *Thunderer*. To be completed in 1943.
1940 *Vanguard*. To be completed in 1944.

As events would prove, the demand on resources, technical, materials and labour, would make this number of battleships impossible to build once the pressure of war was felt through competing demand for resources.

The *King George V* class

Throughout the 1920s and 1930s, various capital ship designs had been developed in preparation for scenarios that might develop should the Treaty system collapse. A measure of this effort can be gained from a note dated 9 March 1937, buried in the *King George V* ships covers, in which the DNC, Stanley Goodall, states that since the construction of *Nelson* and *Rodney*, sixty different designs of capital ships had been prepared of which eighteen were for 14in-gun ships.

The origin of the *King George V* class began in 1935 when the DNC and his staff were working on a series of designs for battleships and battlecruisers mounting 14in guns in quadruple turrets. These designs ranged from small battleships of 22,000 to 24,000 tons displacement and battleships and battlecruisers up to the maximum size permitted of 35,000 tons. Design 14P, subsequently to become the

King George V class, was considered to be closest to requirements and by July 1936 a cost had been worked out as follows:

	£
Machinery	825,000
Hull	2,050,000
Armour	1,425,000
Gun mountings	1,500,000
Air conditioning	14,000
Guns	580,000
Ammunition	805,000
Aircraft equipment	66,500
Power boats	20,000
Dockyard labour & materials	156,000
Incidental charges	27,000
TOTAL	7,468,500

No formal tendering process appears to have been followed and in July 1936, contracts were awarded to Vickers-Armstrongs (*King George V*) and Cammell Laird (*Prince of Wales*). The Vickers-Armstrongs ship would be built at Walker Naval Yard and the machinery at their Barrow works. The urgency with which the Admiralty was proceeding is perhaps explained by the request for a quotation from both builders which was made two months later in September – these two shipyards had built *Nelson* and *Rodney* at a loss a decade earlier. Preparations were made for a further three ships to be laid down soon after and in October 1936, the DNC wrote to John Brown, Fairfield and Swan Hunter, providing them with the basic dimensions of the ship to enable a berth to be prepared and advising that the maximum weight to be lifted would be the quadruple 14in turntables at 187 tons. Goodall stated that at this stage it was not known if the three new ships would be repeats of the first two already ordered.

The original prices quoted in September excluding armament and armour were:

	Vickers-Armstrongs (£)	Cammell Laird (£)
Hull	2,262,000	2,271,000
Electrical	225,000	220,000
Machinery	898,014	900,896
Auxiliaries	65,254	64,659
Total	3,450,268	3,456,555

Both *King George V* and *Prince of Wales* were laid down on 1 January 1937, that being the day after the termination of the London Naval Treaty. It was not until July 1937 however, that the builders' tenders were accepted with figures subsequently adjusted in September of that year.

Below: Queen Elizabeth and King George VI walking to the launching platform at Clydebank on 28 February 1940 where the Queen will launch *Duke of York*. Winston Churchill, First Lord of the Admiralty but soon to be Prime Minister, is behind the King while Sir Stephen Pigott, managing director of the Clydebank works is behind the Queen. The Chairman of John Brown & Co, Lord Aberconway is to the right of the King. (*Author's Collection courtesy of NRS*)

In anticipation of the impact that the future battleship programme would have, a conference had been held on 16 April 1936 on board the new Cunard liner *Queen Mary* to discuss likely annual requirements.[13] In attendance were the top executives and their teams from Firth-Brown (Lord Aberconway), English Steel Corporation (Sir Charles Craven) and Wm Beardmore & Co (Sir James Lithgow). The Admiralty was represented by the Controller (Vice-Admiral Sir Reginald Henderson), the Director of Naval Construction (Sir Arthur Johns), the Engineer-in-Chief (Vice-Admiral Sir H A Brown), Director of Contracts (E C Jubb) and others. The Controller estimated that 21,000 tons of cemented armour and 18,500 tons of non-cemented armour would be required on average over the next few years. The three firms thought that, with extensions to their plant, they could produce 42,500 tons of armour annually, ESC 19,000 tons, Firth-Brown 13,500 tons and Beardmore 10,000 tons, compared with their current combined capacity of 18,000 tons a year. The firms also agreed that in order to produce this amount without harming their existing steel trade a capital expenditure of £1,500,000 was necessary – see Chapter 9. This was an example of the Treasury beginning to relax the purse strings to rebuild Britain's war potential as the threat from Germany increased.

In September 1936, orders were placed with the above firms for 9000 tons of deck armour for the two *King George V*s to keep their armour plant working at full capacity with deliveries aligned to shipyard construction timetables. The English Steel Corporation was allocated the contract for all of the deck armour for *King George V* while Beardmore and Firth-Brown split the deck armour for *Prince of Wales* between them. At the same time the armour for two quadruple turret barbettes each was allocated to Beardmore and Firth-Brown. ESC was allocated both twin turrets' barbette armour. In November 1936 orders were placed with Vickers-Armstrongs for the main armament of the three *King George V* class battleships of the 1937 programme, the armament for the first two having been ordered in May 1936.

In February 1937, John Brown submitted a tender price to the Admiralty for one ship at a total of £3,409,000 – see details on pp.294-5. This price, slightly lower than that of the first two ships, benefitted in cost savings from work already done in the drawing office and pattern shops as well as from the purchase of forgings.

ORIGINAL TIMETABLE FOR COMPLETION OF *KING GEORGE V* CLASS, SEPTEMBER 1939

	A	B	C
King George V	mid-March 1940	mid-September 1940	mid-December 1940
Prince of Wales	August 1940	mid-December 1940	end December 1940
Anson (Duke of York)	mid-April 1941	mid-August 1941	end August 1941
Jellicoe (Anson)	August 1941	mid-December 1941	end December 1941
Beatty (Howe)	mid-December 1941	mid-April 1942	end April 1942

By the end of April, sufficient building drawings had been provided to the shipbuilders to allow *Duke of York* to be laid down at Clydebank on 5 May. *Howe* was laid down on 1 June 1937 at Govan and *Anson* on 20 July 1937 at Wallsend.

On 3 September 1939, war with Germany was declared bringing a new level of urgency to the construction of the *King George V* class battleships. Germany had already launched the 15in battleships *Bismarck* and *Tirpitz*. The Admiralty wrote to the five shipbuilders on 20 September advising them of hoped for completion dates. These were based on three criteria, A, the delivery of the last gun mounting; B, steam and gun trials and C, fully completed ships after returning to the shipyard for fire control gear and adjustments (see above).

To achieve this timetable for *King George V*, Vickers-Armstrongs were instructed to give this ship priority over the aircraft carrier *Victorious*. It was further noted that if the delivery of mountings was improved, *Beatty* could be completed by December 1941. On 28 November, Winston Churchill, First Lord of the Admiralty, wrote to the Controller saying it was 'absolutely necessary that the five battleships now building with 14in guns should be ready by the summer of 1941'. He then asked if there were improvements in the last three of the class over the first two adding 'Let me see the legends'. The DNC replied to the Controller that all five were the same with minor modifications but that *King George V* was fitted as a flagship, although the decision was taken later to fit *Duke of York* as a flagship also.

Completion of *King George V* and *Prince of Wales*

At a conference held at the Spa Hotel, Bath[14] on 8 May 1940, the completion of *King George V* was discussed and the following decision made to bring her into service as quickly as possible. As the ship had only two propellers fitted at this time, it was agreed that she would be capable of being steamed to Devonport in this condition at 18 to 20 knots and docked there where the other two propellers could be fitted. As another month was required to complete A and Y 14in mountings and half of the eight 5.25in mountings, the ship could not be completed and receive her crew until the end of September. It was therefore proposed to commission her on 1 October at Walker with a full engine room complement and sufficient personnel to fight A and Y mountings as well as half the 5.25in mountings. A further three weeks would be required to ammunition the ship and complete various drills. This would leave B turret to be completed and the remaining half of the 5.25s. In the event, four of *Prince of Wales'* 5.25in mountings were taken from Barrow to complete *King George V* and B 14in was shipped in August so the Devonport diversion was not necessary. *King George V* left the Tyne on 17 October for Rosyth where she was drydocked and eventually completed on 11 December 1940.

The Admiralty overseer at Cammell Laird worked out a rough timetable for *Prince of Wales* which was based on the possibility of receiving the 14in mountings one month early.

Early November: Dry dock (about ten days).

Inclining and tilt test and alignment of gun sights.
Late November: Undock, ammunition ship and complete storing (about ten days).
Early December: Sea trials and completion.

However, this timetable proved overly optimistic and *Prince of Wales* was completed at Rosyth on 31 March 1941.

Duke of York was launched on 28 February 1940 and completed on 4 November 1941 but work on *Anson* and *Howe* had to be suspended during fitting out because of the need to finish other vessels that were closer to completion, as well as the pressure that urgent war work had placed on the gun mounting manufacturing capacity at Barrow and Elswick. *Anson* was completed on 22 June 1942 and *Howe* on 29 August 1942.

Lion class

In 1938 the governments of Britain, France and the USA agreed that as a consequence of Japan's failure to sign up to the London Naval Treaty that battleships up to a displacement of 45,000 tons mounting 16in guns could be constructed. The British government however, stated that it did not intend to build in excess

of 40,000 tons standard displacement, probably in the hope that the other signatories would follow suit. This decision set the scene for the *Lion* class although other designs were produced including a 12 x 16in gunned ship of 45,000 tons and a 12 x 14in-gunned ship of 43,000 tons.

After examining several design options and weighing up the likely international reaction to the design chosen, a ship of 40,000 tons and nine 16in guns was selected. On 15 December 1938, the Board approved the legend and drawings of the *Lion* class battleships. Tenders for hull and machinery were invited from John Brown, Fairfield, Vickers-Armstrongs, Cammell Laird, Harland & Wolff and Swan Hunter (hull only). Parsons Marine and Wallsend Slipway were also invited to tender for the machinery. Tenders were submitted on 31 January 1939 and on 6 February they had been reviewed and it was the decision of the Board to place orders with the two lowest tenders: Vickers-Armstrongs and Cammell Laird, both of whom offered a 42-month delivery subject to sufficient labour being available. Letters accepting these tenders were sent out to the shipbuilders on 21 February.

In compliance with the 1936 London Naval Treaty, in December 1938 the Admiralty disclosed the particulars of the 1938 Battleships. See table top right.

The contracts for armour and gun mountings were placed well ahead of that of the hull and machinery and by December 1938, before any keels had been laid, the DNC memoed his staff to say that the machining of armour plate was at present the bottleneck in armour production and that as a consequence this should be cut to the minimum, citing the practice of machining a radius on plate edges which was to stop.

The order for the next two *Lions* could have been allocated to either John Brown, Fairfield, Harland & Wolff or Swan Hunter. On 12 June 1939, both John Brown and Fairfield and presumably Harland & Wolff and Swan Hunter, were invited to tender. These were received between 22 and 27 July 1939, and the tenders from John Brown and Fairfield accepted. Thus the third and fourth units of the *Lion* class, *Conqueror* (John Brown) and *Thunderer* (Fairfield) were ordered in August 1939. *Temeraire* was the first to be laid down on 1 June 1939 at Birkenhead followed by *Lion* on 4 July at Walker on Tyne. On 3 July however, the first intimation that these contracts were

BASIC PARTICULARS OF THE *LION* CLASS DECEMBER 1938

Names:	*Lion* and *Temeraire*
Standard displacement (tons)	40,000
Length at waterline at standard displacement	80ft
Mean draught at standard displacement	30ft
Extreme beam at waterline or below waterline at standard displacement	105ft
Designed hp	120,000
Designed speed	29.75 knots
Type of machinery	Turbines, geared
Number and calibre of guns above 3in	9 x 16in and 16 x 5.25in

going to be troublesome came when both shipbuilders were told that the 16in mountings would be delivered nine months late. Cammell Laird wrote to the Admiralty reminding them that in their letter of 23 June, the Admiralty had anticipated that delivery of the 16in mountings for *Temeraire* would be in April, May and June 1942. The nine months delay now indicated would make the August 1942 completion date impossible to keep and would result in higher building costs. At the Walker Naval Yard, where the delivery of the main armament should have been in January, February, March 1942, completion of *Lion* would now be February 1943.

With work on the four *Lions* now underway, collaboration between the four shipbuilders began, starting with the division of drawing office work. Details already worked out by Vickers-Armstrongs and Cammell Laird were passed to on John Brown using the frame offsets laid off at Barrow. John Brown's naval architect, James McNeill, wrote to A J Hendin, shipyard manager at Naval Yard, asking if he would 'lend' him tracings for the shaft brackets; stern casting; rudder; vertical and flat keels; longitudinals, arrangement and detail; transverse framing in double bottom and the body plan to enable the ordering of materials.

The beginning of the construction process for the *Lions* coincided with the start of the war which forced a re-evaluation of priorities requiring the manufacture of weapons and the production of armour for use in more immediate circumstances. With the five *King George V* class well advanced in the shipyards and the armour and ordnance shops, the *Lions* were more than could be managed and on 3 October 1939, the Admiralty requested the shipbuilders to suspend work on the battleships pending instructions. Initially, it was intended that the contracts should be suspended for one year pushing back *Lion*'s completion until March 1944 and *Temeraire*'s to September 1944.

Under the revised timetable the John Brown
ship would be laid down in January 1941 and
the Fairfield ship in April 1941. A significant
contributory factor in suspending the *Lion*s was
the slow and late production of armour drawings from a hard-pressed DNC's department.
This brought with it the concern that the
heavy armour plate mills would not be running
at capacity and skilled labour dispersed or
diverted to other purposes such as tank armour.
To obviate this situation it was agreed that the
production of armour for *Conqueror* and
Thunderer should be stopped and considered
again in June 1940 but that bulkhead and lower
deck armour for *Lion* and *Temeraire* should
proceed, subject to the realistic appraisals of the
shipbuilders and armour manufacturers. It was
a question of the effective utilisation of vital
defence manufacturing capacity within the
expected duration of the war.

This delay enabled an accumulation of war
experience at sea to be brought to bear on the
Lion design, which was in any case constantly
reviewed and updated. The consequence of this

was that by August 1940, new calculations
showed that additions to the design resulted in
the ships being too deep in the water. After
deliberation between the Controller and the
DNC, the following alterations were approved
for *Lion* and *Temeraire* to be implemented when
construction resumed.

- Maximum beam increased from 105ft to
  108ft.
- Side armour over machinery spaces to be
  reduced from 15in to 14in.
- Barbette armour to be reduced from 15in to
  14in.
- A splinter belt to be fitted forward and aft of
  the main belt from lower to middle deck.
- Sheer of the forecastle to be increased.
- 40lb transverse splinter bulkheads to be fitted
  forward and aft between lower and middle
  deck.

One outcome of these alterations was that the
increased beam would make the ships unable to
be drydocked at Rosyth and Portsmouth.

Vickers-Armstrongs and Cammell Laird were advised of these changes for which a new body plan would have to be prepared. In mid-October, the DNC decided that no work should be done on the new body plan at present and that work on detailed drawings should be dropped. Such a fundamental redesign would, in any case, have required a fresh start on the building slip. A new design 16H was produced with the following basic hull particulars: 780ft on the waterline (unchanged from the original design), 108ft beam, 33ft 3in draught on a deep displacement of 48,000 tons.

The third significant restraint that would have affected the *Lions*, a shortage of skilled labour, soon materialised as it had in the First World War over the *Hood*s. At a meeting between the Controller (Vice-Admiral Sir Bruce Fraser) and the First Sea Lord (Admiral Sir Dudley Pound) on 31 March 1941, Pound was most anxious that both ships should be restarted, while the Controller said that it was now a question of labour and that only a large increase in the labour force on Navy work would enable a restart to be made. Along with armour production, gun mounting capacity was a crucial bottleneck. On 6 September 1941, a meeting between the DNO (Captain W R Slater) and the Controller noted that as the last of the 14in mountings for the *King George V*s were nearing completion, capacity in machine tools and labour was becoming available for the *Lions*' 16in mountings, although some capacity had been given over to other war work. The discussion noted that 'If the capacity were adapted to another purpose, and should the teams of labour for gun mountings be dispersed, it could be a long time before an efficient organisation for constructing gun mountings could be built up again, and it was therefore doubtful if a high state of efficiency could be obtained for a matter of many years. The DNO stressed that if it is desired to proceed at any future time with the building of battleships, now is the moment at which to recommence work on the heavy gun mountings'. According to Vickers-Armstrongs, the mountings could be completed by 1945 although the DNO and Controller thought this was optimistic. In subsequent meetings the DNO asked for three 16in mountings for one battleship to be restarted while the DNC thought a start could be made on the hulls in August 1942. However, the longer the ships remained in suspension, the more likely that

the design was to change as a consequence of war experience. At a Controller's meeting on 30 December 1941, new staff requirements for the *Lion*s were discussed. It was pointed out that for a ship not expected to be completed until 1946/7 and already not in accordance with the latest staff requirements, it would be impossible to incorporate these into the existing design. The meeting nevertheless concluded somewhat contradictorily that *Lion* might still be completed although the Controller thought it unlikely that *Temeraire* would be restarted.

The end came on 19 December 1942 when the Director of Contracts wrote to Vickers-Armstrongs and Cammell Laird requesting them to clear the slips and re-use the material on other naval contracts where possible.[15] In April 1943, the DNC Goodall, wrote to the Controller saying that quantities of worked structural material for *Lion* should be returned to the makers as scrap as even if *Lion* was restarted she would need to be redesigned 'as practice regarding the construction of the bottom of a capital ship has changed since this ship was designed owing to our increased knowledge of the effects of under the bottom explosions'.

Vanguard

Five months before the Second World War began, a paper written by the Director of Plans, Victor H Danckwerts, presented a case for constructing a battleship quickly and at a lower cost (the paper refers to a battlecruiser) utilising spare 15in gun mountings held in store. As evidence for this, his paper included a synopsis of what he thought the future strengths of the British, German and Japanese fleets would be.

Japanese construction of capital ships remains uncertain, but from what evidence is available, it is clear that we shall for many years have to be prepared to face a Japanese fleet in the Far East with a British Fleet considerably inferior to it in numbers of capital ships. Although this inferiority in the Far East will be considerable during the next two or three years, it does not become most marked until Germany has completed her full quota of capital ships under the Anglo-German Treaty, i.e. until the portion of our fleet to be retained in home waters reaches the maximum. It is estimated that this will occur at about the end of 1943, say March 1944, at which date the situation in the event of a simultaneous war against Germany and Japan is likely to be roughly as follows:

British Fleet in Home Waters	Germany
2 1939 Programme	5 new capital ships
5 KGV	2 Scharnhorsts
3 Battlecruisers	3 Deutschlands
10 (capital ships)	7 + 3 (capital ships)

British Fleet in Far East	Japan
2 Lions	4 new capital ships ?
2 Nelsons	2 Nagatos
3 Warspites	4 Fusos
2 Barhams	4 Kongos
3 Royal Sovereigns	2 battlecruisers ?
12 (capital ships)	16? (capital ships)

The paper argued that a ship of 40,000 tons and 30 knots armed with eight existing 15in mountings could join the fleet in the Far East where the inferiority in numbers was greatest and that a further unit of this type could be built when the first *Royal Sovereign* was scrapped in 1942, thereby releasing four additional 15in mountings. It was recognised that the construction of this ship would be dependent on armour production but the ready availability of 15in mountings, albeit that they would require to be modernised, could enable the ship to be completed in early 1944 without delaying the last of the *Lion*s. In the discussion that followed, the DNC, who had himself previously referred to the possibility of such a ship, thought that a ship of *King George V*'s speed and protection mounting eight 15in guns would cost about £7 million, although this did not include the cost of the mountings but only the cost of bringing them up to date. He reiterated that armour production would be the deciding factor in construction time. He also referred to the need to extend the Harland & Wolff works at Scotstoun on the Clyde (the former Coventry Ordnance Works) where conversion of the 15in mountings would take place. In all probability this was because capacity at Barrow and Elswick would be fully occupied by other work, most notably the mountings for the *King George V* and *Lion* classes and cruisers.

Approval to proceed with the design for such a ship was received from various department heads as well as the Controller, Bruce Fraser, and the First Lord, Earl Stanhope, who felt it would be of great value to have a fast powerful ship of the *Hood* type in the Far East.

The Controller's summary of the situation was that:

> The existing 15in mountings would have to be modified before use in a modern ship.
> This modification will have to be done at Scotstoun in a new extension costing £600,000.
> The modification can be done in time to enable the ship to be completed by the end of 1943 but not sooner.
> Armour will be available for this ship in addition to that for the two 1940 *Lions*.

The 15in mountings for what became *Vanguard*'s Y and A mountings were previously the forward turrets from *Courageous* and *Glorious* while X and B were the after mountings from the same ships. With protection for the proposed ship to be equal to that of the *King George V*s, the ex-battlecruiser turrets did not meet these requirements and consequently it was proposed to replace the 170lb roof

Below: Three weeks after the departure of *Duke of York*, the first keel plate for *Vanguard* is laid down on Berth No.3 at Clydebank on 2 October 1941. With 15in turrets already available, the hope was that construction of the battleship could be accelerated, enabling the ship to join the fleet in early 1944. *(Author's collection courtesy of NRS)*

armour with 240lb, the front of the shield with three 520lb plates and the 80lb protective plate under the tail with 120lb. Increasing the elevation of the guns from 20° to 30° would require cutting into the roof plate.

The cost of Design 15C as estimated in July 1939 was:

	£
Hull	3,130,000
Main and auxiliary machinery	1,360,000
Power boats	20,000
Armour and bullet proof plating	1,540,000
Gun mountings and air compressing machinery	750,000
Ammunition and guns	900,000
Dockyard labour and materials	200,000
Total	7,900,000

At this stage the DNC advised the Controller that the construction programme envisaged was 3½ years from the date of keel laying. See table to right showing milestones to completion.

On 15 February 1940, verbal instructions to proceed with the design of the 15in battleship with machinery as in *Lion* were given by the Controller while, three weeks later on 8 March, he wrote to Sir Stephen Pigott, managing director at John Brown's Clydebank yard, in a wonderfully informal manner, placing with him the order for *Vanguard*.

> I have not yet been able to give you the official order for the 'Marshal Soult' [later *Roberts*] but will you on this authority go ahead at full speed, since I intend to put a 15in battleship with you at the beginning of next year. I should also be very grateful if you would give your full assistance to the Director of Naval Construction in all drawing and design work required for the new capital ship, so that we can complete the ship by June 1943. This is an essential requirement and I feel that we can hold to it.

This instruction by the Controller, and his completion date of June 1943 in particular, had a galvanising effect on the DNC's department who noted that 'all questions now under discussion affecting the general design of the ship may be dealt with as soon as possible so that detailed design work may proceed'.

Now a degree of confusion entered proceedings when, on 30 May, W G Sanders of the DNC's Department wrote to Pigott with reference to the Controller's letter of 8 March

CONSTRUCTION OF *VANGUARD* AS ANTICIPATED IN THE SUMMER OF 1939

	Months from zero	Approximate date
Order hull and machinery	0	Nine months after approval of sketch design, say, August 1940
Order armour (rolling sizes)	0	August 1940
Lay down ship	4	December 1940
Launch ship	24	August 1942
1st turret shipped	26	October 1942
2nd turret shipped	27	November 1942
3rd turret shipped	28	December 1942
4th turret shipped	29	January 1943
Line up machinery	30	February 1943
Trials at sea	37/38	September/October 1943
Completion	42	February 1944

saying that this vessel will now not proceed. On the following morning, Pigott telephoned Fraser for clarification following this with a letter on 5 June:

> I think you stated that it is desired that the design of this vessel will continue and I gather that it is the intention that the design for the 16in gun battleships in which design work we are participating will also continue. The object of this letter is to confirm that our Dr McNeill and our special staff are ready to assist or relieve Sir Stanley Goodall's staff of all such work as can be entrusted to us...

Dr McNeill had visited the Admiralty design office at Bath on 19 April where it was agreed his firm would assist in working on *Vanguard*'s design calculations.

The first serious delay in progress was notified on 19 September when the DNC wrote to Pigott advising that *Vanguard*'s beam had been increased from 105.5ft to 108ft for the same reasons that applied to *Lion*. However, some doubt about the ship proceeding at all still persisted and it was not until 26 October 1940 that Goodall wrote to Pigott stating that *Vanguard* would definitely proceed. To alleviate the pressure on the DNC's department, six ship draughtsmen were sent to Bath from Clydebank to work alongside Admiralty constructors on the battleship's design calculations.[16] By mid-October the specification for *Vanguard* was still incomplete, as the calculations needed to be reworked because of the increased beam. The drawings were between 40 and 60 per cent complete. It was not until 25 March 1941 that the design was completed based on sketch design 15D. The formal order to proceed with *Vanguard* was by letter dated 14 March

1941 although it was not until 2 October that it was possible to lay her keel.

At a Controller's meeting on 30 December 1941, the first following the loss of *Prince of Wales* and *Repulse* off Malaya, the Controller asked for *Vanguard* to be completed urgently. However, there were competing demands for labour at the shipyard not least the fleet carrier *Indefatigable*. It was agreed that to put more workers on *Vanguard* and *Indefatigable*, the cruiser *Bellerophon* (later *Tiger*) should be suspended and that the sloops *Snipe* and *Sparrow* be transferred to Devonport Dockyard.[17] Progress on a Port Line merchant ship, which had been laid down in November 1941, was decelerated. It was also agreed that the highest priority, priority 1A, be sought for *Vanguard*'s construction. The bureaucratic machinery necessary to acquire this level of priority precipitated a revealing exchange of letters, not least for the insight it offers into the demands placed on officials managing their corners within a pressurised Admiralty department during wartime.

The exchange took place between the Assistant Secretary to the Admiralty, A S Le Maitre, and C Hannaford, Director of Contract Work, and is reproduced here in full.

6 January 1942

Dear Hannaford,

The First Lord has informed the Controller that the Prime Minister has granted 1A for the Vanguard. I now have to get the necessary certificate from the Chairman of the Central Priority Committee, Colonel Llewellin. There is, of course, no difficulty, but in asking for the certificate, which formally authorises the priority rating of 1A to be applied, I must have some ammunition. All I know is that the Vanguard, building at John Browns, has a part of her keel laid, that she is due to finish at the end of 1944, but that we might knock three months off that. The engines, I suppose, are also being built at John Browns. I suppose that her main mountings are already in hand and are fully manned. Can you tell me in any detail what we are likely to gain by 1A at this very early stage, which contractors are involved, and who is likely to suffer, i.e., other naval work which is no one's business but our own, or the work of some other department?

Material is not affected by 1A and in any case I presume that we can so organise our own material allocation that there will be no hitch except such as we impose ourselves, such as the delay of something else.

Labour, again is outside the Priority Direction, and as we are now transferring labour from John Brown to Fairfield, it seems to follow that if any yard is especially short of labour it is not John Brown.

Where then exactly does 1A come in? If it is purely psychological, I should have thought it better to keep for emergencies – i.e. you may need it for auxiliary aircraft carriers or Tank Landing Craft, and you have already asked for it

Below: Last of the *King George V* class to join the war. *Howe* during her brief trials period in August 1942, still fitted with aircraft-handling equipment. *(Author's collection)*

for submarine equipment, and have got it for two battleships at a late stage in their completion.

Can you please give me some advice on what this priority is needed for?

Hannaford replied on 17 January 1942:

Dear Le Maitre,

The ammunition you require will, I hope, be contained in the following.

1. Both the hull and machinery are being constructed by Messrs John Brown, Clydebank. The mountings for the big guns are already in existence and have only to be adapted for the ship and are fully manned for this purpose. Vanguard's date of completion could not have been earlier than the middle of 1945.

2. It is now proposed to suspend the construction of the cruiser Bellerophon for at least 12 months and it is also in mind to transfer the order for two sloops. With these steps and with minor adjustments together with

priority 1A as directed by the Prime Minister it appears feasible to complete the vessel in September 1944. This would be within three years of laying the keel and compares with four years for the quickest construction of the King George V Class.

3. In attempting to accelerate the construction of work of such magnitude as a battleship it is essential that protection should be given against any possible hold up in her construction otherwise the effect of previous concentration would be lost. We expect to be able to restrict the effects of any priority direction largely within our own department but the future may bring us into conflict with the requirements of other departments and we want to ensure that Vanguard has the highest ranking. One example that occurs to me is the construction of tanks. Tanks require armour and the major part of this armour is being made in armour works which were maintained and built up in peace time by the efforts of the Admiralty and the requirements for tank armour may at some time come into

Above: Gleaming in a fresh coat of paint, Britain's last battleship, *Vanguard*, is ready to leave Clydebank to run trials in this photograph taken at the beginning of May 1946. Next to *Vanguard* is the cruiser *Tiger*, soon to be laid-up and eventually reconstructed to a new design. The third vessel, the Port liner *Port Wellington*, marks the start of the rapid transition from naval to merchant tonnage. Note the east yard building berths are being re-equipped with new 40-ton tower cranes and the machinery castings stored at the head of the fitting-out basin. *(Author's Collection courtesy of NRS)*

Right: Although this graph from Admiralty sources shows John Brown shipyard labour to 1946, it appears that actuals are only to 1943, with 1944 onwards projected to show resources potentially available to build aircraft carrier *Malta* (cancelled in 1945) and merchant ships. LST hulls were built elsewhere although some were fitted out by John Brown at Dalmuir.

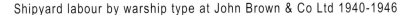

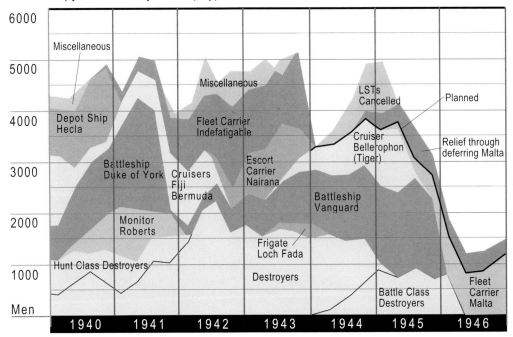

Shipyard labour by warship type at John Brown & Co Ltd 1940-1946

conflict with the requirements for Vanguard and for other of our armoured ships, though as far as can be seen we shall be able to get over any difficulties that may arise. If any adjustment becomes necessary for the requirements for Tanks and Vanguard we want to be sure that Vanguard is not handicapped by a lower ranking.

4. You seem to see a paradox in the fact that labour is being transferred from John Browns to Fairfields while we are clamouring for John Brown to be priority 1A for Vanguard. The explanation is quite simple. Howe is in the completion stage at Messrs Fairfields and requires the services of finishing trades such as electricians, fitters and painters whereas Vanguard is only a few plates on the stocks and requires those men skilled in plating work.

The long and the short of it is we want priority 1A because the Prime Minister wants the ship at the earliest possible moment.

In March 1942, Pigott advised the Admiralty that even given priority 1A, completing *Vanguard* by September 1944 would be a 'notable achievement'. At that time, *Indefatigable* was fully manned and *Vanguard* manned as fully as material available allowed. The only outcome of pressing the Admiralty for additional labour was the voluntary transfer of one squad of platers from Stephen's shipyard further up the

River Clyde. Pigott had no alternative but to tell the Admiralty that *Vanguard* would not be completed in 1944.[18] In a letter of 4 April 1942, the Admiralty nevertheless complained about lack of progress on the ship. When Admiral Lord Chatfield made further criticisms of the battleship building programme, Pigott met the Controller on 23 April. At this meeting it emerged that *Vanguard* was intended to have priority only over the *Lion* class battleships and that it was still the Admiralty's view that *Indefatigable* was more important than *Vanguard*. Pigott was told that Admiralty priorities for Clydebank that year were, in order of importance, repairs to naval ships already in service; destroyers to fullest capacity of number 7 and 8 berths; the light cruiser *Bermuda*, then *Indefatigable* and lastly *Vanguard*.[19]

The manpower required to fulfil the decision to convert a suspended merchant ship into an escort carrier in July 1942, subsequently *Nairana*, pushed *Vanguard*'s projected completion date back until June 1945. Pigott met with District Shipyard Controller, Vice-Admiral Troup, on 2 July 1942 to discuss the implications. Troup claimed that the Admiralty was hopeful of getting 2000 skilled men, who had been out of the industry for some time, to return and that *Vanguard* should benefit from this.[20] At a further meeting at St Enoch's Hotel in Glasgow on 2 July 1942, Pigott submitted that representation should be made to Mr

Bevin, Minister of Labour, for the complete interchange of labour within and between all establishments as the most meaningful way in which production could be accelerated. At the John Brown ordinary general meeting in July, the Chairman, Lord Aberconway, summed the situation up: '…it would appear that manpower is now the measure of output.' Nevertheless, in December 1942, the best that could be provided for *Vanguard* was an additional 500 steelworkers although a further 500 would have been needed to adequately man the contract. The troubled history of *Vanguard*'s construction continued into 1943 when, in August and September, the Admiralty transferred men to *Indefatigable* and *Nairana*; the diagram shows the allocation of the Clydebank labour.

In March 1944, construction of *Vanguard* was finally given Priority 1A and completion was now projected to December 1945.[21] To ensure that sufficient numbers of the finishing trades were retained at Clydebank to work on the battleship after launching in November, John Brown entered into negotiation with Harland & Wolff to complete four of their frigates. After an agonisingly long time on the building slip, Princess Elizabeth finally launched *Vanguard* on 30 November 1944.

With the end of the European war in sight, the emphasis of war production began to change. In October 1944, Pigott met the Director of Naval Construction to discuss the completion of Admiralty contracts. It was agreed there would be no slowing down of naval contracts for ships that could be completed by June 1946. After the end of the war there was no hurry to complete *Vanguard* and it was not until the summer of 1946 that she ran trials on the Firth of Clyde.

CONCLUSION

Vanguard was the last British battleship to be completed, although this might not necessarily have been so had the *Lion* contracts been revived. Design work on an improved *Lion* continued until 1945 when it was finally recognised that battleship's role had gone with the changing nature of war at sea.[22] As it was, *Vanguard* was the last of the line. But what a line it had been. In the Dreadnought era alone, fifty-four battleships and battlecruisers had been laid down in British yards up until 1920 for the Royal Navy alone of which fifty-one were completed. In the last phase of construction from 1921 onwards, a further sixteen were contracted for, of which eight were completed. If battleships for foreign governments are added from 1906 onwards, the total built by the British naval construction industry was sixty-nine.

The vulnerability of the battleship to air attack, considered by some at the end of the First World War to be good enough reason to stop such vessels, was demonstrated many times during the Second World War. The aircraft carrier's overwhelming ability to project power over the horizon put the big-gun battleship into perspective, and it was now relegated to an escort and shore bombardment role. If industry had struggled to build six out of ten projected battleships between 1936 to 1946, fourteen fleet carriers and twenty-five light fleet carriers were projected of which seven and twenty respectively were completed by 1946 and two further fleet carriers, *Eagle* and *Ark Royal* in the early 1950s. In these numbers it is perfectly clear that of the shipbuilding capacity available to the Admiralty in 1939, a far greater portion was allocated to the aircraft carrier than to the battleship.

4: THE BUILDERS

SOME OF THE COMPANIES THAT formed the backbone of the armaments and naval construction industries in the first half of the twentieth century owed their origin to the early 1800s when iron as a construction material and steam as a power source came into use, spurred by the expansion of the railways and steam navigation. None of these companies began with naval construction in mind but grew from small beginnings, stimulated by the dynamic of industrialisation that swept across Britain as their products found ready markets at home and abroad.

Perhaps more than most industries, shipbuilding typified this experience through an early lead in steam marine engineering that pioneered the adoption of iron-hulled steam-driven vessels and the shipyards to build them from the late 1830s onwards. The new shipyards benefited greatly from two other prize assets, both a consequence of British domination of the high seas and its creation of a globe-spanning empire. The first was the size of the merchant marine and its transportation of people and goods to far-flung posts of Empire; the second was the Royal Navy, overwhelmingly the largest in the world, charged with projecting British political influence and defending the homeland and sea lanes alike. While merchant shipbuilding was the staple diet of British shipbuilding, over a period of time and in particular from 1860 onwards, the Admiralty made increasing use of private shipyards in addition to its own Royal Dockyards.

The largest of the twentieth-century armaments firms, Armstrong and Vickers, started out quite differently, the first as a manufacturer of hydraulic dock gear in Newcastle, the other as a maker of steel goods in Sheffield. Other businesses followed different routes to reach the same end as is the case with two other Sheffield firms, John Brown and Charles Cammell, whose expertise in the manufacture of iron and steel products led to the rolling of armour plate and later, the acquisition of ordnance capacity and finally shipbuilding. Increasingly, as the nineteenth century reached an end, this process of vertical integration became a significant business objective for companies hitherto limited in the scope of their manufacturing capability.

The Royal Dockyards were the traditional and almost exclusive builders of large Admiralty warships during the era of wooden hulls and sail. With the arrival of iron construction, steam propulsion and sophisticated ordnance, the ability of the Dockyards to build ships completely on their own was diminished. The decision to proceed with the construction of *Warrior* and *Black Prince* in 1859, ships that might be described as the first iron-hulled, steam-powered battleships, was made in the knowledge that they would be built by private yards. The reason was the Dockyards' lack of experience in iron construction. This was understandable given the accumulation of expertise over many decades in proven and tested but conservative wood-based technologies, managed by a distant bureaucracy. If a degree of inertia militated against the rapid uptake of new ideas, the opposite was the case for private yards where competitive interest lay in pioneering new technologies, particularly if that enabled ships to be built more quickly or cheaply or were faster, more fuel-efficient or had greater carrying capacity.

From this time onward, although the Dockyards retained their workforce and most re-equipped for iron construction, the private yards had a permanent and growing presence as contractors to the Admiralty, even if the Dockyards still dominated warship output. The

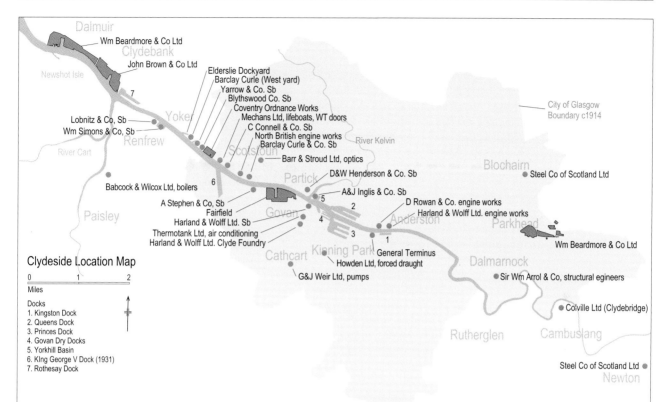

Clydeside Location Map

Wm Beardmore & Co Ltd
John Brown & Co Ltd
Elderslie Dockyard
Barclay Curle (West yard)
Yarrow & Co. Sb
Blythswood Co. Sb
Coventry Ordnance Works
Mechans Ltd, lifeboats, WT doors
C Connell & Co. Sb
North British engine works
Barclay Curle & Co. Sb
Barr & Stroud Ltd, optics
D&W Henderson & Co. Sb
A&J Inglis & Co. Sb
D Rowan & Co. engine works
Harland & Wolff Ltd. engine works
Lobnitz & Co, Sb
Wm Simons & Co, Sb
Babcock & Wilcox Ltd, boilers
A Stephen & Co, Sb
Fairfield
Harland & Wolff Ltd. Sb
Thermotank Ltd, air conditioning
Harland & Wolff Ltd. Clyde Foundry
General Terminus
Howden Ltd, forced draught
G&J Weir Ltd, pumps

City of Glasgow
Boundary c1914
Steel Co of Scotland Ltd
Wm Beardmore & Co Ltd
Sir Wm Arrol & Co, structural egineers
Colville Ltd (Clydebridge)
Steel Co of Scotland Ltd

0	1	2

Miles

Docks
1. Kingston Dock
2. Queens Dock
3. Princes Dock
4. Govan Dry Docks
5. Yorkhill Basin
6. King George V Dock (1931)
7. Rothesay Dock

A generic upper Clyde map set against Glasgow City boundaries c.1914.
The principal firms associated with shipbuilding are shown with works area plans for the battleship builders. In comparison to the Tyne and Mersey, the Clyde was narrow which required alignment of building berths at acute angles to the river to afford an adequate launching run. The West of Scotland with Glasgow at its centre was host to a myriad of firms large and small supporting the heavy industries of which shipbuilding and marine engineering were among the most significant. Other major industries included steel, locomotives and structural steel work such as cranes and bridges. Not shown on this map were other important shipbuilding yards at Old Kilpatrick and Dumbarton and a major complex of shipyards and engine works at Port Glasgow and Greenock.

The river Tyne was second only to the Clyde for twentieth-century warship building, but was the primary armaments producer with Armstrong Whitworths's Elswick Ordnance Works and its nearby Scotswood works. Armstrong also had three shipyards – at Elswick itself, Low Walker (mainly merchant ships) and Naval Yard, completed in 1914 to avoid the limitations of the upriver bridges. While Palmers and Swan Hunter were the only other Tyne battleship builders, there were three battleship machinery builders – Hawthorn Leslie, Wallsend Slipway and Parsons Marine. Most of the steelworks and engineering works supplied material for battleships, while most of the smaller shipbuilders built naval vessels in the First World War.

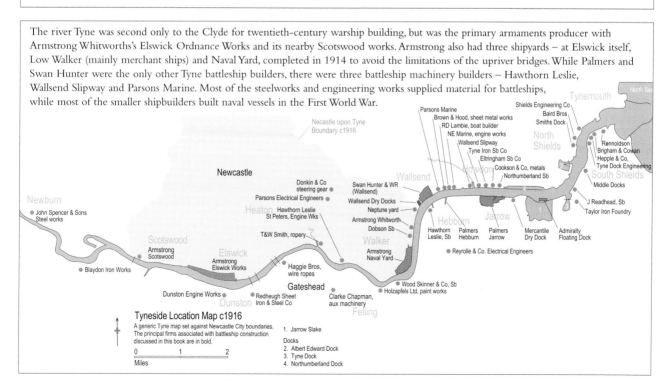

Parsons Marine
Brown & Hood, sheet metal works
RD Lambie, boat builder
NE Marine, engine works
Wallsend Slipway
Tyne Iron Sb Co
Eltringham Sb Co
Cookson & Co, metals
Northumberland Sb
Shields Engineering Co
Baird Bros
Smiths Dock
Rennoldson
Brigham & Cowan
Hepple & Co,
Tyne Dock Engineering
Middle Docks
J Readhead, Sb
Taylor Iron Foundry

Necastle upon Tyne
Boundary c1916
Newcastle
Donkin & Co
steering gear
Parsons Electrical Engineers
Hawthorn Leslie
St Peters, Engine Wks
T&W Smith, ropery
Swan Hunter & WR
(Wallsend)
Wallsend Dry Docks
Neptune yard
Armstrong Whitworth
Dobson Sb
Armstrong
Naval Yard
Hawthorn
Leslie, Sb
Palmers
Hebburn
Palmers
Jarrow
Mercantile
Dry Dock
Admiralty
Floating Dock
Reyrolle & Co. Electrical Engineers

John Spencer & Sons
Steel works
Armstrong
Scotswood
Armstrong
Elswick Works
Haggie Bros,
wire ropes
Blaydon Iron Works
Dunston Engine Works
Redheugh Sheet
Iron & Steel Co
Gateshead
Clarke Chapman,
aux machinery
Wood Skinner & Co, Sb
Holzapfels Ltd, paint works

Tyneside Location Map c1916

A generic Tyne map set against Newcastle City boundaries.
The principal firms associated with battleship construction
discussed in this book are in bold.

0	1	2

Miles

1. Jarrow Slake

Docks
2. Albert Edward Dock
3. Tyne Dock
4. Northumberland Dock

same applied to the construction of steam machinery, ordnance and armour. From the advent of steam propulsion, the Admiralty relied exclusively on private firms to construct machinery, although naval establishments were created to enable naval staff to operate and maintain machinery. Although the Admiralty did have access to significant gun manufacturing capability in the form of the Royal Gun Factory at Woolwich run by the War Office, innovation in this field tended to come from the private sector, not just for the manufacture of sophisticated ordnance but the design and manufacture of the hydraulically-operated gun mountings which were the most complicated mechanisms on any ship.

The growing technical sophistication of warships required considerable investment in new construction and manufacturing processes. Such investment was largely met by the private firms on the expectation that contracts for both naval and merchant ships would be forthcoming. Over the final decades of the nineteenth century, the Admiralty became increasingly reliant on the private sector and sought to strike a balance between maintaining the Dockyards and their staff, partly as a strategic reserve in time of war, and positively encouraging private manufacture with the required investment in new technology and plant through the prospect of substantial contracts.

The following sections trace the development of the main firms that emerged from the early days of industrialisation to form the naval construction industry, or in the context of this book, the battleship builders of the twentieth century. This industry can be divided into three groups: the armaments companies who developed the manufacturing capacity to build a battleship within their own works, the private shipbuilders who essentially remained as such although some developed links with armaments companies, and the government-owned Royal Dockyards and Royal Gun Factory.

1 THE ARMAMENTS COMPANIES

These are the companies that either developed or acquired industrial capability which enabled them to build most of the hull, machinery, armament and armour that comprised a battleship. Some firms claimed capability for all aspects of the ship although this was not strictly true, as items such as capstan gear, steering gear and a multitude of minor but important items including watertight doors and scuttles were often manufactured elsewhere.

By the description above, five companies have a reasonable claim to being described as fully integrated armaments companies. The first of these is Sir W G Armstrong & Co Ltd not simply because it is first in the alphabet but because this company set the pattern for others to follow and became the first of the large armaments companies in Britain.

1.1 Sir W G Armstrong, Whitworth & Co Ltd

Like many of the companies described in these pages, the driving force behind this company was one individual of talent and passion. William George Armstrong abandoned a career in law at the relatively late age of 37 to follow his interest in hydraulics, applied to the working of dock cranes and machinery. In 1846 Armstrong established the Newcastle Cranage Company, a non-manufacturing entity intended to manage the hydraulic cranes designed (but not built by) Armstrong for Newcastle quayside. The following year he established a works at Elswick on the north bank of the Tyne nearly two miles west of the centre of Newcastle. Here, Armstrong designed and manufactured hydraulically-powered dock cranes and equipment for the new and expanding market in ports around the British Isles and abroad. In 1850 he invented the hydraulic accumulator which provided water at constant pressure to dock appliances where no natural head existed and incidentally provided recognisable landmarks in ports in the form of distinctive towers. As the hydraulics business grew, Elswick became a major engineering centre for other mechanical and structural products such as winding engines, bridges and pumping engines.

Although Armstrong's contribution to the field of hydraulics was significant enough on its own, his entry into the business for which his company is best known, ordnance, seemed to be unplanned and quite by chance. Soon after the Crimean War (1853–6) broke out, he was asked to apply his engineering expertise to an underwater mine capable of blowing up Russian vessels sunk in Sevastopol harbour. However, it was while staying with eminent dock engineer James Rendel, with whom Armstrong had worked on many dock projects, that both men railed against what they considered to be the archaic nature of military ordnance, in particular field guns, evident from press coverage of the Battle of Inkerman fought in 1854. The outcome of this interest was that

Armstrong resolved to forward ideas for a new type of field gun to the Secretary of State for War. Armstrong's design was an engineered product far in advance of anything then in existence employing a breech-loading gun with a rifled barrel firing an elongated steel shell. This produced a more rapid and accurate fire than was possible with existing weaponry. Over the next two years, Armstrong provided a variety of guns to be evaluated by the Ordnance Committee to consider the type of gun most suitable for future use in the Army. Armstrong's proposals did not go unchallenged however, and were contested by Joseph Whitworth, often in rancorous circumstances. Whitworth, a talented engineer renowned for precision measuring methods in engineering and the screw thread named after him, had established a large works at Openshaw, Manchester, where machinery, tools, steel forgings and guns were manufactured. The Committee found in favour of Armstrong and he was appointed in 1859 as Engineer of Rifled Ordnance at the Royal Gun Factory, Woolwich, receiving a knighthood in

SIR W.G ARMSTRONG, WHITWORTH & CO. LTD,

ARMSTRONG NAVAL YARD,

HIGH WALKER,

NEWCASTLE-ON-TYNE.

21st November, 1917.

Left: The letterhead in use by Armstrong Whitworth during the First World War.

recognition of his contribution to British arms. To avoid a conflict of interest, Armstrong set up the Elswick Ordnance Company (EOC), separate from his hydraulic machinery company, but with manufacturing capacity at the Elswick site. But the EOC was not the only private supplier of guns, and there was a continuing challenge from Whitworth with his own gun designs. A considerable service opinion against Armstrong's gun brought about a brief return to the old style muzzle-loading guns. In 1862, after a series of financial issues concerning public funding at Elswick, all government contracts were cancelled. In 1863 Armstrong resigned from his government post and in the

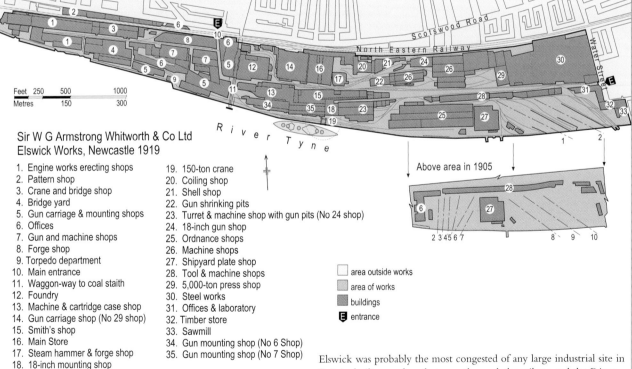

Sir W G Armstrong Whitworth & Co Ltd
Elswick Works, Newcastle 1919

1. Engine works erecting shops
2. Pattern shop
3. Crane and bridge shop
4. Bridge yard
5. Gun carriage & mounting shops
6. Offices
7. Gun and machine shops
8. Forge shop
9. Torpedo department
10. Main entrance
11. Waggon-way to coal staith
12. Foundry
13. Machine & cartridge case shop
14. Gun carriage shop (No 29 shop)
15. Smith's shop
16. Main Store
17. Steam hammer & forge shop
18. 18-inch mounting shop
19. 150-ton crane
20. Coiling shop
21. Shell shop
22. Gun shrinking pits
23. Turret & machine shop with gun pits (No 24 shop)
24. 18-inch gun shop
25. Ordnance shops
26. Machine shops
27. Shipyard plate shop
28. Tool & machine shops
29. 5,000-ton press shop
30. Steel works
31. Offices & laboratory
32. Timber store
33. Sawmill
34. Gun mounting shop (No 6 Shop)
35. Gun mounting shop (No 7 Shop)

Above area in 1905

☐ area outside works
☐ area of works
☐ buildings
E entrance

Elswick was probably the most congested of any large industrial site in Britain, built on a slope between the road, the railway and the River Tyne, employing around 16,000, many of whom lived in terraced houses just across the road. To the west was the Engine Works making the original product of dock machinery, to the north east the Steel Works, to the south east the Shipyard, and squeezed in between scores of workshops making the guns and mountings. In the modern day Elswick business park, nothing remains visible of the ironclad berths at 54-57-38N 01-38-04W. To overcome site and bridge limitations, a new shipyard was completed downstream at High Walker in 1914, while a new factory for smaller components and ammunition was built at Scotswood to the west. *Monarch* is shown alongside the fitting-out quay.

Opposite: Taken from the 250-ton crane this excellent view over *King George V* looking aft in mid-August 1940 gives a good indication of the scale of activities at Walker. S4 5.25in mounting has yet to be delivered – some of *Prince of Wales'* had to be diverted to her – as have the HA/LA directors. The berth layout is clear with travelling tower cranes. On the nearest No. 1 berth are three 'P' class destroyers, on No. 2 the keel of *Lion* has been laid (4 July 1939) but with construction suspended (subsequently broken up on the slip), on either side are the hulls of 'Hunt' class destroyers *Oakley* (completed as the Polish *Kujawiak*) and *Liddesdale* about to be launched. The two 'Hunts' alongside are *Eglinton*, nearest, and *Exmoor*. *(Author's collection)*

following year he merged the ordnance works with the rest of his business at Elswick to form Sir W G Armstrong & Co. which, by the mid-1860s, employed about 4000 persons most of whom were in the Ordnance Department. With an uncertain future for ordnance manufacture at Elswick, now shorn of British government contracts, Armstrong successfully developed his business with overseas governments. In this, Armstrong's principal competitor was the Essen-based ordnance works of Alfred Krupp.

In 1867 Armstrong made direct connection with naval construction when he signed an agreement with Charles Mitchell whereby the latter's shipyard at Low Walker, five miles downstream from the Elswick works, undertook to build hulls for Armstrong's guns. This development was managed by George Rendel, son of James Rendel mentioned previously, a naval architect and engineer. Under his direction a series of gunboats, small unarmoured cruisers and later protected cruisers were designed and built.

The beginning of naval shipbuilding proved to be a prescient move given the strong demand for naval vessels worldwide that resulted from Armstrong's innovatory designs. The arrangement with Mitchell was formalised in 1882 when the business became Sir W G

Armstrong, Mitchell & Co Ltd. The following year the decision had been taken to add shipbuilding berths for warship construction at the eastern end of the Elswick works and it was from here that many innovative protected cruisers were launched from 1885. At the same time a steel works covering ten acres at the eastern end of the Elswick works was commissioned to produce steel by the Siemens-Martin process for forgings and ordnance components. Rendel also turned his attention to the machinery necessary to work naval guns – the hydraulic mechanisms necessary to repeatedly supply shell and propellant to guns which in turn had to be trained and elevated, i.e. aimed at a target, as well as fired. A gun mounting department was consequently established where the design and manufacture of these elaborate and large mechanisms could be undertaken. Another key individual adding to the success of the company was Andrew Noble, a captain in the Royal Artillery and ballistics expert, who joined the company in 1860, eventually to become Armstrong's successor as managing director and Chairman – see Personalities on p.105.

By the 1880s, the sprawling but congested works at Elswick were capable of turning out every type of modern warship and its armament, the only one of its kind in the UK. There

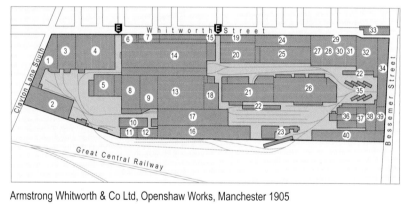

Armstrong Whitworth & Co Ltd, Openshaw Works, Manchester 1905

1. New gun mounting shop
2. Oil hardening shop
3. Plate shop
4. Gun machine shop
5. Joiners and patternmakers shop
6. Drawing office
7. General office
8. Iron foundry
9. Smiths shop
10. Gas works
11. Brass foundry
12. Pattern shop
13. Steel works
14. Engineering shop

15. Gauge room
16. Steel foundry
17. Steel melting furnaces
18. Soaking and casting pits
19. Dining rooms, laboratory over
20. Small gun shop
21. New steel works
22. Gas producers
23. Ammonia recovery plant
24. Armour plate machine shop
25. Armour plate grinding and erecting shop
26. Armour plate machine shop
27. Drilling shop
28. Machine shop

29. Armour plate dept.
30. Bending shop
31. Furnaces
32. Armour plate treatment shop
33. Cottages
34. Oil tempering dept.
35. Cementation furnaces
36. Steel stores
37. Crucible making
38. Rolling dept.
39. Steam hammer shop
40. Crucible melting shop

Feet	250	500	1000
Metres	75	150	300

☐ area outside works
▨ area of works
▓ buildings
🄴 entrance

Joseph Whitworth had established a new works at Openshaw, Manchester in 1880. After the merger with Armstrong in 1897, it was extended to manufacture armour on the north east of the site at a cost of half a million pounds, while most gun mounting work was moved to Elswick, although it continued to make guns, machine tools and general engineering products. Although Openshaw was not included in the merger with Vickers in 1927, Vickers-Armstrongs took over the works again in the Second World War to manufacture anti-aircraft weapons, employing about 4000, similar to pre-First World War figures. The site remains in industrial use at 53-28-20N 02-11-03W.

were however two major exceptions in this otherwise seamless array of warship components, which was the capacity to manufacture propelling machinery and armour plate. In the former, Armstrong was well served by several marine engineering works on Tyneside.

Such was Armstrong's standing that in 1886, at the behest of the Italian Government, an arsenal was established at Pozzuoli near Naples where Armstrong manufactured ordnance for the Italian navy and army. Previously it had exported such material from Elswick.

In 1897, undoubtedly with a degree of satisfaction, Armstrong amalgamated with Manchester-based rival Sir Joseph Whitworth & Co Ltd. The new company, Sir W G Armstrong, Whitworth & Co Ltd, set about further extending its capability by laying down a new armour plate mill at Openshaw. In 1899 the company opened a new works at Scotswood to the west of Elswick for the manufacture of munitions. Armstrong's company had come a long way over the preceding fifty years and now stood as a large manufacturing concern producing all manner of engineering products but principally ordnance, armour and warships. By the end of the nineteenth century the company employed about 20,000 across its three main sites – see p.258 for twentieth-century figures.

An important aspect of the success of Armstrongs was the very high regard with which it was held by the Admiralty, not simply because of its manufacturing capability but also its innovative influence on warship design exemplified by its cruisers. The interchange of senior personnel is a good example of this regard. Sir William White, Sir Philip Watts and Sir Eustace Tennyson d'Eyncourt worked as naval architects at Armstrong, each later to become the Director of Naval Construction at the Admiralty, a period spanning the years 1885 to 1924.

The successful development of Armstrong's company through various stages and change of direction had brought it to the forefront of naval construction with leading-edge design and manufacturing capacity and experience in naval weapon systems and warship protection schemes. Armstrong's had, in many ways, defined the modern armaments company. For their hard work and innovation they would soon be imitated by other firms seeking to challenge them for a share if not outright leadership of this lucrative market. For his services, Sir William was raised to the peerage in 1887

becoming Baron or Lord Armstrong of Cragside, after his Northumbrian estate. He died in 1900.

The first battleship to be built at Elswick was the turret ship *Victoria*, completed in 1890. This was followed by a trio of battleships for the Japanese Navy: *Yashima*, launched in 1894, *Hatsuse* in 1899 and *Kashima* in 1905. The Chilean battleship *Constitucion* ordered in 1902 was completed as *Swiftsure* for the Royal Navy in 1904. A new yard with two, later three, large berths was built at the east end of the works leaving the original West Yard to concentrate on smaller vessels. The new East Yard, sometimes referred to as the Ironclad Yard, was overtaken by the increasing size of dreadnoughts and the three berths re-organised as two larger berths in 1910. While these berths may have been sufficient for the immediate future, the arrangement of bridges, particularly the Newcastle swing bridge, imposed a width restriction on ships passing down river from Elswick and this would effectively limit continuing battleship construction at Elswick. In 1908 the Armstrong Board had considered the purchase of Hawthorn Leslie's shipyard at Hebburn, a company with whom Armstrong had placed many of its machinery contracts. Instead the Board agreed to purchase ground at High Walker, just up river from the original Armstrong Mitchell yard where a new shipyard was laid out, subsequently known as the Naval Yard – see p.139. The topography of the site was difficult, requiring the removal of higher ground where the shops and building slips were to be laid out. However, the yard represented a great improvement over Elswick with the largest berth capable of accommodating ships 1000ft long. The new yard was finally completed in 1914 and the first ship to be laid down there in October 1913 was *Malaya* followed by *Courageous* (1915) and *Furious* (1915). The Naval Yard was awarded the contract for a *Hood* class battlecruiser (*Anson*) which was cancelled in early 1919. The battleship *Nelson* was laid down in 1923 but it was not until 1937 that Armstrong's last battleship, *King George V*, was laid down at Walker, albeit under the Vickers-Armstrongs name – see p.64.

Armstrong was the only major private shipbuilder without its own engine works. It considered from time to time whether they should set up their own marine engine works – while they had a division named 'Engine Works' at their Elswick works, it mainly made hydraulic machinery for docks and cranes, although it did make the hydraulic pumps for gun mountings. H F Swan was not only a director of Armstrong, but also Chairman of Wallsend Slipway & Engineering. He advised the Armstrong Board confidentially in October 1902 that Swan Hunter was proposing to take a controlling interest in the Slipway, but Armstrongs declined to make an offer.[1] Armstrongs had considered obtaining a Parsons licence and building a turbine manufacturing plant in 1905. In 1908 with the advice of J M Allan, managing director of Hawthorn Leslie's marine engine department, they explored the possibility of setting up a marine engine and boiler works. But in order to produce the necessary 60,000 hp a year, it would need a site of about 20 acres.[2] This was not possible even on their Scotswood site and would still require hulls to be brought through the Newcastle bridges which limited both breadth and height of ships. They also investigated taking over Hawthorn Leslie itself with its St Peters engine works. But they did not want to buy the company's shipyard as well (at Hebburn, which was similar in size to their Low Walker yard) or need its locomotive works at Forth Banks in Newcastle. The Board then gave up such ideas, relying on the existing companies to quote them competitive prices for the machinery required. Ironically, they did enter the marine engineering market after the First World War, but this was to provide civilian work in the absence of warship and armaments orders. Some marine steam reciprocating engines were built at Elswick, while a Sulzer diesel engine licence was taken out in 1921 and some two dozen such engines built at Scotswood, together with steam locomotives.

1.2 Vickers, Sons & Maxim Ltd

While Armstrong was the first of the big armaments firms to become established, Vickers grew to become its principal rival and ultimately take it over to become the most significant and long-lived of all the British armaments firms. Unlike Armstrong, Vickers' primary business was steel. In the early 1800s when Sheffield was earning a reputation as a steel town, there were many small businesses, some of whom would emerge years later as major industrial concerns. Three of them form a large part of this history: Charles Cammell, John Brown and Vickers, all of whom shared a similar growth pattern in the early years of their development.

The Vickers company began in 1829 when William Vickers became a partner in the steel firm of Naylor, Hutchinson, Vickers & Co., with works at Mill Sands in Sheffield. He was joined by his brother Edward who until then had been a miller by trade. Two of Edward's four sons, Tom and Albert, who had received a technical training in Germany, became involved in the business which began a profitable trade exporting railway and other steel products to America. In 1863 expansion of the business necessitated a move to new works which were built at Brightside on the River Don. In the following year the business was split with one of the new companies, Naylor Vickers & Co, carrying on the manufacturing business of the old firm and the other the commercial activities. Three years later in 1867, the business was restructured as a limited liability company under the title Vickers, Sons

Above: From the same location and time as the preceding photo, this shows the forward part of *King George V*, the carrier *Victorious* and the cruiser *Nigeria*. B turret's roof plates have yet to be fitted. *Victorious* is out of reach of the quayside cranes so a travelling crane has been erected on her flight deck. Note the extensive workshops to the left and the large volume of fittings and materials waiting to be lifted on board these ships. *(Author's collection)*

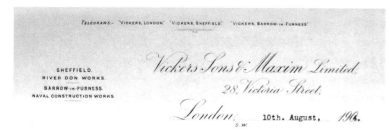

TELEGRAMS:- "VICKERS, LONDON" "VICKERS, SHEFFIELD" "VICKERS, BARROW-IN-FURNESS"

SHEFFIELD.
RIVER DON WORKS.
BARROW-IN-FURNESS.
NAVAL CONSTRUCTION WORKS.

Vickers Sons & Maxim Limited
28, Victoria Street,
London, 10th. August, *1914.*
S.W.

Above: An example of the letterhead used by Vickers Sons & Maxim Ltd.

& Co Ltd. By this time the company was producing a variety of cast, crucible steel products such as bells, cog wheels, and components for railway tyres. Marine shafting and screw propellers were soon to follow. The new company prospered, adding a rolling mill in 1874, while in 1882 a steel forge was added and in 1888 the manufacture of steel armour plate for warships started. Until this time the development of the Vickers company had followed a somewhat predictable path of expansion based on steel products. From the mid-1880s onwards however, it laid the foundation for a series of developments in ordnance and naval construction that would later establish it as a serious rival to Sir W G Armstrong & Co.

During the 1890s, three companies that would play an important role in this expansion became inter-connected, either through formal amalgamation or common business interests. The longest established of these companies was the Barrow Shipbuilding Co Ltd established by the Duke of Devonshire and James Ramsden, the general manager of the Furness Railway, at Barrow-in-Furness in 1871. The yard was laid out and managed initially by Robert Duncan, a Clyde shipbuilder. The first vessel launched at Barrow was the small steam yacht *Aries* in May 1873 for Ramsden, although the passenger-cargo steamer *Duke of Devonshire* launched the following month was more representative of the vessels to be built and engined at Barrow. Four years later the yard produced its first warship, the gunboat *Foxhound*, and in 1881, progress to the higher ranks among shipbuilders was marked by the completion of the Inman Line's *City of Rome*, then the largest ship in the world with the exception of Brunel's gigantic white elephant *Great Eastern*, albeit a technical and financial failure. James Ramsden, together with other backers, had begun the transformation of Barrow from a small town into an industrial hub. In addition to the shipyard, he set up a steel works in the mid-1870s to convert locally mined iron ore to supply the shipyard with plate and sections.

The origins of the second company began in

1881, when the American mechanical engineer and inventor Hiram Maxim emigrated to England where over the next few years he took out patents concerning the operation of an automatic machine gun. In 1884 he approached the Vickers family to get their backing for its development and manufacture. Albert Vickers was evidently impressed with what he saw and became the Chairman of a new company, the Maxim Gun Company Ltd, established in the autumn of that year. By 1885 the new company was manufacturing Maxim guns at works in Crayford, south east of London. Tom and Albert Vickers were among the shareholders of the new company although it had no formal association with the Vickers company at this stage.

In 1888 Vickers successfully submitted its first all-steel armour plate for testing by the Admiralty. In the same year they opened an ordnance department to manufacture medium calibre guns. In the early 1890s Vickers, like John Brown and Charles Cammell, began the manufacture of Harvey armour, soon to be superseded by the Krupp process for which patents were acquired in 1897. Now firmly established as an armaments company, Vickers turned their attention to the logical next stage – naval construction.

The third company that would soon become part of Vickers expanding business also owed its origins to the early 1880s when Swedish arms manufacturer Thorsten Nordenfelt acted on an approach from the Manchester inventor George William Garrett to develop the latter's patents for a submarine. The first submarine was built in Sweden; however, the second was built by the Barrow Shipbuilding Co Ltd and launched in 1886 followed by another the next year. By this time Nordenfelt had set up his own armaments company in England called the Nordenfelt Guns & Ammunition Company Limited and in the following year works were opened at Erith close to the River Thames for the manufacture of his machine gun. In 1888 Nordenfelt became a director of the Barrow Shipbuilding company, which was then styled The Naval Construction & Armaments Co Ltd. However, in that year, the interests of the Nordenfelt and Maxim companies were merged to form Maxim Nordenfelt Guns & Ammunition Co Ltd, in which Vickers had a substantial shareholding.

Finally, in 1897, the same year that Armstrongs acquired Whitworths, cash-rich Vickers swept up both the Naval Construction

& Armaments Co Ltd for £430,000 and Maxim Nordenfelt for £1.353 million, helped by Rothschild finance. The new company took the title Vickers, Sons & Maxim Ltd with works at Sheffield, Barrow, Erith, Crayford, Dartford and Birmingham. Not content with these major additions to its manufacturing capacity, Vickers began a major programme of investment across their works. At the Barrow shipyard improved building berths, cranes, foundries and a large gun mounting shop were added which, according to reports in the contemporary engineering press, virtually doubled the size of the yard making it among the largest in the country. By 1900 the new gun mounting shops employed 1500 men alone. Rapid expansion on this scale imposed serious strains on the town of Barrow and it became a matter of urgency to construct over one thousand new homes to accommodate the influx of workers. The rapid growth and capitalisation of Vickers as a thoroughly modern armaments company of the first rank could only have been viewed with some alarm at Elswick, where it was recognised that their leadership in the arma-

ments business had been checked. By the early 1900s Vickers rivalled Armstrong in overall manufacturing capacity and had realised their aim of building warships entirely from their own resources. In 1898 Vickers won its first battleship contracts, one from the Japanese Navy to construct *Mikasa* and the other from the Admiralty for the *Canopus* class battleship *Vengeance*. On completion in 1902, *Vengeance* became the first British battleship completely built at Barrow and the first to be constructed in every respect, hull, machinery, ordnance and armour, by one firm, a claim that Armstrong's could not quite make. In 1900 the Vickers board was prescient in recognising the potential of the submarine, licensing the Holland design from the Electric Boat Company of USA. Thus began its long association with submarine construction, a factor that has contributed to the longevity of the Barrow shipyard into the twenty-first century under BAE Systems.

While in terms of numbers the bulk of warship output from Barrow from then on was for submarines, the yard also produced most other classes of warship as well as merchant

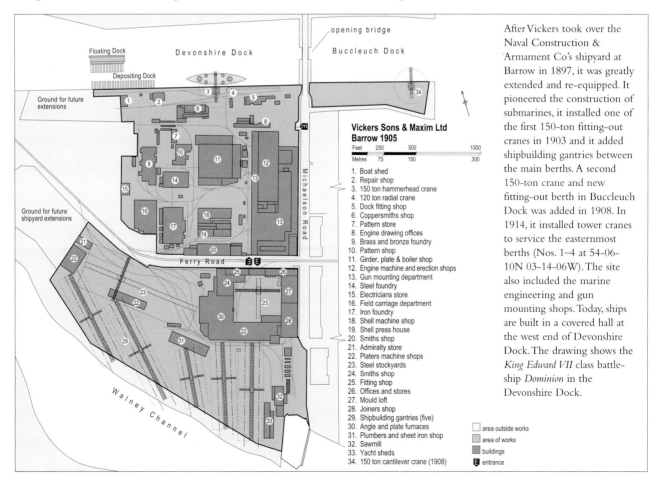

**Vickers Sons & Maxim Ltd
Barrow 1905**

Feet   250   500   1000
Metres 75   150   300

1. Boat shed
2. Repair shop
3. 150 ton hammerhead crane
4. 120 ton radial crane
5. Dock fitting shop
6. Coppersmiths shop
7. Pattern store
8. Engine drawing offices
9. Brass and bronze foundry
10. Pattern shop
11. Girder, plate & boiler shop
12. Engine machine and erection shops
13. Gun mounting department
14. Steel foundry
15. Electricians store
16. Field carriage department
17. Iron foundry
18. Shell machine shop
19. Shell press house
20. Smiths shop
21. Admiralty store
22. Platers machine shops
23. Steel stockyards
24. Smiths shop
25. Fitting shop
26. Offices and stores
27. Mould loft
28. Joiners shop
29. Shipbuilding gantries (five)
30. Angle and plate furnaces
31. Plumbers and sheet iron shop
32. Sawmill
33. Yacht sheds
34. 150 ton cantilever crane (1908)

☐ area outside works
▨ area of works
▨ buildings
🄴 entrance

After Vickers took over the Naval Construction & Armament Co's shipyard at Barrow in 1897, it was greatly extended and re-equipped. It pioneered the construction of submarines, it installed one of the first 150-ton fitting-out cranes in 1903 and it added shipbuilding gantries between the main berths. A second 150-ton crane and new fitting-out berth in Buccleuch Dock was added in 1908. In 1914, it installed tower cranes to service the easternmost berths (Nos. 1–4 at 54-06-10N 03-14-06W). The site also included the marine engineering and gun mounting shops. Today, ships are built in a covered hall at the west end of Devonshire Dock. The drawing shows the *King Edward VII* class battle-ship *Dominion* in the Devonshire Dock.

Right: The Evolution of Vickers' and Armstrong's Works into Vickers-Armstrongs.

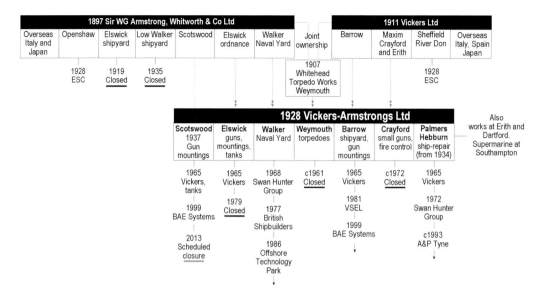

Above: The shipyard stamp applied to drawings at the Walker Naval Yard.

vessels. In the dreadnought era the yard launched four battleships and two battle-cruisers: *Vanguard* 1909, *Princess Royal* 1911, *Kongo* (Japanese Navy) 1912, *Emperor of India* 1913, *Erin* 1913 and *Revenge* 1915. The latter ship brought battleship construction at Barrow to an end. In any case, after 1927 with the amalgamation with Armstrong, future battleship hulls would be better constructed at the Walker Naval Yard.

Prior to the First World War, Vickers developed significant armaments interests overseas in Spain, Italy, Japan, Russia, Sweden, Turkey and Canada, as discussed from p.199 onwards.

Vickers–Armstrongs Ltd
The virtual cessation of arms production after the end of the First World War followed by the depressed years of the 1920s was a trial of survivability for the armaments industries from which Vickers emerged as a more astute and financially stronger company than Armstrong. When the latter ran into serious financial difficulties, it laid itself open to takeover. In 1927 a major restructuring supported by the Bank of England, which also included large sections of the steel industry, resulted in the formation of a new company, Vickers-Armstrongs Ltd, in which all of the armaments and naval shipbuilding activities of both firms were merged under Vickers control. Nevertheless the outlook remained bleak and the decision was taken to temporarily close the Walker Naval Yard in 1928, not reopening fully until 1934. Two further battleship contracts were secured by Vickers-Armstrongs, *King George V* and *Lion*, both of which were laid down at Walker. *King George V* was completed in 1940 although work

on *Lion* was stopped in 1939 and the contract subsequently suspended and then cancelled, owing to more urgent wartime demands. Vickers-Armstrongs' other interests included aircraft and tanks, also products where the Government was anxious to maintain a core manufacturing capacity despite defence cuts in the 1930s. Chapters 11 and 12 discuss the products, finances and employment in the company.

Fate
Under the restructuring of the shipbuilding industry undertaken by the government-sponsored Shipbuilding Industry Board following the Geddes Report, in 1968 the Naval Yard became part of newly formed Swan Hunter Shipbuilders Ltd. On nationalisation of the shipbuilding industry in 1977, Swan Hunter became part of British Shipbuilders, only to be privatised in 1986. The Naval Yard launched its last ship in 1980 although the fitting out quay was used for shipbuilding for several years after that. By 1988 the shipyard had been demolished, although the 250-ton cantilever fitting-out crane erected in 1931 remains in service with the offshore manufacturing companies that currently occupy the site, which is at latitude 54-58N longitude 01-13-15W.[3] Both the Elswick (54-57-40N 01-38W) and Scotswood Works closed in 1979 and the buildings were subsequently demolished. A new tank factory was later built on the site of the Scotswood Works, now part of BAE Systems, but this is due to close in 2013, the last vestige of the enormous Armstrong Tyneside industrial empire.

Barrow shipyard is one of only four large shipbuilding sites to have survived in Britain from the heyday of British shipbuilding. Its role as the leading yard for submarine construction since they were first ordered for the Admiralty in 1900 has kept it in the forefront of shipbuilding technology as the submarine has become the pre-eminent nuclear weapon delivery system. Ship construction is now carried out in the huge Devonshire Dock Hall, located at 54-06-13N 03-14-10W.

In 1954 the company was reorganised and the shipbuilding activities separated from engineering under a new name, Vickers-Armstrongs (Shipbuilders) Ltd. In 1965 the Armstrong name was dropped and the company became simply Vickers Ltd. Following the 1966 Geddes Report on the British shipbuilding industry, the Tyneside yard became part of the Swan Hunter group. In 1977 both Swan Hunter and Vickers shipbuilding interests were nationalised becoming part of British Shipbuilders, taking a variety of company names. In 1986 the Barrow yard was subject to a management buy-out under the title Vickers Shipbuilding & Engineering Ltd (VSEL). Shortly before, the Cammell Laird yard at Birkenhead had become a subsidiary, which it operated until 1993. In a period of consolidation among British defence contractors, VSEL was acquired by GEC Marconi Marine in 1995 to become Marconi Marine. When British Aerospace merged with GEC Marconi in 1999, it became BAE Systems Marine. Thereafter a succession of BAE Systems names resulted in the 2012 title for Barrow becoming BAE Systems Maritime – Submarines.

1.3 John Brown & Co Ltd

Even before John Brown & Co Ltd acquired the Clydebank shipyard in 1899, it had built some significant warships. The yard continued to do so under Brown throughout the twentieth century until 1968, being responsible for some of the best known British ships of that era. The early business trajectory of John Brown was similar to Vickers and Cammell, and came close to emulating Vickers in becoming a fully integrated armaments business.

John Brown (1816–96) was a Sheffield man who began his association with the steel industry by taking an apprenticeship with a local steel firm, Earl Horton & Co, traders and later makers of files and cutlery. In 1838 at the age of 22 John Brown left this company to establish his own business making cutlery, pocket knives, scissors and files for which he made his own crucible steel. This business expanded rapidly and Brown removed it to

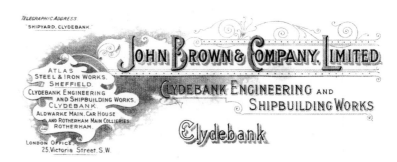

Above: The letterhead used by John Brown & Co's Clydebank shipyard in the early years of the twentieth century.

larger premises in Furnival Street which he named the Atlas Steel Works. In 1848, Brown invented a conical spring buffer that found a ready market in the rapidly growing railway network. The success of his business was assured and in 1856 the Atlas Works were moved to new premises of three acres in extent at Savile Street. In 1857 he started wrought iron making and, finding a ready outlet for his products, expanded production to 100 tons per week. In 1859 Brown began the manufacture of steel by the Bessemer process, then a largely untried method. This gamble paid off and demand for his products required numerous additions to plant to keep pace with orders. Many of these were for railway products, including axles, tyres and rails.

By this time John Devonshire Ellis, a brass founder, and William Bragge, an engineer, both from Birmingham, had joined John Brown as partners and together they set about establishing the manufacture of rolled armour plate, the first to do so in Britain. They had been encouraged in this direction by the technical revolution which had taken place in the 'line of battle ship' following the appearance of the first ironclad, the French *Gloire* in 1858. It was recognised that the wooden walls of the Royal Navy were no longer adequate and a programme of ironclad building was initiated, beginning with *Warrior*. At first armour was usually wrought iron rolled to the required thickness and did not differ in composition from the normal wrought iron plates used widely by industry.

In 1864, to permit adequate financing of what was now a large manufacturing concern, the business was converted into a limited liability company, taking advantage of the first Companies Act which had been passed in 1862. The flotation of the company attracted the attention of several wealthy Manchester businessmen who had previously invested in a number of iron and coal companies. Most

Below: The *Majestic* class pre-dreadnought *Jupiter* was launched from J & G Thomson's Clydebank shipyard (later John Brown & Co Ltd) on 18 November 1895. Here the hull is being prepared for that event. Shoring is being removed, transferring the weight to the sliding launchways, the forward poppet is in place and drag chains are being positioned down the ship's side. Either the photographer has told everyone to stand still as he is about to make a time exposure or his actions have proven to be irresistible for the workforce. *(Author's collection courtesy of NRS)*

prominent of these was Henry Davis Pochin, a talented chemist who had made important contributions to the manufacture of paper and soap. From profits made, Pochin invested in a number of businesses and became the majority shareholder in John Brown & Co Ltd. Pochin took a seat on the Board but John Brown was elected Chairman and John D Ellis and William Bragge were both appointed as managing directors.

By 1867 the majority of ironclads in the Royal Navy were protected by simple wrought iron armour plate much of which had been rolled in the Atlas Works. The effect of this was to transform the business from 200 employees and three acres in 1857 to 4000 employees and 21 acres in 1867. Armour plate making accounted for half of the output, although the production of rails remained important. John Brown, who was knighted in 1867 for his part in establishing the steel industries of Sheffield, resigned from the business in 1871 to set up a new steel company

and take up a directorship of Earle's Shipbuilding & Engineering Co Ltd of Hull.

Under the chairmanship of J D Ellis, John Brown & Co Ltd continued to grow, acquiring collieries at Rotherham and ore mines in Northern Spain. In 1878 the company shifted the emphasis of production away from railway products and started the manufacture of ships' plates and boiler end-plates. In 1879 the Siemens-Martin open hearth steel making process was adopted in addition to the Bessemer and crucible steel processes.

The 1880s and 1890s saw the introduction of new plant and processes most of which were in response to rapidly evolving technical advances in the manufacture of armour plate and naval ordnance. Firstly, the company began making compound armour in which a hardened steel plate was welded to a backing plate of wrought iron. In 1886 a 4000-ton forging press for use in the manufacture of forgings for ships and guns was installed. In 1892 Captain T J Tresidder, an expert in ballistics and a manager

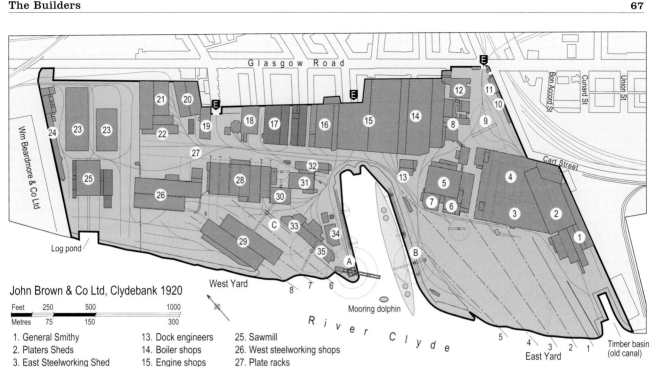

John Brown & Co Ltd, Clydebank 1920

Feet	250	500		1000
Metres	75	150		300

1. General Smithy
2. Platers Sheds
3. East Steelworking Shed
4. Scrieve boards, mould loft over
5. Joiners shop
6. Electricians shop
7. Stores
8. General Offices
9. Plate racks
10. Electrical drawing office
11. Admiralty overseers offices
12. Engine pattern shop

13. Dock engineers
14. Boiler shops
15. Engine shops
16. Foundry
17. Sheet iron shop
18. Galvanising station
19. Brass finishing shop
20. EW pattern store
21. Funnel shed
22. Condenser shop
23. Wood drying sheds
24. Experiment tank

25. Sawmill
26. West steelworking shops
27. Plate racks
28. Plate and riveting sheds
29. Coverd building berths
30. Beam smithy
31. Beam shed
32. Riggers loft
33. Electrical store
34. Dock engineers
35. Plumbers shop

A. 150 ton cantilever crane
B. 150 ton derrick crane
C. 10 ton travelling crane

☐ area outside works
☐ area of works
■ buildings
🄴 entrance

in company employment, patented his quenching process for face-hardening steel armour plate, a method similar to the American Harvey process which was introduced in the early 1890s, as discussed in Chapter 9. The year 1896 saw the introduction of Krupp cemented armour which, through treating a nickel-chromium alloy steel, was superior to all previous armour and was to remain the basic type throughout the life of the armoured warship.

In the late 1890s the logic that had directed Armstrong and Vickers to acquire a shipbuilding capability was followed by the John Brown Board. Although Brown had supplied armour and heavy forgings to Dockyards and shipyards, they had hitherto seen no direct advantage in acquiring their own shipbuilding capacity. At this time, a number of privately controlled shipyards were theoretically available for take-over, most notably the Thames Iron Works at Blackwall, Laird at Birkenhead, Palmers on the Tyne and both Fairfield and the Clydebank Engineering & Shipbuilding Co. on the Clyde. Surprisingly, the Board initially approached none of these and instead considered the

purchase of Earle's Shipbuilding & Engineering Co Ltd at Hull. This medium-sized firm had achieved a good record of naval construction but was verging on financial collapse.

However, the Board made the decision to purchase the Clydebank shipyard on the Clyde, formerly known as J & G Thomson Ltd until 1897 and from then until 1899 as the Clydebank Shipbuilding & Engineering Co Ltd. The works were large and had built many prestigious ships. Ground was available for future extensions and profits over the last decade had been impressive. It had an excellent record in naval shipbuilding including battleships and, in the form of the Union Bank of Scotland which was its largest shareholder, it had a willing vendor. Negotiations for the purchase of the works by John Brown started early in 1899 and by 31 March the basis of the sale had been agreed at a purchase price of £923,255 3s 3d.

On 5 June 1899 Charles Ellis, John D Ellis's son and managing director, wrote to the Company's London solicitors with the form of words to be put to the John Brown shareholders.

Above: When Clydebank shipyard opened on a greenfield site in 1871, it was restricted to the area of the East Yard only. Over the next four decades, an engine works was built, the West Yard developed and the fitting-out basin created and subsequently enlarged. The remote rural setting also caused major problems in bringing workers and materials to the yard. Over time the town of Clydebank was built around the works and rail and tram links were added. The site selected for the shipyard was a good one however, facing the mouth of the River Cart which enabled the largest warships *Hood* and passenger liners such as the Queens to be launched into the otherwise narrow River Clyde. *Hood* is shown in the fitting-out basin.

Below: Crew members of *Barham* on the quarterdeck ready for the commissioning ceremony which took place in the yard on 18 August 1915. The 150-ton giant cantilever crane is in the immediate background with the covered sheds of the West Yard behind that. *(Author's collection courtesy of NRS)*

A favourable opportunity has arisen for strengthening the position of the Company by the acquisition of one of the best equipped and most successful shipyards and engine works in the United Kingdom. A provisional contract has been made with the Clydebank Engineering & Shipbuilding Co. Ltd. for the purchase of their property and business as a going concern on terms which the Directors believe are favourable to the shareholders.[4]

J & G Thomson Ltd

The Clydebank shipyard had its origins in the Finnieston area of central Glasgow in 1847, when two brothers, James and George Thomson, established a marine engine-building business at the Clyde Bank Foundry overlooking the river Clyde. Both James and George had worked under the pioneering engineer and entrepreneur Robert Napier, who did so much to establish marine engineering and iron shipbuilding on the Clyde. James and George earned a reputation for building reliable steam engines and by 1851 they decided to expand the business by building a shipyard on ground at Govan. This made good sense as the mind-set of the marine engineer and boiler maker was readily transferred to the construction of iron ships, as all used similar plant and skills.

The Thomsons quickly earned a reputation for building well-appointed passenger vessels, and established a good trade with Samuel Cunard's steam ship line, for whom a third Thomson brother worked as superintendent engineer. During the American Civil War, the company built its first warships, the 4750-ton displacement ironclad *Santa Maria* (later purchased by the Danish Government and named *Danmark*) and the frigate *Canton*, both ordered for the Confederate Navy.

After family difficulties during the mid-1860s, including the death of the principal partner George, the business was faced with a crisis that might have proved terminal. A compulsory purchase order was placed on the shipyard to make way for the expansion of port facilities. The Trust formed to manage the business was of a mind to cease trading but George's young son James was set on relocation and expansion. As a result, in 1871, the business was transferred to new works on a 32-acre green-field site at Dalmuir. The new works suffered in both a practical and economic sense from its isolated situation and only after many years did this improve when the town of Clydebank grew around the yard, providing housing for workers and better transport links.

Despite these difficulties, the Thomsons built large and impressive liners at Clydebank, including *Servia*, launched in 1881 and *City of New York* in 1888. The first Admiralty contracts were for two gunboats, *Firebrand* and *Firefly*, launched in 1877. Orders for torpedo boats and cruisers followed, some of which were for the Russian, Spanish and Japanese governments. The first battleship was *Ramillies*, launched in 1892, followed by *Jupiter* in 1895. At the time of its purchase by John Brown & Co Ltd, the yard was building the Japanese battleship *Asahi*. Its fourth and last pre-dreadnought battleship was *Hindustan* launched in 1903.

With Clydebank shipyard now part of John Brown & Co Ltd, the company further strengthened its manufacturing capacity through an exchange of shares with the well-known Sheffield steel maker and producer of gun forgings, Thomas Firth & Sons Ltd, whose Norfolk Works were adjacent to the Atlas Works.

In 1908 the company took out a licence with the General Electric Co of USA to manufacture Curtis steam turbines. The design was modified at Clydebank and the turbines thereafter known as Brown-Curtis. They found great favour with the Admiralty and were fitted in many British warships of the period, earning John Brown considerable sums licensing the technology to other marine engineers.

The yard appeared to specialise in constructing battlecruisers, having completed *Inflexible* in 1908, *Australia* 1913, *Tiger* 1914, *Repulse* 1916 and *Hood* 1920 with a G3 battlecruiser ordered in 1921, although the latter was cancelled. One battleship, *Barham* (1915), was also constructed.

After the First World War conditions were difficult but Clydebank seemed to be weathering the storm with orders for large liners such as *Empress of Britain* 1928 and *Queen Mary* 1930. However, in 1931 the inability of Cunard to finance *Queen Mary* after one year of construction closed the yard, which did not reopen until 1934. Re-armament and the order for the liner *Queen Elizabeth* in 1936 brought the yard fully back to life and new orders for warships flowed, including the battleships *Duke of York* 1937 and *Vanguard* 1941. The order for the *Lion* class battleship *Conqueror* was placed with Clydebank in 1939 but suspended before it could be laid down; its yard number 567 was used for *Vanguard*.

Fate

The period after the war saw the yard resume its mixed tonnage of passenger liners, cargo ships, tankers and warships. By the early 1960s, however, the yard was uncompetitive, especially against foreign shipyards, and was trading at a loss. The *Queen Elizabeth 2* was laid down at Clydebank in 1965, the contract taken at a loss making price. Government sponsored restructuring of the shipbuilding industry resulted in the formation of Upper Clyde Shipbuilders Ltd in 1968, of which the former John Brown yard became the Clydebank Division. Upper Clyde Shipbuilders collapsed spectacularly in 1971 and a campaign was mounted to save the yards. No place was seen for Clydebank in the company that emerged from the ashes and closure seemed inevitable. A buyer was found in the US Marathon Manufacturing Company. The yard was operated as Marathon Shipbuilding Co (UK) Ltd until 1980 building jack-up oil rigs, after which it was acquired by French owned UiE, part of the Bouygues Group, and operated as UiE Scotland Ltd building jack-ups, integrated decks and floating production unit conversions. The yard closed in 2001 and the entire site, shipyards and engine works, was demolished, with the exception of the 200-ton cantilever fitting-out crane which remains as an A-listed historic structure, located at 55-53-50N 04-24-30W.

1.4 Charles Cammell & Co Ltd

Charles Cammell was born in Hull and moved to Sheffield in 1830 where he, like John Brown, became a traveller in cutlery and steel goods. In 1837 he began a business with the brothers Thomas and Henry Johnson as Johnson, Cammell & Co, maker of files and other steel

Above: John Brown's shipyard stamp applied to drawings of the battlecruiser *Australia*, initialled by the chief draughtsman and countersigned by Admiralty Overseer H J Blandford.

Right: The letterhead in use by the company after the First World War.

products at premises in Furnival Street, Sheffield. The business expanded largely through the boom in railway construction and by 1845 new works were opened on Savile Street and given the name Cyclops Works. In 1855 the company was renamed Charles Cammell & Co specialising in the manufacture of steel railway springs, buffers and tyres. In 1862 Cammell followed John Brown's lead in laying down plant for rolling armour plate. In the mid-1860s, with great demand for rails, new works were opened at Grimesthorpe in Sheffield and at Penistone and later again at Dronfield and Workington. As the manufacture of rails became less profitable in the face of intense competition, Cammell like Brown turned increasingly to the manufacture of armour. New methods were constantly being sought to improve the resistance of armour and by the late 1870s wrought iron was superseded by compound armour, which was in use until the early 1890s when Harvey armour was developed. The final development came in the middle of that decade with the introduction of the Krupp process.

Developments in armour manufacture together with the production of large steel forgings for guns and marine products such as shafting required significant investment in plant at the Grimesthorpe and Cyclops Works. In 1903, six years after Vickers and four after John Brown but driven by the same business objectives, Charles Cammell & Co Ltd also decided to acquire shipbuilding capacity. The yard chosen was one with which the company had many dealings in the past – the Birkenhead shipyard and engine works of Laird Brothers Ltd. The new company was called Cammell, Laird & Co Ltd.

Laird Brothers

William Laird arrived in Liverpool from Greenock prior to 1810, turning his hand to shipping and acting as an agent for fellow Greenockian James Watt's steam engines. In 1824 he established the Birkenhead Ironworks with Daniel Horton at Wallasey Pool to begin work as boilermakers. Four years later the partnership was terminated and Laird was joined by

his son John and the business renamed William Laird & Son. In 1829 the company constructed its first vessel, the 50-ton lighter *Wye*, built of iron. In 1833 shipbuilding began in earnest with the construction of the iron paddle steamer *Lady Lansdowne*. Laird was a pioneer and early advocate of iron-hulled warships and among the first to mount guns in an iron-hulled ship in a series of vessels for the East India Company, shipped in pieces to India in the late 1830s. In 1842 the iron frigate *Guadalupe* was built for the Mexican Navy, which appears to have influenced the Admiralty into ordering five steam frigates, one of which was the *Birkenhead*, launched by Laird in 1845 to become one of the Royal Navy's first iron ships.

In 1857 a new shipyard complete with engine works was opened at Monks Ferry and by the following year it employed 2000 people. This yard comprised five graving docks and four building slips. By then the company had been renamed John Laird & Sons and in 1862, with four of John's sons now in the business, the company was renamed Laird Brothers. By this time the population of Birkenhead had grown to 36,000 from 2500 in 1831. In 1862 the company built the successful commerce raider *Alabama* for the Confederate Government, and was by then among the leading British shipbuilding firms with an impressive list of ships for British and overseas owners. Many warships were built for overseas governments while four battleships were built for the Royal Navy: *Royal Oak* launched in 1892, *Mars* 1896, *Glory* 1899 and *Exmouth* 1901.

By the late 1890s the shipyard had become too small to build the larger sizes of ship then required, both mercantile and naval. In 1902 the Tranmere Bay Development Co Ltd was formed in partnership with the nearby shipyard of John Jones & Sons to develop a 98-acre site at Tranmere, just upriver from the existing works. Here a completely new shipyard and engine works was laid out capable of building the largest ships then envisaged. Six new building slips, the largest of which could accommodate a ship 800ft in length, were provided along with new engine and boiler shops and a great 15-acre fitting-out basin served by a 150-ton fitting-out crane plus two large drydocks.

While Cammell was the last of the big Sheffield firms to acquire shipbuilding capacity, they nevertheless saw the desirability of further extensions into the ordnance industry by

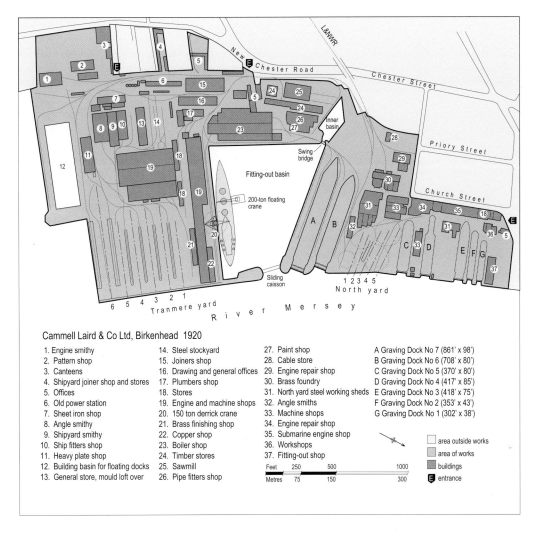

Cammell Laird & Co Ltd, Birkenhead 1920

1. Engine smithy
2. Pattern shop
3. Canteens
4. Shipyard joiner shop and stores
5. Offices
6. Old power station
7. Sheet iron shop
8. Angle smithy
9. Shipyard smithy
10. Ship fitters shop
11. Heavy plate shop
12. Building basin for floating docks
13. General store, mould loft over
14. Steel stockyard
15. Joiners shop
16. Drawing and general offices
17. Plumbers shop
18. Stores
19. Engine and machine shops
20. 150 ton derrick crane
21. Brass finishing shop
22. Copper shop
23. Boiler shop
24. Timber stores
25. Sawmill
26. Pipe fitters shop
27. Paint shop
28. Cable store
29. Engine repair shop
30. Brass foundry
31. North yard steel working sheds
32. Angle smiths
33. Machine shops
34. Engine repair shop
35. Submarine engine shop
36. Workshops
37. Fitting-out shop

A Graving Dock No 7 (861' x 98')
B Graving Dock No 6 (708' x 80')
C Graving Dock No 5 (370' x 80')
D Graving Dock No 4 (417' x 85')
E Graving Dock No 3 (418' x 75')
F Graving Dock No 2 (353' x 43')
G Graving Dock No 1 (302' x 38')

area outside works
area of works
buildings
E entrance

Feet 250 500 1000
Metres 75 150 300

acquiring in 1903 the Coventry-based Mulliner Wigley & Co Ltd, manufacturers of field guns and to whom Cammell had previously supplied steel castings. This was the origin of the Coventry Ordnance Works set up shortly after and described below.

Cammell, Laird & Co Ltd

The new company Cammell, Laird & Co Ltd oversaw the completion of the Tranmere shipyard development, which opened in 1906. By 1909 close on £1 million had been spent on this yard, which was now comparable with the best in the UK. The old yard, known as the North Yard, was retained for the construction of smaller vessels. In 1914 Cammell Laird had shipbuilding and marine engineering works at Birkenhead, and steel works at the Cyclops and Grimesthorpe Works in Sheffield and at Penistone. The shipyard continued to be known locally however as 'Lairds'.

Despite the investment made at Birkenhead,

only one battleship, *Audacious*, was built in the dreadnought era until the First World War. A contract for a *Hood* class battlecruiser was placed with the firm and laid down in 1916, although cancelled and broken up in 1919. The contract for *Rodney* was placed in 1922 and for *Prince of Wales* in 1936. The *Lion* class battleship *Temeraire* was ordered in 1939 but suspended the year after and cancelled outright in 1944.

Fate

Cammell Laird continued as significant shipbuilders after the end of the Second World War, building several notable warships including the aircraft carrier *Ark Royal* launched in 1950 and two nuclear ballistic missile submarines in 1967, a nuclear attack submarine following in 1969. Along with the rest of the industry, the yard became a member of nationalised British Shipbuilders in 1977 only to be privatized in 1986, shortly before which it became a subsidiary of Vickers

Left: The Cammell Laird site as it was after the First World War, showing the original North Yard with small building berths and numerous graving docks, the new Tranmere Bay Yard and the engine works both completed in 1906. With a wide expanse of river the shipbuilding berths could be arranged at 90° to the river. The large 14-acre fitting-out basin was served by a 150-ton capacity derricking crane built by the German firm Duisburger Maschinenbau AG. However, Cammell Laird found it necessary to acquire a 200-ton non-revolving floating crane to fit out larger vessels including *Rodney* shown here. At this stage in the development of the shipyard, the berths were equipped with steel derricks although these were subsequently upgraded to tower cranes and later in the 1950s, to level luffing cranes of up to 100-tons capacity by Butters Bros & Co Ltd.

Shipbuilding & Engineering Ltd for the construction of three diesel attack submarines. On the completion of these in 1993 the shipyard was closed, although the company name continued in ship repairing until bankruptcy in 2001, following the building of a mid-body extension for an Italian cruise ship. Thereafter the drydocks were operated as Northwestern Shiprepairers & Shipbuilders Ltd until renamed Cammell Laird Shiprepairers & Shipbuilders Ltd in 2008 with a diversified range of engineering products and ship repair, located at 53-23-13N 03-00-30W. In 2010 shipbuilding was again added to the company's activities with the award of a contract to build sections of the aircraft carrier *Queen Elizabeth*, plus two ferries ordered in 2012.

1.5 William Beardmore & Co Ltd

While Vickers began to challenge Armstrong in ordnance and naval construction, another company with similar aspirations prepared to enter the market. This was William Beardmore & Co Ltd with extensive steel and armour works at Parkhead, 2½ miles to the east of central Glasgow. Beardmore's spectacular rise as an armaments empire and entry into naval shipbuilding would last just thirty years before crashing in the austerity of the late 1920s.

This company had its origins in the forge which was established at Parkhead in 1837 supplying forgings to the shipbuilding and marine engineering industries that were then rapidly multiplying on Clydeside. In 1848 the forge came under the control of Robert Napier, who had an iron shipyard at Govan and engine works at Finnieston. In the late 1850s, Napier built rolling mills at Parkhead princi-

pally to make armour in anticipation of winning Admiralty work. In 1859 Napier was successful in winning the contract for the second iron-hulled ironclad warship, *Black Prince*, near sister-ship of the preserved *Warrior*, whose plates were rolled at Parkhead. In 1861 Napier disposed of his interest in the Parkhead Forge, which then came under the control of William Rigby and William Beardmore, who continued the expansion of plant and facilities to meet demand. In the early 1880s a steel foundry was added while in 1888 a steel armour plate mill was installed. This was followed by a new plate mill in 1892 and a 12,000-ton forging press in 1898. Beardmore was subject to the same technical developments in the manufacture of armour plate described elsewhere, including a licence to manufacture Harvey armour in 1895. By the end of the 1890s the Parkhead Forge under the sole direction of William Beardmore junior, had become one of the most important suppliers of steel castings, forgings and armour plate in the UK. However, William was ambitious and had determined that he could develop the industrial infrastructure to challenge Armstrong and Vickers in naval construction including shipbuilding and an ordnance works. In 1900 he took the first step towards that aim in acquiring the old Govan shipyard of Robert Napier & Sons Ltd.

Robert Napier & Sons Ltd
Robert Napier was one of the prime movers in the development of marine engineering and shipbuilding on the river Clyde and subsequently hailed as the father of Clyde shipbuilding. His early successes lay in the design

and construction of marine engines, with which he broke down Admiralty reservations hitherto shown toward Clydeside engineers in favour of Thames builders. With engine works at Lancefield, Napier began iron shipbuilding in 1842 at Govan and here built a succession of important and well-appointed steamships for Cunard and other owners.

His long association with naval construction included the *Black Prince*, completed in 1862 but surprisingly not with Napier's own engines but Penn's. A succession of battleships and a coast defence ship for the Admiralty followed during the 1860s and 1870s. Following Napier's death in 1876, the company's position as the leading Clyde yard began to wane and was overtaken by two of his protégés, John Elder of the Fairfield Works and J & G

ALL COMMUNICATIONS TO BE ADDRESSED TO THE COMPANY

WILLIAM BEARDMORE & Cº LIMITED.

TELEGRAMS.
BEARDMORE, DALMUIR.
BEARDMORE, GLASGOW.
BEARDMORE, LONDON.

IN REPLY PLEASE REFER TO
ENGINE DEPARTMENT,
AND QUOTE REF.

Naval Construction Works
Dalmuir,
AD/Pr. *Dumbartonshire.*

20th. October 1922.

Thomson, later John Brown, at Clydebank. By 1900 Napier's old Govan yard was all but exhausted and Beardmore's acquisition of the shipyard was purely temporary, although orders were quickly won for the armoured cruisers *Berwick* and *Carnarvon*.

At the same time as the small Govan yard was acquired, Beardmore purchased a large green-

Above: The letterhead used by Beardmore's Naval Construction Works at Dalmuir.

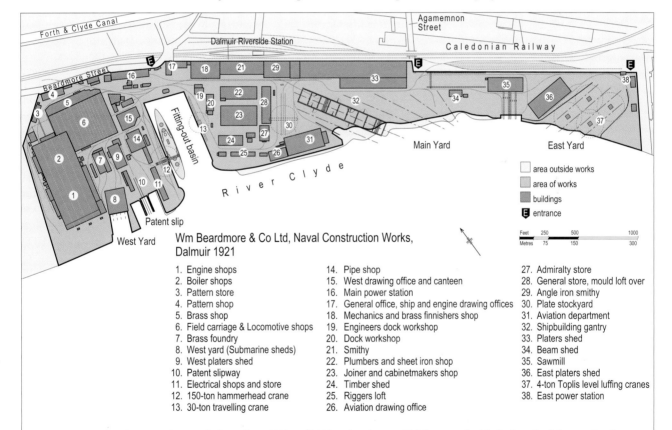

Wm Beardmore & Co Ltd, Naval Construction Works, Dalmuir 1921

1. Engine shops
2. Boiler shops
3. Pattern store
4. Pattern shop
5. Brass shop
6. Field carriage & Locomotive shops
7. Brass foundry
8. West yard (Submarine sheds)
9. West platers shed
10. Patent slipway
11. Electrical shops and store
12. 150-ton hammerhead crane
13. 30-ton travelling crane
14. Pipe shop
15. West drawing office and canteen
16. Main power station
17. General office, ship and engine drawing offices
18. Mechanics and brass finnishers shop
19. Engineers dock workshop
20. Dock workshop
21. Smithy
22. Plumbers and sheet iron shop
23. Joiner and cabinetmakers shop
24. Timber shed
25. Riggers loft
26. Aviation drawing office
27. Admiralty store
28. General store, mould loft over
29. Angle iron smithy
30. Plate stockyard
31. Aviation department
32. Shipbuilding gantry
33. Platers shed
34. Beam shed
35. Sawmill
36. East platers shed
37. 4-ton Toplis level luffing cranes
38. East power station

Wm Beardmore's Dalmuir works were laid out from 1902 until 1906 when it was officially opened with the launch of the pre-dreadnought *Agamemnon*. At the time, over £1 million was spent in creating the works, a sum Beardmore was able to realise after the exchange of shares with Vickers Sons & Maxim. Poor trading in the 1906–09 shipbuilding depression prevented the completion of Beardmore's intention to build a large graving dock where the patent slips were and the extension of the gantry over more of the building berths.

Numerous additions were made to the works before and during the First World War, most notably ordnance departments for small- to medium-calibre guns (both naval and land), a four-berth submarine yard (West Yard), an aviation department and after the war, the East Yard. The shipbuilding gantry constructed by Sir Wm Arrol & Co in 1904 built all four of Beardmore's battleships but would have had insufficient width to accommodate the G3 battlecruiser that the company was awarded in 1921 (and cancelled in February of the following year) The fitting-out basin, shown here with *Ramillies*, was equipped with a 150-ton hammerhead crane manufactured by the Benrather Maschinenfabrik AG in 1903.

Above: Stamp used by the Design Office at Beardmore's Dalmuir works.

Right: 17 May 1911 at Dalmuir. Very few parts of ships were pre-assembled in the days of riveted construction, tripod mast assemblies and funnels being major exceptions. This was also the case with ring bulkheads which supported the main armament mountings and outboard of which was the barbette armour. Sixteen days after her launch, the ring bulkhead for *Conqueror*'s B turret has been lifted into place, while the ring bulkhead for Q turret is sitting on the dockside waiting to be shipped. To the immediate right of that is a pile of side armour plates possibly for the starboard side of the battleship where work is in progress off staging rigged above the waterline. The 150-ton crane, unusually equipped with lifting gear on both sides of the cantilever, would be kept busy shipping machinery, armament and most of the armour plates for this ship. The *Weymouth* class light cruiser *Falmouth* is nearing completion, although she did not commission until September 1911. Both Beardmore's shipyard and the adjacent John Brown yard looked across the river to open countryside. *(Author's collection)*

field site at Dalmuir on the Clyde where he planned what would be at the time the largest shipbuilding and marine engineering works in the UK. However, Beardmore's investment in plant at Parkhead over-extended his financial resources, and unable to make further borrowings, he entered into negotiations with Albert Vickers. Vickers, perhaps taking the view that it was best to be close to the competition, agreed to an exchange of shares which took place in 1902, resulting in the formation of a new company, William Beardmore & Co Ltd, in which Vickers held a 50 per cent shareholding and two of the five seats on the Board. Vickers wished to control a greater share of the lucrative armour market after Armstrong's entry. Vickers had some influence on Beardmore if not full control, although it was agreed under the terms of the merger that Beardmore would not establish capacity for the manufacture of heavy gun mountings.

Over the next four years, heavy investment was made at Dalmuir where the new yard was given the title Naval Construction Works, which was opened with the launch of the battleship *Agamemnon* in 1906. For Beardmore, securing this important contract was a *tour de force*, the first ship to be built in a new and untested yard, as inclusion on the Admiralty list usually required high levels of confidence in facilities and expertise; it was a demonstration

of the excellence and modernity of the facilities at Dalmuir. However, with few established customers among merchant shipowners, Beardmore now struggled to find fresh Admiralty contracts. When Beardmore tendered for a *Bellerophon* class battleship in late 1906, it was for the hull only, as the company was not permitted to tender for the machinery. At this time the company had just completed and equipped what was the largest marine engineering works on Clydeside. While the Admiralty would have had justifiable reservations about employing an untried and untested facility, it nevertheless drew an interesting response from the company which illustrates the wider point of Government recognition where private firms had invested in new plant. The Admiralty was undoubtedly approving if not positively encouraging of Beardmore's new works while the latter expected, quid pro quo, to at least have the opportunity to tender.

On 29 November 1906, the Marquis of Graham, a director of Beardmore, wrote to the First Lord of the Admiralty

I would like to say to you privately that we have sunk an enormous amount of capital in establishing the great naval construction works at Dalmuir, and it is a serious thing to be denied any chance of getting Government work to do in any particular line... All I respectfully ask is

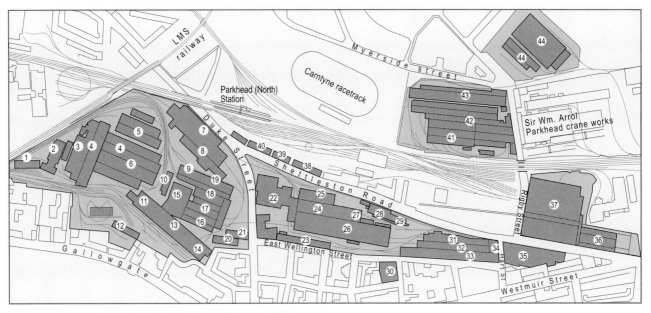

William Beardmore & Co Ltd, Parkhead Forge, Glasgow 1945

1. Scrap breaking
2. Armour carburizing shop
3. Armour treating shop
4. Armour bending shop
5. U shop
6. Armour machine shop
7. No 1 and No 2 press shops
8. Armour machine shop D
9. Boiler plant
10. Mill fitting shop
11. Open hearth furnaces
12. Boiler shop
13. No 2 melting shop
14. Electric furnace
15. Armour mill

16. Billet stores
17. Smithy
18. Inspection bay
19. O shop
20. B shop
21. C shop store
22. No 8 press shop
23. F machine shop
24. Press shop (No 9)
25. L machine shop
26. Steel foundry and No1 melting shop
27. Core shop
28. Gun treating shop
29. Gun tempering shop
30. Pattern shop

31. I machine shop
32. H machine shop
33. G machine shop
34. K shop
35. M shop
36. E shop extension
37. Howitzer shop
38. General offices
39. Government offices
40. Research laboratory
41. Bullet proof treatment shop
42. Bullet proof plate shop
43. Armour barbette erecting shop
44. Admiralty gun mounting & armament depot

area outside works
area of works
buildings
E entrance

that you may see your way clear to give Wm Beardmore & Coy. permission to tender for engines and machinery as well as for hull and armour for the new battleships, and in some degree grant us encouragement in return for the efforts we have made to establish naval construction works which may be of as great credit as of use to the nation.[5]

Beardmore was nevertheless unsuccessful in this round of orders, not receiving its first naval machinery contract until 1909, for the cruiser *Gloucester*. Coupled with the slump that befell the shipbuilding industry between 1908 and 1910, the works were brought to the point of closure almost before they had been properly established. It was not until January 1910 that Beardmore won another battleship contract, *Conqueror*, of the *Orion* class, one of the 'We Want Eight', followed by *Benbow* in 1912, and *Ramillies* in 1913. Vickers had reason to be

concerned about their large investment in Beardmore, the company having passed its dividend since 1907. They tried to persuade Armstrong Whitworth to acquire a one-third share in 1910, but the latter wisely declined.[6] Vickers finally disposed of their Beardmore shareholding in 1926.

In 1921 Beardmore was successful in winning the contract to build one of the G3 battlecruisers although, despite the large and well equipped engine works, the machinery was subcontracted to Vickers. The cancellation of this contract a few months later coincided with the general downturn in trade that affected the shipbuilding industry throughout the 1920s. Despite interesting and innovative ideas about diversification into modern forms of transport – airships, aircraft, cars and locomotive building – Beardmore's greatly expanded wartime organisation was unable to develop these interests sufficiently to fully

Above: When the forge at Parkhead was first built in the late 1830s, it was in a rural setting to the east of Glasgow which at that time had a population of over 200,000. Rapid industrialisation saw major extensions to city boundaries and a rise in population to over 1.1 million by the mid-1920s. As the heavy industries boomed, the Parkhead Forge was extended southwards and eastwards from its original site at the north west of Duke Street. New works were erected at Rigby Street and Myreside Streets to cope with the volume of work. The end result was a major steel and ordnance works nearly two miles to the east of the city centre. During the First World War, 20,000 people were employed at the Parkhead Works.

utilise its extensive facilities and thus secure its future. By the mid-1920s it was in serious financial difficulties, prompting a restructuring which saw many of the post-1900 additions trimmed back or closed altogether. The shipyard fell into the latter category and although it had attracted a number of naval contracts in the last half of the 1920s, the volume of work was insufficient to sustain such a large yard.

The formation of National Shipbuilders Security Ltd in 1930, described on pp38-9, provided the vehicle for disposal of the loss making works, so reducing the competition for the few shipbuilding orders available. The yard was purchased in March 1930 for £200,000 and closed at the end of that year with the departure of its last ship. The engine works was retained, however, on the basis that Admiralty orders for cruiser machinery offered a profitable future, but this too failed and in 1934 the Engine Works were also acquired by NSS and closed.

Fate

The main shipyard site was taken over by Turner & Newall to become an asbestos factory. The fitting-out basin was used by John Brown as Admiralty agents to fit out some Clydebank ships and escorts launched elsewhere during the Second World War. From 1946 Arnott Young & Co Ltd used the basin and nearby workshops as a shipbreaking site where ships of all kinds, including several British battleships, were broken up – see Appendix 3. Arnott Young ceased operations there in 1985. In 1938 the East Yard was dug out to become a tidal basin for use by Post Office cable ships.

Beardmore's Engine Works were extensive and capable of large-scale engineering work, which made them of value especially after re-armament began in the latter 1930s. In 1939 they were acquired by the Ministry of Supply and became a Royal Ordnance Factory specialising in the manufacture of medium calibre guns. Beardmore received an order in 1938 for nine of the new 16in guns intended for the *Lion* class battleships, completing two of them.[7] Armour plant capacity was installed at Dalmuir and the management of the works returned to Wm Beardmore & Co Ltd as agents for the Ministry of Supply from 1941 until 1944. The Dalmuir ROF continued after the war, manufacturing tanks including the Conqueror main battle tank. In 1957 the ROF closed and the works were operated by Babcock & Wilcox Ltd until 1969 for a variety of purposes including crane manufacture. After Babcock & Wilcox's departure, no further use could be found for the works, which were demolished from 1970 to 1973. From 1981 the former Beardmore site was designated an enterprise zone in what proved a successful attempt to attract new business to the site. The fitting out basin was infilled, the slipways levelled, and the site decontaminated. A private hospital, subsequently acquired by the National Health Service, and hotel complex stand on the site of the shipyard, located at 55-54-21N 04-25-40W. The site of the Engine Works is now an industrial estate. No trace now remains of Beardmore's Naval Construction Works, apart from the former East Yard time office, which is now a private dwelling, and slipway ends visible at low tide.

1.6 Coventry Ordnance Works Ltd

In 1905 John Brown, Cammell Laird and Fairfield established Coventry Ordnance Works Ltd to challenge the duopoly that Armstrongs and Vickers had in the highly profitable and complex business of manufacturing heavy gun mountings. The core of this business had been established in Birmingham in the late 1880s as Mulliner Ltd, machine tool makers, manufacturers of carriages and later car bodies. By the end of the nineteenth century the business, accelerated by the Boer War, had diversified into the manufacture of army vehicles and mountings for field guns. In early 1902 the company, now named Mulliner Wigley Co Ltd after its two principals, was concentrated on a large site at Coventry. Two years earlier Charles Cammell & Co had decided that they should

Below: Beardmore's engine works and former West Yard was greatly extended as Dalmuir Royal Ordnance Factory in the years before the Second World War for the manufacture of medium-calibre guns and armour. Had the *Lion* class battleships not been cancelled, some of their 16in guns would have been made here. This photograph was taken in the 1950s when Babcock & Wilcox used some of the works. The entire site was demolished twenty years later. *(Author's collection)*

acquire an ordnance capacity through the purchase of the Hotchkiss Ordnance Company. Although this did not materialise, Mulliner Wigley, for whom Cammell produced steel forgings, emerged as a potential candidate. In January 1903 Cammell purchased Mulliner Wigley for over £140,000. Later that year, as already recounted, Cammell acquired Laird Brothers and thus by the end of 1903 Cammell Laird & Co Ltd stood in a potentially similar position to that of Armstrong and Vickers. However, both Armstrong and Vickers were naturally resistant to others entering the market for gun mountings. At the same time there was a concern expressed by Cammell Laird and John Brown that the Admiralty might in future place the contract for a ship, its ordnance and armour with one company, with the expectation of a lower tender price. Such an arrangement would seriously disadvantage Cammell Laird and Brown. However, in reality the Admiralty were better off inviting competition for machinery, armour and gun mountings separately from hulls, as there were different specialist firms for each product.[8] Despite last minute attempts by Vickers to persuade them otherwise, both companies formed a new business, Coventry Ordnance Works Ltd, in which John Brown had a 50 per cent shareholding and Cammell Laird and Fairfield 25 per cent each. Fairfield's inclusion is explained by an exchange of shares that took place between Cammell Laird and the Fairfield Shipbuilding & Engineering Co Ltd in October 1905. Under the terms of this arrangement each company provided two directors to sit on each other's Board. Fairfield's concern, however, was that the armament combinations that had recently taken place between Vickers with Beardmore and Armstrong with Whitworth potentially shut them out from the supply of steel forgings, guns and armour, except at high prices. Hitherto much of Fairfield's requirements for forgings had been met by Beardmore's Parkhead Forge. The arrangement with Cammell Laird and the Coventry Ordnance Works (COW) cleared all of these hurdles for the Clydeside firm.

A programme of investment was initiated to provide the new company with the tools and expertise to construct the largest naval mountings. New plant was provided at Coventry to enable the largest guns to be manufactured, while a gun mounting works was constructed on a 20-acre site at Scotstoun on the Clyde in 1907. This plant included five pits where

THE
COVENTRY
ORDNANCE
WORKS
LIMITED.

LONDON-COVENTRY-SCOTSTOUN-
CLIFFE-BOSTON.

NAVAL AND LAND SERVICE GUNS AND MOUNTINGS.
PROJECTILES, CARTRIDGE CASES, FUZES
AND ALL ACCESSORIES.
HIGH-SPEED TWIST DRILLS, MILLING CUTTERS,
TURNING TOOLS.

CONTRACTORS TO THE BRITISH, COLONIAL AND
FOREIGN GOVERNMENTS.

completed gun mountings including turrets and guns could be assembled and tested before being dismantled and dispatched to the shipyard. However, COW struggled at a number of levels, much of it to do with having no track record in the manufacture of these complex mechanisms, coupled with resistance from the two existing gun mounting contractors. Armstrong and Vickers were both disinclined to help a competitor in this lucrative business, while the Admiralty was initially reluctant to entrust a newcomer with such critical components – there was less risk ordering smaller guns and mountings. The result was high expenditure in setting up the works and for manufacturing and testing prototypes, with little income from sales. It was only after the increase in battleship orders under the 1909 programme, when eight vessels were ordered, that the Coventry Ordnance Works began to receive more substantial orders, with a contract for the five 13.5in twin mountings for *Conqueror*, the hull and machinery for which were to be constructed at Beardmore's Dalmuir yard. Coventry's initial difficulties had serious

Above: An advert for the Coventry Ordnance Works dating from 1913.

Below: Part of the former Coventry Ordnance Works at Scotstoun in the early 1970s while owned by Harland & Wolff Ltd. The basin and gantry system supporting the heavy overhead crane that lifted completed 13.5in and 15in guns and mountings into coasters for transportation to the shipyards can be seen. *(Author's collection)*

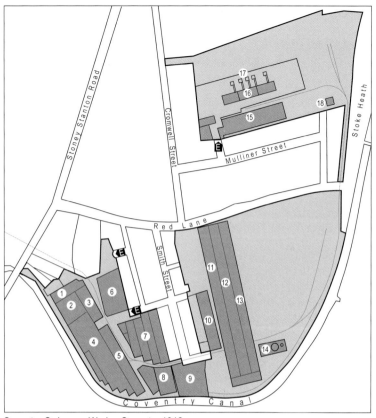

Coventry Ordnance Works, Coventry 1912

1. Offices and stores
2. Tool room & twist drill dept.
3. Wood mill
4. Heavy machine shop
5. Gun carriage erecting shop
6. Wagon shop & timber store
7. Light machine shop
8. Repair & polishing shops
9. Shrapnel filling shop & repair shop

10. Limber shop
11. Large machine shop
12. Large erecting shop
13. Large gun bay
14. Large gun pit
15. Machine shop & store room

16. Assembly room
17. Powder magazines
18. Erosion chamber

□ area of works
■ buildings
E entrance

Feet	250	500	1000
Metres	75	150	300

Above: The modest ordnance works at Coventry was greatly extended once John Brown, Cammell Laird and Fairfield had taken over in 1905. The Coventry site was used to manufacture guns, transferable and field mountings and ammunition, with heavy gun mountings built at Scotstoun. Guns were shipped out on rail wagons across Stoney Stratford Road to the main line, either to the test range at Freiston or to an ordnance depot. The site is visible today at 52-25-10N 01-29-30W.

financial consequences, particularly for Fairfield, which was the smallest and least robust financially of the three parent companies who had to underwrite losses. From January 1906 onwards the new company required significant funding from the three controlling firms and by October 1911, it owed Fairfield £190,000. By 1913 they had resolved to dispose of their holding in the Coventry business at the earliest moment.[9] However, COW was to become more profitable given the demand for its products from a country at war, and between October 1914 and June 1916 COW had repaid all debt owed to Fairfield.

From 1914–18 the Coventry Ordnance Works at last became profitable[10] producing a wide range of guns, ammunition and mountings, including 13.5in and 15in, as listed on p.191. When the war ended and demand reduced drastically however, it was clear there

was little future for the continuation of the two works and Coventry was disposed of by majority shareholder John Brown & Co to the newly formed English Electric Co Ltd to manufacture electrical generating equipment. In 1920 the Scotstoun Works were sold to Harland & Wolff, who began the construction of marine diesel engine parts, although the gun pits were retained under the terms of the sale but filled in later. Scotstoun was closed between 1927 and 1936 because of lack of work. With the beginning of re-armament, Harland & Wolff re-opened the plant with Admiralty support as their Scotstoun Ordnance Works. Large new shops were added to the west of the existing shops and plant supplied by the Admiralty for the manufacture of naval mountings of various calibres up to 5.25in. In 1944 the Scotstoun Ordnance Works refurbished and modernised the 15in mountings from *Glorious* and *Courageous* for the battleship *Vanguard* which was under construction at Clydebank.

Fate

The Scotstoun works continued to manufacture twin 4.5in naval mountings until the late 1960s when it ceased ordnance manufacture to become part of the Albion Motor Co. In 1993 the works was taken over by Albion Automotive, which was in turn acquired by American Axle & Manufacturing in 1998. These large heavy engineering factory buildings located at 55-52-35N 04-21-24W are among the very few that have survived in Britain today, which are typical of the ones manufacturing the ships and their components forming the subject of this book.

2 THE PRIVATE SHIPYARDS

While the previous section discussed the careers of companies that had been transformed into major armaments companies, several of the battleship builders remained as simply that, shipbuilders and marine engineers, relying on the armaments firms to supply armour and ordnance. These firms included Thames Iron Works, Palmers Shipbuilding & Iron Co Ltd and Scotts' Shipbuilding & Engineering Co Ltd.

2.1 Fairfield Shipbuilding & Engineering Co Ltd.

The origins of the Fairfield works can be traced to 1834 when Charles Randolph and Richard Cunliff set up as engineers and machinery makers at Tradeston in Glasgow. In 1852 John

Elder joined the company where his talent for marine engineering would prove significant. The first marine steam engine built by the company, now Randolph, Elder & Co, was put into service in 1853, although that year also marked a more significant event in the development of the steam engine when, in January, Elder took out the first patent for the compound steam marine engine. Compounding greatly increased fuel efficiency by using both a high and a low pressure cylinder. In 1854 the first vessel so fitted, the screw steamer *Brandon*, demonstrated a 30 to 40 per cent saving in coal expended during trials, thereby reducing operating costs and allowing longer voyages to be undertaken. The company filed several other patents in marine engineering and, in 1860, it followed the example of other Clydeside engineers by expanding the business into shipbuilding. At first a small existing yard at Govan was taken over but in 1864 the company purchased a large tract of land occupied by Fairfield farm. Here Elder planned a large integrated shipyard and engine works. The first ship was launched from this yard in 1864 and in 1868 work constructing the engine shops began, moving manufacture from the restricted Tradeston site. Elder died at the early age of 45 in 1869 and on the retirement of Charles Randolph in 1870 the business was renamed John Elder & Co in a tribute to Elder and his achievements. In 1878 William Pearce, a naval architect trained at Chatham Dockyard and partner in the business, took control of the yard and under his direction it rose to the first rank, enjoying a deservedly high reputation internationally for, amongst many others, a series of record-breaking Atlantic liners, seven of which held the prestigious Blue Riband for the fastest Atlantic passage.

In 1886 the company converted to a limited liability status, becoming the Fairfield Shipbuilding & Engineering Co Ltd, at that time the largest shipbuilding and marine engineering organisation on the Clyde, although subsequently exceeded by the John Brown and Beardmore works at Clydebank and Dalmuir. Warship construction had begun in 1868 with the gunboat *Midge*, although what might be loosely termed a battleship (armoured cruiser) *Nelson* was launched in 1876 followed by a series of cruisers. The only pre-dreadnought battleship to be constructed was *Commonwealth*, launched in 1903.

In 1905 an exchange of shares took place between Fairfield and the much larger business

of Cammell Laird & Co. The strengthening of relations between the two companies did not affect the autonomy of the Fairfield company but did prepare them for the venture into the manufacture of guns and mountings through Cammell Laird's (and John Brown's) Coventry Ordnance Works described above under that heading.

In the same year as the accommodation with Cammell Laird, Fairfield tendered successfully for one of the first battlecruisers, *Indomitable*, and thereafter for the battlecruisers *New Zealand*, *Renown* and the battleship *Valiant*. Fresh investment was made at this already well equipped works, including in 1911 the installation of a 200-ton cantilever fitting-out crane by Arrol to enable the lifting of increasingly heavier guns, gun mountings and machinery components. Despite the volume of high value contracts that earned annual gross profits of about £100,000 in the first decade of the century, from 1911 onwards Fairfield's shipbuilding department made a series of losses.

Difficulties for the company were not over in what they described in December 1915 as 'repeated failures to maintain dates stated for progress and completion of contracts of which the position of HMS *Renown* and the delay in delivery of HMS *Mischief* are glaring examples.'[11] Nevertheless, *Renown* was still completed in a remarkably short space of twenty-one months for such a large and complex ship. In April 1916 Fairfield was awarded the contract for the *Hood* class battlecruiser *Rodney*, one of three sister-ships of *Hood*. This contract proceeded slowly until 1917 when it was suspended although not finally cancelled until March 1919. During the war submarine building sheds were added to the west of the fitting-out basin and this was followed after the end of the war in the general optimism that pervaded the shipbuilding industry by two new berths served by a large shipbuilding gantry. Fairfield was successful in winning the contract for a G3 battlecruiser in 1921, although the contract was suspended after just three weeks and cancelled outright in February 1922 under the terms of the Washington Treaty.

In 1919 the Fairfield yard, along with several

THE FAIRFIELD SHIPBUILDING & ENGINEERING C? LT?

GOVAN.

GLASGOW, 17th November, 1921.

Left: The letterhead in use by the company after the First World War.

Below: Fairfield's stamp.

Right: The Fairfield Works were conceived by John Elder in the early 1860s as the first of the large private integrated shipyards and marine engineering works in the UK. Because of the narrowness of the Clyde at Govan, a fitting-out basin was an essential element in the layout enabling vessels to be completed without obstructing the river channel. Similarly, building berths had to be arranged at an acute angle to provide an adequate launching run. To illustrate this, *Renown* is shown here stopped in the river after launching and in the fitting-out basin. This yard, despite many threatened closures over the last fifty years, is presently owned by BAE Systems building the lion's share of the aircraft carriers *Queen Elizabeth* and *Prince of Wales*.

Below: Like all of the larger private yards, Fairfield built most classes of ship. This advert from 1913 shows recently constructed warships.

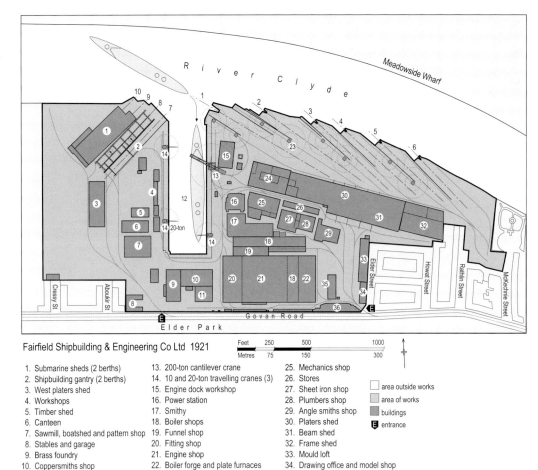

Fairfield Shipbuilding & Engineering Co Ltd 1921

Feet 250 500 1000	
Metres 75 150 300	

1. Submarine sheds (2 berths)
2. Shipbuilding gantry (2 berths)
3. West platers shed
4. Workshops
5. Timber shed
6. Canteen
7. Sawmill, boatshed and pattern shop
8. Stables and garage
9. Brass foundry
10. Coppersmiths shop
11. Pipe shop
12. Fitting-out basin
13. 200-ton cantilever crane
14. 10 and 20-ton travelling cranes (3)
15. Engine dock workshop
16. Power station
17. Smithy
18. Boiler shops
19. Funnel shop
20. Fitting shop
21. Engine shop
22. Boiler forge and plate furnaces
23. 12-ton fixed tower cranes (8)
24. Joiners shop
25. Mechanics shop
26. Stores
27. Sheet iron shop
28. Plumbers shop
29. Angle smiths shop
30. Platers shed
31. Beam shed
32. Frame shed
33. Mould loft
34. Drawing office and model shop
35. Electrical workshop and stores
36. Main office and drawing offices

☐ area outside works
▨ area of works
▨ buildings
E entrance

other British shipbuilding firms including Doxford at Sunderland and Workman Clark at Belfast, was acquired by the Northumberland Shipbuilding Co Ltd. This small and unlikely business was used by financiers Sperling & Co as a vehicle for acquiring shipbuilding capacity to take advantage of the expected boom in merchant shipbuilding after the end of the war. This boom proved to be very short-lived, ending in 1920, and in the depressed market that followed the Sperling Combine collapsed in 1927. Fairfield was inherently sound and continued until 1935 when the company was taken over by Lithgows Ltd. In 1930 under the auspices of National Shipbuilders Security Ltd, a company brought into existence to buy out redundant shipyards, Fairfield's comparatively new but under-utilised West Yard which had cost over £150,000 a decade earlier was acquired for £30,000 and demolished.

After the expiry of the London Naval Treaty in 1936 there was considerable haste on the part of the Admiralty to order new battleships. In the second round of orders for *King George V* class battleships, Fairfield was awarded the contract for *Howe* in April 1937. In August 1939 they were awarded the contract for the *Lion* class battleship *Thunderer*, although very little work on her was undertaken; her keel was never laid down and the contract was cancelled in 1944.

THE FAIRFIELD
SHIPBUILDING AND ENGINEERING CO., LTD.,
DESIGNERS AND BUILDERS OF

Battleships, Cruisers, Destroyers and War Vessels of every description
COMPLETE IN ALL RESPECTS.

PART OWNERS OF THE COVENTRY ORDNANCE WORKS, LTD.

Mail and Passenger Steamers of the Largest Size and Type.
TURBINES, GEARED TURBINES, RECIPROCATING ENGINES, INTERNAL COMBUSTION ENGINES.

OUTPUT OF S.H.P. IN 1913, 202,200.

Head Offices:—FAIRFIELD WORKS, GOVAN, GLASGOW. | London Offices:—9, VICTORIA STREET, WESTMINSTER, S.W.
Telegrams and Cables: "FAIRFIELD GLASGOW." | Telegrams and Cables: "KENTIGERN, LONDON."

H.M.S. "GLASGOW."   H.M.S. "FORTUNE."

H.M.S. "INDOMITABLE."   H.M.S. "UNDAUNTED."   H.M.S. "NEW ZEALAND."

Left: The effect on the skyline at Fairfield of the new Arrol 200-ton cantilever crane (completed in 1911) is plain to see as it towers over *New Zealand* in the fitting-out basin. The battlecruiser is not far from completion which indicates that this photograph was probably taken about October 1912. *(Author's collection)*

Left: A view across the fitting-out basin of the shipyard as it is today, the cantilever crane having been demolished in 2007. A section of the aircraft carrier *Queen Elizabeth* extends out of the assembly hall. For comparison with the above photograph, the only building in both images is the 'sawtooth' roof building at right also visible behind *New Zealand*'s funnels. *(Author's collection)*

At the end of the war Fairfield, like the rest of the British shipbuilding industry, enjoyed a prolonged period of profitable activity and during the 1950s a major programme of investment re-equipped the works for welded fabrication. By the early 1960s severe overseas competition and low prices began to impact on the British shipbuilding industry and in 1965 the company filed for bankruptcy despite a large order book. Its recent modernisation and the prestige hitherto enjoyed as one of the big names in British industry won it a reprieve through Government intervention. Restruc-tured as Fairfield (Glasgow) Ltd, it was made the subject of a high-profile experiment in labour relations and production control aimed at increasing productivity. Before this could be brought to a conclusion, the yard was swept into the Government's industry-wide strategy of restructuring in line with the Geddes Report. This envisaged regional groups and thus in 1968 Fairfield became part of Upper Clyde Shipbuilders as the Govan Division.

Large sums of public funding were made available to assist the groups in making a hoped for transition to profitable trading. This Upper Clyde Shipbuilders was unable to achieve owing to poor productivity and high wages and in the summer of 1971 the group went into liquidation. Following a memorable and highly politicised campaign to save the yards, Fairfield emerged as the centrepiece of a new publicly funded company, Govan Shipbuilders Ltd. In 1977 the shipbuilding industry was nationalised and Govan Shipbuilders was incorporated into British Shipbuilders. Ten years later Government support for the shipbuilding industry came to an end and the companies were sold off. The Govan yard was bought by the Norwegian industrial conglomerate Kvaerner in 1988 under the title Kvaerner Govan Ltd. Investment into new production facilities was made in the yard to enable construction of liquefied gas tankers. In 1999 Kvaerner withdrew from British shipbuilding and the Govan yard became part of BAE Systems formed out of the amalgamation of Marconi Electronic Systems and British Aerospace. BAE Systems has undergone a number of structural changes since then. Currently (2012) the Govan yard is a part of its BAE Systems Maritime – Naval Ships, one of three divisions of BAE Systems Surface Ships Ltd.

Although the Fairfield yard continued as a major builder of warships after the end of the Second World War, warship construction ceased in 1970 with *Antrim*, in line with a greatly reduced Royal Navy and the concentration of naval construction in designated warship yards. Throughout the 1970s, 1980s and 1990s, the Govan yard built merchant ships exclusively, with the exception of the hull of the helicopter carrier *Ocean* launched in 1995 for VSEL. As part of BAE Systems, the yard returned to warship construction and is currently working on large blocks for the two new British aircraft carriers, having built five of the six Type 45 destroyers. Along with Barrow shipyard, Govan is the only other battleship yard to have survived from the heyday of British shipbuilding that is still building ships, located at 55-52N 04-19-17W.

2.2 Harland & Wolff Ltd

At its peak Harland & Wolff had an enormous shipbuilding and ship repair organisation in the UK, building a large number of well-appointed passenger liners and merchant ships; but the only capital ship constructed at their works was the battlecruiser *Glorious*, launched in 1916.

The business of Harland & Wolff was formed in 1861 when Edward Harland set up in partnership with Gustav Wolff. Harland, born in Scarborough in 1831, had previously served an apprenticeship at Robert Stephenson's engineering works in Newcastle, leaving there in 1851 to become chief draughtsman at J & G Thomson's Clyde shipyard and two years later manager at Toward's shipyard on the Tyne. While serving his apprenticeship, Harland met Gustav Schwabe, a German financier resident in Liverpool and partner in the shipping line John Bibby & Sons. Schwabe was destined to play an important role in shaping what would become Harland & Wolff. It was through him that Harland met Schwabe's nephew Gustav Wolff, then an engineering student.

In 1854, encouraged by Schwabe, Harland became manager of Robert Hickson's shipyard at Queen's Island, Belfast to be followed two years later by Wolff who became Harland's assistant at Queen's Island. In 1858, probably financed by Schwabe, Harland purchased Hickson's yard for £5000, which was then styled Edward James Harland & Co. In 1861 Edward Harland and Gustav Wolff entered into partnership and from then onwards the business of Harland and Wolff was begun, although it would not be until 1888 that the name Harland & Wolff Ltd was adopted following conversion to a limited liability company.

The early success of the partnership initially rested on building ships for John Bibby, but as the business grew Schwabe brokered a deal with shipowner Thomas Ismay in 1868, resulting in the formation of the Oceanic Steam Navigation Co, better known as the White Star Line. In return for finance, Ismay agreed that White Star ships would be built by Harland & Wolff on a cost-plus basis, also known as 'time and line'.

By 1875 the partnership was expanded to include shipyard manager Walter Wilson and chief draughtsman William Pirrie. Pirrie proved himself most able and from 1884 onwards gradually assumed control of the business, becoming Chairman in 1894. The cost-plus system of financing contracts first implemented with White Star was expanded to include other shipping lines in what became known as the Commission Club. With the boom in passenger liner construction, this system was a spectacular

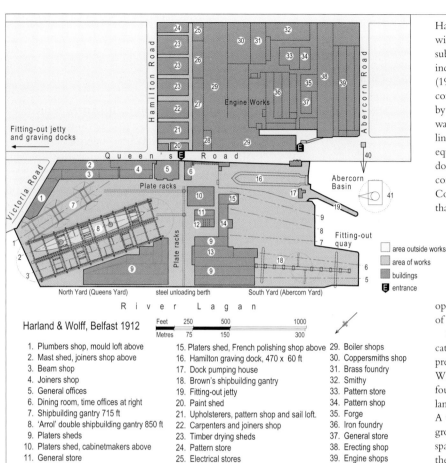

Harland & Wolff, Belfast 1912

1. Plumbers shop, mould loft above
2. Mast shed, joiners shop above
3. Beam shop
4. Joiners shop
5. General offices
6. Dining room, time offices at right
7. Shipbuilding gantry 715 ft
8. 'Arrol' double shipbuilding gantry 850 ft
9. Platers sheds
10. Platers shed, cabinetmakers above
11. General store
12. Rivet and tool store
13. Smiths shop
14. Platers shed, polishing shop above
15. Platers shed, French polishing shop above
16. Hamilton graving dock, 470 x 60 ft
17. Dock pumping house
18. Brown's shipbuilding gantry
19. Fitting-out jetty
20. Paint shed
21. Upholsterers, pattern shop and sail loft.
22. Carpenters and joiners shop
23. Timber drying sheds
24. Pattern store
25. Electrical stores
26. Fitting and bolt shop
27. Electric power station
28. Pneumatic & hydraulic shop
29. Boiler shops
30. Coppersmiths shop
31. Brass foundry
32. Smithy
33. Pattern store
34. Pattern shop
35. Forge
36. Iron foundry
37. General store
38. Erecting shop
39. Engine shops
40. 60 ton sheerlegs
41. 150 ton floating crane

Harland & Wolff began in the early 1860s with one yard (later the Abercorn Yard) and subsequently expanded the business to include four yards, Queens (1886), Musgrave (1918) and Victoria (1935), making the company the largest shipbuilder in the UK by a considerable margin. In 1907 when it was decided to construct the *Olympic* class liners for White Star, plans were made to equip the Queens yard with a massive double gantry system designed and constructed by Sir William Arrol & Co. Completed in 1909, it was under this gantry that Harland & Wolff's only capital ship, *Glorious*, was built. The company had access to the Alexandra and Thomson dry docks owned by Belfast Harbour Commissioners, as well as fitting-out wharves to the north-east of the Queens yard. In 1918 the company opened the Musgrave Yard to the south-east of the engine works.

In 1969 a large building dock and fabrication shops were opened on what had previously been the Musgrave Channel. While part of this facility remains today, the four shipyards have been demolished and the land used or earmarked for other purposes. A visitor attraction has been built on the ground of the old Queens Yard and the space the gantry occupied preserved to mark the construction and loss of RMS *Titanic*. The 1912 plan of the yard shows *Glorious* under the gantry as in 1916.

success and enabled the company to begin a major expansion in its operations. Engine works were built in 1880 and in 1886, ground was acquired to the north east of the existing yard, which latter was renamed the Abercorn Yard, where four building slips and steel working shops were laid out. The new North Yard, later the Queen's Yard, brought the number of building slips up to nine.

Under Pirrie, Harland & Wolff became a key player in a number of ambitious developments, including in 1902 the formation of International Mercantile Marine Company (IMM) by the US financier J P Morgan, who bought up many well-known shipping lines including White Star. The arrangement was that Harland & Wolff would meet all of IMM's ship-building requirements on a similar cost–plus basis as the Commission Club. One outcome of this was the construction of the three *Olympic* class liners ordered from 1907 onwards, including the infamous *Titanic* for which the yard is best known today.

In 1907 John Brown & Co Ltd took a 51.7 per cent shareholding in Harland & Wolff to further secure the output from its Sheffield works, in addition to that of its Clydebank shipyard. Under this arrangement, Clydebank supplied Harland & Wolff with expertise in turbine technology, building a number of sets until the engine works at Belfast were suitably equipped. With great demand for merchant ships to replace those lost to U-boats, in 1918 a new shipyard, the East or Musgrave Yard, with six berths was opened in the Musgrave channel for the construction of standard ships.

While facilities were expanded at Belfast, Harland & Wolff established major repair yards in Southampton (1907), Liverpool (1913) and London (1924) and on the Clyde no fewer than five shipyards were acquired and operated from 1913 onwards: London & Glasgow yard in 1912, Caird & Co in 1916 and A&J Inglis, D&W Henderson, A McMillan & Co all in 1917.

Naval contracts began in 1868 with the small

gunboat *Lynx*, although they were few and far between thereafter with only five small contracts placed over the next forty years, including the yacht *Enchantress* in 1903. With as much merchant work as it could handle, it is likely that Harland & Wolff were not seriously interested in naval contracts, although it unsuccessfully tendered for a *Majestic* class battleship in 1895, and thereafter the occasional dreadnought. With no serious experience in Admiralty work for which there was great competition with low prices for hulls, this is perhaps understandable. They were more successful bidding for machinery contracts, including for the pre-dreadnought *Queen* in 1900. At the beginning of the First World War naval orders began to flow, particularly for monitors built at Belfast and destroyers at Govan. Early in 1915 Harland & Wolff were given the contract for the battlecruiser *Glorious*, as following the cessation of passenger liner building, the company had spare capacity.

After the end of the war, Harland & Wolff, with a huge number of ships on order, purchased the Clydeside steel works of David Colville to secure steel supplies. Soon after, it became financially entangled with the Royal Mail Group with serious consequences that threatened the future of the company. In 1935 part of Workman Clark, Belfast's other shipbuilder, was acquired, and its South Yard became Harland & Wolff's Victoria Yard. Prior to the Second World War the company again became involved with warship construction, laying down no fewer than nine aircraft carriers among other warship types, the first being *Formidable* ordered in 1937.

Harland & Wolff had one further connection with battleship construction through its purchase of the Coventry Ordnance Works gun mounting shops at Scotstoun on the Clyde in 1920. Although used primarily for the construction of diesel machinery parts, at the beginning of re-armament in 1936 the works reverted to ordnance production, becoming known as the Scotstoun Ordnance Works. In 1944 four 15in turrets that had been kept in store were redesigned and modernised at Scotstoun for *Vanguard*.

From the 1960s onwards, in common with the general decline of shipbuilding in Britain, Harland & Wolff disposed of its shipyards and repair yards on mainland Britain to concentrate on its Belfast yard. Investment in a new shipyard centred on a building dock in the Musgrave Channel was completed in 1969, located at 54-

36-35N 05-53-55W. But here too shipbuilding ceased in 2003 although the firm continues in offshore work, ship repair and other engineering manufactures as Harland & Wolff Heavy Industries Ltd.

2.3 Palmers Shipbuilding & Iron Co Ltd.

The impetus behind the establishment of the Jarrow shipyard was coal and its trans-shipment. In 1851 Charles Mark Palmer and his brother George with interests in local coal mines set up a small shipyard known as Palmer Brothers & Co at Jarrow, then a mining village of about 1000 persons. In 1852 Palmer designed and

Below: Glorious fitting out at Belfast in the summer of 1916. Harland & Wolff's 150-ton floating crane, completed in 1908, looks positioned to erect her forward twin 15in turret, the aft one already installed. *(National Museums of Northern Ireland)*

built the first successful 486-grt iron steam driven collier, the *John Bowes*, which transformed the transportation of coal from the Tyne to London compared with existing wooden sailing vessels. In 1856 the company constructed the floating battery HMS *Terror* for the Admiralty, for which Charles Palmer employed rolled armour, supplied by Beale of Rotherham, rather than hammered armour.

In 1857 work began erecting blast furnaces at Jarrow, followed by rolling mills the year after. In 1860 a shipyard at Howdon on the opposite bank of the Tyne was acquired and by the following year Palmer had a total of 6000 employees at his by now extensive Jarrow and Howdon works. In 1865 the company was converted to limited liability under the designation Palmers Shipbuilding and Iron Co Ltd. In the same year a graving dock was opened at the Jarrow works to develop the ship repair side of the business. Over the last half of the nine-

Below: An example of the stationery used by Palmers in the early years of the twentieth century.

Right: The Palmers site at Jarrow included a steel works at the western end, a shipyard, an engine works, graving dock and a patent slip. The works were responsible for much of the town's development in the last half of the nineteenth century and up to 80 per cent of the male working population of the town was employed there. The installation of the shipbuilding cableways in the early 1900s gave the yard an unmistakable appearance and a skyline visible for miles around. The width of the River Tyne could support launching the largest ships unlike the Clyde where slipways had to be arranged at acute angles to the river to enable large ships to be launched. The plan shows the battlecruiser *Queen Mary* at the East fitting-out quay.

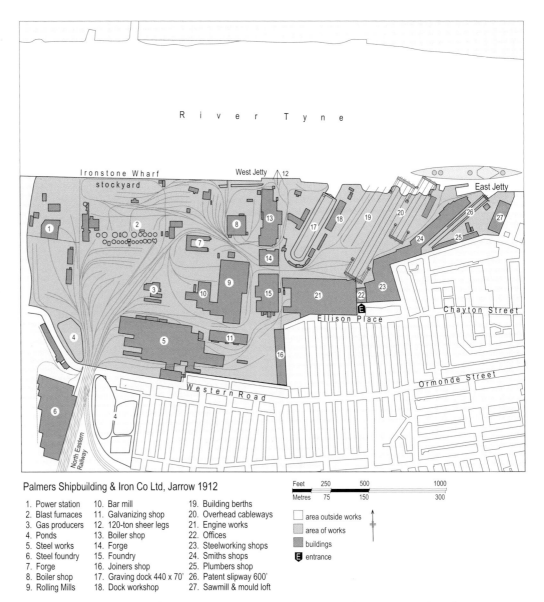

Palmers Shipbuilding & Iron Co Ltd, Jarrow 1912

1. Power station	10. Bar mill	19. Building berths
2. Blast furnaces	11. Galvanizing shop	20. Overhead cableways
3. Gas producers	12. 120-ton sheer legs	21. Engine works
4. Ponds	13. Boiler shop	22. Offices
5. Steel works	14. Forge	23. Steelworking shops
6. Steel foundry	15. Foundry	24. Smiths shops
7. Forge	16. Joiners shop	25. Plumbers shop
8. Boiler shop	17. Graving dock 440 x 70'	26. Patent slipway 600'
9. Rolling Mills	18. Dock workshop	27. Sawmill & mould loft

Feet 250 500 1000
Metres 75 150 300

☐ area outside works
▨ area of works
▨ buildings
🅴 entrance

teenth century, Palmers built a number of armoured warships. including *Defence* launched in 1861, *Cerberus* in 1868, and *Swiftsure* and *Triumph* in 1870. Although smaller classes of warships were also built, twenty years elapsed before the battleships *Resolution* and *Revenge* were constructed, both launched in 1892, followed almost ten years later by *Russell* in 1901. Palmer's also developed a reputation for building fast destroyers. By the end of the nineteenth century the Jarrow works had a shipyard, engine and boiler works, blast furnaces, rolling mills, steel works, and galvanising works as well as their own iron ore mines elsewhere.

In the early years of the twentieth century the yard was acquired by Christopher Furness, who began a programme of investment, including two new berths served by the iconic overhead cableway system that dominated the Jarrow skyline. The pre-dreadnought battleship *Lord Nelson* was launched from the smaller of these berths in 1906 and the dreadnought *Hercules* in 1910. Two other capital ships were built by Palmer's, the battlecruiser *Queen Mary* launched in 1912 and battleship *Resolution* in 1915. A unit of the *Royal Sovereign* class, the battleship *Repulse* had been awarded to Palmer's in 1914 but when the design of this ship was hastily reworked as a battlecruiser, the contract was switched to John Brown at Clydebank because the increased length could not be accommodated at Jarrow. In 1911 Robert Stephenson's shipyard at Hebburn was leased, to be purchased outright in the following year, at which time the old Howdon yard was sold to Eltringham.

No further capital ship contracts were awarded to Palmer's, although it continued to build many other warship types for the Admiralty. As for most other yards in Britain, the 1920s proved to be very difficult owing to the general downturn in trade. Large loans had been taken out, incurring high interest charges, while losses at the steelworks mounted. The onset of the Depression from 1930 brought the works to its knees and in 1933 it was purchased by National Shipbuilders Security Ltd, closed, and its plant either sold off or demolished. As the single largest employer in Jarrow, the closure of Palmer's, which at its peak employed 10,000, inflicted serious distress on the district and resulted in the 'Jarrow Crusade', a protest march which took place in 1936. The Hebburn yard was sold off to become Palmers Hebburn ship repair yard that became a subsidiary of Vickers-Armstrongs in 1934. It is still in business today as A&P Tyne, located at 54-59-05N 01-31-09W (Jarrow at 54-59-07N 01-29-30W).

2.4 Scotts' Shipbuilding & Engineering Co Ltd

During the nineteenth and twentieth centuries, the lower Clyde at Port Glasgow and Greenock had a large concentration of shipyards. Of these only one became a major builder of warships, Scotts' of Greenock.

Scotts' traced its origins back to 1711 when John Scott began building small fishing vessels at West Burn in Greenock. Throughout much of that century the company was preoccupied building fishing and coastal sailing vessels. In the early nineteenth century the company undertook work for the Admiralty, constructing the revenue cutter *Prince of Wales* in 1803, although it was not until 1838 that a further Admiralty contract was won, this time the machinery for the sloops *Hecla* and *Hecate*. The advent of steam propulsion encouraged the firm to enter that field in 1825 as Scott, Sinclair & Co and in 1839 iron was first used as a material for constructing hulls. The screw driven iron frigate *Greenock* of 1835 tons displacement was launched in 1849 but thereafter there was little Admiralty work, with exception of engines for Dockyard-built sloops and gunboats. In 1857 Scott & Co, as the company had become, formed links with the Liverpool ship owner Alfred Holt, building many of that company's vessels thereafter. In the early 1870s this pattern was repeated with John Swire, who formed the China Navigation Co. Subsequently Scotts' supervised the construction of Swire's Taikoo Dockyard & Engineering Co at Hong Kong.

In 1883 the company effectively doubled in size when it took over Robert Steele's yard at Cartside, later known as the Cartsburn Dockyard. Admiralty work resumed in 1889 under the impetus of the Naval Defence Act of that year with machinery orders to the associated Greenock Foundry Co for the turret ships

Below: *Hercules* lying at Palmers East Jetty in June 1911, with the two cableway gantries prominent in the background; she was built under the larger right hand one. *(NMM)*

Centurion and *Barfleur*. At the end of that decade further machinery orders followed for the battleships *Canopus* and *Prince of Wales*. In 1902 with the laying down of the armoured cruiser *Argyll*, the volume of Admiralty work had become a significant feature of the Greenock company's output. To secure this, the company began a major programme of invest-

ment at the engine works and both shipyards. To facilitate this, the company had decided in 1899 to merge its engine works, the Greenock Foundry Co., with the shipbuilding company, Scott & Co. This process appears not to have been completed until 1904 when the merged businesses formally became Scotts' Shipbuilding & Engineering Co Ltd. Between 1900 and 1912 the company spent £500,000 on these works, providing new shops and machine tools, building slips up to 700ft in length and a new fitting-out basin served by a 100-ton derrick fitting-out crane. A steady flow of Admiralty work followed, including the machinery contract for the battleship *St Vincent*, the turbines of which were sub-contracted to Parsons Marine on Tyneside as Scotts' new engine shops were incomplete. This was followed by the contracts for the hull and machinery for the battleships *Colossus* and *Ajax*, launched in 1910 and 1912 respectively. Tenders for succeeding classes of battleships and battlecruisers up to and including *Nelson* were unsuccessful.

In 1925 the works were extended eastwards by the acquisition of Ross & Marshall's yard, while in 1934 Scotts' Cartsdyke shipyard was exchanged with the adjoining Greenock Dockyard Co's yard to provide a contiguous site. This was further extended in 1966 when Scotts concluded the agreement to purchase the Greenock Dockyard Co's Cartsdyke yard. Throughout this period, and particularly

Scotts' Shipbuilding & Engineering Co Ltd
Engine Works and Cartsburn Dockyard, Greenock 1912

1. Pattern shop
2. Laboratory
3. Ironfinishing shop
4. Fitting shop
5. Engine test bed
6. Boiler shops
7. Heavy machine shop, blading shop, brass shop above
8. Turbine shop
9. Smithy
10. Brass foundry
11. Offices
12. Copper shop
13. Boiler tube shop
14. Light boiler shop
15. Sheet metal shop
16. Plumbers shop and store, pattern shop above
17. Counting house
18. Joiners shop, mould loft over
19. Platers sheds
20. Power house
21. Bending blocks
22. Smiths shop
23. Angle smithy
24. Beam shed
25. Sawmill
26. Slipways
27. Electrical workshop
28. Spar maker and yard store
29. Graving dock 370 x 47 ft
30. Boat shed
31. Engineers workshop
32. 100-ton derrick crane
33. Joiners store
34. 20-ton travelling crane

area outside works
area of works
buildings
E entrance

In 1912 Scotts' had three separate sites in Greenock; Cartsburn Dockyard, Cartsdyke shipyard and an engine works at Cartsburn Street. *Colossus* and *Ajax* were built at Cartsburn. To the east of this yard was the Greenock and Grangemouth Co's shipyard and to the east of this, Scotts' yard at Cartsdyke. All three shipyard sites were eventually integrated into Scotts. A railway linked the engine works and the shipyards. With naval work in mind, Scotts invested large sums at Cartsburn to enable them to tender for battleship contracts. The shipbuilding berths were equipped with Arrol steel derrick cranes while a fitting-out basin was cut and equipped with a 100-ton fitting-out derrick crane, later uprated to 120 tons. *Ajax* is shown in the fitting-out basin.

during the Second World War, the company continued to receive orders for cruisers and destroyers, with submarine construction also becoming a specialist activity. The last surface warship built at Cartsburn was the frigate *Euryalus*, completed in 1964, although the non-combatant seabed operations ship *Challenger* was completed in 1984. The last submarine built at Cartsburn was HMAS *Otama* in 1978.

Fate

Under the restructuring of British shipbuilding prompted by the Geddes Report of 1966, Scotts' yard was merged with neighbouring Lithgow yard at Port Glasgow to form Scott Lithgow Ltd. This was the holding company name, as Scott and Lithgow continued to trade under their own names with (1969) added. In 1977 Scott Lithgow became part of nationalised British Shipbuilders and in 1980 part of British Shipbuilders Offshore Division. Under this reorganisation the Cartsdyke shipyard, which had been a merchant yard, was closed. In

1984 Scott Lithgow was privatised, becoming part of Trafalgar House plc. In the same year Scotts' Cartsburn shipyard, where *Colossus* and *Ajax* and numerous other warships were built, was closed. The shipyard site was cleared by the end of the 1980s, since when it has been redeveloped as a shopping complex, located at 55-56-42N 04-44-35W.

2.5 Swan, Hunter & Wigham Richardson Ltd

Swan Hunter, as the company was generally called, was the last of the big private yards to build a battleship, constructing *Anson* of the penultimate class of battleships constructed for the Royal Navy.

The company could trace its origins back to the very early days of iron shipbuilding on the Tyne when John Coutts set up a shipyard at Walker on the Tyne in 1842. He is credited with building the first iron ship, *Prince Albert*, on the Tyne and the first if not entirely successful iron steam collier, *QED*, in 1844. Coutts' yard

Below: The incomplete *Ajax* has been swung out from her berth in the small Scotts' fitting-out basin to allow a coasting vessel space to unload her cargo, most likely main armament components from the Coventry Ordnance Works upriver at Scotstoun, under the 100-ton derrick crane. Note the ship's boat derrick and parts of the foremast tripod lying on the quayside. *(NRS)*

Right: The company letterhead from the Second World War.

SWAN, HUNTER, & WIGHAM RICHARDSON, LIMITED,

Telegraphic Address :   WALLSEND SHIPYARD.
SWANHUNTER, WALLSEND.   WALLSEND-on-TYNE.
London Office : 7, East India Avenue, E.C.

IN REPLY PLEASE QUOTE

Below: Swan Hunter & Wigham Richardson stamp applied to drawings of the battleship *Anson*.

was not a financial success and the site was later acquired by Miller, Ravenhill & Co, who operated a shipyard there between the years 1851 and 1855.

During Coutts' time at Walker, he employed Charles Mitchell as a ship designer and in 1852 Mitchell began shipbuilding on his own behalf at Low Walker. Through marriage, Mitchell acquired two capable brothers-in-law, Henry Frederick and Charles Sheridan Swan, who later took up employment with Mitchell at his Walker yard. In 1871 Mitchell acquired another shipyard up-river at St Peters which was operated on his behalf by Coulson, Cooke & Co. Two years later this business relocated to a larger site at Walker, near Coutts' old yard, only to fail one year later in 1874. Mitchell then placed the management of the yard in the hands of his brother-in-law, C S Swan. Swan was involved in a fatal accident, falling from a ferry while returning from a business trip in 1879. Mitchell and Swan's brother Henry then entered negotiations with George Hunter from Wearside to form a partnership between the latter and C S Swan's widow, entitled C S Swan & Hunter.

In 1883, with Hunter pushing the business forward, land to the east of the existing yard was purchased, extending the total area of the works from 7 to 23 acres. In 1895 the business was converted to limited liability status, while two years later further westward extensions were made, this time by the acquisition of the old 7-acre shipyard of Schlesinger Davis & Co.

Three decades earlier the origins of the Wigham Richardson enterprise can be traced to when, in 1860, John Wigham Richardson, a young draughtsman, bought Coutts' old shipyard with a £5000 loan from his father. The business was titled Wigham Richardson & Co and the shipyard became known as the Neptune yard. Richardson appointed shipbuilder John Denham Christie as manager of the Neptune Works and the business prospered. In 1879 an engine and boiler works was acquired near the shipyard and further additions in the 1880s extended the yard to over 18 acres in extent. In 1899 the business was converted into a limited company, becoming Wigham Richardson & Co Ltd.

In 1902 an opportunity presented itself that would transform both shipbuilding companies in the form of a potential contract from Cunard to build one of two very large express liners, *Lusitania* and *Mauretania*. George Hunter realised that if his and the neighbouring Wigham Richardson businesses were combined, they would have the financial muscle as well as the facilities to be in contention with the larger British shipbuilding firms for one of the Cunarders. The amalgamation was successfully accomplished in the following year and the contract for *Mauretania* signed in 1904. This was a significant achievement for businesses that had not built such a large and prestigious ship before. Moreover, at the same time Swan Hunter acquired a majority stake in marine engineers Wallsend Slipway & Engineering Co Ltd, although operationally this company retained a high degree of autonomy. The new company, Swan, Hunter & Wigham Richardson Ltd (SHWR), with the Wallsend Slipway, became immediately one of the largest shipbuilding and marine engineering companies in the UK, set to pursue the highest calibre of merchant and naval work. In 1912 it would extend its operation by purchasing the well-known Clydeside shipyard and engine works of Barclay Curle & Co Ltd.

With his sights on the *Mauretania* contract, Hunter invited Sir William White, recently retired as DNC, to join the SHWR Board in 1903, bringing his experience of large fast ships. John Wigham Richardson was a Quaker and thus opposed to building warships, so there was no immediate attempt to enter the warship building market, although the former Swan Hunter company had built a floating dock for the Admiralty in 1902. Although the Admiralty declined to add SHWR's name to the list of builders invited to tender for a *Lord Nelson* class pre-dreadnought in 1904, the new company was in any case fully occupied with work on *Mauretania*, which together with *Lusitania* were the largest, most powerful and most costly merchant ships of their day. But by 1908 *Mauretania* had successfully entered service and Richardson had died, so it was time to test the warship building market.

In 1909 the first warship order was received for the destroyer *Hope*, engined by Wallsend Slipway. By 1911, by which time White had resigned from the Board, Swan Hunter was tendering for battleship contracts, although unsuccessfully. However, further orders for destroyers, cruisers and monitors followed in

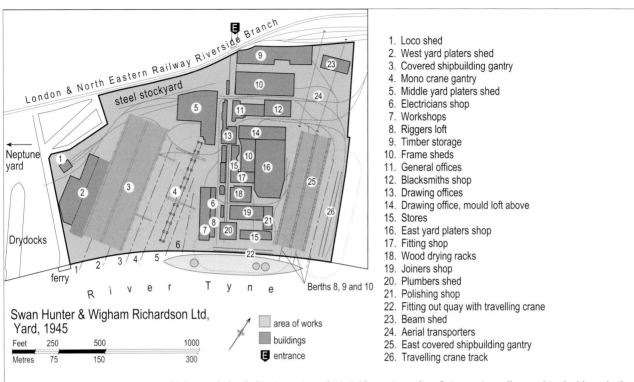

1. Loco shed
2. West yard platers shed
3. Covered shipbuilding gantry
4. Mono crane gantry
5. Middle yard platers shed
6. Electricians shop
7. Workshops
8. Riggers loft
9. Timber storage
10. Frame sheds
11. General offices
12. Blacksmiths shop
13. Drawing offices
14. Drawing office, mould loft above
15. Stores
16. East yard platers shop
17. Fitting shop
18. Wood drying racks
19. Joiners shop
20. Plumbers shed
21. Polishing shop
22. Fitting out quay with travelling crane
23. Beam shed
24. Aerial transporters
25. East covered shipbuilding gantry
26. Travelling crane track

Swan Hunter & Wigham Richardson Ltd, Yard, 1945

Feet 250 500 1000
Metres 75 150 300

area of works
buildings
E entrance

Although Swan Hunter did not build their only battleship (*Anson*) until 1942 (shown in outline fitting out), smaller warships had been built from 1909. The Wallsend site had been used for shipbuilding for the previous seventy years, gradually extended under George Hunter to include other nearby yards. The shipyard was modernised in 1904 to build *Mauretania* including two new covered berths (Nos 1 and 2). This layout remained little changed until the 1950s when the increasing size of tankers required the covered berths to be cleared, with larger open slipways, bigger cranes and new workshops. The associated Neptune shipyard just to the west built few warships. The last ship built on the Tyne was launched at Wallsend in 2005.

the years leading up to and including the First World War. It was not until 1921 that the company was finally successful with the contract for a G3 battlecruiser, although the machinery order was awarded to Parsons Marine and not to Wallsend Slipway. Before the battlecruiser could be laid down the contract was cancelled in February 1922 as a consequence of the signing of the Washington Treaty aimed at reducing armaments. It was not until another fifteen years had elapsed and the start of re-armament that the company was awarded the contract for the battleship *Anson*, which was laid down in 1937 and completed in 1942.

Fate

Although the battleship era was over, after the end of the Second World War Swan Hunter continued to be a major builder of naval as well as merchant ships. By the mid-1960s the British shipbuilding industry was under threat from overseas competition, prompting the Government to fund a restructuring. The outcome of this was the eventual formation of Swan Hunter Shipbuilders Ltd which, by the

end of the 1960s, included most of the Tyne shipbuilding facilities as well as two yards on the Tees. In 1972 the company took over the Hebburn drydock from Vickers for use in newbuilding. In 1977 the company was nationalised, only to be privatised nine years later. Despite significant investment in plant and facilities, the company along with the rest of the shipbuilding industry was fundamentally uneconomic in the face of overseas competition, so Swan Hunter survived mainly on Ministry of Defence contracts. The Neptune yard launched its last ship in 1988, while the main yard at Wallsend went into receivership in 1993 following the loss of the contract for the helicopter carrier *Ocean* to VSEL. Two years later a new company was set up as Swan Hunter (Tyneside) Ltd centred on the Wallsend yard, which then worked on a diversified series of offshore contracts. A contract from the Ministry of Defence for two Royal Fleet Auxiliaries was won in 2000, by bidding an unrealistically low price. With new staff and little experience of MoD work, cost overruns and delays mounted, resulting in the cancellation of the contract after only the first ship, *Largs Bay*, had been completed. The shipyard was effectively closed in 2007 and its plant sold to an Indian shipyard. The site continues to do offshore related work such as oil rig dismantling, located at 54-59-08N 01-31-46W.

2.6 Thames Iron Works Shipbuilding & Engineering Co Ltd

The Thames Iron Works company originated in 1837 at Deptford as a partnership between Thomas Ditchburn and Charles Mare. The company became an important builder of Admiralty ships, one of several such Thames based shipbuilders during the latter part of the nineteenth century. Proximity to the Admiralty and the many naval establishments located on the Thames encouraged business opportunities, in contrast to the late nineteenth and early twentieth centuries when these yards became uncompetitive in comparison with the big northern shipbuilding and marine engineering centres.

The yard was among the first to build ships of iron, one of which was the small steamer *Daylight* built in 1838. In that year the business was transferred from Deptford to a new location at Bow Creek, Blackwall. Ditchburn left in 1846, when the company became C J Mare & Co and expanded onto a new site to the east side of Bow Creek, where another and larger yard was laid out. The first vessel to be laid down at the new yard was the iron brig HMS *Recruit*, a 12-gun brig. About this time a small iron works was established on site for making iron plate, bar and forgings for shipbuilding purposes. In 1855 the business, which by now employed about 3000 to 4000 and covered an area of 10 acres, overreached itself and was declared bankrupt. It was reconstructed in 1857 as the Thames Iron Works & Ship Building Co Ltd. In 1859 the company was successful in winning the contract to construct the first iron-hulled, armoured steam-driven warship, HMS *Warrior*, now preserved at Portsmouth. Building this ship brought the company to the

Right: Although Thames Iron Works had built many ironclads starting with *Warrior* in 1861, by the end of the nineteenth century its facilities were outdated and it was uncompetitive with northern shipyards. The congested site off the main River Thames also produced structural steelwork and a range of engineering products. The main building berth had to be lengthened and strengthened in 1910 to take their last battleship *Thunderer* but given her size, she had to be fitted out at a new deepwater jetty and workshops at Dagenham built by Samuel Williams & Sons Ltd at 51-30-56N 00-08-29E. Although the battleship *Duncan* is shown at the fitting-out quay, most pre-dreadnoughts were fitted out at nearby Victoria Dock, which had deeper water – the Admiralty requirement was that ships should be afloat at all times.

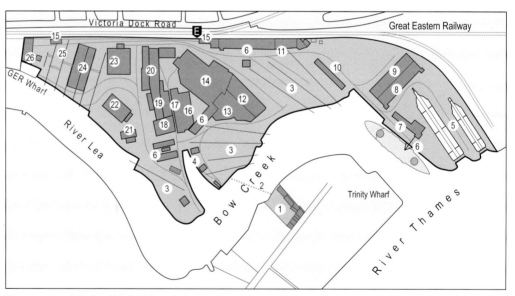

Thames Iron Works Shipbuilding & Engineering Co Ltd, Blackwall 1894

1. General and drawing office and site of original Ditchburn & Mare yard
2. Shipyard ferry
3. Building berths
4. Stores
5. Graving docks (470' x 64' and 335' x 46')
6. 80 ton sheer legs and fitting-out quay
7. Press shed
8. Marine engineering shop
9. Girder shop
10. Mast house with mould loft over
11. Angle iron shop
12. Plate mill
13. Bar mill
14. Steam hammer shop and smithy
15. Offices
16. Engineering shop
17. Press shop
18. Plate bending shop
19. Angle smiths shop
20. Fitting shop
21. Sawing shed
22. Joiners shop
23. Iron foundry
24. Structural steel shops
25. Steel erecting bays
26. Smithy

edge of bankruptcy, however, and survival was only enabled through the Admiralty increasing its payments to the company. Unlike some other Thames shipbuilders, Thames Iron Works survived the financial crisis of 1866 when bankers Overend Gurney & Co failed and, together with Samuda Brothers at Isle of Dogs, became the leading Thames private builders of warships for the Admiralty as well as for other governments. The Thames Iron Works in particular became the most successful of all the private companies in Britain to construct battleships, completing no fewer than fifteen including *Warrior* until the end of the pre-dreadnought era in 1904, of which seven were for overseas governments. In 1899, on taking over the long established engine builders John Penn & Sons Ltd, who had works at Greenwich and Deptford, the business was reconstructed as the Thames Iron Works Shipbuilding & Engineering Co Ltd. The turret ship *Sans Pareil* was launched in 1887 and their last pre-dreadnoughts *Duncan* and *Cornwallis* in 1901.

By the 1890s many Thames yards had either closed or were experiencing great commercial pressure from the major shipbuilding centres on the Clyde and the North East Coast. There, an abundance of labour, lower wages, nearby steel works and a multitude of suppliers to the shipbuilding industry existed. Samuda Brothers closed in 1893 and Yarrow moved from Isle of Dogs to the Clyde in 1907. In 1909 the Thames Iron Works won the contract to construct the *Orion* class battleship *Thunderer* but this proved to be the last major ship built on the Thames, as discussed on p.126. In 1910 the firm was excluded from tendering for an *Indefatigable* class battlecruiser because of what the Admiralty described as 'inadequate facilities'. The works closed in 1912 after calling in the receiver in November 1911. The main site is now buried under new roads located at 51-30-35N 00-09-35E.

3 THE ROYAL DOCKYARDS

Unlike the private yards, the Royal Dockyards had a lineage that in many cases was as old as the Royal Navy itself. The Dockyards covered large areas and were laid out to build, maintain and refit the fleet. In a report written for the US naval authorities in 1889, Philip Hichborn, a constructor with the US Navy, compiled some interesting statistics. At this time the main Dockyards were Chatham, Sheerness, Portsmouth, Devonport with Keyham, and Pembroke. Wooden shipbuilding Dockyards at

Woolwich and Deptford had closed in 1869. Quoting Admiralty figures submitted in 1884, the total value was $75 million (about £15 million) including land, buildings and material, while the total number of employees was 18,000. Portsmouth was the largest yard covering an area of 115 acres on which were accommodated five building slips, fifteen drydocks and numerous sheds and shops; 5660 employees were working at Portsmouth in 1889.

Taking *Warrior* as the starting point, the Dockyards that participated in iron and steel battleship construction from 1860 onwards were Chatham, Pembroke, Portsmouth and Devonport. The first iron-hulled battleship built in a Royal Dockyard was *Achilles*, laid down in drydock in August 1861 at Chatham. Given the inexperience of Dockyards in iron construction, demonstrated by awarding *Warrior* and *Black Prince* to private yards, this was a creditable performance at Chatham in converting to iron in such a short time. By the early 1900s however, a strategy had to be developed concerning the constructional locations for future battleships given the steady increase in the size of these ships and the topography of each of the Dockyards. Although Chatham and

Above: The Thames company's letterhead used in tendering for battleship contracts in 1904.

Below: Festooned with flags and bunting, the Japanese battleship *Shikishima* is launched into Bow Creek with the River Thames beyond on 1 November 1898. The ship will be secured to the quay where the sheerlegs stand to begin fitting-out. Note the timber and sliding ways in the water to the left of shot where a light pole derrick can be seen at the end of the building slip. *(NMM)*

Pembroke had both made great contributions to the battlefleet over previous decades, the former had restricted covered berths and comparatively narrow entrance locks, while the latter could not fit out ships after launch. The decision was made to concentrate facilities for dreadnought construction at Portsmouth and Devonport. From *Dreadnought* onwards, all Dockyard battleships and battlecruisers were built at these two yards.

3.1 Portsmouth

In the modern era, Portsmouth has been regarded as the premier Dockyard, the one which more than any other symbolises the Royal Navy and its traditions. It can trace its maritime history back to the twelfth century, although it was not until the very late fifteenth century that it opened its first drydock. With the arrival of the steam era, a series of extensions were provided for, beginning in the early 1840s with the building of a new steam basin, later named No.2 Basin. This was not completed until 1849, after which other shops including an engineering shop or 'steam factory', pattern shop and an iron foundry were added. In the late 1860s the Dockyard was again extended to handle the large ironclad warships then being built, adding three drydocks, four new basins (one tidal), two new

locks, machine and electrical shops and a 100-ton capacity sheerlegs, bringing the total area of the Dockyard from 115 acres to 295 acres on completion in 1876. By 1890, Portsmouth employed over 7600 people – later figures are given on p.256.

The launch of the turret ship *Devastation* in 1871 began Portsmouth's career as a builder of iron-hulled warships, although a number of wooden-hulled ironclads had been built previously. In 1876 *Inflexible* mounting four 16in guns was launched. From then until the end of the pre-dreadnought era, Portsmouth completed *Colossus* (1885), *Camperdown* (1889), *Trafalgar* (1890), *Royal Sovereign* (1892), *Centurion* (1894), *Majestic* (1895), *Prince George* (1896), *Caesar* (1898), *Canopus* (1899), *Formidable* (1901), *London* (1902), *New Zealand* (1905) and *Britannia* (1906).

Portsmouth's status as the most important of the Royal Dockyards was underlined in 1905 when the decision was taken to build *Dreadnought* there. Ships of this size demonstrated the need for new facilities capable of dealing with the ever increasing size of battleships. These alterations and extensions, which were completed just before the outbreak of the First World War, included new locks/drydocks and the addition of a 250-ton cantilever crane in the enlarged No 3 Basin to

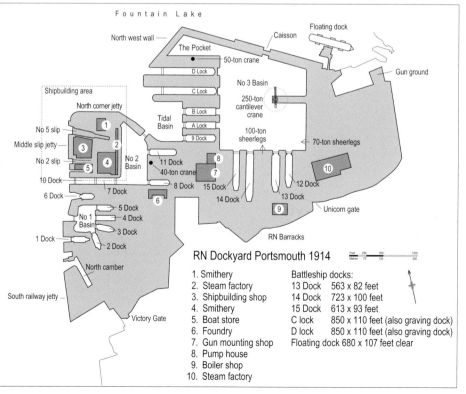

Portsmouth Dockyard had been building wooden warships for the Royal Navy for four centuries, but only started iron construction in 1869. With the increasing size of battleships, the old covered slipways were inadequate, so No. 5 Slip was continually extended to cope with battleships as large as *Queen Elizabeth*. Ships were fitted out in Basin No 3 under the 100-ton sheerlegs or when completed in 1914, the 250-ton cantilever crane. New locks and drydocks were built so that by 1914, the dockyard was well placed to cope with the demands of war. The last warship launched from No 5 Slip was frigate *Andromeda* in 1967, but from 2003 Vosper Thornycroft set up a shipbuilding facility between No 12 and 14 drydocks, launching from a covered hall onto barges a succession of offshore patrol vessel types as well as sections for Type 45 destroyers and aircraft carriers.

RN Dockyard Portsmouth 1914

1. Smithery
2. Steam factory
3. Shipbuilding shop
4. Smithery
5. Boat store
6. Foundry
7. Gun mounting shop
8. Pump house
9. Boiler shop
10. Steam factory

Battleship docks:
13 Dock   563 x 82 feet
14 Dock   723 x 100 feet
15 Dock   613 x 93 feet
C lock   850 x 110 feet (also graving dock)
D lock   850 x 110 feet (also graving dock)
Floating dock 680 x 107 feet clear

H.M.S. BELLEROPHON

handle the heaviest machinery and armament loads then foreseen.

Portsmouth, like the other Royal Dockyards, required a vast area to rebuild, refit and replenish a large number of warships at any one time, as well as provide facilities and services to naval personnel. The area devoted to ship-building was comparatively small, roughly equal in size to a medium-sized private yard. The yard was located on the western side of the Dockyard with slipways aligned towards Gosport, located at 50-48-21N 01-06-37W. All of the dreadnought battleships were built on No 5 Slip with one annually after the completion of *Dreadnought* in 1906: *Bellerophon* (1909), *St Vincent* (1910), *Neptune* (1911), *Orion* (1911), *King George V* (1912), *Iron Duke* (1914), *Queen Elizabeth* (1915) and *Royal Sovereign* (1916). The latter would be the final battleship built at Portsmouth; the rapid increase in the size of battlecruisers put them beyond the capabilities of the yard to construct without a major programme of investment, although some enquiries were made in 1920. Portsmouth did, however, undertake the major reconstruction of *Queen Elizabeth* between the years 1937 and 1940. The last warship built at the Dockyard was the frigate *Andromeda* completed in 1968. Since then refits of naval and merchant ships and base support for the fleet have become the

main activities, with BAE Systems operating most of the facilities. When Vosper Thornycroft closed their Southampton shipyard, they moved to a site at Portsmouth Dockyard on the south side of No 3 Basin in 2003. The company merged with BAE Systems to become BVT Surface Fleet Ltd in 2008, fully taken over by BAE in 2009. They have been building modules for the *Queen Elizabeth* aircraft carriers for assembly at Rosyth, but the building facility is due to close in 2014.

3.2 Devonport

Work began on the construction of a Dockyard at Plymouth in 1691. It was not until a century and a half later, in 1841, that the name Devonport Dockyard was officially applied to the yard after the town of Devonport that had sprung up around the yard rather than Plymouth which was some distance away. The advent of steam propulsion required that significant additions be made but expansion of the existing yard was restricted on the two land-ward sides by housing and other developments. The most suitable ground was identified half a mile northwards at Keyham and here in 1846 the foundation stone was laid of what would be the new Steam Factory Yard, later known as the North Yard. On completion in 1853 this 74-acre development included drydocks, north

Above: The completion of *Dreadnought* in December 1906 marked the laying down of Portsmouth's second dreadnought, *Bellerophon*. Similar to *Dreadnought* with a few improvements, she is seen here by the 100-ton sheerlegs on the south wall of No 3 Basin. With guns shipped and steam up, this suggests that the photo was taken at the end of 1908. *(Brian Newman)*

Opposite: Collingwood was the second dreadnought constructed at Devonport, with machinery by Hawthorn Leslie. She is seen here fitting-out in 1909 under the new 160-ton Cowans Sheldon cantilever crane (1909) in Basin No. 5. Most of her superstructure is in place, while the installation of her Elswick main armament is underway aft with X turret in position. With these very heavy weights onboard, the ship's machinery and shafting could be aligned and fitted. Devonport Dockyard completed its northern extension in 1907, just in time to fit out and drydock a succession of dreadnoughts launched from its South yard.
(Brian Newman)

and south basins, and various shops, including boiler, platers, engine smiths, fitting, erecting, millwrights and copper shops, as well as a foundry. By the end of the nineteenth century the yard was again in need of major extension to reflect the increased size of the navy and growing size of warships. In 1895 approval was given for a 118-acre extension to the immediate north of the Keyham Yard at a little under £3 million. Work began in the following year and it was not until the end of 1906 that work was completed. Two large new basins, one of 10 acres and one of 34 acres, served by three docks and one lock formed the essential features of the extension. Shipbuilding facilities had been concentrated in the original South Yard and here, to enable large warships to be constructed, new shops were added, starting in the late 1890s and No 3 Slip upgraded eventually to a length of 750ft. This berth would be used extensively for the construction of a series of dreadnoughts.

Devonport's introduction to battleship construction began in the early 1860s, with two wooden-hulled ironclads *Gibraltar* (1860) and *Ocean* (1864). Thereafter, Devonport played no role in their construction until the shipyard in the South Yard was upgraded; the area located

at 50-21-58N 04-10-48W, No 3 Slip, is still visible. The first battleship launched from this slipway was *Ocean* in 1898. She was followed by *Implacable* (1899), *Bulwark* (1899), *Montagu* (1901), *Queen* (1902), *King Edward VII* (1903) and lastly in the pre-dreadnought era, *Hibernia* (1905). Dreadnought construction began with *Temeraire* launched in 1907 and thereafter annually with *Collingwood* (1908), *Indefatigable* (1909), *Lion* (1910), *Centurion* (1911), *Marlborough* (1912), *Warspite* (1913) and *Royal Oak* (1914). Thereafter some fifty smaller warships were built, the last being the frigate

Devonport Dockyard, with a history going back several centuries, was destined to become the largest of the Royal Navy's dockyards. The shipbuilding area was located in the South Yard and was equivalent to a medium private yard in size. From 1900 onwards, a continuous succession of battleships was built including five pre-dreadnoughts and eight dreadnoughts, a number only exceeded by Portsmouth Dockyard. Devonport's last dreadnought was the battleship *Royal Oak*, launched as with the others from No 3 Slip. Although No 3 Slip had sufficient length for ships larger than *Lion*, the longest dreadnought built at Devonport, the increased beam would have made it impossible to take ships into Basin No 5 for completion, although its entrance was widened in the 1930s.

The area plan shows the overall extent of the dockyard which covered over 300 acres. The general area used for shipbuilding is shown at a larger scale in the inset.

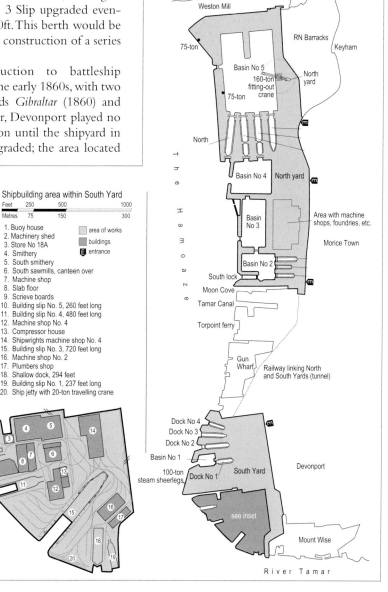

Shipbuilding area within South Yard

Feet 250 500 1000
Metres 75 150 300

1. Buoy house
2. Machinery shed
3. Store No 18A
4. Smithery
5. South smithery
6. South sawmills, canteen over
7. Machine shop
8. Slab floor
9. Scrieve boards
10. Building slip No. 5, 260 feet long
11. Building slip No. 4, 480 feet long
12. Machine shop No. 4
13. Compressor house
14. Shipwrights machine shop No. 4
15. Building slip No. 3, 720 feet long
16. Machine shop No. 2
17. Plumbers shop
18. Shallow dock, 294 feet
19. Building slip No. 1, 237 feet long
20. Ship jetty with 20-ton travelling crane

area of works
buildings
E entrance

RN Dockyard Devonport 1912

Feet 1000
Metres 300

Weston Mill

RN Barracks
Keyham

75-ton

Basin No 5
160-ton
fitting-out
crane

North
yard

75-ton

North

Basin No 4   North yard

Basin
No 3

Area with machine
shops, foundries, etc.

Morice Town

Basin No 2

South lock

Moon Cove

Tamar Canal

Torpoint ferry

Gun
Wharf

Railway linking North
and South Yards (tunnel)

Dock No 4
Dock No 3
Dock No 2

Basin No 1

100-ton
steam sheerlegs   Dock No 1

South Yard

Devonport

see inset

Mount Wise

The Hamoaze

River Tamar

Scylla completed in 1970. Management of the Dockyard was handed over to Devonport Management Limited (DML) in 1987, owned by Brown & Root, Weir Group and Balfour Beatty. It was bought by DML in 1997, with its main activity now being the refit of nuclear-powered submarines, as part of Babcock International since 2007.

3.3 The Royal Gun Factory, Woolwich

The Royal Arsenal, dating back to the seventeenth century, was located on the Thames east of Woolwich Dockyard and was one of many military and naval establishments concentrated on the Thames, including several important private shipbuilding firms. It was under War Office control, so the Admiralty's needs could take second place to the Army's. The Royal Gun Factory remained at Woolwich long after the Thames became less important and shipbuilding ceased altogether.

In the first half of the twentieth century, the main part of the vast Royal Arsenal that played an active role in battleship construction was the Royal Gun Factory at Woolwich, which manufactured a variety of guns fitted on dreadnought battleships and battlecruisers in calibres from 9.2in to 16in. The Gun Factory did not manufacture the 'non-transferable' mountings for these large guns as they were designed and made exclusively by the private firms of Armstrong, Vickers and Coventry Ordnance Works. It did, however, make smaller 'transferable' mountings, as well as testing and storing guns.

Fate

The Gun Factory closed in 1967 while elements of the Royal Arsenal remained opera-

Below: The heavy gun finishing shop at the Royal Gun Factory, Woolwich Arsenal in 1897. The guns look to be 12in Mark VIII designed at Woolwich.

tional until 1994. Much of the site has been developed for housing, located at 51-29-39N 00-04-20E. The National Maritime Museum houses its plans and photographs department in the old Brass Foundry on this site.

4 THE ENGINE BUILDERS

Although the Admiralty developed iron and steel shipbuilding manufacturing capability during the nineteenth and twentieth centuries, they did not do so for marine engine building. 'Steam Factories' were built at the principal Dockyards during the nineteenth century, where marine steam engines could be repaired, but not built. This created an opportunity for private marine engineering firms. In the mid-nineteenth century, Thames-based marine engineers dominated the production of machinery for the Admiralty. The principal firms included the works of John Penn & Sons at Greenwich, Maudslay, Son & Field at Lambeth, Humphrys & Tennant at Deptford and Miller & Ravenhill at Blackwall. Other early manufacturers of steam machinery for the Admiralty were Boulton & Watt in Birmingham and Robert Napier at Glasgow. However, by the early twentieth century all of the above mentioned except Napier had given way to the engine works that had been established in the large northern shipbuilding centres in the second half of the nineteenth century.

The machinery, including boilers and engines, for every battleship built in a Royal Dockyard, from the beginning of the steam era to the last constructed in the First World War, was contracted out. Often this contract would be awarded to an engine works already part of a shipyard such as Vickers at Barrow, John Brown at Clydebank or Hawthorn Leslie on Tyneside. However, a number of companies had established themselves solely as marine engine builders, like the Wallsend Slipway, and these firms also competed for the machinery of Dockyard-built battleships along with shipyards with engine building capacity. Chapters 7 and 11 discuss the performance of such companies.

While a shipbuilder with his own engine works would submit a tender for both hull and machinery, the Admiralty also received separate tenders for machinery from engine builders such as Hawthorn Leslie. They might therefore decide to allocate the machinery contract to other than the shipbuilder, as occurred with Beardmore's *Agamemnon*. This was always the case with Armstrong contracts as they had no

engine works. Sometimes the main machinery contractor might have to subcontract a key part to another engine builder: for example, Humphrys, Tennant & Co ordered *Invincible*'s turbines from John Brown, but remained responsible for the design, installation, boilers and auxiliaries.

This happened again with the Portsmouth-built battleship *Neptune*. The machinery contract was awarded to Harland & Wolff at Belfast but this firm sub-contracted the turbines to Clydebank because turbine manufacturing capacity had yet to be installed at Belfast. Similarly the machinery contract for Dockyard-built *St Vincent* was awarded to Scotts, who sub-contracted the turbines to Parsons Marine because their new turbine shops were incomplete.

During the First World War, when the shipyard and engine works were declared controlled establishments, the Admiralty could move contracts around to where spare capacity existed in the best interests of rapid completion. This happened with the battlecruiser *Furious* under construction at Armstrong. The machinery contract was awarded to the Wallsend Slipway but two of her four geared turbine units were sub-contracted to Clydebank, who had available capacity.

Three engine builders on the Tyne constructed machinery for battleships of the dreadnought era: the Parsons Marine Steam Turbine Co Ltd, Wallsend Slipway & Engineering Co Ltd and R & W Hawthorn Leslie & Co Ltd.

4.1 R & W Hawthorn, Leslie & Co Ltd.

Hawthorn Leslie was a significant shipbuilder and marine engineer. Although the shipyard built many warships for the Admiralty, it did not build any battleships, a limitation that did not apply to propelling machinery.

Robert Hawthorn began business at Forth Banks in Newcastle in 1817 manufacturing stationary and marine steam engines. Locomotive construction began in 1829. In 1871 the company as R & W Hawthorn, erected new engine works at St Peters on the north bank of the Tyne for the exclusive construction of marine engines, leaving the inland Forth Banks works to concentrate on locomotives. In 1853 Andrew Leslie acquired eight acres of ground at Hebburn Quay, on the south bank about three miles downstream from St Peters, to lay out an iron shipyard. The business R&W Hawthorn, Leslie & Co Ltd was formed by the amalgamation of both firms in 1885.

Hawthorn Leslie enjoyed good relationships with Armstrong Mitchell/Armstrong Whitworth, supplying machinery for many ships built at Elswick and at Low Walker. However, the arrival of Philip Watts as naval architect at Armstrong's from his previous post as a Constructor at the Admiralty brought with it his preferences in the placement of machinery contracts. As a consequence, the balance of machinery orders for overseas orders shifted to Humphrys, Tennant & Co at Greenwich. Nevertheless, Hawthorn Leslie was the most successful of all the separate engine builders in winning machinery contracts for battleships. The first set of turbine machinery ordered was for *Temeraire* early in 1907 followed by *Collingwood* later in 1907, *Monarch* and *Centurion* in 1910, *Marlborough* in 1911, *Warspite* in 1912 and *Royal Oak* in 1913.

Fate

Hawthorn Leslie continued as a significant warship engine builder until the RN switched to gas turbines in the 1960s. The engine works was formed into a separate company in 1954 as Hawthorn Leslie (Engineers) Ltd. After nationalisation in 1977 this became a subsidiary of British Shipbuilders. With the latter rationalising engine building, it was paired with George Clark & NEM Ltd at Wallsend to become Clark Hawthorn Ltd in 1979. But with smaller and less modern plant, St Peters was closed in 1984. The site was developed into a housing estate and marina located at 54-57-57N 01-34-20W

4.2 Parsons Marine Steam Turbine Co Ltd.

After Charles Parsons had developed his new steam turbine and tested it successfully in his experimental 'yacht' *Turbinia*, he set up The Parsons Marine Steam Turbine Co Ltd in 1897. The new Turbinia Works of 14 acres was built on the north bank of the Tyne at Wallsend just east of the Swan Hunter shipyard.[12] The company undertook the design of complete steam turbine installations, and manufactured the key components – the turbines, condensers and later the gearing. Its first warship contract was for the quadruple-screw destroyer *Cobra* of 11,000 shp, ordered as a speculation by Armstrong Whitworth in 1898, but bought by the Admiralty in 1900. The Clyde passenger steamer *King Edward*,

built by Denny, was the first commercial vessel, completed in 1901. These early vessels showed the superiority of the steam turbine for fast high-powered vessels, so rapid acceptance followed. Parsons designed turbines were selected for the 70,000 shp *Mauretania* and *Lusitania* in 1904 and *Dreadnought* herself in 1905. Parsons then licensed other engine builders, including John Brown, Wallsend Slipway & Engineering and Denny.

Parsons' designed turbines propelled the majority of RN battleships and battlecruisers ordered before the First World War, but the company itself only won the contracts for building two such complete installations, that of *King George V* and *Royal Sovereign*. However, they built the turbines for three other such ships, as their main machinery contractors had not yet acquired a turbine licence or the necessary plant and experience. By 1914 the company claimed that 10.51 million shp for warships had been completed or was under construction by itself or licensees and 1.85 million shp for merchant ships.[13] Parsons introduced geared turbines in warships from 1913, producing such machinery for *Courageous* in 1916. It became a specialist in gearing manufacture and supplied other machinery contractors.

The company continued to be the Admiralty's main designer of steam turbines, although some Brown-Curtis designs were

Left: Marine engineering companies' advertisements often featured notable warships. One for Parsons in 1938 illustrated *Warspite*, re-engined by them in 1936, and the pioneer *Turbinia*. (*Shipbuilding & Shipping Record*)

built. All post-war British battleships had turbines of Parsons design with single reduction gearing, both new and re-engined ships; however the company supplied only two of the latter installations in the 1930s, for *Warspite* and *Valiant*. Parsons was more successful with destroyer machinery contracts, often being the prime contractor to the Admiralty, with the hull sub-contracted usually to Vickers-Armstrongs' Tyne shipyard. Machinery was built for thirty warships during the Second World War of 1.159 million shp.[14]

Fate

Parsons' R&D activities and those of its licensees were transferred to the Parsons & Marine Engineering Turbine Research & Development Association (PAMETRADA) in 1944, with a new research station built next to the Turbinia Works at Wallsend. A much smaller business than C A Parsons, the Marine Steam Turbine company was acquired by the Richardsons, Westgarth group in 1957, and renamed Parsons Marine Turbine Co Ltd, to include gas turbines. But by the 1960s the steam turbine had been largely displaced by the diesel in merchant ships and by the gas turbine in warships. In 1964 the company was wound up and parts of the works used for other industrial purposes, today including the successful Soil Machine Dynamics company, located at 54-59-16N 01-31-17W. PAMETRADA was merged into the British Ship Research Association on the same Wallsend premises, now transformed into British Maritime Technology (BMT), whose offices are spread throughout the world.

4.3 Wallsend Slipway & Engineering Co Ltd.

This company was jointly set up by shipbuilder Charles Mitchell and two firms of shipowners at Wallsend in 1871 mainly to repair vessels owned by them. The works, initially called the Wallsend Slipway Co, were laid out over the next year and work began on its first repair contracts in 1872. Two patent slips were provided where ships could be hauled out of the river and brought up close to the repair shops. Boilermaking was undertaken from the start, as the then common employment of sea water as boiler feed resulted in rapid corrosion in these units and hence frequent replacement. In 1875, under the direction of William Boyd, formerly of Thompson, Boyd & Co, the construction of marine engines was begun, initially as a means of retaining the skilled workforce through the commercial vagaries of repair work, although this would later constitute the main activity of the firm. The addition of marine engine building was subsequently reflected in the title of the company, which became the Wallsend Slipway & Engineering Co Ltd in 1878. Locally it was always known as 'the Slipway'. In 1882 a large boiler shop was erected to enable the separation of engine and boiler making.

When Sir W G Armstrong & Co Ltd merged with Charles Mitchell & Co in 1882, it seemed likely that the Wallsend Slipway would be

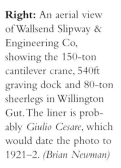

Right: An aerial view of Wallsend Slipway & Engineering Co, showing the 150-ton cantilever crane, 540ft graving dock and 80-ton sheerlegs in Willington Gut. The liner is probably *Giulio Cesare*, which would date the photo to 1921–2. *(Brian Newman)*

acquired by the new company but Armstrong decided against this. In 1896, Andrew Laing became the general manager of the works, having recently been the engine works director at the Fairfield works on the Clyde. Laing determined that the business would compete for the highest class of work and under his direction substantial additions were made to the works, including a new erecting shop, boiler shop, pattern shop, brass foundry plus new machine tools and overhead cranes. These additions were not completed until 1904, just in time to build *Mauretania*'s pioneering steam turbine machinery. The facilities at Wallsend were further enhanced in 1910 with the installation of a 150-ton giant cantilever crane at the riverside quay; in addition an 80-ton sheerlegs served vessels in Willington Gut, as shown on the plan on p.159. By this time the Wallsend Slipway had been transformed into one of the largest and best-equipped engine works in the UK.

The company started constructing compound reciprocating engines, graduating to triple and quadruple expansion engines and later again to turbine manufacture of the direct drive and geared type. Over the same period the company manufactured cylindrical, locomotive and later water tube boilers, and were pioneers in the development of oil firing equipment for boilers.

In 1903 the shipbuilders Swan & Hunter Ltd and Wigham Richardson & Co Ltd merged to form Swan, Hunter & Wigham Richardson Ltd. This merger, crucial to winning the contract for the Cunard liner *Mauretania* in 1904, brought Wallsend Slipway under the control of the new shipbuilding company through a 63 per cent shareholding. Although having Swan Hunter directors on their Board, the 'Slipway' enjoyed a high degree of autonomy under the autocratic Laing and continued to tender separately for machinery contracts from its shipbuilding parent.

The Wallsend Slipway had previously constructed machinery for the Admiralty, the first being for the sloop *Espiegle* in 1899. The first contract for battleship turbine machinery in the dreadnought era was *Superb* ordered in 1907, followed by *Orion* in 1909, *Queen Elizabeth* in 1912, *Malaya* in 1913, and *Furious* in 1915.

Fate

The Slipway continued to be a significant warship steam turbine engine builder until the RN switched to gas turbines in the 1960s. It ceased main engine building in 1967 under full Swan Hunter management, but continued making boilers, repairing ships at its single drydock and general engineering work into British Shipbuilders days. As Wallsend Slipway Engineers, it was sold to Marske Machine Co Ltd in 1984, who sold the site for construction of offshore production platform modules, with most of the shops being demolished. Combined with the neighbouring North Eastern Marine site, modules of up to 12,000 tons were built, latterly by AMEC. The site continues to be used for a variety of offshore work, located at 54-59-25N 01-30-25W.

5 SHARE CAPITAL

The relative size of the major companies associated with battleship building can be judged from the table of share capital overleaf.

6 BUSINESS LINKS

Starting in the early 1800s, a large number of businesses contributed to the development of the British naval construction industry as it became known in the twentieth century. Not all of these businesses survived this process as indeed very few have survived into the twenty-first century. Companies bought out other companies routinely, there were mergers and sometimes there was an exchange of shares with directors on each other's boards, although the day-to-day autonomy of the businesses thus linked usually remained unchanged. There were other forms of association or linkages, however, where it was less clear what was happening and where the power lay. While the technical and financial press of the day occasionally reported such links, they were rarely reported in the then prevalent uninformative company annual reports to shareholders. Where a company's Directors Minute Books have survived in archives, more information is sometimes revealed. The diagram on p.64 shows how complex such links might be in the case of Vickers and Armstrong.

It was less well known at the time that a direct link existed between Palmer's Shipbuilding & Iron Co Ltd and John Brown & Co Ltd. At some time from 1865 onwards when Palmer's was converted into a limited liability company, Henry Davis Pochin, a wealthy manufacturing chemist from Manchester, purchased a majority shareholding in Palmer's. Although he remained as Chairman, it seems that Charles Mark Palmer (he was made a baronet in 1886) took less interest in the running of the business from this

MAJOR COMPANIES' SHARE CAPITAL

Company	Date	Ordinary shares (£)	Preference shares (£)	Total (£)
Sir W G Armstrong, Whitworth & Co Ltd	31 Dec 13	4,012,500	2,000,000	6,012,500
Vickers Ltd	31 Dec 13	4,440,000	1,500,000	5,940,000
John Brown & Co Ltd	31 Mar 14	1,823,000	1,750,000	3,573,000
William Beardmore & Co Ltd	1913	1,700,000	1,300,000	3,000,000
Cammell, Laird & Co Ltd	31 Dec 13	1,147,670	1,225,225	2,372,895
Swan, Hunter & Wigham Richardson Ltd*	31 Dec 13	855,532	722,845	1,578,377
Harland & Wolff Ltd	1 Jul 14	600,000	164,890	764,890
Palmers Shipbuilding & Iron Co Ltd	30 Jun 13	497,560	200,000	697,560
Thames Iron Works Shipbuilding & Engineering Co Ltd	1910	300,000	300,000	600,000
Fairfield Shipbuilding & Engineering Co Ltd	30 Jun 13	250,000	250,000	500,000
R & W Hawthorn, Leslie & Co Ltd	30 Jun 13	467,700	–	467,700
Scotts' Shipbuilding & Engineering Co Ltd	1914	275,000	25,000	300,000
Wallsend Slipway & Engineering Co Ltd	31 Dec 13	149,030	109,000	258,030
Parsons Marine Steam Turbine Co Ltd	30 Jun 13	211,280	–	211,280
Vickers-Armstrongs Ltd #	31 Dec 39	7,864,412	9,599,839	17,464,251

Excludes loan capital like debentures, and retained profits.

Not all of each company's activities were directly related to warship building but the majority were, including hull building, engine building, armour manufacture, ordnance manufacture, forgings etc, but certainly over 80 per cent in the case of Armstrong and Vickers.

* Although they did not receive their first battleship order until 1937, they tendered pre-war (e.g. *Benbow*) and would have built one of the cancelled G3s in 1921.

After merger of Armstrong Whitworth and Vickers in 1927.

time onwards, later pursuing a career as an MP (from 1874) and Mayor of Jarrow. In 1864, when John Brown was similarly converted, Pochin effectively acquired that company too through a majority shareholding. Pochin took a seat on both Boards but never took the role of Chairman of either company and left the running of it to those better qualified. In 1883 Pochin's son-in-law Charles McLaren, a barrister, joined him on the Board of John Brown & Co Ltd. At a date unknown, McLaren also joined the Board of Palmer's, no doubt due to the influence of his father-in-law. In 1907 he became Chairman, Palmer having relinquished the role in 1893. In 1897 McLaren became Deputy Chairman of John Brown & Co Ltd and Chairman in 1906. In 1902 Charles McLaren was knighted and in 1911 he was raised to the Peerage becoming Baron (Lord) Aberconway of Bodnant. Both Palmer's and John Brown were managed independently and usually in competition with one another and there is no direct reference in surviving John Brown records to suggest any collusion – no detailed Palmer company records have survived. However, as can be seen from the John Brown list of tenders in Appendix 1, in contracting for capital ships, Palmer's sometimes sought machinery or turbine prices from John Brown, and the figures suggest that prices were quoted to them on favourable terms. It could be argued that switching *Repulse* from Palmer's to John

Brown in January 1915 was a product of shared knowledge but this seems unlikely given the controlling role the Admiralty had in the placement of warship orders and the very high esteem in which they, in any case, held the John Brown company.

In 1907, John Brown also acquired a controlling interest in Harland & Wolff. One reason given was to provide a ready outlet for the products of the Atlas Works, much as it had been for the purchase of Clydebank shipyard in 1899. However, with one of the finest shipbuilding works in the UK, could it be significant that Harland & Wolff, as important as any British shipbuilder, was never successful in winning any of the fifty-one capital ships built until one of the very last, *Glorious* in 1915? Harland & Wolff were usually invited to tender by the Admiralty but either declined to submit a tender or priced it too highly. The probable reason was that the shipyard was busy pre-war with cost-plus orders for passenger ships and saw no need to pursue marginally profitable battleship contracts. The turbines for *Neptune*, whose main machinery contract was won by Harland & Wolf, were sub-contracted to Clydebank, as was a series of other mercantile turbine contracts. Perhaps one outcome of the John Brown control was that Harland & Wolff would not seriously pursue capital ship contracts and equally, perhaps there was a tacit unwritten agreement that turbine work would be undertaken at Clydebank for a certain period of time.

Sensitivity over perception and business esteem ran high. When John Brown built the centre shaft turbines for the liners *Olympic* and *Titanic* at Clydebank, progress photographs of them were requested by the journal *Engineering* for publication. John Brown's shipyard director, Thomas Bell, wrote, 'We have sent some photographs of the turbines to H&W but please do not refer to them unless they furnish them to you, nor make any reference to our name, as this is a sore point with them'. Even today many *Titanic* aficionados do not realise that H&W did not build all of her machinery.

7 NOTABLE PERSONALITIES
Admiralty Personnel
(Sir) William White (1845–1913)

Director of Naval Construction 1885–1901, over the period of the expansion of the British battle fleet. Shipwright apprentice Devonport Dockyard 1859. Admiralty draughtsman and constructor 1867–83. Warship designer Armstrong Mitchell 1883–5. Design responsibility for battleships from *Royal Sovereign* class onwards, in total 245 warships. Championed many technical developments including armoured turtle deck, steel and armour, new machinery. Prolific author, including *A Manual of Naval Architecture*. Expanded Royal Corps of Naval Constructors. KCB 1894. Supportive of professional engineering institutions, including Presidency of Civil, Mechanical and Marine Institutions. Retired from Admiralty in 1902 from ill health. Director of Swan, Hunter & Wigham Richardson 1903–07, on £1000 p.a. and 1.5 per cent of profits. Great warship designer with wide knowledge of every aspect of shipbuilding and engineering.

(Sir) Philip Watts (1846–1926)

Director of Naval Construction 1902–12 over the period of introduction of dreadnoughts. Shipwright apprentice Portsmouth Dockyard 1860. Admiralty draughtsman and constructor 1870–85. Assistant to William Froude at the Admiralty towing tank, then at Torquay, 1870–2. Design of evolving ironclad types including *Inflexible*. Naval architect at Armstrong, Mitchell's Elswick shipyard 1885, later general manager and director (1895) to 1901. Developed export warship designs especially for Japan. At Admiralty responsible for *Dreadnought* design (and member of 1905 Committee on Designs) including new arma-

ment layout, steam turbines, underwater protection. Battlecruisers and submarine development. KCB 1905. Retained as Admiralty consultant after 1912. Armstrong, Whitworth local director at Elswick 1912. Main Board and London office director 1916. Managing shipyards 1916–17. Wrote extensive section on 'Ships and Shipbuilding' for 10th Edition of *Encyclopaedia Britannica*.

(Sir) Eustace Henry William Tennyson d'Eyncourt (1868–1951)

Director of Naval Construction 1912–24 responsible for battleships from *Royal Sovereign*s to *Nelson*s. Premium apprentice at Armstrong Mitchell 1886. Royal Naval College Greenwich 1888. Naval architect at Elswick. Naval architect at Fairfield 1898. Returned to Elswick 1902 as naval architect and salesman after Watts became DNC. Negotiated for foreign sales to Brazil, Argentina, Chile, Turkey. First civilian DNC 1912. Responsible for massive First World War construction programme, including battlecruisers and monitors, for which underwater bulge protection developed. Knighted 1917. Director of Armstrong Whitworth 1924–7. Director Parsons Marine Steam Turbine.

(Sir) Stanley Vernon Goodall (1883–1965)

Director of Naval Construction 1936–44, the period of First World War battleship modernisation and Second World War new construction. Transferred from RN engineer officer training to constructor 1901 at RN College Greenwich. Worked on cruiser design and armour plating and at Admiralty Experiment Works, Haslar. Assessed damage on ships after Jutland 1916. Washington 1917 to share British experience with US. 1919 design work on *Hood* and post-war battleship proposals including *Nelson*. Assessed German battleship *Baden* 1921. Constructor at Malta Dockyard including use of floating docks for battleships 1925–7. In charge of destroyer design. Chief Constructor 1930, working on modernisation of battleships. DNC 1936 responsible for *King George V* class battleships, and large re-armament programme including aircraft carriers, cruisers and submarines. KCB 1938. Responsible for design of *Lion* class and *Vanguard*. In parallel, Assistant Controller of Warship Production 1942–5, allocating Britain's stretched shipbuilding resources. Retired to devote time to professional affairs including Institution of Naval Architects.

Sir John Arbuthnot Fisher, Admiral of the Fleet Lord Fisher of Kilverstone (1841–1920)

First Sea Lord who modernised the Royal Navy and was the progenitor of *Dreadnought*. Midshipman 1856. Lieutenant 1862. HMS *Excellent* Gunnery School, Portsmouth. Commander 1869. Gunnery and torpedo specialist. CO of *Bellerophon* 1872. Captain 1876. CO of new battleship *Inflexible* 1881. Captain of *Excellent* 1883–5. Director of Naval Ordnance 1886–91. Increased control of naval armaments from War Office. Rear-Admiral 1890. Admiral Superintendent of Portsmouth Dockyard, observing construction of *Royal Sovereign*. Third Sea Lord (Controller) 1892–7 in charge of materiel, and building of new battlefleet and destroyers. KCB 1894. Vice-Admiral 1896. Commander in Chief North America and West Indies station 1897. Admiral 1901. C-in-C Mediterranean Fleet 1899–1902, improving fighting ability. Second Sea Lord 1902 introducing reforms to training of executive and engineer officers. C-in-C Portsmouth 1903. First Sea Lord 1904. Ruthlessly cleared out obsolete ships, improved administration of RN and reserve ships, set up Committee on Designs in 1905 which proposed the *Dreadnought* concept. Admiral of the Fleet 1908. Encouraged development of battlecruisers, submarines, turbines, diesels, oil fuel. Retired in 1911 aged 70. Re-appointed First Sea Lord October 1914. Instigated massive new construction programme of battlecruisers, destroyers, submarines, monitors. Resigned May 1915 over Dardanelles campaign. Board of Invention and Research 1915.

Engineer Vice-Admiral Sir Albert John Durston (1846–1917)

Engineer-in-Chief who introduced watertube boilers, steam turbines and oil fuel into the RN. Engineering student Portsmouth 1861 and London. Entered RN in 1866. On staff of chief engineer Portsmouth Dockyard 1872–81. Chief engineer Sheerness Dockyard 1881–3. Chief engineer Portsmouth Dockyard 1883–8. Admiralty as Engineer in Chief 1889. Oversaw transition from unreliable steam reciprocating engines with cylindrical boilers to steam turbines with watertube boilers. KCB 1897. Engineer Rear-Admiral 1903, Vice-Admiral 1906 – the first to hold that rank. Retired 1907. President Institute of Marine Engineers 1895.

Sir John Rushworth Jellicoe, Admiral of the Fleet Earl Jellicoe (1859–1935)

Distinguished naval officer in key positions during the construction of dreadnoughts and their armament. Naval cadet 1872. Lieutenant 1880, specialising in gunnery. At HMS *Excellent* gunnery school 1884–6 and experimental department 1886–8. Assistant to Director of Naval Ordnance 1888. Commander 1891, Captain 1897. Assistant to Controller (Third Sea Lord) 1902. Committee on Designs 1905. DNO 1905–07, completing transfer of all Admiralty ordnance activities from War Office, and supporting development of fire control systems. Rear-Admiral 1907. Controller 1908–10, in charge of battleship and battlecruiser building programme. Supported development of 13.5in gun. KCB 1911. Vice-Admiral in command of Atlantic Fleet 1910. Second Sea Lord 1912–14. Admiral Commander in Chief of Grand Fleet 1914–16, including Battle of Jutland. First Sea Lord 1916–17. Admiral of the Fleet 1919. Governor General of New Zealand 1920–4. Earl 1925.

Admiral Sir Reginald Hugh Spencer Bacon (1863–1943)

Technically brilliant naval officer playing a key role in the development of submarines, *Dreadnought* and heavy ordnance. Joined RN 1877. Lieutenant 1883 specialising in torpedoes and electrical. Commander 1895. Captain 1900. Appointed Inspecting Captain of Submarines 1901, playing a key role in development of early boats to 1904. Committee on Designs 1905. First CO of *Dreadnought* 1906. Director of Naval Ordnance 1907. Retired 1909 as Rear-Admiral to become managing director of Coventry Ordnance Works. Recalled to RN in First World War becoming Vice-Admiral Dover Patrol 1915–17, deploying monitors for shore bombardment with guns up to 15in. KCB 1917. Naval author.

Admiral Sir Frederic Charles Dreyer (1878–1956)

Naval officer whose fire control system greatly improved dreadnought gunnery. RN College Dartmouth 1891. Lieutenant 1898 specialising in gunnery. Gunnery officer in *Scylla*, *Hawke*, *Exmouth*. Commander and Assistant to Director of Naval Ordnance 1907–09. Developed fire control table bearing his name, fitted in most battleships by Jutland. Flag Commander *Hercules* 1911, Flag Captain *Orion* 1913, *Iron Duke* 1915. DNO 1917, overseeing development and production of new AP projectiles. Director of Naval Artillery and Torpedo 1918. Director of Gunnery Division 1920–2. Assistant Chief of Naval Staff as Rear-Admiral 1924, Deputy Chief of Naval Staff as Vice-Admiral 1930. KCB 1932. C-in-C China Station 1933–6 as Admiral. Came out of retirement in the Second World War to assist in various roles, before finally retiring in 1943.

Industry Personnel

(Sir) William George Armstrong (later Lord Armstrong) (1810–1900)

Lawyer turned engineer and industrialist who founded the Armstrong company in Newcastle, pre-eminent in ordnance and warship building. Started the Elswick Engine Works to build hydraulic cranes and machinery in 1847. Developed rifled breech-loading guns made of steel from 1855. Inspector of Rifled Ordnance at War Office 1859. Knighted 1859. Elswick Ordnance Company set up separately from W G Armstrong & Co until 1864 when Armstrong returned to Elswick to develop the merged businesses. Merged with Charles Mitchell's Low Walker shipyard in 1882 to build ships, with a new warship building yard laid out at Elswick in 1884. Major supplier of heavy hydraulically operated gun mountings for the Admiralty. Major exporter of warships to foreign navies. Created a baron in 1887. Generous local benefactor. Twice President of Institution of Mechanical Engineers, once of Civil Engineers. His house at Cragside, north of Newcastle, is now open to the public.

(Sir) Andrew Noble (1831–1915)

Notable artillerist and key contributor to the rise of Armstrong company. Commissioned into Royal Artillery 1849. Secretary of Rifled Cannon Committee 1858. Invited by William Armstrong to join the Elswick Ordnance Company in 1860. Experimented with explosives, ordnance and ballistics. In charge of all Elswick works 1881. Developed hydraulic gun machinery, ordnance sales to Admiralty, War Office and foreign governments, and warship exports. Director of Armstrong Mitchell. KCB 1893. After merger with Whitworth in 1897, started manufacture of armour plate at Openshaw. Succeeded Armstrong as Chairman of Armstrong, Whitworth in 1900. Oversaw expansion of ordnance manufacturing facilities at Elswick and Armstrong shipyards in the dreadnought era. Ruled the company as an autocrat with subservient staff until his death in 1915.

(Colonel) Thomas (Tom) Edward Vickers (1833–1915)

Metallurgist who transformed Vickers from a specialist steel maker into a major armaments and shipbuilding company. Educated in Sheffield and Germany. Joined his father's firm c1854 which became Vickers, Sons & Co Ltd in 1867. Developed crucible steels for tools, castings and railway material. Chairman 1873–1909. CO of Hallamshire Rifle Volunteers 1871–99. Took company into manufacture of armour plate and guns late 1880s. Took over Maxim Nordenfelt Guns & Ammunition and Naval Construction & Armaments at Barrow in 1897. Took half share in Wm Beardmore 1902 and Whitehead Torpedo in 1906. In 1909 handed over chairmanship to brother Albert (1838–1919), who had been responsible for commercial affairs and sales.

(Sir) Benjamin Chapman Browne (1839–1917)

Engineer, manager and chairman of Hawthorn Leslie, major supplier of machinery for battleships built by Armstrong and Royal Dockyards. Apprentice engineer Elswick 1856. Civil engineering work on docks and harbours 1861–70. Partner in R & W Hawthorn, Newcastle making mainly locomotives 1870. Set up new marine engine works at St Peters, Newcastle 1871. Merged with shipbuilder Leslie at Hebburn in 1885 to form R & W Hawthorn, Leslie & Co Ltd. Chairman 1886–1916. Interest in industrial relations and business economics. Knighted 1887. President North East Coast Institution of Engineers and Shipbuilders 1898.

Francis Elgar (1845–1909)

Naval architect and manager at battleship building yards. Shipwright apprentice Portsmouth Dockyard 1859. Admiralty assistant overseer of HMS *Captain* building at Birkenhead 1867. General manager Earle's Shipbuilding & Engineering, Hull 1874–6. Consultant naval architect. First Professor of Naval Architecture at Glasgow University 1883–6. The Admiralty appointed him as Director of Dockyards 1886–92, building and repairing battleships. Director and naval architect of Fairfield Shipbuilding & Engineering when the company built its first battleships

1892–1907. Chairman of Cammell Laird (an associated company) 1907 and Chairman of Fairfield. Very active in the affairs of the Institution of Naval Architects.

Josiah Richard Perrett (1848–1918)
Manager of Elswick shipyard during the main dreadnought building period. Dockyard school Devonport. Admiralty as assistant to William Froude at Torquay tank 1871–85. Principal assistant to Philip Watts at Armstrong Mitchell 1886. Designer of many warships, especially for foreign navies, and hull forms. Succeeded Watts as general manager at Elswick 1902. Responsible for construction of eleven battleships there and at new Naval Yard until retirement in 1916.

(Sir) James McKechnie (1852–1931)
Vickers engineering manager and director who established the Barrow works as a world leader. Apprentice engineer Glasgow. Draughtsman at Fairfield. Chief draughtsman at J & G Thomson engineering works c1882, then assistant manager. Engineering manager at Nervion shipyard, Bilbao 1889, building machinery for three armoured cruisers. Engineering manager Naval Construction & Armaments, Barrow 1895. Special (local) director of Vickers, Sons & Maxim at Barrow 1899. Oversaw the massive expansion of Barrow works including manufacture of heavy gun mountings. In fifteen years the area of the works trebled and workforce quadrupled, focussing on warship construction. Developed design of diesel engines for submarines. General manager Barrow. Main Vickers board 1910. KBE 1918. Retired 1923.

(Sir) Charles Algernon Parsons (1854–1931)
Pioneer of the steam turbine, which revolutionised warship propulsion in the early twentieth century. Sixth son of Earl of Rosse. Passed out of Cambridge University in mathematics in 1877. Premium apprentice at Armstrong's Elswick works to 1881. As junior partner at Clarke, Chapman & Co at Gateshead, formed their electrical engineering department and developed his steam turbine concept to drive electrical generators in 1884. Set up his own business at Heaton in Newcastle in 1889 to build turbo-generators. Parsons Marine Steam Turbine Co set up in 1897 at Wallsend to develop the turbine for ships. 100ft launch *Turbinia* (now on display in Newcastle's Discovery Museum) used for experiments.

Successful patented design of turbine and propellers by 1897. First application in destroyers and ferries. Bold decision to use 70,000shp turbines in *Mauretania* and *Lusitania* in 1904 encouraged the selection of turbines for *Dreadnought* in 1905. The company remained in the forefront of marine propulsion licensing manufacture in UK and overseas. Every subsequent RN battleship and battlecruiser had steam turbine propulsion, which was extended to cruisers and destroyers. KCB 1911. Many awards including Order of Merit 1927. Parsons continued to develop turbines for land and marine use to the end of his life, as well as other products including astronomical telescopes.

(Sir) John Harvard Biles (1854–1933)
Prominent naval architect for both naval and merchant ships. Apprentice Portsmouth Dockyard. RN College Greenwich 1875. Admiralty 1877. Chief of Staff J & G Thomson 1880, responsible for foreign warship design. Professor of Naval Architecture, Glasgow University 1891. Own consultancy business from then on. Committee on Designs 1905. Knighted 1913. Author of two-volume *Design and Construction of Ships*, 1908.

Andrew Laing (1856–1931)
Marine engineer during the dreadnought era. Educated at James Baillie's School in Edinburgh, followed by an engineering apprenticeship at Hogg & Walker. In 1877 he entered the drawing office at John Elder's Govan engine works and by his mid-twenties had been promoted to chief draughtsman. By 1890 he had assumed the rank of engine works director. During his time at Govan, vessels built and engined by the firm were at the cutting edge of power, speed, size and reliability, including the Cunard liners *Campania* and *Lucania*. In 1896 he moved to Wallsend Slipway & Engineering as general manager and by 1901 had assumed full control as managing director, a position he held until his death. He was responsible for the design of the machinery for many warships, including six battleships, as well as his greatest achievement, the machinery for the liner *Mauretania*. He was awarded the CBE for services to marine engineering in 1917.

(Sir) Robert Abbott Hadfield (1858–1940)
Metallurgist who developed alloy steels, armour piercing projectiles and cast steel

armour. Apprentice steelmaker Jonas & Colver in Sheffield. Father formed Hadfield's Steel Foundry in Sheffield in 1872. Run by son Robert from 1888, Chairman and managing director. Hard manganese steel developed in 1882 for railway and dredging applications. High tensile silicon steel for deck protection. Heclon armour-piercing capped projectiles from 1905. Era armour steel castings for conning towers etc 1908. Under his leadership, Hadfield became largest UK manufacturer of heavy projectiles in First World War, up to 18in calibre.

(Sir) Alexander Gracie (1860–1930)

Prominent Clyde marine engineer during the dreadnought era. Engineer apprentice J & G Thomson, Glasgow, then Clydebank drawing office. Draughtsman Wm Denny & Bros 1887. Engine design department Clydebank 1889. Engineering manager Fairfield 1895. Director 1901. Committee on Designs 1905. Managing director 1905, Chairman 1909–19. Director Cammell Laird 1905 after share exchange with Fairfield. KBE 1918.

(Sir) Thomas Bell (1865–1952)

Manager at Clydebank during battleship era. Trained at Royal Naval Engineering College, Keyham as RN engineering officer. Poor eyesight so left RN to join John Brown's engineering works at Clydebank in 1886. Manager 1902 overseeing manufacture of machinery for *Lusitania* and battleships and battlecruisers. Responsible for the introduction of the Brown-Curtis turbine to Clydebank 1908. Managing director of the John Brown works at Clydebank from 1909 until retirement in 1935. John Brown main board director 1909–46. Deputy Controller of Dockyards and War Shipbuilding 1917–19. Knighted in 1918.

(Sir) Arthur Trevor Dawson (1866–1931)

Naval officer who became Vickers ordnance expert in the battleship era. RN cadet 1879. Lieutenant 1889, specialising in gunnery. Staff of HMS *Excellent* gunnery school. Experimental officer, Woolwich Arsenal 1892. Joined Vickers as Superintendent of Ordnance 1896. Director 1898. Developed ordnance design and manufacture at Sheffield and Barrow. Managing director of group 1909. Knighted 1909. Temporary rank of Commander RN 1915. Director Vickers-Armstrongs 1928. Author of *The Engineering of Ordnance*. Junior Institution of Engineers 1909.

(Sir) Thomas George Owens Thurston (1869–1950)

Vickers chief naval architect during dreadnought era. Trained in Liverpool shipyard. Naval architect at Elswick under Philip Watts. Joined Vickers, Sons & Maxim 1898. London office. Appointed naval designer 1905 at £800 p.a. Company naval architect 1909. Produced many battleship designs especially for foreign navies, e.g. *Kongo*. Changed his name in 1915 from Thomas George Owens. KBE 1920. Vickers naval director until 1930. Consultancy business thereafter.

(Sir) Stephen Pigott (1880–1955)

Marine engineer contributing to Clydebank's eminence in dreadnought era. Born in US, studied mechanical and marine engineering at Columbia University 1903. Invited by Thomas Bell to develop Brown-Curtis turbine at John Brown in 1908. Manager of engine works 1920. Oversaw construction of machinery for liner *Queen Mary*. Managing director of Clydebank 1935–49, building liner *Queen Elizabeth*, and battleships *Duke of York* and *Vanguard*. Knighted 1938.

(Sir) Charles Worthington Craven (1884–1944)

Naval officer who became managing director of Vickers-Armstrongs and sustained its shipbuilding and armaments capability during 1930s depression ready for the demands of the Second World War. RN cadet 1899. Lieutenant serving in submarines 1905–12, latterly as CO of an 'A' class boat. Joined Vickers as submarine technical adviser 1912. Returned to serve in RN with submarines 1914-16 as Commander. Rejoined Vickers to oversee submarine construction. Special (local) director 1919. General manager Barrow 1923. Director Vickers Ltd 1925. Managing director Vickers-Armstrongs 1931. Managing director English Steel Corporation 1932. Knighted 1934. Chairman V-A and ESC 1936. Admiralty and Ministry of Aircraft Production 1940–2, Chairman and Managing Director V-A and ESC 1942-3. Baronet 1943. President Institute of Marine Engineers 1932.

5: BUILDING

HULL CONSTRUCTION

While battleships were constructed in a broadly
similar fashion to merchant vessels, there were
differences in the more substantial components
and notably in the strong influence of the
owner, the Admiralty. The latter provided the
basic design, it supplied to the shipbuilder
about half of the vessel's content, including
armament and armour, and it supervised
construction closely. Until about 1904 it also
undertook final completion in a Royal
Dockyard. Once a contract to build a battleship
had been awarded, the shipbuilder needed to
make an immediate start if he was to deliver in
only two to three years' time. Typical contracts
had many clauses, covering a wide variety of
issues. For example, the ship had to be fitted out
afloat at all times, it was to be delivered at open
water near the port of construction, no
foreigners were to be allowed in the shipyard
during construction, the Official Secrets Act
applied, all materials and equipment were to be
weighed, only the best materials and workmanship were to be used, overseers were to be given
facilities for inspecting the vessel and had
power to reject materials or workmanship,
responsibilities during trials including payment
for fuel, trial records to be taken. Commercial
conditions included details of instalment
payments e.g. one-eightieth when 850 tons of
steel bars, plates, rivets, and metal were on the
contractor's premises (exclusive of armour to
be supplied by the Admiralty and of nickel
steel) and appropriated to the ship. Once
payment had been made, the work completed
vested in the Admiralty. If the shipyard went
bankrupt, the contract could be determined
(ended) and only the Admiralty could complete
the ship, no sub-letting of work without
Admiralty approval, hull and machinery to be
insured, e.g. against fire, drawings to remain the
property of the Admiralty, penalties for lateness

or machinery over weight, fair wages to be paid
as current in the district, no member of the
House of Commons to have any share in the
contract.

The Admiralty provided the specification and
important drawings including:

– Sheer drawing i.e. lines plan.
– Profile.
– Rig.
– Sections fore and aft.
– Armour.
– Midship section structure.
– Deck plans, typically eight.
– Key machinery drawings.

The shape of the hull was the starting point.
The lines plan usually at a scale of ¼in = 1ft
(1:48) defined the shape in two dimensions,
being based on previous experience of the ship
type and the results of model tests at the
Admiralty Experiment Works at Haslar near
Portsmouth. Private shipbuilders preparing a
design for foreign navies might be able to use
Haslar, but John Brown built their own 400ft
towing tank at Clydebank in 1903 and Vickers
a 440ft one at St Albans (near their London
office) in 1912. Together with the general
arrangement plans and main structural drawings, the shipyard had to convert all this design
intent into working drawings which were used
both to order materials like steel plates and to
guide the workshops on how to manufacture.

In the mould loft, a large flat area often above
a workshop, the loftsmen drew out (in chalk)
on the screive boards the hull shape to full size,
showing the shape of every transverse frame.
Some fairing (smoothing in three dimensions)
was needed before a final table of building
offsets could be produced. These gave the half-
breadths from the centre line (ships are usually
symmetrical on both sides) at various waterline

Midship section
Royal Sovereign class battleship
based on drawing from Manual of Seamanship 1932

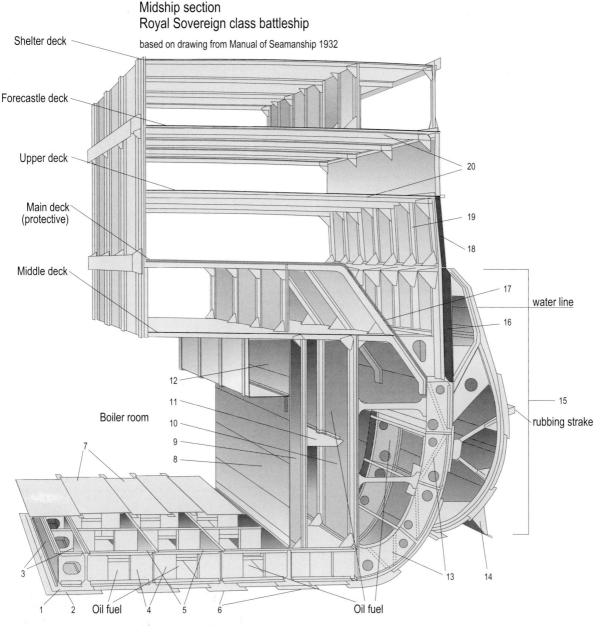

Shelter deck
Forecastle deck
Upper deck
Main deck (protective)
Middle deck
Boiler room
Oil fuel
Oil fuel
water line
rubbing strake

1. Inner flat keel plate
2. Outer flat keel plate
3. Vertical keel plates
4. Bracket plates
5. Longitudinals
6. Outer bottom plating
7. Inner bottom plating
8. Longitudinal bulkhead
9. Air space
10. Longitudinal protective bulkhead
11. Oiltight flat
12. Electric lead and pipe passage
13. Lightened plate frames
14. Bilge keel
15. Protective side bulge (added post WW1)
16. 520lb (13in) side armour
17. Sloped protective deck
18. 240lb (6in) side armour
19. Zed bar frames
20. Deck beams

heights above the keel. It was thus possible to make wooden templates defining the exact shape of every shell (skin) plate and frame. In parallel a wooden half-block model would be made at 1:48 scale, on which the lines of the shell plate seams (longitudinal joints) and butts (transverse joints) could be worked out to minimise plates curved in two dimensions and reduce scrap from non-rectangular plates.

Allowance had to be made for the overlap of riveted joints when working out the size of each plate, and a margin added on length and breadth as a cutting allowance (green material). The scrap percentage (the difference between ordered and finished steel weight) on structure was around 15–20 per cent – the offcuts could be sold back to the steelworks.

Preliminary launch calculations would

already have been made to check that a ship of the required size could be safely launched into what might be quite a narrow and shallow river. The selected building berth would need not just to be long and wide enough, but also have a suitable slope (declivity), typically ⅝in per foot, or 1 in 19, for safe launching and of course have foundations strong enough to take the weight. The shipwrights would lay the keel blocks, usually of timber, in the chosen location, each about 4ft high, which allowed enough room for men to work underneath the hull as well as accommodate the launchways to be built later under the hull.

The drawing office would order the steel plates and sections (stiffeners) from the steelworks, giving the identifying mark that each was to receive. Port and starboard plates and frames were usually mirror images so were ordered in pairs. Delivery time was usually only a few weeks, with wagons full of steel arriving regularly by rail in the yard. Steel was placed in acid 'pickling' tanks to remove millscale, and was then passed through the plate straightening rolls (mangle) – there was usually some slight waviness as plates cooled after rolling at the steel mill. The loftsmen provided the templates for shaped plates and sections, and the platers marked off the positions of rivet holes, both around the periphery of the plate and where stiffeners were to be attached. The size of the rivets and their spacing was shown on each steelwork drawing: to give an example, for a bulkhead, typically ½in to 1½in diameter spaced 4 to 8 diameters apart, single or double rows depending on the structural loads.

The marked plates were then ready to go to the machines in the plater's shed, where they were cut to final dimensions by shears – oxygas cutting was not used regularly until after the First World War. The shearing machine was usually worked by leather belts from an overhead lineshaft driven by a steam engine – electric drive of machine tools was not yet in widespread use, except in the newest yards such as Beardmore. The shears was often combined with a punch which formed the rivet holes rhythmically as the plating squad manipulated the plate to the next hole punch position. For critical plates and higher tensile steel plates, the slower but more precise method of drilling holes was used. If the plate was curved, it was moved on a bogie on a narrow gauge railway to the plate rolls where successive passes between an upper and two lower rollers bent it cold to the right shape as checked by a template.

Frames (side stiffeners) often had quite marked curvature, especially towards the ends

Right: Mould lofts were necessarily large, well-lit spaces to enable ships' sections and other data to be laid out at full scale. This photograph shows Beardmore's mould loft about 1906 soon after it had been built. It shows a light wooden template which has been made to conform exactly to a particular frame on a body plan. The template will be taken to the plater's shed where a frame will be bent to this shape. *(Author's collection)*

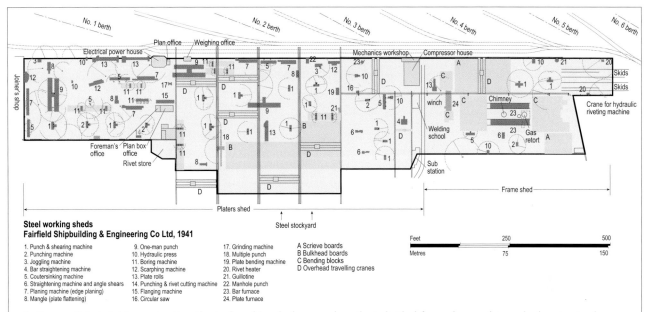

Steel working sheds
Fairfield Shipbuilding & Engineering Co Ltd, 1941

1. Punch & shearing machine
2. Punching machine
3. Joggling machine
4. Bar straightening machine
5. Coutersinking machine
6. Straightening machine and angle shears
7. Planing machine (edge planing)
8. Mangle (plate flattening)
9. One-man punch
10. Hydraulic press
11. Boring machine
12. Scarphing machine
13. Plate rolls
14. Punching & rivet cutting machine
15. Flanging machine
16. Circular saw
17. Grinding machine
18. Multiple punch
19. Plate bending machine
20. Rivet heater
21. Guillotine
22. Manhole punch
23. Bar furnace
24. Plate furnace

A Scrieve boards
B Bulkhead boards
C Bending blocks
D Overhead travelling cranes

In the era of riveted ship construction, the steel working sheds were where the individual frames, beams, plates and other structural components that comprised the hull were formed.

Information in the form of lines describing all aspects of the hull shape was transferred from the mould loft to the scrieve boards, a large cast-iron surface, located in the plater's shed. From this, steel was marked off and worked either cold or heated in gas-fired furnaces and bent into shape on bending blocks. The machines employed to cut, punch, bend and plane steel were necessarily large and powerful, either hydraulically or electrically powered. Over twenty different types of machine were employed, each in a specific capacity.

Handling steel was paramount to efficient working and each machine was served by a jib of up to 5 tons capacity. Other radial cranes spanned local work areas while overhead travelling cranes handled heavier components or built-up sections quickly from one work area to another. Manual labour was still used extensively with up to four 'helpers' for each plater.

Plater's sheds, while covered, were generally open on either side to permit the easy flow of unworked steel from the stockyard on one side through to the berths on the other. With a full order book a workforce of about 8500 men were employed in the Fairfield works with 6000 in the shipyard and 2500 in the engine works. Of the 6000, approximately 3000 were steel workers employed either around the plater's shed or outside at the building berths.

Today this area of the shipyard, occupied with fabrication sheds and a Ship Block and Outfit Hall, is building major sections of the aircraft carriers *Queen Elizabeth* and *Prince of Wales*.

of the hull, so were generally bent hot. The cast-iron bending slab had hundreds of holes in it to accept pins and dogs (an angled clamp) to hold down the workpiece against a sett, a thin strip of metal set to the correct shape. The frame would be heated red-hot in a nearby gas-fired furnace, drawn out with tongs, forced against the sett with hammers or a hydraulic jack, and held down by dogs until it had cooled to the correct shape.

The formed plates and stiffeners were now ready to go to the building berth, their identity and location marked in white paint. Most larger shipyards had a railway track down each side of the berth, where material from the shops could be moved on bogies, either pushed by hand or by a steam locomotive, the latter sometimes fitted with a small crane. There was usually a series of timber pole derricks supported by guys at intervals on each side of the berth to provide coverage over most of the hull. Although they could typically only lift about 3 tons, that covered a 1in plate about 27ft x 6ft. Some larger Clyde yards substituted 5-ton steel derricks from about 1906, e.g. John Brown. Each plate or stiffener would be erected one at a time, either involving muscle power on a block and tackle to the derrick or a wire taken to a nearby winch. The plate would be manoeuvred into position and temporarily bolted to adjacent structure. It was then faired to mate closely with adjoining plates or stiffeners, with any rivet holes not in exact alignment reamered out. The riveters were then ready to begin the joining process using red-hot rivets to join two (or sometimes three) thicknesses of plate or a stiffener to a plate, or an angle bar connecting two plates at right angles. Rivets could be hammered down manually by two men striking alternate blows, or a hydraulic riveter could be used if its jaws could reach both sides of the plate, or increasingly in the dreadnought era a pneumatic

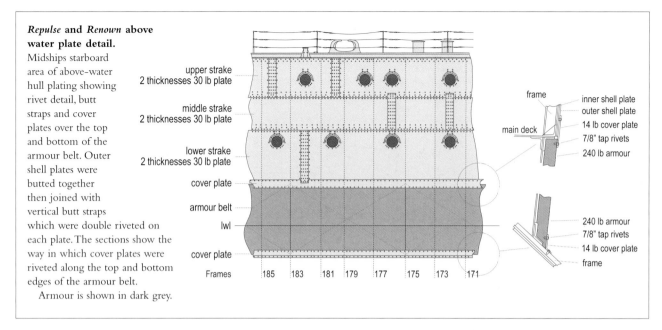

***Repulse* and *Renown* above water plate detail.**
Midships starboard area of above-water hull plating showing rivet detail, butt straps and cover plates over the top and bottom of the armour belt. Outer shell plates were butted together then joined with vertical butt straps which were double riveted on each plate. The sections show the way in which cover plates were riveted along the top and bottom edges of the armour belt.

Armour is shown in dark grey.

upper strake
2 thicknesses 30 lb plate

middle strake
2 thicknesses 30 lb plate

lower strake
2 thicknesses 30 lb plate

cover plate

armour belt

lwl

cover plate

Frames   185 183 181 179 177 175 173 171

frame
main deck

inner shell plate
outer shell plate
14 lb cover plate
7/8" tap rivets
240 lb armour

240 lb armour
7/8" tap rivets
14 lb cover plate
frame

hammer driven by compressed air held by one man. Welding was not used in battleship building until the *King George V* class and then only for non-critical structure or where oil-tightness was desired as in fuel tanks.

A riveting squad consisted or four or five men: a rivet boy who heated the rivets in a nearby coke furnace, a catcher who placed the red hot rivet in the correct hole, and a holder-up on the side of the rivet head who held up his heavy dolly to take the force of the blows from the riveter(s) on the other side who then hammered the point down. As the rivet cooled, it contracted, pulling the pieces of metal closely together. If water or oil-tightness was required, a caulker would use a hammer or pneumatic tool to force the overlapping plate edge into the plate beneath. Access at higher levels both inside and outside the ship was from wooden planks, precariously spanning between upright

Right: The hull of Japanese *Kashima* takes shape on No 8 ironclad berth at Elswick. The sloped protective deck is being fitted. The timber derricks could only lift a single plate. The other uprights are to support staging. Steel beams and timber planks are visible in the typical shipyard ground clutter.
(Newcastle University Marine Technology Special Collection)

Above: A view looking forward of Yard No.755, *Kashima* under construction at Elswick in the summer of 1904. Curved side frames, deck beams and deck plates are in position but not yet riveted up. *(Newcastle University Marine Technology Special Collection)*

wooden or steel staging posts, sometimes with a wooden gangway for vertical access, more usually ladders.

For a battleship, this process continued for about twelve months, starting with laying the flat plate keel about 3ft wide nearly the length of the ship, upon which was erected the vertical keel or centre girder. The rest of the double bottom structure consisted of bottom plates, transverse floors (actually vertical) with manholes cut in them for access and lightness, fore and aft girders (longitudinals), all closed in by the inner bottom plating. Side frames extended vertically at each side of the ship, sometimes as double hulls with inner and outer plating much like the double bottom. Vertical bulkheads were erected on the double bottom, both transverse and longitudinal to form compartments, usually watertight, such as machinery spaces and magazines. Transverse beams and fore and aft girders stretched between the tops of the bulkheads and the side of the ship to support the decks. Deck plates were laid on these supports, usually a single thickness, although the protective deck was laid

in two thicknesses, leaving holes and hatchways where needed. Shell plates were bolted to the frames, faired, riveted and caulked. Where the shape was complex, templates might be lifted off the ship to give the correct shape for bending the plate, a process also used to make moulds for shaping side armour plates. This process continued deck by deck until the weather deck (upper or forecastle) was reached. Large openings would be left in the upper decks to allow the machinery and barbettes and gun mounting hoists to be installed.

During the battleship building era, many well illustrated textbooks were published on shipbuilding practice. Two that focussed on warships were *Shipyard Practice* by N J McDermaid in 1911 and *Practical Construction of Warships* by R N Newton in 1941, both authors being members of the Royal Corps of Naval Constructors.

FORGINGS AND CASTINGS

Complex shaped objects could be forged or cast from iron or steel, or occasionally non-

Above: Heavy forgings and castings like propeller shaft brackets were usually erected by temporary sheerlegs, as the berth cranes had insufficient capacity. The holes in the palm of this starboard outer bracket at Frames 293-4 will be riveted to *Duke of York*'s supporting structure in the hull. *(Upper Clyde Shipbuilders)*

Above, right: Fifteen months after keel laying, the plating of *Duke of York*'s middle deck (two below the upper) is being laid over the aft machinery spaces. The rectangular opening aft is for Y turret. Beyond lies the Cunarder *Queen Elizabeth* nearly ready for launch. *(Upper Clyde Shipbuilders)*

Opposite, top: The stern casting for *Hood* shown in the machine shops at Beardmore's Parkhead Forge. The four-piece casting has already been drilled in preparation for riveting. *(Author's collection courtesy of NRS)*

ferrous metals. Forgings were formed from red-hot ingots under a hydraulic press or a steam hammer, such as turbine rotors or gun components. Castings were made from molten metal poured from a ladle into a mould. The shape of the object was made in wood by patternmakers (the core), and then placed in a lower box full of sand, closed with an upper sandbox. After the core was removed, the molten metal was poured in to fill the space. Some shipyards and most engine works had their own foundries and forges, generally handling simpler parts like mooring bollards. But they relied on outside specialists like Darlington Forge Co Ltd for complex items such as sternframes to support the rudder, or shaft brackets to support the propeller shafts. Large items might have to made in more than one piece for transport to the shipyard, usually by rail, and then bolted or riveted together. Other suppliers included Walter Somers & Co Ltd of Halesowen, Spencer & Sons of Newcastle and Barrow Hematite Steel Co.

At each end of the ship such heavy steel castings were erected with the help of temporary wooden sheerlegs, the sternframe and the stem piece, the latter of ram form in most dreadnoughts. Similar sheerlegs could be used to lift in any heavy items required to be fitted before launch like transverse bulkhead armour plates at each end of the armour belt, and sometimes boilers.

Manufacture would be spread over several companies, in the case of *Repulse*:

– Stern casting A – The Steel Company of Scotland, Glasgow.

– Stern casting B – Wm Beardmore & Co, Glasgow.
– Stern casting C – The Steel Company of Scotland and Thomas Firth & Sons Ltd, Sheffield.
– Stern and shaft tubes – Thomas Firth.
– Shaft tubes – Thomas Firth and F H Lloyd & Co.
– Shaft brackets – Beardmore.
– Rudder – Beardmore.

In 1933 a market-sharing agreement for Admiralty forgings was arranged between English Steel Corporation (which included Darlington Forge), Firth-Brown and Beardmore, to preserve capacity, soon to be needed for re-armament.[1]

LAUNCHING A BATTLESHIP

Once the hull was reasonably complete and watertight (tested by filling compartments with water to check for leaks), it could be painted and launched. A suitable date on which there was a high enough tide would be agreed with the Admiralty about two months in advance, or more if a royal sponsor was involved. Admiralty Dockyard Regulations governed the procedure at Portsmouth or Devonport. The Superintendent, often an Admiral, had to send the

Admiralty an estimate of expected expenditure for the ceremony for gravelling roads, floral decorations and providing a band. If a royal personage was present, up to £120 could be spent on a luncheon and carriages, but if not, only £40. The general public might be admitted, with tickets of approved design issued to control numbers.[2] After the launch, a telegram had to be sent to the Admiralty advising of a successful launch (or otherwise) plus a form recording the actual measured hull dimensions and weight. More elaborate ceremonies were held by private shipbuilders launching battleships for foreign navies. Vickers shared the cost of such events between their London, Sheffield and Barrow offices, including a special train for guests from London to the shipyard. In the case of the Japanese *Kongo* (with a launch weight of 13,220 tons) Sheffield paid £1296.[3]

The shipwrights were responsible for carrying out the launch operation itself. Some heavy timbers were kept from previous launches, but new timber was used to make up the fore and aft poppets to match the exact narrow shape of the ship at each end to transfer the weight out to the launchways. As the hull entered the water and gained buoyancy aft, it would pivot about the fore poppet, which would thus take a large load. As the launch date neared, the two fixed launchways (groundways) would be manoeuvred under the hull, each spaced about 15–20ft from the centreline for a

dreadnought, and each about 4–5ft wide. Above them were placed the sliding ways temporarily attached to the hull, between which was a layer of grease and tallow. As launch time approached, all the keel and other blocks supporting the hull would gradually be removed, transferring the weight to the launchways. Shortly before the launch, there would be only a trigger each side preventing the ship from sliding down the launchways. After the sponsor had uttered the words 'I name this ship

Below: *Kashima* about to be launched at Armstrong Whitworth's Elswick shipyard on 22 March 1905. The two propellers are fitted, the tide is high, and two steam cranes are posed each side. *(Newcastle University Marine Technology Special Collection)*

Right: The starboard shafts of *Hood* with launching poppet visible in place underneath her hull a few days before launching on 22 August 1918. Note the recessed area where side armour will be fitted after her launch. The underwater part of her shell plating has internal riveted butt straps to give a smooth surface. *(Author's collection courtesy of NRS)*

… May God bless her and all who sail in her', a signal would be given to drop the triggers and release the ship. All being well, the ship would glide gracefully into the water amid the cheers of the spectators, but if the ship was slow to move, perhaps due to frozen grease, a hydraulic ram would be used to give it a push. As the fore end was about to reach the water, the wires attached to the hull and to piles of drag chains alongside the berth would tighten, and the friction of the drags on the ground would bring the vessel to a halt, hopefully before it struck the opposite bank, as could happen in the narrow rivers Clyde or Tyne. Drags were not much needed where there was clear water off the berth as at Portsmouth, Devonport or Birkenhead. The poppet and sliding way structure would float clear of the hull to be recovered by boats, the drag chains were disconnected and the tugs would take the hull to the fitting-out berth.

FITTING OUT A BATTLESHIP

Naval architects often classify elements of a warship into Structure, Machinery, Outfit, Armament and Armour. Fitting out, nowadays called outfitting, is the transformation of a bare steel hull into a finished ship ready for sea. In the battleship building era, nearly all this work took place after launch, although today 'pre-outfitting' is practised whereby steel blocks are fitted out with equipment, piping etc before erection on the building berth or dock. The labour content is much less when done in workshops under cover, but needs much more investment in planning and facilities, such as much larger berth cranes to lift heavier units into place.

Some fitting out was carried out by the shipyard's own workforce, with joiners fitting accommodation, shipwrights laying wood decks and plumbers installing piping. Semi-finished materials like timber and pipes were ordered, bought in and processed in the shipyard's own workshops like the joiner's shop or the plumber's shop. In other cases a specialist manufacturer supplied the equipment as ordered by the drawing office for the shipyard to fit, like anchors and cables and galley equipment. In others, the sub-contractor both supplied and fitted, e.g. ventilation systems. Sometimes shipyards, like Thames Iron Works, had their own electrical departments to do all the electrical work, but others relied on local specialist firms.

For ships ordered before 1903, final fitting

out, especially of Admiralty Supply Items (ASI) such as guns and boats, took place at a naval Dockyard, a process taking months after leaving the shipyard. 'Owing to the great pressure of work in the Dockyards [for refits and repairs], it has been decided to allow contractors who are building the ships to complete them in all respects ready for commission, by which means all the shipbuilding firms who construct war vessels will gain further experience and be better prepared to undertake Naval work.'[4] Thereafter the private shipyards completed the ship ready for sea, so shipyard 'completion' date was now similar to ship completion date. Previously commissioning for sea could be many months after shipyard delivery.

Specialist suppliers needed to get on to the Admiralty List for their class of product. A company could apply to the Director of Contracts to be included. Its works would be inspected and it might be given a small trial order and if satisfactory could be invited to tender in future. Where there were only a few suppliers, all would be invited to tender, but for general items there could be scores, so only a proportion would be invited to tender each time. If the equipment selected was a special design by a company (say electrical), they would be given a sizeable order as a reward, but the Admiralty expected free use subsequently; the Director of Contracts claimed firms accepted such terms.[5]

Manufacturers to the Admiralty of important equipment fitted in battleships are listed overleaf.

Battleships carried a dozen or more boats, ranging from a 16ft dinghy to 50ft or 56ft steam pinnaces or picket boats. Some of the latter could carry 14in torpedoes, with a boat hoisting weight of 18 tons and costing about

Above: *Indomitable* in Fairfield's fitting-out basin. The ship appears to be fully rigged so this probably dates the photograph to June 1908 when she was completed. Note the box section nature of the sheerlegs built to the shipyard's own design. These were soon to be replaced by a 200-ton giant cantilever crane. *(Author's collection)*

Opposite: Although most machinery was shipped after launch, sometimes boilers were shipped earlier, allowing decks over to be closed up. One of *Furious'* eighteen Yarrow water-tube boilers is being shipped into her hull at Armstrong Whitworth's Naval Yard in the spring of 1916. The 10-ton travelling tower cranes seen on each side of Berth No 1 were not sufficient to lift a boiler weighing about 30 tons. Pole derricks at right were rigged to lift the boiler off the ground from its rail wagon, it was then skidded across the main deck on timber baulks, and lowered by the gantry at left into a boiler room. *(Brian Newman)*

ADMIRALTY EQUIPMENT MANUFACTURERS

Clarke Chapman & Co Ltd, Gateshead	Winches, capstans, deck cranes, steering gear, auxiliary boilers, electric generators, feed pumps, searchlights, electric motors, motor generators, fans, boat hoists, ammunition hoists, steam launches
J Stone & Co, London	Propellers, ash hoists and ejectors, watertight doors
J & E Hall Ltd, Dartford.	Refrigerating equipment for storerooms and magazines, evaporators, (WW2) ammunition hoists
Haslan Foundry & Engineering Co Ltd, Derby	Refrigerating and magazine cooling machinery
Thermotank Ltd, Glasgow. (Hall and Thermotank merged in 1959 to form Hall-Thermotank Ltd)	Heating and ventilating systems, air-conditioning
Napier Brothers, Glasgow	Steering gear, capstans, winches
Bow, McLachlan & Co Ltd, Paisley	Steering gear (also built small ships and steam engines)
Harfield & Co, London	Steering gear, capstans, winches, boat hoists
Brown Brothers & Co Ltd, Edinburgh	Steering gear, telemotor controls, (WW2) Cordite aircraft catapults
MacTaggart, Scott & Co, Edinburgh	Steering gear, telemotor controls, helm signal displays, hydraulic hoists, (WW2) Cordite catapults
John Hastie & Co Ltd, Greenock	Steering gear
W L Byers & Co Ltd, Sunderland	Anchors
Samuel Taylor & Sons Ltd, Brierley Hill	Anchors
Fielding & Platt, Gloucester	Hydraulic boat hoisting machinery
Veritys Ltd, London	Electric ammunition hoists, winches, ventilation fans
General Electric Co Ltd, Birmingham	Ventilation fans, motor generators, winches, electric lamps, cables, switchboards, telephones
Moorwood	Galley (kitchen) equipment
Baker & Sons	Galley equipment
Henry Wilson & Co, Liverpool	Galley equipment
International Paint Ltd, Gateshead	Interior and exterior paints
Rahtjens Composition Co, London	Paint
Wailes Dove Bitumastic Ltd, Newcastle	Paint
T & W Smith Ltd, Newcastle (merged into British Ropes Ltd 1924)	Wire ropes
R Hood, Haggie & Son Ltd, Newcastle. (merged into British Ropes Ltd 1959)	Wire and manila ropes
Bullivant & Co Ltd, London (merged into British Ropes Ltd 1924)	Wire ropes, torpedo net defence
Cowan	Switchboards, telephone systems
Alfred Graham & Co, London	Telephone systems
Chadburn's (Ship) Telegraph Co Ltd, Liverpool	Engine room telegraphs
Metropolitan-Vickers Electrical Co Ltd, Manchester (AEI subsidiary from 1928)	Winches, WW2 high angle directors, searchlights, radar, remote power control for guns
English Electric Co Ltd, Bradford	Ammunition hoists, WW2 rangefinder directors
Vickers Ltd, Barrow	Boat hoists
Armstrong, Whitworth & Co Ltd, Elswick	Ammunition and boat hoists, winches
Evershed & Vignoles Ltd, London	Steering & other telegraphs, helm indicators, turret danger signals. WW2 high angle control systems
Callender's Cable & Construction & Co Ltd, Erith (later BICC)	Electric cables
Turner Brothers Asbestos Co Ltd, Rochdale (Turner & Newall Ltd from 1920)	Asbestos for insulation and jointing
Newalls Insulation Co Ltd, Washington and Paisley	Asbestos and cork insulation
R Waygood & Co Ltd, London (Later Waygood-Otis Ltd)	Lifts
Stothert & Pitt Ltd, Bath	WW2 aircraft cranes
Mechans Ltd, Scotstoun, Glasgow	Watertight doors, ventilators

THOS. & WM. SMITH, L^{TD.}
WIRE ROPE MANUFACTURERS,
NEWCASTLE-UPON-TYNE, ENGLAND.

150-ton Electric Crane, at the North Eastern Marine Engineering Co.'s Works, Wallsend-on-Tyne, fitted with Thos. & Wm. Smith's Steel Wire Ropes.

WIRE ROPES of the HIGHEST QUALITY,
combining strength, flexibility, and durability for every kind of special work in shipyards.
CRANE ROPES, LAUNCHING CHECKS, SLIPWAY ROPES,
ETC. ETC.
For launching modern Battleships and Liners, and for working on modern Giant Cranes,
THE BEST WIRE ROPE OBTAINABLE
is always the safest and cheapest in the long run.

Launch of H.M.S. "Princess Royal," at Messrs. Vickers' Works. Launching Checks 8-in. circ., of a total length of about 5,000 feet, with a guaranteed test breaking stress of 200 tons.

£2500. Boats were an ASI, ordered centrally and allocated as required to each battleship. While the Dockyards both maintained and built boats, regular shipbuilders like Thames Iron Works, John Brown, J Samuel White & Co of Cowes, J I Thornycroft of London and Yarrow & Co of Poplar built steam launches and machinery. A whole range of smaller firms also built hulls and/or machinery – see table on p.120. Stapleton notes 433 steam boats built for the Admiralty between 1895 and 1902.[6]

Installing propulsion machinery was a major operation, nearly all carried out after launch, leaving large openings in the decks to ship boilers, turbines etc. But this was a separate operation undertaken by the main machinery contractor, either the shipyard's own engine works or a specialist manufacturer like Wallsend Slipway. Fitting out consisted of carrying on board thousands of components from a plank of timber on a man's back to a boat hoisting winch lifted by a light crane. The fitting-out berth needed enough depth of water for the battleship to remain afloat all the time, and ideally should be alongside the outfitting work-shops, as at Armstrong's Naval Yard. Yards like Thames Iron Works were handicapped by having to use a fitting-out berth some distance

Left: Clydebank ship-yard and engine works from the air in May 1946 showing *Vanguard* and *Port Wellington* in the fitting-out basin. The east and west yard machine shops are close to their respective building berths while the engine works shops are at the head of the basin to right of shot. Tenement buildings for the workers line the main Glasgow road bottom right. *(Author's collection courtesy of NRS)*

Below: If somewhat obscured by smoke from tugs, an otherwise excellent view in September 1916 of the new battle-cruiser *Renown* passing Clydebank from the Fairfield yard upriver after a remarkably short construction time. *(NRS)*

SMALLER BOAT BUILDERS FOR THE ADMIRALTY

Hull and machinery	Hulls only	Machinery only
Vosper & Co, Portsmouth	J T Crampton, Portsmouth	A G Mumford & Co, Colchester
Simpson, Strickland & Co Ltd, Dartmouth	Philip & Son, Dartmouth	G E Belliss & Co, Birmingham
	Forrestt & Co Ltd, Wivenhoe	Plenty & Son, Newbury
	J Read Jnr, Portsmouth	T & J Hosking, Bermondsey
	W White & Sons, Cowes	
	H S Hansen & Co, Cowes	

Right: John Brown's 150-ton derrick crane lifts *Duke of York*'s foremast into place using its auxiliary hoist on 10 November 1940. *(Upper Clyde Shipbuilders)*

Right: *New Zealand* with tug assistance fore and aft, on her way from Fairfield's yard to the Firth of Clyde. This photograph was taken off John Brown's east yard at Clydebank. The lack of crew on deck and general air of incompleteness, including lack of a top coat of paint, suggests this is early in her trials period. She is not in commission so possibly on her way to drydocking at Devonport at the end of September 1912. The large number of boats is typical of ships of the period – a significant factor in superstructure and mast design. Although *New Zealand* is sailing down the Clyde, the river Cart is in the background. *(NRS)*

from their main facilities, with all the difficulties of moving material and workers to and from the shipyard and supervising them.

The table on p.255 (Chapter 12) gives some idea of the activities and trades involved in fitting out *Temeraire* at Devonport. Fitting out and installing machinery, armament and armour could take longer than building the steel hull. Pre-war dreadnoughts built in Dockyards took typically nine months on the berth and eighteen fitting out, while in private yards the figures were typically fourteen and twelve months. Equipment and systems would be tested both alongside and on seagoing trials, with manufacturers' representatives in attendance.

Testing and trials of equipment and machinery would be spread over several months; typical machinery trials are listed on p.157 (Chapter 7). The Admiralty would make a Report of Inspection previous to passing a vessel into the Fleet – *Monarch*'s was carried out at Jarrow on Tyne on 26 March 1912 before completion on the 28th and commissioning on 6 April.

ELSWICK SHIPYARD REPORTS TO THE ARMSTRONG WHITWORTH BOARD

The Elswick shipyard manager J R Perrett prepared a report before each meeting of the Armstrong Board every two months. A selec-

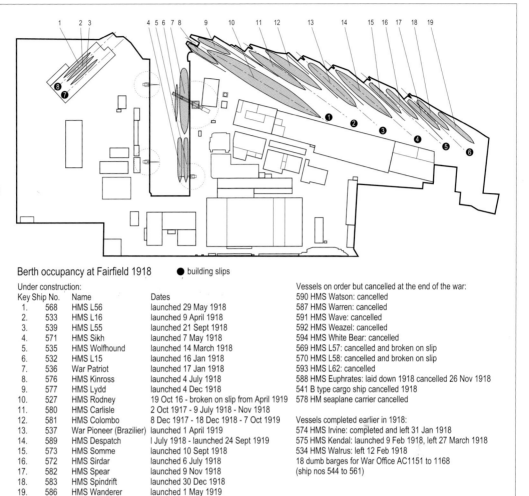

A revealing plan of the Fairfield yard showing wartime construction in the early summer of 1918. The suspended and soon to be dismantled (April 1919) hull of *Rodney* occupies the big No 1 berth but this has not prevented two minesweepers being accommodated on the same slip. No 2, 5 and 6 berths have been doubled up while *Wanderer* has been laid down on the ground to the east of No.6 berth. Destroyers and light cruisers predominate reflecting the relative shortage of these classes. The cancellation of naval orders in the last months of the war did not create a significant problem for Fairfield as in common with other builders they anticipated a prolonged boom in merchant work.

Berth occupancy at Fairfield 1918   ● building slips

Under construction:

Key	Ship No.	Name	Dates
1.	568	HMS L56	launched 29 May 1918
2.	533	HMS L16	launched 9 April 1918
3.	539	HMS L55	launched 21 Sept 1918
4.	571	HMS Sikh	launched 7 May 1918
5.	535	HMS Wolfhound	launched 14 March 1918
6.	532	HMS L15	launched 16 Jan 1918
7.	536	War Patriot	launched 17 Jan 1918
8.	576	HMS Kinross	launched 4 July 1918
9.	577	HMS Lydd	launched 4 Dec 1918
10.	527	HMS Rodney	19 Oct 16 - broken on slip from April 1919
11.	580	HMS Carlisle	2 Oct 1917 - 9 July 1918 - Nov 1918
12.	581	HMS Colombo	8 Dec 1917 - 18 Dec 1918 - 7 Oct 1919
13.	537	War Pioneer (Brazilier)	launched 1 April 1919
14.	589	HMS Despatch	I July 1918 - launched 24 Sept 1919
15.	573	HMS Somme	launched 10 Sept 1918
16.	572	HMS Sirdar	launched 6 July 1918
17.	582	HMS Spear	launched 9 Nov 1918
18.	583	HMS Spindrift	launched 30 Dec 1918
19.	586	HMS Wanderer	launched 1 May 1919

Vessels on order but cancelled at the end of the war:
590 HMS Watson: cancelled
587 HMS Warren: cancelled
591 HMS Wave: cancelled
592 HMS Weazel: cancelled
594 HMS White Bear: cancelled
569 HMS L57: cancelled and broken on slip
570 HMS L58: cancelled and broken on slip
593 HMS L62: cancelled
588 HMS Euphrates: laid down 1918 cancelled 26 Nov 1918
541 B type cargo ship cancelled 1918
578 HM seaplane carrier cancelled

Vessels completed earlier in 1918:
574 HMS Irvine: completed and left 31 Jan 1918
575 HMS Kendal: launched 9 Feb 1918, left 27 March 1918
534 HMS Walrus: left 12 Feb 1918
18 dumb barges for War Office AC1151 to 1168
(ship nos 544 to 561)

tion of entries from 1907–09 gives a good impression of the problems of battleship building. Authors' notes in square brackets.[7]

27th November 1907
No.785 [*Invincible*]

As far as our work and that of the Engineering Contractors [Humphrys, Tennant & Co] are concerned this vessel could be got ready to proceed down the river in December as previously arranged and be completed by the contract date. In consequence, however, of the backward state of the electrical work, for which the Admiralty is responsible, and of the late delivery of the gun mountings, there does not appear to be any possible chance of taking the ship down the river for some four or five months yet, and her final delivery will probably be delayed to this extent.

Brazilian Battleship "Minas Geraes" No.791

This vessel is now framed fore and aft to the height of the main deck. The inner bottom, shell plating behind armour, upper and main decks, store rooms and magazines are well advanced. All the main castings have been fitted in place. We are working with the object of having the vessel ready for the Engineers [Vickers, Barrow] to commence boring out early in the new year, and of launching the vessel in March or April next. The weight at present on the blocks is 3560 tons.

H.M.S. "Superb" No.800

A considerable amount of water testing, including the filling of one of the engine rooms, and one of the boiler rooms having been completed, she was successfully launched on the 7th instant. At the launch of the vessel 1750 tons of armour were in position, comprising the main belt, armour bulkheads and screens, and since the launch about half of the barbette armour has been put on board. The magazines, shell rooms etc as far as the steel work is concerned, are practically completed. The Engineers [Wallsend Slipway] are now proceeding with the installation of the main machinery and boilers, the boilers in one boiler room having been already installed. The weight of the vessel at the time of launch was 9000 tons, and is the heaviest weight yet launched from this Shipyard.

21st January 1908
H.M.S. "Superb" No.800
The rapid progress made with the construction of this vessel since her commencement has been well sustained during the past two months. Since the launch of the vessel the whole of the armour and barbettes, with the exception of a few closer plates, have been placed in position, and the forward barbette is practically ready for the machining of the roller path. Work in connection with the ventilation, drainage, cabins, store rooms etc is well in hand and the arrangements for cooling the magazines having been approved, this work will also be proceeded with at once. Some delay has taken place in the delivery of the turbines by the Engineering Contractors owing to a defective casing for the L.P. [low pressure] starboard turbine, and some trouble has been occasioned by the bearings of the port L.P. turbine, but with these exceptions the work on the machinery and boilers has generally made satisfactory progress.

The number of men at present employed in the Shipyard is 4998

18th March 1908
The work generally in the Shipyard has been very seriously interfered with by the strike of Shipwrights, Joiners and Drillers which commenced on the day following the date of my last report, and the stoppage of these trades has made it so difficult to carry on the work of other trades, that, whilst the men actually on strike number some 700 only, the total number of men who have had to be discharged or suspended, including those on strike, now exceeds 2500. This strike, and the discharges and suspensions arising therefrom, directly affect this Department, but the work of the Engineers on some of the vessels in hand has also been brought up by the Engineers' strike thus the work on the machinery of H.M.S. "Superb" is at a standstill, and the trials of H.M.S. "Afridi" cannot at present be completed. [Machinery sub-contractors

Humphrys, Tennant and Vickers were not affected so continued to work on *Invincible* and *Minas Geraes*]

Brazilian Battleship "Minas Geraes" No.791
Our work on this vessel is practically at a standstill, but the Engineers are proceeding with the boring out and the fixing in position of the underwater fittings. We had hoped to launch this vessel early in April, but it will now be quite impossible to do this in less than two months after the conclusion of the strike. The weight on the blocks is 5200 tons.

H.M.S. "Superb" No.800
With the help of the apprentices of various trades and men belonging to trades not on strike for whom we can economically find employment, we are doing everything possible to keep the work, including the electrification, on this vessel going. The barbette structures are all ready for receiving the 12" mountings which, we understand, will be ready to put in place next week, and we shall be in a position to claim by the end of the Financial Year all the instalments we undertook to claim at the commencement of the year. The new casing to replace the defective casing for the L.P. starboard turbine, referred to in my last report, is nearing completion but the fracture of one of the L.P. rotor wheels when under steam test on the 2nd instant at the works of the Wallsend Slipway & Eng Co, together with the strike, will still further delay the completion of the vessel.

The number of men at present employed in the Shipyard is 2467.

19th May 1908
During the past two months very little progress has been made with any of the work in hand at this shipyard owing to the continuance of the strike of Shipwrights, Joiners and Drillers; the work of these trades has been entirely stopped with the exception of such work as could be done by the apprentices and the few mechanics whose services it has been advisable to retain, viz. Fitters, Plumbers, Coppersmiths, Sheet iron workers and Pattern makers. The work in connection with other trades has been entirely suspended. Fitters' and sheet iron work for the various vessels under construction has been advanced as much as possible in view of the fact that a large number of these workmen will shortly have to stand aside for two or three

weeks to permit the machinery in the old shops to be dismantled and installed in the new shops, which are rapidly approaching completion.

No.785

As many apprentices as could be have been employed on this vessel to keep the work of sub-contractors going, but apart from this, our own work is practically at a standstill. The propelling machinery is almost complete and ready for trials.

H.M.S. "Superb" No.800

With the aid of the apprentices as much work as possible has been carried out on this vessel, consisting chiefly in the preparation of the barbettes for the reception of the 12 inch guns and mountings in connection with which we have succeeded so far as not to delay the installation. Our Electricians, with the help of the Drillers apprentices, have been able to make fast progress with the electrical work on the vessel. With respect to the machinery department, the fractured L.P. rotor wheel, referred to in my last report, has been replaced by a forged wheel, and on board the vessel a certain amount of pipe work has been carried out, but beyond this the work generally is at a standstill.

The total number employed in the Shipyard is 1255, comprising 716 men and 539 apprentices.

22nd July 1908

The strike of shipyard workers having ended, the men returned to work on June 1st. Since this date, notwithstanding some difficulty we have experienced in obtaining approval of drawings by the Brazilian and Argentine inspectors, good progress has been made with the various vessels under construction. The continuance of the strike of Engineers, however, is very seriously affecting the installation of the machinery of H.M.S. "Superb" and has prevented any further trials being made with H.M. Torpedo Boat Destroyer "Afridi". This vessel is still moored in one of the basins at Chatham Dockyard awaiting the return of the engineers to work.

No.785

The shipyard work on this vessel is rapidly approaching completion. The Engineers have carried out a satisfactory trial of the machinery alongside, and provided the gunnery and electrical work be sufficiently advanced, the vessel will be ready to be taken down the river about the end of August, in which case the official trials should commence towards the end of September.

Brazilian Battleship "Minas Geraes" No.791

Considerable progress has been made with this vessel. A large number of armour plates have been delivered by Openshaw; the armour backing has been trimmed; the bolt holes and other work completed in readiness for fitting the whole of the armour in place. The work on the magazines, store rooms, cabins and other internal structural arrangements is well advanced. We hope to be in a position to launch the vessel about the 10th September. The weight at present on the blocks is 5950 tons.

H.M.S. "Superb" No.800

In this vessel also satisfactory progress is being made so far as the work in this dept is concerned, and we are doing all we can to make up for the great delay caused by the recent strike. The Engineer Contractors succeeded a fortnight ago in shipping the remaining four turbines, this has enabled us to proceed with the closing in of the decks so as to allow the remaining guns and gun mountings to be installed. The Engineers' strike however continues to cause delay in this department.

The total number of men at present employed in the shipyard is 4420.

15th September 1908
No.785

This vessel left Elswick on the 1st instant and after a safe passage through the bridges, was moored at Pelaw Buoys. On the 12th instant she was removed from Pelaw and docked in Messrs Stephenson & Co's dock at Hebburn where she will remain for ten or twelve days. During this period, the bottom will be coated with anti-fouling composition, new propellers will be put on and the whole of the underwater fittings examined. On leaving dock, the vessel will be taken to the buoys at Jarrow to be coaled and prepared for official trials, which we hope to commence about the middle of October.

Brazilian Battleship "Minas Geraes" No.791

This vessel was successfully launched on the 10th instant and is now moored alongside the jetty at the 150 ton crane in readiness for the

installation of her machinery and boilers, which will shortly arrive from Barrow. Previous to the launch, about 1500 tons of armour were placed in position, and the remainder will be fitted as soon as received from Openshaw. The weight of the vessel when launched was 9000 tons.

18th November 1908

The Engineers' strike having terminated, work is now in full progress on all ships.

No.785

This vessel was taken out of Messrs Stephenson's dock at Hebburn on September 26th, and moored at Jarrow, where she was coaled and prepared for trials. On October 21st a preliminary trial off the mouth of the Tyne was carried out with satisfactory results, and on the 22nd October the vessel left for Spithead, carrying out the 30 hours one-fifth power trial *en route*. The whole of the speed trials, gun, torpedo and anchor trials, turbine cruising, stopping, starting and turning trials, auxiliary machinery and cooling of magazine trials have since been carried out without a hitch, and I am now pleased to report that the speed attained by this vessel is higher than that of the other two vessels of the class. The vessel returned to the Tyne on 13th inst and was moored at Jarrow Buoys. The opening out of the machinery and all other work necessary to the completion of our contract will now be pressed forward with the view of delivering the ship at the earliest possible date.

Brazilian Battleship "Minas Geraes" No.791

Since the launch of this vessel on the 10th September, a large amount of armour including that of the barbettes, has been placed in position. The machinery and boilers have all been installed, and the decks are being closed in. As soon as this work is completed the upper structures of the vessel will be proceeded with. Our work has been somewhat hindered through difficulty in obtaining approval of our proposals; this difficulty however has now been overcome to a great extent and everything possible is being done to complete the ship at the earliest possible date.

H.M.S. "Superb" No.800

In this vessel the cabin work, magazines and shell rooms, pumping, draining, ventilation and other internal work, including the electrical installation, are in an advanced state, and so far as this Department is concerned, the vessel could be ready to go on trials in the course of a very few weeks. It is not, however, expected that the Machinery Contractors will be ready for the ship to be taken down the river for docking for at least two months, but every effort is being made to prevent her completion being delayed more than is absolutely necessary beyond the contract date. [4 Jan 1909]

20th January 1909
No.785

The opening out of the machinery of this vessel has been completed, and we are pushing on with the work of painting, upholstery etc. Provided the balancing of the electrical circuits, and the electrical work generally, be completed, [*Invincible* had electric gun mountings] the vessel will be ready for delivery on the 15th

March, as arranged with the Controller of the Navy on his recent visit to these Works. It has been arranged to dock the vessel on the 23rd instant.

H.M.S. "Superb" No.800

So far as the Shipyard Department is concerned, this vessel is nearly ready to be taken down the river to prepare for trials. The Machinery Contractors are carrying out their steam testing and it is hoped that their work will be sufficiently advanced to enable us to dock the vessel at the end of next month and proceed on trials early in March.

17th March 1909
No.785

This vessel was docked at Hebburn on the 23rd January and undocked on 6th February, since which date the work of completion has proceeded satisfactorily at Jarrow Buoys. She was formally handed over to the representatives of the Admiralty on the 15th instant and left the Tyne on the morning of the 16th instant to carry out the final 24 hours completion trial. At the conclusion of this trial the vessel will sail for Portsmouth to be commissioned. As at present arranged the rapidity gun trials which were not completed during the gun trials in November will take place during the passage from the Tyne to Portsmouth.

Brazilian Battleship "Minas Geraes" No.791

Fair progress continues to be made with the work on this vessel, and a large portion of the internal work is well advanced. The installation of the gunhouses, turntables etc is proceeding satisfactorily, but the electrical work continues in a backward state. The Engineers have made rapid progress with the installation of the machinery and will be ready to steam alongside at an early date. Notwithstanding the difficulty we continue to experience in obtaining approval of our submissions to the Brazilian Representatives, we are doing all we can to hasten the completion of the vessel.

H.M.S. "Superb" No.800

This vessel steamed alongside on February 8th and on February 20th she was taken from Elswick and moored at the Pelaw Buoys. On the 22nd February she was safely placed in the dock of Messrs Stephenson & Co at Hebburn, where the underwater fittings were examined, gun sights tested, the alignment of the torpedo tubes completed, and the vessel's bottom coated

with antifouling composition. She was undocked on the 9th instant and returned to the Buoys at Pelaw to be prepared for official trials which are arranged to commence on the 19th instant. The vessel generally is in an advanced state and provided the trial programme is carried through without interruption we expect to be able to hand her over by the end of May or early in June.

In consequence of the completion of H.M.S. "Invincible" and the advanced state of H.M.S. "Superb", the services of a large number of workmen in this Department will have to be dispensed with during the next few weeks.

The number of men at present employed in the Shipyard is 5061.

26th May 1909
No.785

The 24 hours completion trial of this vessel was concluded on the 17th instant, and she proceeded immediately afterwards to Portsmouth.

Brazilian Battleship "Minas Geraes" No.791

The work on the cabins and in connection with the pumping, drainage, ventilation etc is progressing satisfactorily. No settlement has however been arrived at in regard to our magazine cooling proposals and this is preventing the completion of the magazines, whilst other portions of our work have been brought to a standstill awaiting certain electrical parts, including a large number of motors which are required to enable us to proceed with such items as ventilating fans, hoists etc.

Below: The Brazilian *Minas Geraes* heads down the Tyne nearly completed by Armstrong Whitworth. *(Newcastle University Marine Technology Special Collection)*

The vessel was steamed at moorings on the 19th instant.

H.M.S. "Superb" No.800

The trials of this vessel were brought to a successful termination on the 4th April, when she returned to the Tyne and was moored at Pelaw to be completed. She was handed over on the 24th instant, and proceeded to sea yesterday to carry out the 24 hours completion trial which was successfully completed this morning. It has been found expedient to arrange for the final docking to take place at Portsmouth, whither the vessel sailed immediately after the conclusion of the completion trial.

The number of men at present employed in the Shipyard is 4375.

THAMES IRON WORKS AND *THUNDERER*

For over forty years, Thames Iron Works (TIW) had been a major builder of battleships, starting with *Warrior* in 1861, delivering five to the RN and seven to overseas navies in the nineteenth century. But with the RN expansion in the 1890s and as the Clyde and Tyne shipbuilders became more active in warship construction, its competitiveness declined. Although receiving orders for three pre-dreadnoughts in 1896–9, *Albion*, *Duncan* and *Cornwallis*, it faced increasing problems. All three were delivered about a year late, although some of the delay was due to late delivery of armament, armour and machinery. But the Admiralty also had concerns about build quality. When *Albion* was drydocked at Chatham in early 1901 (there was no suitable dock on the Thames, with TIW's largest dock being 470 x 64ft) it was found that

her keel line was irregular, up to 2in out of true in places. Apart from questions of quality control, such hull distortion could cause shaft alignment as well as structural problems. It was then found that *Duncan* and *Cornwallis* had similar distortions. The cause was found to be subsidence of the two main building berths under heavy loads – each launch weight was about 7000 tons. The upper part of the slipways had been built up from cinders and blast furnace slag, into which water from high tides and rain had percolated, rotting the upper part of the timber piles.[8]

But this was not the only concern of the Admiralty. The narrow and twisting Bow Creek was not really wide or long enough to launch large ships easily – see yard plan on p.92. At her launch on 21 June 1898 *Albion* had washed away a platform full of spectators, resulting in the deaths of 38 (there is a William McGonagall poem commemorating the event). At her launch, *Cornwallis* had struck Trinity Wharf on the opposite bank, damaging her hull. Fitting out conditions were not ideal, there being no suitable berth at the shipyard itself. Instead ships were taken into the nearby commercial Royal Albert or Victoria Docks, but the entrance lock was only 80ft wide, impossible to get a dreadnought through.

The Admiralty insisted that if TIW were to receive an order for another large warship, they would not only have to replace the rotten piles but add new ones to spread the load over a wider area. Some work had been done on the *Duncan* slipway by 1903, when *Black Prince* was ordered, 75ft longer than their pre-dreadnoughts. But the Admiralty was not entirely satisfied that enough had been done, and was unhappy at the layout of the timber launchways, too close together and with not enough camber in their length to counteract any settlement.[9] By 1906 when *Black Prince* was completed, TIW's shipbuilding output was little more than local ferries, lifeboats and barges, hardly enough to sustain a company of its size, despite having other divisions like electrical engineering and civil engineering plus the former Penn engine works. Perhaps not surprisingly, TIW were omitted from the list of shipyards invited to tender for *Lord Nelson* in 1904 and *Vanguard* in 1907.

But apart from a restricted building site, TIW also faced much higher costs than its northern competitors for large ships. It had not only higher material costs with steel and equipment manufactured in the north having to be

Below: This advertisement for Thames Iron Works shows the wide range of the company's products. Although published in *Syren & Shipping* in 1911, it features pre-dreadnoughts of a decade earlier.

The Thames Iron Works, Shipbuilding and Engineering Company, Ltd.,
CANNING TOWN, LONDON, E.

Builders of
WARSHIPS
CAISSONS
BRIDGES
PONTOONS
ROOFS
GIRDERS
TANKS
DOCK GATES
STRUCTURAL
IRON AND STEEL WORK.
MARINE ENGINES
OF THE LARGEST TYPE.
LIFEBOATS.
TUGS.
BARGES.
TURBINES.
150-TON FLOATING CRANE

Manufacturers of
BUOYS
MOTOR LORRIES
MOTOR CABS
PUMPING MACHINERY
BOILERS
CONDENSERS
SHIP WIRING
ELECTRIC FANS
DYNAMOS
MOTORS
MODEL
TESTING TANKS
SWITCHES
("STRUT" & "SNAP")
SEARCH LIGHTS

IRON & BRASS
FOUNDRIES
Two DRY DOCKS
50-TON SHEER LEGS

A GENERAL VIEW OF THE YARD, SHOWING BATTLESHIPS AND STEAMERS IN COURSE OF CONSTRUCTION

brought south at high cost, but higher coal prices and wage rates. In 1907 Thames shipwrights were paid about 42 shillings (£2.10) for a shorter working week of 48 hours, compared with 37 or 39 shillings on the Tyne or Clyde for 54 hours, i.e. an hourly rate over 20 per cent higher.[10] It is extremely unlikely that their productivity (e.g. tons per man-hour) was 20 per cent higher to compensate, given their fluctuating workload. The ordnance manufacturers charged more to erect on the Thames gun mountings built at Barrow or Elswick than at Clyde or Tyne yards – Vickers quoted £23,000 for the Thames in 1909 as against £17,300 at Barrow (32 per cent higher). This was needed to cover additional transport costs plus the costs of accommodation and allowances for their skilled erection staff working away from home. Yarrow and Thornycroft had already left the Thames for the Clyde and Southampton respectively for similar reasons.

Skills and tradition had counted for something when placing battleship orders in the late nineteenth century, especially for overseas navies. But after the northern shipyards had built up their facilities in the early 1900s and gained an impressive track record, this counted for little. With the decline of a once proud company and significant unemployment in east London, TIW's ever–optimistic chairman Arnold Hills and local worthies lobbied the Admiralty for a battleship contract in 1909. John Middlemore, MP for Birmingham North, asked a question in the House of Commons on 26 May 1909, to which the First Lord, Reginald McKenna, gave the non-committal answer 'The Thames Ironworks Company will be invited to tender for such contract work as it is considered the firm is capable of undertaking.' A delegation led by the local MP Sir John Bethell met him at the House of Commons on 12 August, but he was not prepared to give preferential treatment to the Thames, 'no order would be given unless the price permitted'. Advised by W E Smith, Superintendent of Contract Work, he also insisted that if they were awarded a contract to build one of the three *Orion* class shortly to be tendered for, they would have to put in the necessary plant to ensure completion on time. In practice this meant lengthening the building berth by 80ft, strengthening it for a 9184-ton actual launch weight, and building a new fitting out jetty, as the class at 88.5ft were too wide to enter the Royal Albert Dock. They also had to build a new floating crane pontoon, with a

150-ton German-built crane to lift the heavy gun mounting and machinery components arriving by coaster. The jetty at Dagenham would need a depth of 27ft at low water, and was for long called Thunderer Wharf. TIW had to raise £100,000 of fresh capital to finance these works.

However, TIW (or to give it its official title from 1899 Thames Iron Works Shipbuilding & Engineering Co Ltd) were determined to win this contract, despite previous complaints about unfair competition from northern shipyards. Invited to tender on 7 October 1909, they submitted a very keen price on 5 November, along with eight other builders (Vickers, Cammell Laird, Armstrong, Palmers, John Brown, Fairfield, Beardmore, Scotts). Almost certainly this included only partial recovery of overheads – the cost of the new plant would have to be spread over several assumed future contracts, but the cash still had to be spent now. In the event TIW's bid turned out to be the lowest, although DNC had reservations: 'The staff of the shipbuilding department of the Thames Co as it exists at present is known to be quite inadequate to deal successfully with a contract of this magnitude in the time allowed for completion and there is inevitable risk of uncertainty and delay in the steps necessary to augment it.'[11] When contract award letters went out from the Admiralty on 4 January 1910 for delivery by 31 March 1912, the successful tender prices were noted as:[12]

Price (£)	Thunderer	Monarch	Conqueror
Hull etc	546,220	576,550	577,056
Machinery	175,625	113,100	141,660
Boilers	51,816	91,500	81,860
Spares etc	4504	5250	4630
Total	778,165	786,400	805,206

In addition there was a further amount of about £22,000 for auxiliary machinery contracts, while armament and armour were to be ordered by the Admiralty and supplied to the shipbuilder as construction progressed.

Left: Good construction photos of *Thunderer* are rare. This view shows her nearly complete in 1912 at the fitting-out wharf specially built for Thames Iron Works at Dagenham. *(World Ship Society D K Brown Collection)*

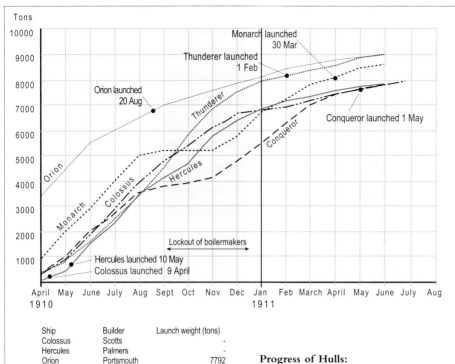

Tons

Monarch launched 30 Mar

Thunderer launched 1 Feb

Orion launched 20 Aug

Conqueror launched 1 May

Lockout of boilermakers

Hercules launched 10 May
Colossus launched 9 April

April May June July Aug Sept Oct Nov Dec Jan Feb March April May June July Aug
1910   1911

Ship	Builder	Launch weight (tons)
Colossus	Scotts	-
Hercules	Palmers	-
Orion	Portsmouth	7792
Monarch	Armstrong, Whitworth	10877
Thunderer	Thames Iron Works	9184
Conqueror	Beardmore	9246

The Admiralty required shipbuilders to make regular reports of quantity of material worked, collated here onto a graph showing a maximum of about 1000 tons per month. The launch weight included some armour and machinery in addition to the hull. The construction of *Colossus* and *Hercules* had been completed 12 months earlier and was used here to make a comparison with the *Orion* class. Between 3 September and 14 December 1910, a national lockout affecting 20,000 boilermakers took place over a wage dispute. The construction of *Conqueror* and *Monarch* were particularly affected by this action on the part of the Employer's Federation which affected a similar number of men of other trades. Traditionally steelworkers in the Royal Dockyards were organised by the Shipwrights' Association and not the Boilermakers Society.

Progress of Hulls:
***Colossus, Hercules, Conqueror, Monarch, Orion* and *Thunderer*.**
Weights added month by month. Based on graph from *Orion* Class Ships' Cover.

Given this low price, the Admiralty had no alternative but to accept the TIW tender despite their reservations. The award letter for *Thunderer* (so named on 16 February 1910) included conditions requiring the new plant to be installed. The company was also required to provide the standard financial guarantee of 10 per cent of the price, or about £80,000, so that should the company fail before delivery, there was some funding to ensure completion. The Admiralty appointed as overseer Arthur Johns, a later Director of Naval Construction.

The *Marine Engineer* magazine of March 1910 noted that 40 additional draughtsmen were being engaged, while 'nearly 1000 additional men will be put on'. New 100ft high derricks were erected alongside the slipway to lift the steel plates and sections into position. Work on the machinery also started at the former Penn engine works at Greenwich, although manufacture of the turbines had to be sub-contracted to Parsons at Wallsend. Work on the hull progressed rapidly, indeed faster than her sisters *Monarch* and *Conqueror* (handicapped by a lock-out) – see graph.

Although TIW was receiving progress instalments regularly, actual costs far exceeded their income. Furthermore their capital structure included a high proportion of debentures and

loans demanding large interest payments.[13] Inevitably the money ran out; in November 1911 some nine months after launch, TIW was effectively bankrupt, so an Official Receiver was appointed. Arnold Hills, the eternal optimist, even submitted a TIW bid for an *Iron Duke* class battleship only weeks before the company failed. *Thunderer* was eventually completed in June 1912, throwing over 2000 men out of work. The shipyard finally closed its doors on 21 December 1912.[14] Attempts were made to persuade the winners of 1911–12 Programme battleship and cruiser contracts (Vickers and Beardmore) to undertake the work on the Thames at the same price. But when they found that the Thames workers had a 48-hour week and were unwilling to change to the 54 hours worked elsewhere even though the hourly rates would remain the same so weekly wages would go up, they understandably declined.

The end had been a long time coming, but inevitable given that shipbuilding on the Thames was totally uncompetitive with northern shipyards and TIW facilities completely outdated. Indeed both *Conqueror* and *Monarch* made profits (£44,148 and £109,466 respectively) albeit on a slightly higher contract price, so were not submitting loss-leading prices. But even today there are claims from east London that it was unfair competition from northern shipyards and deliberate under-pricing by shipbuilders who were also armaments manufacturers that caused the company to close. But in practice, by 1906 TIW no longer had any high-value cards to play, while having to spend £100,000 on new plant and quoting a hull price £30,000 less than a Clyde or Tyne yard was likely to result in failure; it was just a question of when.

Anson's Contract[15]

Anson, *Duke of York* and *Howe* were the last British battleships ordered under competitive tendering. The Admiralty invited tenders for hull and machinery on 21 December 1936 to be submitted by 15 February 1937, giving less than eight weeks for the shipbuilder to prepare their cost estimates and work out a price to quote. As well as estimating the hull work content and labour cost, they had to get material and equipment prices from sub-contractors. Swan, Hunter & Wigham Richardson sought quotations for the main machinery from Wallsend Slipway and from Parsons. The former was slightly cheaper than the latter, as well as being a subsidiary of SHWR, so its price of £911,200 was included in their tender,

plus £65,149 for auxiliary machinery. Their hull and electrical quotation was £2,512,500, which included an estimated profit margin of £274,965 and £100,000 for estimated wage increases over the build period. Various extras were also quoted including spare parts and deep load trials (£8000). Drydocking was to be at Portsmouth or Southampton, with delivery off the River Tyne by 15 January 1941. Anticipated launch date was May 1939 and sea trials July 1940. (Actual completion date was 22 June 1942.)

After the Admiralty acceptance letter of 28 April 1937, the Director of Navy Contracts, E C Jubb, sent a more detailed letter on 8 July, with contract prices for the battleship to be called *Jellicoe*.

Left: Unlike merchant ships, British warships rarely carried a hull builder's plate, but an engine builder's plate was usually fitted in the engine room. *Anson* had an oval brass plate 20 x 13in on a mahogany backing, showing her Wallsend Slipway engine contract number (926). *(Author's collection)*

Below: The fitting-out basin at Clydebank in September 1941 with *Duke of York* at the far side and the monitor *Roberts* in the fore-ground. The battleship, which is soon to leave the yard, is flying the White Ensign so has already been commissioned into the Royal Navy. B turret guns are at maximum elevation. The fleet carrier *Indefatigable* is in frame on No.4 berth to the left of shot. *(Author's collection courtesy of NRS)*

	£
Hull	2,279,100
Electrical	229,500
Machinery	910,336
Auxiliary machinery	65,149
Total	3,484,085

Below: *Colossus* on the stocks at Cartsburn Dockyard on 9 April 1910, the day she was launched. The steel stockyard and plater's shed are in the foreground and the ferry *Cascapedia* and a puffer are in the fitting-out basin, the former being modified for Canadian service after sale as *Fastnet*. Steel lattice derricks are replacing light pole versions on the building berths. *(Author's collection)*

The £65,149 was a token figure, as the Admiralty selected the sub-contractors for the main items of auxiliary machinery and agreed a final price. Further contract documents, specifications and drawings were sent separately to SHWR – the company had had to return such material to the Admiralty after submitting their tender.

It was the shipbuilder's responsibility to insure the hull during construction, for which their brokers, Bowring, quoted 2s 6d per £100 (0.125 per cent) for three years on £2 million cost (£2500). The Admiralty also supplied approximate values of their main supply items, including:

	£
Armour and bulletproof plating	1,200,000
Gun mounting gear	1,400,000
Guns and naval ordnance stores	366,400
Anchors, cables, boats and naval stores	237,500
Miscellaneous auxiliary machinery and catapult	114,200
Total	3,318,100

The latter figure was about the same as the hull and machinery, giving a total estimated cost of nearly £7 million.

The Admiralty requested the shipbuilder to distribute sub-contracts for materials evenly over the country as far as possible, to spread employment. They also desired that overtime should not be worked in the present state of unemployment. The hull and electrical contract had 97 progress payments averaging 1 per cent each, totalling £2,508,600, while the machinery contract had 122 totalling £910,336. Auxiliary machinery sub-contracts included:

	£
Six turbo generators by W H Allen	32,360
Two diesel generators by P Brotherhood	10,836
Steering gear by Brown Brothers	14,267
Distillers by Caird & Rayner	13,576

The printed fifteen-page contract 'First Schedule' spelled out conditions relating to the performance of the work on hull and machinery. Amongst the clauses were:

- Only British subjects to be employed.
- Drawings and patterns to be the absolute property of the Admiralty.
- Quarterly progress reports to be supplied to Admiralty (SHWR shipyard manager N M Hunter to Admiralty overseer W J Hatchard).
- Not less than two months' notice to be given of proposed launch date. If the contractor did not nominate an Officiating Minister and a lady to perform the launching ceremony, the Admiralty would nominate.
- Contractors to weigh all materials.
- Contractors to supply armour manufacturers with drawings and moulds for shaping the plates.
- After the first payment, all materials and equipment to vest in and be the absolute property of the Admiralty.
- Vessel not to touch the ground while fitting out.
- 'Fair wages' to be paid, i.e. rates and hours not less favourable than prevailing in the trade and the district.
- Admiralty may terminate the contract if contractors bankrupt or a liquidator appointed.
- Admiralty may complete the contract, hiring workmen at the yard or take the vessel away.
- Admiralty to have the power to reject the machinery if over 3 per cent in excess of specified weight (2600 tons).
- If contractors require drydocking at a Royal Dockyard, Admiralty will do their best to provide a dock at not less than six weeks' notice. Rent £130 per 24 hours.
- Trials to be run at Talland (near Plymouth), Skelmorlie (Clyde), Arran (Clyde) or St Abb's (near Berwick) or as approved by Admiralty.
- Trials to be at the expense of contractors, with fuel oil to be purchased from the Admiralty at £3 per ton.
- Records to be taken of horsepower developed, revolutions, steam pressure, temperature etc.

Final payments for the hull extended into 1943, totalling about £2.53 million but T McPherson, managing director of the Wallsend Slipway, was able to advise SHWR director C S Swan on 14 October 1942 that the machinery figures excluding auxiliaries for their Contract 926 were:

	£
Final contract price	915,436
Total cost	842,600
Profit	72,836
	(8.6 per cent on cost)

SHEFFIELD AND BATTLESHIP BUILDING

While the battleship-building industry might be considered as mainly based on the rivers Tyne and Clyde, Sheffield, far inland, was almost equally important. Three out of the five armour manufacturers were there, the two largest projectile manufacturers and one of the largest gun manufacturers, Vickers, with their headquarters there until 1911, Britain's second largest armaments manufacturer. It was the largest

Above: Despite many tenders for battleships for foreign navies, John Brown only built one such, the Japanese *Asahi*, although ordered when Clydebank Shipbuilding & Engineering. She is seen in 1900 resplendent in a new coat of paint, but her armament has yet to be fitted by Armstrong Whitworth. *(Author's collection)*

Below: The concentration of steel companies in the north eastern part of Sheffield including the principal manufacturers of armour and heavy forgings. The largest of these sites, River Don Works, proved to be the longest-lasting and continues today as Sheffield Forgemasters.

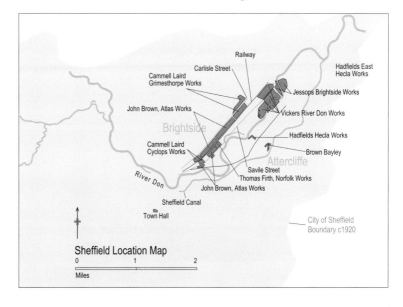

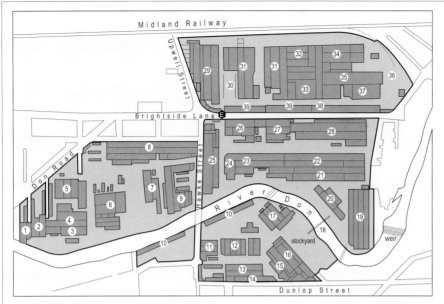

Vickers River Don works at Sheffield was continually extended as new products were added to the original steelworks and forge, first to manufacture guns, then armour (south of Brightside Lane) then an extension south of the River Don, then west of Hawke Street. It covered over 90 acres (about 380,000 sq m) by 1915. It housed the company head office until it moved to London in 1911 to be nearer to its main defence customers. The site is still in industrial use, visible at 53-24-20N 01-25-30W.

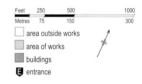

Vickers Ltd, River Don Works, Sheffield 1915

1. Crucible melting furnaces	11. Die cutting shop	21. Gun inspection department	31. Steel melting houses
2. Steel Warehouse	12. Stamping shops	22. South gun machine shop	32. Tyre rolling mill
3. Tilting hammers	13. Shrapnel shell making plant	23. Armour plate treatment plant	33. Railway material machine shop
4. Sheet and bar rolling mills	14. Canteen	24. Projectile machine shops	34. Hammer shop
5. Tube rolling mills	15. Steel foundry	25. Armour plate planing shop	35. Forge hydraulic presses
6. Gun building and hardening plant	16. Electric steel melting house	26. Armour plate rolling mill	36. Sidings
7. Structural steel shop	17. Blacksmiths shops	27. Forging and bending press shop	37. North gun machine shop
8. West gun machine shop	18. Gantry crane over river	28. Armour plate carburizing plant	38. Marine shafts & gun machine shop
9. Fitting and machine shop	19. Electric machinery manufacture	29. North armour plate planing shop	39. Offices
10. South projectile machine shops	20. Central power station	30. Gun building up & hardening plant (100 ton goliath crane)	

Below: Launch of the battlecruiser *New Zealand* at Fairfield on 1 July 1911. Light pole derricks on the building berths are being replaced with steel lattice derricks. Clyde Shipping Co's 800-hp tugs *Flying Swallow* (left) and *Flying Linnet* will move her to the fitting out basin at right. *(Author's collection)*

centre for steel forgings and castings, which went into battleship ordnance, propulsion machinery and hulls. Over a thousand members and guests of the Iron and Steel Institute spent a week in September 1905 inspecting the various works.[16] The report of the visit describes the many works, from which the table opposite showing the extent of the main businesses has been prepared. See map on p.131.

BATTLESHIP CONSTRUCTION DATES

The table opposite shows battleships in completion date order from the *Majestic* class

on, including those built for Japanese [IJN] and Brazilian [Br] navies. A battleship could have several 'completion' dates, but not all were recorded. The final 'trial' (t) was usually shortly before the shipbuilder 'delivered' (d) to the Admiralty but earlier and later trials were also carried out. Sometimes the only available date may be when it 'left the shipyard' (l). 'Completion' (c) is noted where the exact event is not defined. For ships completed after about 1904, all these dates would usually be quite close. But before that, a RN ship would be delivered contractually by a private shipbuilder to the Admiralty and then sent to a Dockyard where ASIs would be fitted, a process that sometimes took a year. Hence the completion date of such ships (ready for sea) is best measured by 'commissioning' (m).

Dockyards did not allocate yard numbers to ships built, unlike private yards. Most shipbuilders used the same contract number for machinery as for hulls.

For the totals, Equivalent Navy List displacement (nl) adds 5 per cent to standard displacement (sd). For Equivalent shaft horsepower, 80 per cent of indicated horsepower is taken.

MAJOR SHEFFIELD WORKS IN 1905

Company	Directors hosting visit	Works	Location	Started	Area, acres	Approx annual iron & steel output	Major products	Approx employees	Major tools
Vickers, Sons & Maxim Ltd	Colonel T Vickers, Douglas Vickers	River Don	Brightside	1863	60	100,000	Armour plate, guns, forgings, shafting, railway material	5000	10,000-ton bending press, 8000-ton forging press
Cammell, Laird & Co Ltd	Colonel Sidebottom, Sir A Wilson, S Roberts, B Whitehead, Mr Longden, Mr Fairholme	Cyclops; Grimesthorpe	Carlisle St	1845; 1864	60	600,000 (group)	Armour plate, bullet proof plate, gun and other forgings, castings, projectiles, railway material, tools	6000 (in 1912)	6000-ton armour press
John Brown & Co Ltd	J D Ellis, W H Ellis	Atlas	Carlisle St	1856	36	94,500	Armour plate, gun forgings, castings, shafting, railway material, tools	c5000	10,000-ton armour press, 4000-ton forging press
Thomas Firth & Sons Ltd	B A Firth, L J Firth, E Willoughby, J R Hoyle	Norfolk	Savile St	1840	c20	35,000	Gun forgings, projectiles, shafting, railway material	c2000	3000 ton forging press
Hadfield's Steel Foundry Co Ltd	R A Hadfield, A G M Jack, B Freeborough, H Cooper, W H Dixon	Hecla Works; East Hecla Works	Attercliffe; Tinsley	1872; 1892	80		Projectiles, armour castings, tramway equipment	c5000	
Davy Bros Ltd		Park Iron Works		1830			Rolling mills, forging presses and boilers		

BATTLESHIP CONSTRUCTION DATES

Name of vessel	Displacement	Shipbuilder	Yard No	Machinery Builder	IHP	Ordered	Keel Laid	Launched	Completed	
Pre–Dreadnoughts										
Majestic	14,900 nl	H M Dockyard Portsmouth		Naval Construction & Armaments Co Ltd	12,000	3rd qtr 1893	5 Feb 1894	31 Jan 1895	12 Dec 1895	m
Magnificent	14,900 nl	H M Dockyard Chatham		John Penn & Sons Ltd	12,000	2nd qtr 1893	18 Dec 1893	19 Dec 1894	12 Dec 1895	m
Prince George	14,900 nl	H M Dockyard Portsmouth		Humphrys, Tennant & Co	12,000	2nd qtr 1894	10 Sep 1894	22 Aug 1895	26 Nov 1896	m
Victorious	14,900 nl	H M Dockyard Chatham		R&W Hawthorn, Leslie & Co Ltd	12,000	Mar 1894	28 May 1894	19 Oct 1895	8 Jun 1897	m
Mars	14,900 nl	Laird Brothers	603	Laird Brothers	12,000	26 Mar 1894	2 Jun 1894	30 Mar 1896	8 Jun 1897	m
Jupiter	14,900 nl	J & G Thomson Ltd	273	J & G Thomson Ltd	12,000	21 Mar 1894	26 Apr 1894	18 Nov 1895	8 Jun 1897	m
Fuji [IJN]	12,320 nl	Thames Iron Works		Humphrys, Tennant & Co	13,500	7 Jun 1894		31 Mar 1896	17 Aug 1897	c
Yashima [IJN]	12,320 nl	Sir W G Armstrong & Co Ltd	625	Humphrys, Tennant & Co	13,500	Jun 1894	6 Dec 1894	28 Feb 1896	8 Sep 1897	d
Caesar	14,900 nl	H M Dockyard Portsmouth		Maudslay, Sons & Field Ltd	12,000	11 Aug 1894	25 Mar 1895	2 Sep 1896	13 Jan 1898	m
Illustrious	14,900 nl	H M Dockyard Chatham		John Penn & Sons Ltd	12,000	11 Aug 1894	11 Mar 1895	17 Sep 1896	10 May 1898	m
Hannibal	14,900 nl	H M Dockyard Pembroke		Harland & Wolff Ltd	12,000	22 Mar 1894	11 May 1894	28 Apr 1896	10 May 1898	m
Canopus	12,950 nl	H M Dockyard Portsmouth		Greenock Foundry Co	13,500	8 Aug 1896	4 Jan 1897	13 Oct 1897	5 Dec 1899	m
Shikishima [IJN]	14,850 nl	Thames Iron Works		Humphrys, Tennant & Co	14,500	4 Feb 1897	Apr 1897	1 Nov 1898	26 Jan 1900	c
Ocean	12,950 nl	H M Dockyard Devonport		R&W Hawthorn, Leslie & Co Ltd	13,500	8 Aug 1896	15 Feb 1897	5 Jul 1898	20 Feb 1900	m
Goliath	12,950 nl	H M Dockyard Chatham		John Penn & Sons Ltd	13,500	8 Aug 1896	4 Jan 1897	23 Mar 1898	27 Mar 1900	m
Asahi [IJN]	15,200 nl	John Brown & Co Ltd	328	John Brown & Co Ltd	15,000	5 Jul 1897	23 Nov 1897	13 Mar 1899	31 Jul 1900	c
Glory	12,950 nl	Laird Brothers Ltd	630	Laird Brothers Ltd	13,500	1 Aug 1896	1 Dec 1896	11 Mar 1899	1 Nov 1900	m
Hatsuse [IJN]	15,000 nl	Sir W G Armstrong, Whitworth & Co Ltd	680	Humphrys, Tennant & Co	14,500	Sep 1897	10 Jan 1898	27 Jun 1899	21 Jan 1901	d
Albion	12,950 nl	Thames Iron Works		Maudslay, Sons & Field Ltd	13,500	27 Jul 1896	3 Dec 1896	21 Jun 1898	25 Jun 1901	m
Implacable	15,000 nl	H M Dockyard Devonport		Laird Brothers Ltd	15,000	12 Jan 1898	13 Jul 1898	11 Mar 1899	10 Sep 1901	m
Formidable	15,000 nl	H M Dockyard Portsmouth		Earle's Shipbuilding & Engrg Co Ltd	15,000	12 Jan 1898	21 Mar 1898	17 Nov 1898	10 Oct 1901	m
Irresistible	15,000 nl	H M Dockyard Chatham		Maudslay, Sons & Field Ltd	15,000	Jan 1898	11 Apr 1898	15 Dec 1898	4 Feb 1902	m
Mikasa [IJN]	15,140 nl	Vickers, Sons & Maxim Ltd	273	Vickers, Sons & Maxim Ltd	15,000	Mid-1898	24 Jan 1899	8 Nov 1900	3 Mar 1902	c
Bulwark	15,000 nl	H M Dockyard Devonport		R&W Hawthorn, Leslie & Co Ltd	15,000	8 Sep 1898	20 Mar 1899	18 Oct 1899	18 Mar 1902	m
Vengeance	12,950 nl	Vickers, Sons & Maxim Ltd	265	Vickers, Sons & Maxim Ltd	13,500	6 Jul 1897	23 Aug 1897	25 Jul 1899	21 May 1902	d
London	15,000 nl	H M Dockyard Portsmouth		Earle's Shipbuilding & Engrg Co Ltd	15,000	3 Sep 1898	8 Dec 1898	21 Sep 1899	8 Jun 1902	m
Venerable	15,000 nl	H M Dockyard Chatham		Maudslay, Sons & Field Ltd	15,000	8 Sep 1898	2 Jan 1899	2 Nov 1899	12 Nov 1902	m
Russell	14,000 nl	Palmers Shipbuilding & Iron Co Ltd	750	Palmers Shipbuilding & Iron Co Ltd	18,000	18 Jan 1899	11 Mar 1899	19 Feb 1901	19 Feb 1903	m
Exmouth	14,000 nl	Laird Brothers Ltd	638	Laird Brothers Ltd	18,000	18 Jan 1899	10 Aug 1899	31 Aug 1901	2 Jun 1903	m
Montagu	14,000 nl	H M Dockyard Devonport		Laird Brothers Ltd	18,000	3 Aug 1899	23 Nov 1899	5 Mar 1901	28 Jul 1903	m
Duncan	14,000 nl	Thames Iron Works Shipbldg & Eng Co Ltd		Thames Iron Works Shipbldg & Eng Co Ltd	18,000	18 Jan 1899	10 Jul 1899	21 Mar 1901	8 Oct 1903	m

Continued overleaf

Name of vessel	Displacement	Shipbuilder	Yard No	Machinery Builder	IHP	Ordered	Keel Laid	Launched	Completed
Albemarle	14,000 nl	H M Dockyard Chatham		Thames Iron Works Shipbldg & Eng Co Ltd	18,000	3 Aug 1899	8 Jan 1900	5 Mar 1901	12 Nov 1903 m
Cornwallis	14,000 nl	Thames Iron Works Shipbldg & Eng Co Ltd	i33	Thames Iron Works Shipbldg & Eng Co Ltd	18,000	18 Jan 1899	13 Jul 1899	17 Jul 1901	9 Feb 1904 m
Queen	15,000 nl	H M Dockyard Devonport		Harland & Wolff Ltd	15,000	7 Jul 1900	12 Mar 1901	8 Mar 1902	7 Apr 1904 m
Prince of Wales	15,000 nl	H M Dockyard Chatham		Greenock Foundry Co	15,000	7 Jul 1900	20 Mar 1901	25 Mar 1902	18 May 1904 m
Swiftsure	11,800 nl	Sir W G Armstrong, Whitworth & Co Ltd	733	Humphrys, Tennant & Co	12,500	Feb 1902	22 Mar 1902	13 Jan 1903	21 Jun 1904 m
Triumph	11,985 nl	Vickers, Sons & Maxim Ltd	289	Vickers, Sons & Maxim Ltd	12,500	26 Feb 1902	7 Apr 1902	15 Jan 1903	21 Jun 1904 m
King Edward VII	16,350 nl	H M Dockyard Devonport		Harland & Wolff Ltd	18,000	Early 1902	8 Mar 1902	23 Jul 1903	7 Feb 1905 m
Commonwealth	16,350 nl	Fairfield Shipbuilding & Engrg Co Ltd	423	Fairfield Shipbuilding & Engrg Co Ltd	18,000	Early 1902	17 Jun 1902	13 May 1903	9 May 1905 c
New Zealand	16,350 nl	H M Dockyard Portsmouth		Humphrys, Tennant & Co	18,000	Mid-1902	9 Feb 1903	4 Feb 1904	24 Jun 1905 m
Dominion	16,350 nl	Vickers, Sons & Maxim Ltd	290	Vickers, Sons & Maxim Ltd	18,000	Early 1902	23 May 1902	25 Aug 1903	15 Aug 1905 c
Hindustan	16,350 nl	John Brown & Co Ltd	359	John Brown & Co Ltd	18,000	Mid-1902	25 Oct 1902	19 Dec 1903	22 Aug 1905 c
Katori [IJN]	15,950 nl	Vickers, Sons & Maxim Ltd	318	Vickers, Sons & Maxim Ltd	16,000	Jan 1904	27 Apr 1904	4 Jul 1905	20 May 1906 d
Kashima [IJN]	16,400 nl	Sir W G Armstrong, Whitworth & Co Ltd	755	Humphrys, Tennant & Co	16,600	Jan 1904	29 Feb 1904	22 Mar 1905	31 May 1906 t
Britannia	16,350 nl	H M Dockyard Portsmouth		Humphrys, Tennant & Co	18,000	Mid-1903	4 Feb 1904	10 Dec 1904	8 Sep 1906 m
Africa	16,350 nl	H M Dockyard Chatham		John Brown & Co Ltd (No.364)	18,000	Mid-1903	27 Jan 1904	20 May 1905	6 Nov 1906 m
Hibernia	16,350 nl	H M Dockyard Devonport		Harland & Wolff Ltd	18,000	Mid-1903	6 Jan 1904	17 Jun 1905	2 Jan 1907 m
Agamemnon	16,500 nl	Wm Beardmore & Co Ltd	484	R&W Hawthorn, Leslie & Co Ltd	16,750	6 Oct 1904	15 May 1905	23 Jun 1906	25 Jun 1908 m
Lord Nelson	16,500 nl	Palmers Shipbuilding & Iron Co Ltd	783	Palmers Shipbuilding & Iron Co Ltd	16,750	6 Oct 1904	18 May 1905	4 Sep 1906	14 Nov 1908 m
Total 49 Ships	720,565				741,100 shp				
Battlecruisers									
Indomitable	17,250 nl	Fairfield Shipbuilding & Engrg Co Ltd	445	Fairfield Shipbuilding & Engrg Co Ltd	41,000	Jan 1906	1 Mar 1906	16 Mar 1907	25 Jun 1908 m
Inflexible	17,250 nl	John Brown & Co Ltd	374	John Brown & Co Ltd	41,000	Jan 1906	5 Feb 1906	26 Jun 1907	20 Oct 1908 m
Invincible	17,250 nl	Sir W G Armstrong, Whitworth & Co Ltd	785	Humphrys, Tennant & John Brown	41,000	Jan 1906	2 Apr 1906	13 Apr 1907	15 Mar 1909 d
Indefatigable	18,750 nl	H M Dockyard Devonport		John Brown & Co Ltd (No.391)	43,000	Dec 1908	23 Feb 1909	28 Oct 1909	24 Feb 1911 m
Lion	26,350 nl	H M Dockyard Devonport		Vickers, Sons & Maxim Ltd (No.401)	70,000	Sep 1909	29 Nov 1909	6 Aug 1910	4 Jun 1912 m
New Zealand	18,800 nl	Fairfield Shipbuilding & Engrg Co Ltd	477	Fairfield Shipbuilding & Engrg Co Ltd	44,000	Early 1910	20 Jun 1910	1 Jul 1911	20 Nov 1912 d
Princess Royal	26,350 nl	Vickers Ltd	407	Vickers Ltd	70,000	18 Dec 1909	9 Apr 1910	29 Apr 1911	26 Nov 1912 c
Australia	18,800 nl	John Brown & Co Ltd	402	John Brown & Co Ltd	44,000	1 Apr 1910	23 Jun 1910	25 Oct 1911	21 Jun 1913 m
Kongo [IJN]	26,481 nl	Vickers Ltd	414	Vickers Ltd	64,000	17 Nov 1910	17 Jan 1911	18 May 1912	16 Aug 1913 d
Queen Mary	27,000 nl	Palmers Shipbuilding & Iron Co Ltd	818	John Brown & Co Ltd (No.410)	80,000	12 Jan 1911	6 Mar 1911	20 Mar 1912	30 Aug 1913 c
Tiger	28,500 nl	John Brown & Co Ltd	418	John Brown & Co Ltd	85,000	3 Apr 1912	20 Jun 1912	15 Dec 1913	3 Oct 1914 m
Repulse	26,500 nl	John Brown & Co Ltd	443	John Brown & Co Ltd	112,000	29 Dec 1914	25 Jan 1915	8 Jan 1916	14 Aug 1916 l
Renown	26,500 nl	Fairfield Shipbuilding & Engrg Co Ltd	503	Fairfield Shipbuilding & Engrg Co Ltd	112,000	29 Dec 1914	25 Jan 1915	4 Mar 1916	18 Sep 1916 l
Courageous	18,600 nl	Sir W G Armstrong, Whitworth & Co Ltd	895	Parsons Marine Steam Turbine Co Ltd	90,000	Mar 1915	28 Mar 1915	5 Feb 1916	28 Nov 1916 c
Glorious	18,600 nl	Harland & Wolff Ltd	482	Harland & Wolff Ltd	90,000	19 Apr 1915	1 May 1915	20 Apr 1916	30 Dec 1916 c
Furious	19,100 nl	Sir W G Armstrong, Whitworth & Co Ltd	896	Wallsend Slipway & Engrg Co Ltd and John Brown & Co Ltd	90,000	Mar 1915	8 Jun 1915	15 Aug 1916	17 Jul 1917 c
Hood	41,200 nl	John Brown & Co Ltd	460	John Brown & Co Ltd	144,000	19 Apr 1916	1 Sep 1916	22 Aug 1918	5 Mar 1920 c
Total 17 Ships	393,281				1,261,000 shp				
Battleships									
Dreadnought	17,900 nl	H M Dockyard Portsmouth		Vickers (No.332) and Parsons (No.38)	23,000	8 Jul 1905	2 Oct 1905	10 Feb 1906	11 Dec 1906 m
Bellerophon	18,600 nl	H M Dockyard Portsmouth		Fairfield Shipbuilding & Engrg Co Ltd	23,000	7 Sep 1906	3 Dec 1906	27 Jul 1907	20 Feb 1909 m
Temeraire	18,600 nl	H M Dockyard Devonport		R&W Hawthorn, Leslie & Co Ltd	23,000	7 Sep 1906	1 Jan 1907	24 Aug 1907	15 May 1909 m
Superb	18,600 nl	Sir W G Armstrong, Whitworth & Co Ltd	800	Wallsend Slipway & Engrg Co Ltd	23,000	26 Dec 1906	4 Feb 1907	7 Nov 1907	24 May 1909 d

Name of vessel	Displacement	Shipbuilder	Yard No	Machinery Builder	IHP	Ordered	Keel Laid	Launched	Completed	
Minas Geraes [Br]	19,281 nl	Sir W G Armstrong, Whitworth & Co Ltd	791	Vickers, Sons & Maxim Ltd (No.348)	23,500	20 Feb 1907	17 Apr 1907	10 Sep 1908	5 Jan 1910	d
Vanguard	19,250 nl	Vickers, Sons & Maxim Ltd	374	Vickers, Sons & Maxim Ltd	24,500	6 Feb 1908	2 Apr 1908	22 Feb 1909	13 Feb 1910	d
Collingwood	19,250 nl	H M Dockyard Devonport		R&W Hawthorn, Leslie & Co Ltd	24,500	26 Oct 1907	3 Feb 1908	7 Nov 1908	19 Apr 1910	c
St Vincent	19,250 nl	H M Dockyard Portsmouth		Scotts and Parsons	24,500	26 Oct 1907	30 Dec 1907	10 Sep 1908	3 May 1910	m
Sao Paulo [Br]	19,105 nl	Vickers, Sons & Maxim Ltd	347	Vickers, Sons & Maxim Ltd	23,500	20 Feb 1907	24 Sep 1907	19 Apr 1909	22 Aug 1910	c
Neptune	19,900 nl	H M Dockyard Portsmouth		Harland & Wolff and John Brown	25,000	14 Nov 1908	19 Jan 1909	30 Sep 1909	11 Jan 1911	m
Hercules	20,000 nl	Palmers Shipbuilding & Iron Co Ltd	805	Palmers Shipbuilding & Iron Co Ltd	25,000	1 Jun 1909	30 Jul 1909	10 May 1910	4 Jul 1911	m
Colossus	20,000 nl	Scotts' Shipbuilding & Engrg Co Ltd	430	Scotts' Shipbuilding & Engrg Co Ltd	25,000	1 Jun 1909	19 Jul 1909	9 Apr 1910	27 Jul 1911	m
Orion	22,500 nl	H M Dockyard Portsmouth		Wallsend Slipway & Engrg Co Ltd	27,000	Oct 1909	29 Nov 1909	20 Aug 1910	29 Dec 1911	c
Monarch	22,500 nl	Sir W G Armstrong, Whitworth & Co Ltd	828	R&W Hawthorn, Leslie & Co Ltd	27,000	4 Jan 1910	1 Apr 1910	30 Mar 1911	28 Mar 1912	c
Thunderer	22,500 nl	Thames Iron Works Shipbldg & Eng Co Ltd	L60	Thames Iron Works and Parsons	27,000	4 Jan 1910	13 Apr 1910	1 Feb 1911	12 Jun 1912	c
King George V	23,000 nl	H M Dockyard Portsmouth		Parsons Marine Steam Turbine Co Ltd	31,000	End 1910	16 Jan 1911	9 Oct 1911	16 Nov 1912	m
Conqueror	22,500 nl	Wm Beardmore & Co Ltd	500	Wm Beardmore & Co Ltd	27,000	4 Jan 1910	5 Apr 1910	1 May 1911	17 Nov 1912	c
Centurion	23,000 nl	H M Dockyard Devonport		R&W Hawthorn, Leslie & Co Ltd	31,000	End 1910	16 Jan 1911	18 Nov 1911	14 Jun 1913	c
Ajax	23,000 nl	Scotts' Shipbuilding & Engrg Co Ltd	438	Scotts' Shipbuilding & Engrg Co Ltd	31,000	16 Dec 1910	27 Feb 1911	21 Mar 1912	15 Oct 1913	c
Audacious	23,000 nl	Cammell, Laird & Co Ltd	775	Cammell, Laird & Co Ltd	31,000	13 Jan 1911	23 Mar 1911	14 Sep 1912	22 Oct 1913	d
Iron Duke	25,000 nl	H M Dockyard Portsmouth		Cammell, Laird & Co Ltd	29,000	End 1911	15 Jan 1912	12 Oct 1912	9 Mar 1914	c
Marlborough	25,000 nl	H M Dockyard Devonport		R&W Hawthorn, Leslie & Co Ltd	29,000	End 1911	25 Jan 1912	24 Nov 1912	16 Jun 1914	c
Agincourt	27,500 nl	Sir W G Armstrong, Whitworth & Co Ltd	792	Vickers Ltd (No.427)	34,000	3 Jun 1911	14 Sep 1911	22 Jan 1913	7 Aug 1914	m
Erin	23,000 nl	Vickers Ltd	425	Vickers Ltd	26,500	27 Jul 1911	6 Dec 1911	3 Sep 1913	22 Aug 1914	l
Benbow	25,000 nl	Wm Beardmore & Co Ltd	510	Wm Beardmore & Co Ltd	29,000	Early 1912	30 May 1912	12 Nov 1913	7 Oct 1914	m
Emperor of India	25,000 nl	Vickers Ltd	429	Vickers Ltd	29,000	29 Dec 1911	31 May 1912	27 Nov 1913	16 Nov 1914	d
Queen Elizabeth	27,500 nl	H M Dockyard Portsmouth		Wallsend Slipway & Engrg Co Ltd	75,000	3rd qtr 1912	21 Oct 1912	16 Oct 1913	25 Jan 1915	c
Warspite	27,500 nl	H M Dockyard Devonport		R&W Hawthorn, Leslie & Co Ltd	75,000	3rd qtr 1912	31 Oct 1912	26 Nov 1913	5 Apr 1915	m
Barham	27,500 nl	John Brown & Co Ltd	424	John Brown & Co Ltd	75,000	5 Dec 1912	24 Feb 1913	31 Dec 1914	19 Aug 1915	m
Canada	28,000 nl	Sir W G Armstrong, Whitworth & Co Ltd	845	John Brown & Co Ltd (No.416)	50,000	2 Nov 1911	1 May 1912	27 Nov 1913	13 Sep 1915	t
Valiant	27,500 nl	Fairfield Shipbuilding & Engrg Co Ltd	497	Fairfield Shipbuilding & Engrg Co Ltd	75,000	Dec 1912	31 Jan 1913	4 Nov 1914	13 Jan 1916	m
Malaya	27,500 nl	Sir W G Armstrong, Whitworth & Co Ltd	867	Wallsend Slipway & Engrg Co Ltd	75,000	Mar 1913	20 Oct 1913	18 Mar 1915	2 Feb 1916	c
Revenge	25,750 nl	Vickers Ltd	455	Vickers Ltd	40,000	15 Aug 1913	22 Dec 1913	29 May 1915	22 Mar 1916	c
Royal Sovereign	25,750 nl	H M Dockyard Portsmouth		Parsons Marine Steam Turbine Co Ltd	40,000	3rd qtr 1913	15 Jan 1914	29 Apr 1915	17 Apr 1916	c
Royal Oak	25,750 nl	H M Dockyard Devonport		R&W Hawthorn, Leslie & Co Ltd	40,000	3rd qtr 1913	15 Jan 1914	17 Nov 1914	9 May 1916	d
Resolution	25,750 nl	Palmers Shipbuilding &	838	Palmers Shipbuilding & Iron Co Ltd	40,000	15 Aug 1913	29 Nov 1913	14 Jan 1915	5 Dec 1916	c
Ramillies	25,750 nl	Wm Beardmore & Co Ltd Iron Co Ltd	516	Wm Beardmore & Co Ltd	40,000	15 Aug 1913	12 Nov 1913	12 Sep 1916	29 Sep 1917	c
Nelson	33,950 sd	Sir W G Armstrong, Whitworth & Co Ltd	991	Wallsend Slipway & Engrg Co Ltd	45,000	11 Dec 1922	28 Dec 1922	3 Sep 1925	15 Aug 1927	m
Rodney	33,900 sd	Cammell, Laird & Co Ltd	904	Cammell, Laird & Co Ltd	45,000	11 Dec 1922	28 Dec 1922	17 Dec 1925	11 Nov 1927	d
King George V	35,000 sd	Vickers-Armstrongs Ltd	10	Vickers-Armstrongs Ltd (No.727)	110,000	29 Jul 1936	1 Jan 1937	21 Feb 1939	11 Dec 1940	d
Prince of Wales	35,000 sd	Cammell, Laird & Co Ltd	1026	Cammell, Laird & Co Ltd	110,000	29 Jul 1936	1 Jan 1937	3 May 1939	31 Mar 1941	d
Duke of York	35,000 sd	John Brown & Co Ltd	554	John Brown & Co Ltd	110,000	28 Apr 1937	5 May 1937	28 Feb 1940	4 Nov 1941	d
Anson	35,000 sd	Swan, Hunter & Wigham Richardson Ltd	1553	Wallsend Slipway & Engrg Co Ltd	110,000	28 Apr 1937	20 Jul 20 1937	24 Feb 1940	22 Jun 1942	d
Howe	35,000 sd	Fairfield Shipbuilding & Engrg Co Ltd	669	Fairfield Shipbuilding & Engrg Co Ltd	110,000	28 Apr 1937	1 Jun 1937	9 Apr 1940	29 Aug 1942	d
Vanguard	44,500 sd	John Brown & Co Ltd	567	John Brown & Co Ltd	130,000	14 Mar 1941	2 Oct 1941	30 Nov 1944	9 Aug 1946	d

Total 45 ships 1,143,836   2,091,000

Total 111 ships 2,272,050 Equivalent Navy List   3,942,480 Equivalent shp

6: FACILITIES

SHIPBUILDING SITES

The requirements for a shipbuilding site have remained essentially unchanged for centuries. A plot of open ground with firm foundations next to water on which a hull could be safely supported, launched and then fitted out, good access to the necessary construction materials and supplies of equipment, the necessary tools for building the hulls and, most importantly, a supply of skilled labour and local housing. In the days of small wooden sailing ships, a shipwright could lease a plot of land on a river bank, either close to a supply of timber or a friendly timber merchant who would advance

credit. The tools employed were hand tools, saws and adzes (an axe-like tool for shaping timbers). When the shipwright got an order for a vessel, he would hire a few men, while the design was largely in his head, based on experience. Once the ship was completed and paid for, he could continue or close down as the market dictated, as he had little capital invested.

But when iron and steam construction developed rapidly in the mid-nineteenth century, design became more technically based, while a more permanent site was needed, machine tools had to be purchased and workshops erected. A substantial machine tool making

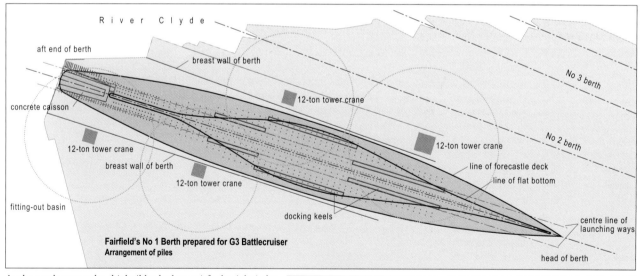

Fairfield's No 1 Berth prepared for G3 Battlecruiser
Arrangement of piles

At the tender stage the shipbuilder had to satisfy the Admiralty that the ship would be built on a suitable berth. This drawing shows the area that a 862 x 106.5ft G3 battlecruiser hull would occupy on No 1 berth at the Fairfield shipyard. This berth has been prepared for vessels up to 900 feet long by driving hundreds of timber piles into the ground shown here as small circles or squares. Note the concentration near the water's edge where launching forces were greatest. Fairfield's tender for this ship was accepted in October 1921 but the ship was cancelled before it could be laid down.

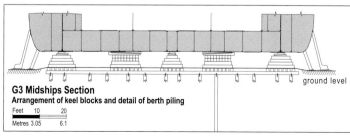

G3 Midships Section
Arrangement of keel blocks and detail of berth piling

industry grew up in the Glasgow area, with companies such as Hugh Smith of Possil making plate rolls, and Craig & Donald of Johnstone and James Bennie & Sons of Glasgow making punch and shears (typical price £200–£300).[1] Building berths (slipways) might need strengthening for heavier hulls, with more substantial lifting appliances. With materials such as iron plates coming from a greater distance, rail access was desirable, as well as an internal network of rail lines, sometimes of narrow gauge. Simple vessels could be engined and fitted out in a few weeks after launch at a nearby wharf, either at the engine works itself, a port authority berth or the shipyard's own quay. But larger vessels such as warships and passenger ships needed more extensive facilities, the fitting-out process lasting for a period of months or even a year or more, with workshops needed for trades such as joiners, plumbers and fitters. All of this required substantial investment capital, from the partners, their families and friends and shareholders and from local banks. A new limited company might be formed, like Thames Iron Works & Ship Building Co Ltd in 1857 with capital of £100,000, but even these usually remained family controlled.

Some longer-established shipbuilders such as Scotts of Greenock or the Royal Dockyards made a successful transition from wood and sail to iron and steam. They expanded their premises to handle larger ships, either by taking over adjacent sites, or in the case of some of the Dockyards, reclaiming land. New shipbuilders entered the burgeoning industry from the 1850s, building only iron ships, like Palmers at Jarrow on the Tyne, who also had their own iron works. Despite their name, Thames Iron Works did build occasional wooden vessels, but soon had to expand from the constricted Blackwall site west of the River Lea to a bigger site on the opposite side of Bow Creek. Like most of the bigger Thames firms, warships (and their machinery), both for the Admiralty and export, formed the major proportion of their business – around two-thirds when warship displacement tonnage is weighted to give the equivalent gross tonnage used for merchant ships.[2] In contrast, in the northern shipyards, like Laird Brothers at Birkenhead, such vessels were a useful supplement to their main merchant shipbuilding business. With ships becoming ever bigger, some shipyards outgrew their original sites, while port authorities sometimes wanted their land for dock construction.

In 1872 J & G Thomson moved from Govan on the south bank of the Clyde to a new green-field site five miles downstream on the north bank, naming the resulting new town Clydebank. The new shipyard was spacious by the standards of the day, covering 32 acres. Ten years later an engine works was added and the site eventually occupied 80 acres, continuing as such until the 1970s – see plan p.67. At Barrow, a new iron shipbuilding yard was set up in 1871 with the help of Clyde shipbuilder Robert Duncan, which later specialised in warship construction as Vickers, Sons & Maxim Ltd – see plan p.63.

At much the same time, William Armstrong had become a successful ordnance manufacturer at Elswick on the banks of the River Tyne just west of Newcastle, but had to get the hulls of any warships, usually for export, built by Charles Mitchell downstream at Low Walker. After the two companies merged in 1882, a

Above: Until the Tranmere Bay development scheme was completed, Laird Brothers built all their battleships in drydock. *Mars* was laid down in No 5 graving dock on 2 June 1894. Only fourteen days later her double bottom is well advanced showing the keel plate and centre girder in the foreground, transverse vertical plate floors, plate longitudinals running fore and aft, with more components being lowered by the wooden pole derricks. *(Navy & Army Illustrated)*

Right: Cammell Laird's Tranmere Bay fitting-out basin at Birkenhead in September 1940, with *Prince of Wales* on the south side. The coaster *Sea Fisher* is alongside having brought her twin 14in B mounting from Barrow, about to be lifted by the 200-ton floating crane. To the right are the cruisers *Dido* (outboard) nearly complete and *Charybdis*. Both ships display the problem of shortage of gun mounting manufacturing capacity: *Dido* has a puny 4in in place of her Q 5.25in twin, while *Charybdis* is having her superstructure rebuilt to take four twin 4.5in mountings instead of the designed five twin 5.25in. To the left, the cargo ship *Springbank* is being converted to an anti-aircraft vessel. (*Author's collection*)

new warship building yard was laid out at the eastern end of the Elswick site, leaving Low Walker to concentrate on merchant ships.

But as battleship (and passenger ship) sizes continued to grow, it became increasingly difficult to build ships of over 400ft length. On the landward side, many shipyards were hemmed in by railways, roads, buildings and higher ground. Even by angling the berths at about 30–40° to the river line, there could be problems making a long enough slipway, and getting a long enough clear run for launching. By the turn of the century, much new investment was clearly going to be needed if major warship builders wished to continue battleship construction. Laird had laid out an extensive shipyard for its time in the mid-1850s opposite Liverpool at Birkenhead, where land was cheaper, which included five graving docks. But they had to use their two larger graving docks to build battleships such as *Mars*, *Glory* and *Exmouth*, which was not an economic use of an asset which could produce better returns repairing ships. In 1902 they decided to expand south-wards by reclaiming mudflats. John Jones & Sons had a small shipyard there, so the two formed the Tranmere Bay Development

Co Ltd. A substantial new shipyard was laid out with six berths up to 800ft long, with associated workshops, a new 14-acre enclosed fitting out basin, a new engine works and two large graving docks – see plan p.71. This stretched Laird's resources, but a merger with Charles Cammell of Sheffield in 1903 provided additional capital. The £959,000 facility was opened in 1906, trading as Tranmere Bay Development Co Ltd (with its own series of yard numbers), with the old shipyard and graving docks trading as Cammell, Laird & Co Ltd.[3] It was not until 1909, by which time Jones' share had been bought out, that both shipyards were integrated and the Tranmere Bay name dropped. That 108-acre layout remained essentially unchanged for the next half century, suitable for both warships and merchant ships.

When steelmaker William Beardmore took over the small Robert Napier yard at Govan in 1900, it was as a temporary measure only until he could lay out a much larger facility to enable him to compete for battleship orders. The brand new Naval Construction Works was laid out on a green-field site at Dalmuir west of Clydebank. The 5382ft long waterfront site initially accommodated six, later ten, berths (one spanned by a gantry – see photograph), a large fitting-out basin covering 7.5 acres, extensive workshops, and a massive new engine works. Up until 1906 when the yard was opened with the launch of *Agamemnon*, his first battleship order and the penultimate pre-dreadnought, Beardmore had invested in excess of £1 million in the new works.

THE ARMSTRONG NAVAL YARD[4]

The next new battleship shipyard to be developed was Armstrong Whitworth's at High Walker, just upstream of their Low Walker yard. This was built on what is now called a brown-field site, but was more accurately described as 'grey-field', having been previously an iron works, gas works and chemical works. Its official name was Armstrong Yard but it was usually called 'Naval Yard' right up until closure in 1985. Ships needed to get downstream from Elswick past two major bridges, both still in use today. Robert Stephenson's High Level Bridge with its cast iron girders opened in 1849 had rail on top and road beneath, with a vertical clearance above the river at high tide of only 82ft. Armstrong's themselves had built the Swing Bridge just downstream in 1876, whose roadway could swing 90° to open up a

Left: The shipbuilding gantry at Dalmuir with *Ramillies* beneath on the day of her launch, 12 September 1916. When it became clear that construction of the battleship would be held back because of delays in supplying her main armament, the decision was taken to fit her with anti-torpedo bulges, thus becoming the first battleship to be so fitted. This required the fitting of some side armour and this together with the desire to do as much work as she lay on the building berth resulted in a launch weight of 18,750 tons compared to a weight of between 9000 and 12,000 tons for other four ships of the class. Minutes after this photograph was taken, the ship was launched into the Clyde hitting the river bed in the process. Both stern and rudder was damaged, although this did not prevent completion of the ship at Dalmuir. With a twisted rudder however, it made for a very difficult passage from the Clyde to Liverpool and the large Gladstone drydock to repair the damage. (*Author's collection*)

waterway on either side. The maximum breadth of battleships that could squeeze through was only 83ft, while masts and upperworks had to be removed or folded down; draught too was limited.

George Carter, a senior manager at Elswick shipyard, submitted a report on building a new shipyard to chairman Andrew Noble on 7 December 1908, outlining the problems. Apart from the restricting bridges, the building berths at Elswick were too short and the outfitting quay inadequate, especially as the Admiralty would not allow a foreign warship building to lie alongside an RN ship, the normal method at the congested shipyard, so a much longer outfitting wharf was needed with a minimum depth of water of 30ft. As battleships nearing completion drew almost this much, Armstrong ships had to lie at buoys down river for completion, adding unnecessary expense. The Admiralty had introduced a requirement that ships be drydocked no more than six months after launch. For smaller ships, it was possible to install machinery in that time and the ship to proceed to a dock under its own power, but a battleship would need to be towed, another risk on the Tyne with its bridges and bends. Among Carter's proposals was taking over and merging the Stephenson and Hawthorn Leslie shipyards at Hebburn – Armstrong already had a shareholding in Stephenson and was on good terms with

Hawthorn Leslie. This would provide a large land area, but the large graving dock at the former needed an adjacent repair quay which would restrict any fitting-out berths. Furthermore there was a smaller labour pool on the south side of the river and poorer rail access than the north. However, by closing the Elswick shipyard, a further advantage was that valuable space would be freed to extend the steel works and ordnance workshops.

A temporary solution to the fitting out of nearly completed ships was achieved in 1909 by acquiring a stretch of riverside frontage at High Walker on a bend in the river just above the Low Walker shipyard. A 7-ton steam crane was installed but no outfitting workshops at what was called the Naval Equipment Yard. This plan had been submitted to the Armstrong Board by Carter, Perrett and d'Eyncourt. None was a member of the Board, despite their long experience – Josiah Perrett had succeeded Philip Watts as general manager at Elswick when the latter was appointed Director of Naval Construction in 1902, naval architect Tennyson d'Eyncourt went on to succeed Watts as DNC in 1912,[5] while Carter was appointed managing director at Cammell Laird also in 1912. Armstrong could ill afford to lose such talented staff, but by declining to appoint them to the main Board (Watts had been on the Board but had been appointed by Armstrong not Noble), they were ripe for being head-hunted.

Right: The new Japanese battleship *Kashima* passes through the swing bridge at Newcastle on her way downriver from Elswick in April 1906, mast lowered to clear the High Level Bridge. This is one of a series of construction photographs from a publicity album prepared by her builders Armstrong Whitworth for actual and potential customers *(Newcastle University Marine Technology Special Collection)*

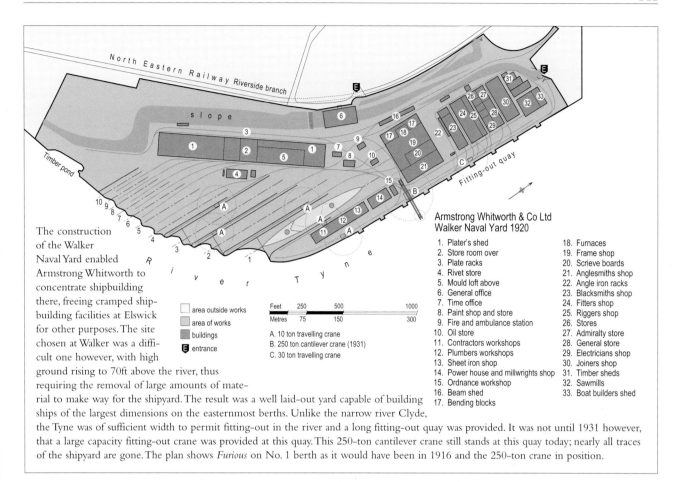

The construction of the Walker Naval Yard enabled Armstrong Whitworth to concentrate shipbuilding there, freeing cramped ship-building facilities at Elswick for other purposes. The site chosen at Walker was a diffi-cult one however, with high ground rising to 70ft above the river, thus requiring the removal of large amounts of mate-rial to make way for the shipyard. The result was a well laid-out yard capable of building ships of the largest dimensions on the easternmost berths. Unlike the narrow river Clyde, the Tyne was of sufficient width to permit fitting-out in the river and a long fitting-out quay was provided. It was not until 1931 however, that a large capacity fitting-out crane was provided at this quay. This 250-ton cantilever crane still stands at this quay today; nearly all traces of the shipyard are gone. The plan shows *Furious* on No. 1 berth as it would have been in 1916 and the 250-ton crane in position.

Armstrong Whitworth & Co Ltd
Walker Naval Yard 1920

1. Plater's shed
2. Store room over
3. Plate racks
4. Rivet store
5. Mould loft above
6. General office
7. Time office
8. Paint shop and store
9. Fire and ambulance station
10. Oil store
11. Contractors workshops
12. Plumbers workshops
13. Sheet iron shop
14. Power house and millwrights shop
15. Ordnance workshop
16. Beam shed
17. Bending blocks

18. Furnaces
19. Frame shop
20. Scrieve boards
21. Anglesmiths shop
22. Angle iron racks
23. Blacksmiths shop
24. Fitters shop
25. Riggers shop
26. Stores
27. Admiralty store
28. General store
29. Electricians shop
30. Joiners shop
31. Timber sheds
32. Sawmills
33. Boat builders shed

area outside works
area of works
buildings
E entrance

Feet 250 500 1000
Metres 75 150 300

A. 10 ton travelling crane
B. 250 ton cantilever crane (1931)
C. 30 ton travelling crane

By this time, the Armstrong Board had become geriatric under the autocratic and conservative Noble, aged 80 in 1911. The elderly directors either died in office (E J Leveson-Gower in 1907, H F Swan in 1908, who had been responsible for the Low Walker shipyard since the merger with Mitchell, J Vavasseur in 1908, Admiral Albini in 1909 and H J Alderson in 1909) or resigned from ill health to die shortly afterwards (P G B Westmacott and W D Cruddas). Instead of appointing an experienced senior manager to the main Board, Noble appointed his son John (his older son Saxton was already on the Board).[6] By contrast, Vickers appointed talented people such as Trevor Dawson, their ordnance expert, when aged only 32, and James McKechnie their engineering manager – see Personalities on p.106. The company was generally more adventurous than Armstrong, e.g. in taking up the highly profitable building of submarines. From being a relative newcomer to the armaments business in the 1890s, by the First World War they rivalled Armstrong in size, and were the senior partner after the merger in 1927 to form Vickers-Armstrongs.

Various plans for a new shipyard were put forward, including taking over the Dobson yard immediately upstream of Low Walker and making a single yard but this too would be limited in size. Although the land to the south of Dobson was generally at a much higher level, due to its topography and slagheaps, all this could be excavated. Initially the Board demurred at the cost, but the only alternative was to build a brand new shipyard elsewhere in the country, which was not viewed favourably. If the company was to retain its position as the principal British warship builder, it would have create a new shipyard despite the civil engi-neering problems and having to acquire land and buy out leases from the present occupiers of the site. Their consultants, Cackett and Burns Dick produced many differing layouts, with building berths up to 1000ft long, but without a marine engineering works, for which there was not enough space.

In July 1910 the Board finally decided to go ahead, starting with purchase of the land and seeking tenders for excavating the site. The excavation contract was let to Edmund Nuttall of Manchester in January 1911 at 1s 4d

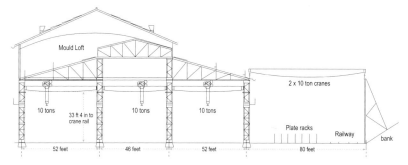

Mould Loft

2 x 10 ton cranes

10 tons   33 ft 4 in to crane rail   10 tons   10 tons

Plate racks   Railway   bank

52 feet   46 feet   52 feet   80 feet

Above: A section through the plater's shed at the Walker Naval Yard which opened in 1914. This building, over 1100ft long, housed the principal steel-working machines used in cutting, punching and forming steel plates, frames and beams. The plate stockyard was served by a gantry crane. Riveted sub-assemblies up to ten tons could be worked and then taken to the berth for erection by 10-ton capacity berth tower cranes. To save space the mould loft was placed above the south-easternmost bays of the shed.

Right: The fitting-out quay at Armstrong Whitworth's Naval Yard was long enough to take three battleships. Alongside on 6 July 1916 are (nearest camera) *Lion* with Q turret removed to Elswick for repair after Jutland, *Courageous* and in the distance the cruisers *Centaur* and *Concord*. At that time the heaviest fitting out crane was a 30-tonner whose jib can be seen over *Courageous'* bow, so a floating crane was used to lift heavy machinery and gun mounting components until a 250-ton cantilever crane was erected in 1931. *(Vickers Ltd)*

(£0.066) per cubic yard, the spoil to be loaded on to hopper barges and dumped at sea. Eventually 4.1 million cubic yards (about 8 million tons) of slag, gravel and clay was removed at a cost of about £270,000. The superficial area was 83 acres, but with the slopes between the upper and lower levels, the flat area of the shipyard was only 50 acres. A wide range of shops from plating to fitting was erected from early 1912, with most of the structural steelwork being provided by A & J Main of Glasgow.[7] An imposing office block costing £60,000, likened to the Egyptian temple at Karnak, was built on the slope, two stories high on the land side, but six on the river side. This allowed the managers a clear view from their high-level offices across the whole shipyard, something not possible on the cramped Elswick site. The total river frontage was 4376ft, half of which was the fitting out quay capable of berthing three battleships, with a minimum depth alongside of 32ft. There were ten building berths, the two largest capable of building ships up to 1000 x 120ft

and 900 x 110ft – see plan p.141. Between the four largest berths, three ferro-concrete piers were built, each supporting one 10-ton travelling tower crane by Arrol of Glasgow, with another on the east side of Berth No.1. On the ferro-concrete fitting-out quay, still in use today, was another 10-ton travelling crane and a 30-ton travelling crane – heavier lifts could be handled by hiring the 140-ton *Titan* floating crane. The six smaller berths were covered by 3-ton derricks. Extensive steel-working shops at the head of the slipways and outfitting workshops alongside the fitting out quay were served by ten miles of internal railways, linked to the North Eastern Railway line 70ft above by a series of inclines.[8]

By the outbreak of the First World War, the Armstrong Naval Yard was virtually complete, with some equipment transferred from Elswick, having cost £1 million, as much as the entire Elswick works excluding land was valued at in the Armstrong books. The first keel was laid on Berth No 3 on 20 October 1913 (the battleship *Malaya*) in the presence of the First Lord of the Admiralty, Winston Churchill. The yard was completed just in time to meet wartime demands, a timely investment indeed. In the meantime, by re-aligning the three main berths at Elswick into two 'armour clad' berths in 1910, vessels up to 700ft long such as *Rio de Janeiro* could be squeezed in. The westernmost berths for smaller vessels at Elswick were also rebuilt, although they had been built over for workshops by 1919. The Tyne Improvement Commission widened the Swing Bridge water-

ways to allow battleships of 92ft beam to pass; *Monarch* at 88.5ft went downstream on 6 November 1911. The intention was to build all future warships at Naval Yard, but in the press of wartime demand, Elswick continued working on warships up to 1918, including submarines.

EXPANSION OF SHIPYARDS FOR BIGGER BATTLESHIPS

Meantime other battleship yards extended their facilities as best they could, given their geography. Portsmouth had been handicapped in the 1890s, building three of the *Majestic* class, although only 421ft x 75ft. No 13 drydock had to be used for the name ship and No 12 for *Caesar. Prince George* was squeezed onto the covered slip from which the cruiser *Eclipse* had recently been launched, with only inches to spare between the hull and the supporting columns, the berth having to be excavated to give enough vertical clearance under the roof, and a building demolished at the head of the slip, while the stern overhung the water.[9] Portsmouth had to extend its largest No. 5 Slip at least twice after 1900, by 50ft then 100ft by demolishing workshops, to accommodate ever

larger ships such as *Orion* and *Queen Elizabeth*. Devonport also had to extend its No.3 Slip to 700ft for *Lion* in 1909. The smaller slipways at both yards tended to be used thereafter mainly for minor vessels such as Dockyard craft, some still covered over from wooden hull days. At Chatham the building berths could take hulls up to about 400ft long and 75ft wide, but as they were covered, it would be costly to extend them. It had four graving docks about 430ft x 82ft, but apart from limiting the size of ships, it was better to reserve any large docks for refit and repair work, rather than tie them up for a year building a hull. While a new longer No 8 Slip had recently been laid out in the open north of the covered berths on which Chatham's last battleship was built, the decision was taken that Chatham would stop building battleships and start building submarines, well suited to their covered berths (which stand to this day), so providing an alternative builder to the previous monopoly supplier Vickers. Two 'C' class boats were ordered in 1906 as *Africa* was completing, and thereafter Chatham was rarely without a submarine to construct until newbuilding ceased in 1968. Pembroke

Below: *Orion* is seen here on No 5 Slip at Portsmouth not far off launching which was on 20 August 1911. This view illustrates the system of light pole derricks used to build all of the dreadnoughts at both Portsmouth and Devonport, capable of loads up to about 3 tons. The derricks are fixed to the ground and to one another with wire guy ropes. Note the booms at the bottom of the berth used to keep timber and other building debris from entering the harbour. Note the extensive use of timber staging. *(National Maritime Museum)*

Below: *Glorious* was the only capital ship built by Harland & Wolff, given three Yard Numbers 482–4 to disguise her size. She is seen on 7 March 1916 under the Arrol shipbuilding gantry under which both *Olympic* and *Titanic* were built.
(National Museums of Northern Ireland)

Dockyard had built battleships up to 1896 when it launched *Hannibal*. It had built in wood up to the 1870s but functioned mainly as a hull building yard with fitting out undertaken at Devonport or Portsmouth. It was not considered worth developing to build larger complete battleships, so concentrated on cruisers and smaller vessels until its closure in 1926.

Portsmouth and Devonport Dockyards also greatly extended their repair facilities to cope with the increasing fleet of battleships, intended for refits and modernisations rather than for newbuilding. The Keyham extension at Devonport was opened in 1907 with large deepwater basins with an entrance lock (which could double as a drydock), together with new graving docks capable of taking the largest modern battleships. At Portsmouth the northern basins, entrance locks and drydocks were extended after *Dreadnought* was built. No 14 and No 15 drydocks were lengthened and widened to take larger battleships, while the two new entrance locks to Basin No 3 could double as drydocks, with C Lock completed in April 1913 and docking *Princess Royal* – all are still in use today. In 1903, a new Dockyard was approved to be built at Rosyth just above the Forth Bridge, but it was never intended for newbuilding. When completed in 1916, its three large graving docks proved invaluable for docking the Grand Fleet's battleships based at Scapa Flow. Today one of those docks is being used to assemble the aircraft carriers *Queen Elizabeth* and *Prince of Wales*.

On the Tyne, Palmers berths were limited to about 700ft. Two gantry cableways had been erected which spanned its two main berths, allowing material up to about 3 tons to be easily placed anywhere on the hull. Swan Hunter's new floating crane *Titan* lifted the river end gantry frames into place.[10] The first ship built under the first 100ft wide gantry was *Lord Nelson* launched in 1906; the second gantry was 700ft long and 150ft wide so could take two cargo ships abreast. When the design of the 1914 620ft (bp) battleship *Repulse* was changed to a 750ft battlecruiser after the outbreak of war, the order had to be diverted to John Brown – see p.22. Palmers received orders for three monitors plus six destroyers in compensation, and thereafter built no warship larger than a cruiser.

Scotts' at Greenock were similarly handicapped in the length of ships they could build, so after 1914, warship orders comprised cruisers and below, plus the increasingly important submarine, although somewhat optimistically they tendered for *Nelson* – rejected with the highest price of the nine bidders (see p.293).

Harland & Wolff had the capability to build battleships but rarely tendered for them. In 1913 the Admiralty Director of Contracts stated: 'We have always asked H&W to tender for the battleships and Workman Clark [also in Belfast] for smaller vessels. H&W are very seldom able to tender. I have looked back over 3 or 4 years. I presume they are so full of White Star and other work that they probably do not care to tender for battleships.'[11]

MARINE ENGINEERING WORKS

Building machinery for ships in the first half of the nineteenth century evolved from building machinery for land based applications: steam locomotives, pumping engines, factory machinery and general engineering. Locating such engineering works at inland sites was no great handicap – Boulton & Watt had their works at Birmingham, shipping components for marine engines by canal barge for erection where the hulls were built. For companies such as Maudslay, Son & Field in London, the switch to building mainly marine engines was gradual. But with the expansion of steamships from 1850, building marine engines became a more specialised business. Waterfront locations super-seded inland works. With the introduction of higher steam pressures, the cylindrical Scotch boiler and the compound engine (where steam expanded from a high to a low pressure cylinder) new engine works were set up, especially on the Clyde and Tyne. Major ship-builders, such as Laird and Palmers, established engine works close to their shipyards. Engine builders also set up their own shipyards, such as Napier, Thomson and Elder on the Clyde, so they could bid for both hulls and machinery, important in winning warship and passenger ship orders. But later in the century companies that started as engine builders, such as Wallsend Slipway & Engineering or Parsons, never made the transition to building hulls.

What all of the engine builders had in common was a continuing expansion of their facilities – the workshops of Wallsend Slipway in 1871 only covered one-third the area of those in 1914 (see plan p.159). While most of the major engine builders sought to get on the Admiralty list, other large firms were content with merchant ship orders; examples of this would be North Eastern Marine on the Tyne and the Wear, and Rowan and Kincaid on the Clyde. The Admiralty tended to look to their preferred contractors for technical advances, as there was a continual cross-fertilisation between merchant ship and warship machinery building.

Most of the larger engine works had rail access as well as an internal network serving their various workshops. Although smaller engine works might buy in castings, the main companies all had their own iron foundries for casting engine items such as bedplates, columns and cylinders. Steel casting and forging was a more specialised business, however, so they tended to buy in such components as shafting and turbine casings – see p.113. Some also cast their own propellers but only in iron – manganese bronze propellers as fitted to high-powered ships from about the 1890s were bought in from specialist manufacturers – see p.166. Rough components went to the machine shops to be machined to finished dimensions before going to the fitting and erecting shops to be assembled. Testing could not be done at full power, largely because there was insufficient boiler capacity, although later on, diesels could be tested at full power connected to a dynamometer to measure output. Most of the larger engine works made their own boilers, either the basic Scotch boiler or later the smaller watertube boilers, the latter usually designs built under licence from the likes of Babcock & Wilcox and Yarrow. A few companies such as Parsons did not build boilers but bought them from companies like Wallsend Slipway, who also did a good business in supplying replacement boilers. In the boiler shops, the heavy steel plates up to 2in thick were formed and riveted together, and fitted with the necessary tubes and furnaces. The complete boiler was water tested to a pressure typically double the working pressure, and then moved complete to the dockside for installation in the ship. Other shops produced engine room pipework and valves, and made fittings such as uptakes and funnels, ladders and gratings. Most auxiliary machinery such as pumps were bought in complete but installed by the engine

Below: A section through the engine and boiler works at Beardmore's Dalmuir shipyard completed in 1906. This building, constructed by Sir Wm. Arrol & Co, housed a multitude of machinery ranging from the smallest drills to the largest machine tools such as crankshaft lathes. These works were manufacturing steam reciprocating and turbine machinery and boilers of the Scotch, Yarrow and Babcock & Wilcox type. The shops were 720ft long.

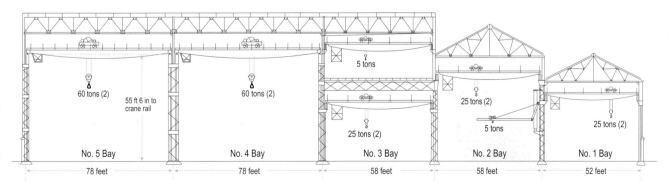

works' own fitters. The heaviest components were found in the boiler and erecting shops, so they had the most powerful overhead travelling cranes, typically 2 x 30 tons in earlier days, later 2 x 60 or 100 tons, especially when steam turbines were being built.

Machine tools like lathes and drills were usually driven by leather belts on pulleys from a lineshaft running the length of a shop at high level, driven by an external steam engine. Such a forest of belts was inefficient and dangerous; the belts often broke and speed control was primitive, requiring the belt to move between different–sized pulleys. Once electric power became more available from about 1900, the major engine builders installed electrically driven tools, or sometimes converted old belt machines to electric drive, giving much better control. Machining precision became more important when steam turbines were introduced, with smaller tolerances than that acceptable in steam reciprocating engines.

Engine builders who wished to build steam turbines in the early 1900s were faced with re-equipping their works with more powerful machine tools capable of handling the large components of direct-drive turbines, including longer lathes, bigger planers and heavier cranes. The availability of electric drive and high-speed steel cutting tools only added to the cost, so some works were slow to re-equip, while others such as the Thames works simply closed down. When gearing was introduced, the companies were faced with installing precision gear-cutting machinery.

Where the shipyard had its own engine works, machinery installation would be undertaken at the fitting out basin or quay, served by a heavy lift sheerlegs or crane. Where the shipyard did not have its own engine works, as with Armstrong and the Dockyards, battleship machinery components were shipped to where the hull was fitting out, adding time and expense. Modest powered merchant ship hulls, however, would usually be towed to a nearby engine works for machinery installation, which took a much shorter time.

LIFTING APPLIANCES
Berth Cranes
Most of the materials forming the hull structure – a single steel plate, for example – were of modest weight, so for much of the pre-dreadnought era simple wooden derricks alongside the berth were sufficient to lift formed parts on to the hull for riveting in place, as described on

p.111. Later, some yards such as John Brown erected steel derricks. For heavier items such as shaft brackets, and occasionally for boilers installed before launch, temporary wooden sheerlegs would be rigged when required. After 1900 a few battleship yards erected gantries: Beardmore with a fixed framework over one berth built by Arrol in 1905, and Palmers with trolley cableways spanning most of the two largest building berths built by Henderson of Aberdeen, the first ordered in 1905 – see opposite.[12] In 1901 Vickers at Barrow had erected two fixed gantries of the patent design by Brown's Hoisting & Conveying Machine Co of Cleveland USA covering four berths, on the top of each of which ran a 15-ton cantilever crane – see plan on p.63 and photograph on p.153. The electrically-driven berth tower crane was only gradually introduced, the first in operation at Barrow in 1914, then at Naval Yard, later at Fairfield and Cammell Laird, giving better coverage of the hull, but typically of only 5–10 ton capacity.[13] The latter yard spent £80,000 in 1936–7 rebuilding and re-equipping the slipway on which Prince of Wales was built. The two main manufacturers of such cranes, both structure and machinery, were Arrol of Glasgow (tower) and Stothert & Pitt of Bath (jib).

Fitting-Out Cranes
Most of the really heavy components were shipped after launch, which also helped keep launch weight and pressures down, but also because one lifting appliance could service many hulls by moving them around. In the early years, such appliances were often common user installed by port authorities, so could be used both for heavy cargo lifts and for fitting out ships. Typically they would be a revolving steam crane of fixed radius capable of lifting up to about 60 tons. In other places, more commonly three-legged sheerlegs were installed, especially by shipbuilders and engine builders. These were cheaper but suffered from only being able to luff, i.e. move the load outwards at 90° to the quay. Hence much manoeuvring of hull and load was needed to position components precisely. Shipbuilder Day, Summers of Southampton was a specialist builder of such sheerlegs from the 1860s until the 1920s. Sheerlegs were structurally simple, so some owners built the legs themselves, buying in the hoisting equipment from a specialist manufacturer. They were robust and long-lived; some were sold second-hand when superseded by a more modern appliance.

Material Handling on the Building Berth

Over the brief period 1900 to 1914, the manner in which material, frames, beams and plates, was handled for erection on the building slip changed significantly. Until then the most common method was the light pole derrick, a timber mast of up to about 80ft in height with a timber jib fixed near the top that could handle loads up to 3 tons. A system of guys kept the mast in place while a winch on the ground attached to the jib by ropes could lift and slew the load. This berth system was used by the Royal Dockyards through their dreadnought building phase 1905–14. However, in the same period, the private shipyards invested heavily in a variety of means whereby material could be erected as efficiently as possible. The four examples illustrated here cover the main types.

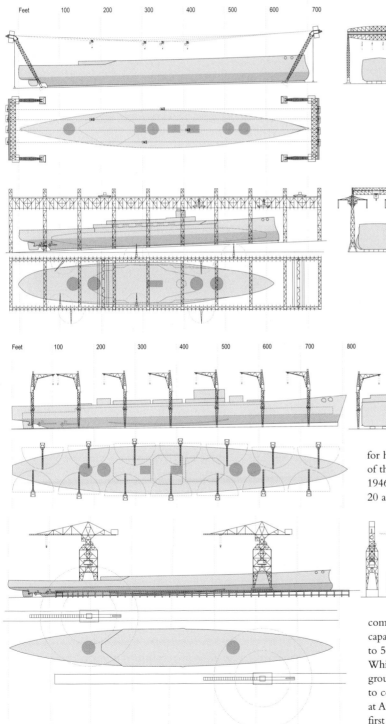

1. Henderson's cable system. Two such cableways were installed at Palmers yard, one installed in 1905 serving a berth 500ft x 100ft used in the construction of *Lord Nelson* and another serving two berths of 700ft x 75ft shown here with *Queen Mary*. The system used overhead trolleys, three in the smaller cableway and four in the larger, capable of handling 3 tons each which could be traversed across the berth as well as running along its length.

2. Arrol gantry system. Sir William Arrol & Co designed this steel gantry system for William Beardmore's Dalmuir shipyard in 1904. It was 750ft in length with 105ft internal clearance. It carried a 20-ton and two 15-ton overhead travelling cranes and a total of eight side-walking jib cranes, each with a capacity of 5 tons. In 1908 Arrol built a larger double gantry of this type for Harland & Wolff at Belfast. *Ramillies* shown.

3. Steel derrick system. Designed and manufactured by Sir William Arrol & Co, steel derricks of this type were first introduced at John Brown's Clydebank shipyard in 1906 to assist in the construction of the Cunard liner *Lusitania*. Essentially sophisticated versions of the wooden pole derrick, these cranes had separate electric motors for hoisting, racking and slewing. Extensive use was made of these cranes on all east yard berths at Clydebank until 1946 when they were replaced with Arrol tower cranes of 20 and 40 tons capacity. *Vanguard* shown.

4. Tower crane system. This system was eventually adopted by most shipyards as the most efficient way of handling material at the building berth. With a large operational radius, these cranes commanded large areas of the building berth, typically capable of lifting a maximum load of about 10 tons out to 50ft and 6 tons out to a maximum of around 100ft. While many examples of this type were fixed to the ground, the ones shown here were travelling cranes able to cover most of the building berth. They were installed at Armstrong's Walker Naval Yard in 1913 – among the first of the type to be installed in the UK. *Furious* shown.

Fitting-out Cranes

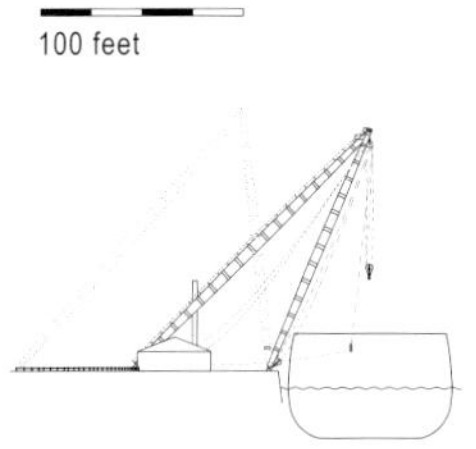

180-ton sheerlegs by Day Summers & Co Ltd for Chatham Dockyard 1905.

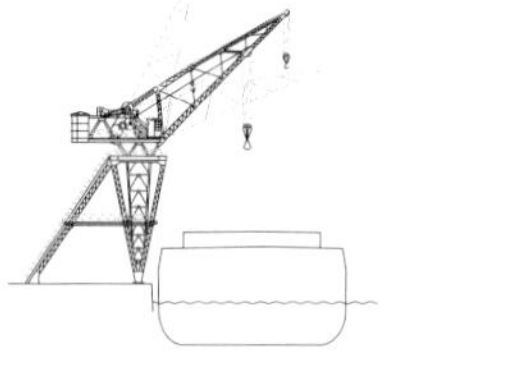

150-ton derricking hammerhead crane by Duisburger Maschinenbau AG. for. Tranmere Bay Development Co 1907, later Cammell Laird & Co Ltd. Audacious shown in section

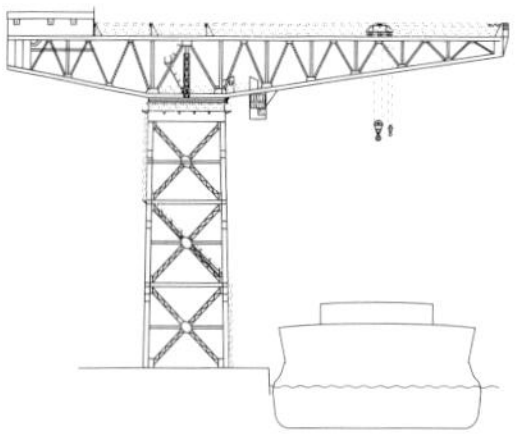

150-ton giant cantilever crane by Sir Wm Arrol & Co. for John Brown & Co Ltd 1907. Hood shown in section.

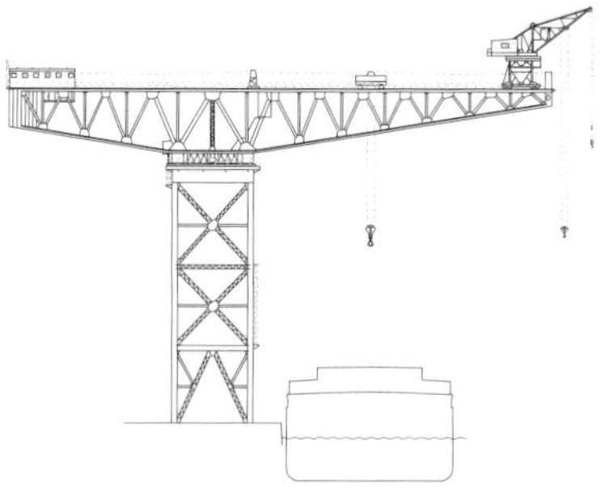

250-ton giant cantilever crane by Sir Wm Arrol & Co Ltd, for Vickers Armstrong, Walker Naval Yard 1931. KGV Class shown in section.

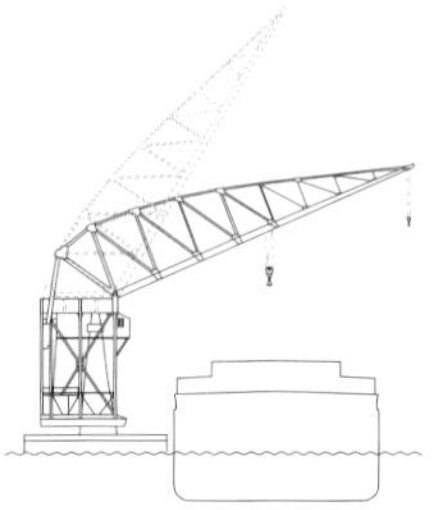

150-ton floating crane *Titan II*, by Werft Gusto for Swan Hunter & Wigham Richardson & Co Ltd, 1922. KGV Class shown in section.

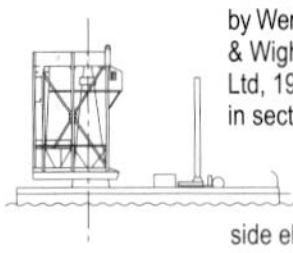

side elevation of pontoon

Lifting loads of exceptional weight such as machinery, guns and mountings required cranes of a special type. Until the end of the nineteenth century, sheerlegs were most commonly used for this purpose. However, from the start of the twentieth century, cranes of a new type were developed that could hoist, rack (move the load along the jib) and slew (rotate) loads with great accuracy. Moreover these characteristics could be applied to floating cranes, usually self-propelled barges on which the crane structure was mounted. One of the first land-based fitting-out cranes of the new type was the giant cantilever crane constructed by Sir William Arrol & Co, for John Brown's Clydebank shipyard. Capable of lifting 150 tons out to 85ft, this crane was upgraded to 200 tons before the Second World War to enable it to lift the quadruple 14in turntables and triple 16in anticipated for the *Lion* class. Although not the last crane of this type built but certainly the largest in the UK, was the 250-ton crane erected by Arrol for Vickers-Armstrong's Walker Naval Yard in 1931. A similar crane was installed at Barrow shipyard.

These commanding and often evocative structures visible for miles around have all but disappeared. Today the A-listed John Brown crane has been preserved as a visitor attraction at the site of the now demolished shipyard. The 250-ton crane at Walker continues to work on Tyneside.

Scotch boilers, being indivisible, were among the heaviest machinery lifts at up to about 100 tons. Most machinery components could be broken down into lighter loads if necessary and re-assembled on board. But for battleships, it was the shipping of the gun mountings that required substantial lifting appliances, not only on account of ever increasing weight but also the need to position turntables precisely on to roller paths, guns into cradles and gun shield armour to interlock with adjacent plates.

The Royal Dockyards installed new sheerlegs all at much the same time: Devonport (100 tons) in 1898, Portsmouth (100 tons) in 1900 (used to ship *Dreadnought*'s machinery and armament) and Chatham (180 tons) in 1905 – see drawing.[14] But these somewhat limited appliances were about to be outclassed by what was loosely called a 'hammerhead' crane, electrically powered. In fact there were different designs, but they all had the feature of a T shape with rotating horizontal jib upon which a trolley or crab ran which carried the actual load, all supported by a fixed tower. Loads of 100 tons or more could be lifted from the quayside and placed anywhere within the crane's working radius on the ship. The minimum radius was determined by the tower dimensions and its setback from the quay face, but maximum load could only be carried out to about 60 per cent of the jib length, typically 80–100ft, with a smaller load at maximum radius.

The first such crane was designed and built in Germany in 1898 for Bremerhaven.[15] At the end of 1902 the Vickers Board ordered such a hammerhead crane for Barrow from the same company, Benrather Maschinenfabrik of Benrath near Düsseldorf, costing £16,500 for the crane, with a total of £23,000 including foundations. At that time, Vickers were preparing a bid for *Mauretania* and *Lusitania*, and were keen to show Cunard that they had the necessary facilities. The new 150-ton crane could service both the engine building and ordnance workshops next to the Devonshire Dock, and largely superseded the existing 120-ton hydraulic crane built by Armstrong for the Furness Railway in 1874 but of only 40ft fixed outreach from the dockside.[16] It was part of the substantial investment the company had been making at Barrow since 1897, on which £840,000 had been spent by 1902, twice what the company had paid for NCA initially. The new engineering facilities were planned by McKechnie, those for the shipyard by manager

A B Gowan, appointed in 1891, who became Palmers' general manager in 1909, later managing director. That expansion had substantially increased the labour force and outrun the housing stock in Barrow. Although Vickers started a large house building programme in July 1899, as an interim measure they bought the liner *Alaska* which was about to be scrapped by T W Ward at Preston for £19,000 to provide accommodation. Houses were built on Walney Island, across the channel from the shipyard, the area being known as Vickerstown.

A 150-ton Benrather crane was also installed at Beardmore's new Dalmuir yard in 1903, although the yard was still being built. Fixed derrick cranes were also installed in British battleship building yards, where the jib normally lay at around 45° to the horizontal and could be raised or lowered for positioning the load; they could slew as well. John Brown installed such a 150-ton crane, built by Cowans Sheldon of Carlisle, for fitting out *Lusitania* in 1906, Cammell Laird a German 150-ton in 1906, Scotts a 100-ton by G Russell & Co of Motherwell in 1905,[17] Elswick a 150-tonner in 1907 – built by Armstrong so naturally hydraulically driven – see photo on p.16. Cammell Laird accounts record that in 1913 (the year of *Audacious*' completion) their crane operated for 3333 hours (10.6 hours per day for a six-day week) at a direct cost of 1s 6d per hour (£0.075), presumably mainly wages and power.[18]

But the most satisfactory design emerged at this time, the giant cantilever crane, sometimes (erroneously) called a Titan crane, a term which was more generally and appropriately applied to travelling cranes used in building harbour breakwaters or blocksetting. It had been developed from earlier hammerhead concepts, particularly by structural engineers Sir William Arrol & Co Ltd at Dalmarnock, Glasgow.[19] The rigid horizontal long arm of the cantilever was balanced by a counterweight on its short arm, the whole resting on roller bearings on the tower which took only axial thrust, with no overturning moment. This meant less deflection under load as well as a more rigid tower structure and lighter foundations. Several of the battleship builders installed these, with the first being of 150-ton capacity for John Brown in 1907, despite their having just installed a 150-ton derrick crane. By positioning this Arrol crane at the outer end of the fitting out quay, it was possible to install heavy gun mountings at

each end of a battleship, by turning the hull round – a crane sited midway along a basin was best suited to handling midship loads such as machinery. Vickers also installed a 150-ton cantilever crane in 1908 (which partially collapsed during erection), but in the wider Buccleuch Dock, built by Appleby & Co, a subsidiary of Vickers and Beardmore. Arrol took over Appleby in 1910 and became the dominant builder of such cranes. Other 'battleship builder' cantilever cranes were:

1909 Devonport Dockyard	160 tons	
1910 Wallsend Slipway	150 tons	
1911 Fairfield	200 tons[20]	
1913 Portsmouth Dockyard	250 tons.	
	(Cost £38,441)	

Several marine engine-building firms installed such cranes, including North Eastern Marine, George Clark and Barclay Curle. Rosyth Dockyard installed not one but two, one of 250 tons in 1917, the other of 100 tons in 1920. Such cranes were exported to overseas Dockyards including Japan and later to Singapore and Sydney, this last still standing. A new 250-ton Arrol cantilever crane capable of handling the heavier gun mounting turntables was completed in 1939 for Vickers-Armstrongs at Devonshire Dock to replace the 1903 hammerhead one. When the Buccleuch Dock 150-ton fitting out cantilever crane was wrecked in an air attack in May 1941, a replacement 150-ton crane was quickly ordered from Arrol, not finally demolished until 2010.

The principal loads were guns and gun mounting components, steam turbines, boilers, and armour plates and, later on for merchant ships, diesel engines. Most such heavy cranes had a secondary hoist capable of lifting 20–40 tons at much higher speeds than the main hoist. In addition they usually featured a high speed whip hoist of 5–10 tons capacity, an invaluable facility used extensively for lighter components and the multitude of outfit items ranging from bundles of timber planks and pipes to deck machinery and masts.

Some shipyards had floating cranes of 150 tons capacity, including Thames Iron Works (1910), Harland & Wolff (1908) and Cammell Laird (200 tons 1919). Swan, Hunter & Wigham Richardson acquired the *Titan* 140-ton floating crane of German Bechem & Keetman design in 1906 to fit out *Mauretania*, which was also hired out for general work on

the Tyne. When that crane was lost in 1921, a new 150-ton floating crane *Titan II* was bought from Smulders' Werf Gusto in Holland in 1922 for £68,500, with ownership later shared between Swan Hunter, Hawthorn Leslie and Wallsend Slipway.[21] Armstrong Whitworth made good use of this crane for fitting out *Nelson*, as shown in the table of typical lifts,[22] while Swan Hunter also used it for work on *Anson* on the berth and afloat. The crane remained in use until 2006, albeit renamed *Titan III* after the original crane was moved to a new pontoon in 1979, before being sold to India in 2008.

The Naval Yard had no crane heavier than 30 tons during the First World War, so probably used *Titan* for heavier lifts, although they built the pontoon for a 250-ton Cowans Sheldon floating crane for the Admiralty in 1916, which

Above: Cammell Laird's 200-ton floating crane was used to ship *Rodney*'s 108-ton 16in guns at Birkenhead in the spring of 1927. The gun had arrived by rail alongside the quay. *(Published by permission of Wirral Council)*

Some Battleship Lifts Carried out by the *Titan II* 150-ton Floating Crane

19 Mar 1924	Lifted two 21-ton sternframes from (Armstrong's) Naval Yard jetty to (battleship) *Nelson* on berth (No 2).
14 Oct 1924	Removed six 50-ton turbine casings from (battlecruiser) *Lion* (being dismantled) at Jarrow Slake.
22 Feb 1925	Lifted three 33-ton and one 31-ton boiler into *Nelson* on berth.
13 Jan 1926	Lifted from Naval Yard and placed aboard *Nelson* 165-ton (16in) turntable (at jetty). Loaded five 40-ton armour plates on (*Titan's*) deck.
19 Mar 1926	Lifted from steamer *Sagenite* (from Barrow) onto jetty at Naval Yard 3 x 33-ton barbettes and 1 x 8-ton ammunition trunk (*Nelson* twin 6in mountings).
15 Sep 1926	Lifted from punt (barge from Elswick) two 108-ton 16in guns and placed aboard (*Nelson*).
2 Oct 1926	Lifted from punt four pieces of armour plate: 1 x 40-ton, 2 x 36-ton, 1 x 29-ton (probably for X gunhouse).
12 Nov 1938	Lifted 38-ton rudder and fourteen armour plates totalling 356 tons from jetty to (battleship) *King George V* (on Berth No 2 at Vickers-Armstrongs).
8 Jul 1939	Lifted rudder frame for HMS *Jellicoe* (*Anson*) 29 tons, from Pontoon Dry Docks to stocks.
18 Nov 1939	Lifted rudder from east yard (Swan Hunter) and placed aboard HMS *Jellicoe*. 35 tons.
25 Nov 1939	Lifted gun planing machine from HMS *Nigeria* to *KGV*, 20 tons (at Naval Yard).
18 Apr 1940	Lifted 47-ton boiler, uptakes and 1 x 27-ton armour plate aboard (*Anson* post launch at Wallsend).
8 Jul 1940	Lifted gearcase 45 tons from barge aboard (*Anson*) one armour plate already aboard placed 34 tons, and lifted 13-ton (cruising) turbine from wherry (barge) aboard.
27 Jun 1941	Lifted guns 84 tons (twin 5.25in mounting) from (Vickers-Armstrongs) punt to battleship (*Anson*) and 40-ton funnel (from Wallsend Slipway) aboard.
3 Dec 1941	Brought 34-ton director from Naval Yard and discharged aboard battleship at Wallsend.
23 Dec 1941	Lifted 65-ton gun turret (twin 5.25in excluding guns) from *Empire Gat* ex H&W Glasgow (Scotstoun) aboard at Wallsend.

was used to ship *Furious*' after 18in gun. When the now merged Vickers-Armstrongs tendered for the Cunarder which became *Queen Mary*, the bold decision was made in April 1930 to install an Arrol 250-ton cantilever crane. The crane was completed very rapidly by March 1931 at a cost of £93,000, and was used to fit out *Monarch of Bermuda* launched that same month, although by then the Cunarder had been ordered from John Brown. Naval Yard was put on care and maintenance from then until 1934, but the crane proved immensely valuable when re-armament started. The 14in mountings built at Elswick for both *King George V* and *Anson* (the latter at a cost of £5000) were installed by it – see photo on p.188. Its 20/5-ton auxiliary crane which travelled along the top of the cantilever was heavily used for fitting out, as well as servicing the crane itself. So well built and maintained was the crane that it is still in use today, lifting items such as cable and pipeline reels at the Walker Offshore Technology Park which was built on the site of Naval Yard after it was closed in 1985 by British Shipbuilders.

To handle their 14in mountings with their heavy turntables, both John Brown's and Fairfield's cranes were uprated from 150 and 200 tons to 200 and 250 tons in 1937 and 1941 respectively at Admiralty expense – a quadruple turntable weighed 200 tons as lifted. The former crane still stands but as a museum, while the latter was demolished in 2007. The Clyde Navigation Trust had also erected a 175-ton cantilever crane at Finnieston, which still stands, used both for handling heavy cargoes such as locomotives and installing machinery from nearby engine works.

For building the hulls of the Second World War battleships, the existing regular berths were used at John Brown, Fairfield, Cammell Laird and Naval Yard, now well covered by tower cranes (also at Barrow), but for *Anson* Swan Hunter used the covered Berth No.2 next to the one used to launch *Mauretania* in 1906. This was a tight squeeze for her 103ft wide hull but had the advantage of some weather protection and good coverage from overhead travelling cranes.

PROBLEMS AT VICKERS' BARROW SHIPYARD

By 1902 Vickers' Barrow shipyard was working well with its new facilities and making profits. But ten years later, the hitherto successful shipyard had become complacent and inefficient,

with the Barrow works as a whole turning in a profit of only £118,310 in 1913, its lowest since 1902. A concerned management started investigations into the poor-quality work and late deliveries of which customers were complaining. They found unsatisfactory work in the 'iron' (i.e. steel working) department, 'indifferently' executed work, poorly-fitting structure requiring remedial rework, lax discipline, excessive overtime, lack of cooperation between trades, highly inflated piecework rates and a dominant influence of 'trade societies' i.e. unions. Encouraged by group managing director Trevor Dawson, Barrow director James McKechnie replaced the shipyard manager, put in place a new management structure and tightened up on the generous piecework rate-fixing. When recruiting for a new manager in September 1912, there were thirteen highly-qualified applicants, some from the Admiralty, happy to work for a company of Vickers' reputation. One was H M MacMillan, works manager at shipbuilders Workman Clark in Belfast, mentioning not only his experience but also a preference to work in England, away

Below: Vickers-Armstrongs took the bold decision in 1930 to order a 250-ton cantilever fitting out crane for their Walker Naval Yard, with only one ship on the order book. Arrol of Glasgow took the contract at a low price of £93,000, completing the crane in March 1931. The fixed tower has already been erected, and the scotch derrick is assembling the cantilever girders, which had been fabricated at Arrol's Parkhead works. The crane remains in service to this day. *(Brian Newman)*

from the Irish troubles. But he applied too late, after W T Davis from the Admiralty had been selected as shipbuilding director. MacMillan was appointed shipyard manager at Fairfield in 1914, when the previous manager was dismissed, a company he had worked for previously for ten years. He later went on to set up the Blythswood shipyard in Glasgow in 1919, after being dismissed from Fairfield for unapproved expenditure.[23]

The new manager put forward his proposals for re-equipping the shipyard in July 1913, pointing out that much of the equipment was old, unreliable and badly sited with regard to where work was being done, e.g. the fitting out quays were some distance from the shipyard building berths and workshops. Nine new fixed tower cranes, two at 30 tons and seven at 10 tons, were erected from late 1913 by Arrol in place of two of the existing gantries, covering the four longest (southernmost) Berths 1–4, costing £51,000. The cantilever crane on the easternmost gantry had been destroyed in a gale in November 1912, resulting in delays to the construction of Emperor of India by having to use temporary lifting gear. New power supplies were needed in place of the elderly inadequate electric, hydraulic and compressed air systems, while a system of narrow gauge railways would improve transport of material within the yard. The plater's shed needed extending and fitting out workshops resited nearer the Buccleuch Dock. A new shipyard management structure was set up, separating the functions of berth, fitting out and submarine building managers. At Admiralty request, submarine work was regarded as secret and the building area fenced off from the rest of the shipyard with its now covered building berths, also being extended with two more berths. Foremen's powers were reduced and a new piecework rate-setting department set up, which helped to reduce excessive wage costs. There was still a shortage of labour, however, with work for another 2000-plus, and a shortage of housing, despite 750 houses being built on Walney Island and more in Barrow itself. Output was therefore restricted, although there were many ships in hand – in July 1913 there were nineteen ships on the slipways: two battleships, two cruisers, a tanker, a floating dock, two river monitors and eleven submarines, plus more fitting out. In September, Churchill visited the yard as First Lord, impressed by the range of work in hand. But Erin, building over this period, turned in a loss of £7000 on hull and machinery, the first

such on a battleship since Vengeance twelve years earlier. Helped by good profits on submarines and gun mountings, however, the Barrow works recovered with profits back up to £301,880 in 1914.[24] The shipyard had been re-equipped just in time to undertake the expanded First World War building programme, especially of submarines.

DRYDOCKS

Every new battleship required to be drydocked before acceptance by the Admiralty. This allowed underwater fittings to be completed and checked, including propellers, shafts, machinery inlets and outlets, submerged torpedo tubes, bilge keels etc, and armament alignment checked. Most importantly, the underwater hull needed cleaning after a year or more in waters that were often polluted, and painted with a fresh anti-fouling coating. When tendering, the shipbuilder was required to state where the ship was to be drydocked. In 1900 no battleship builder other than the Royal Dockyards had its own drydock. Thames Iron Works sent their ships to Chatham Dockyard. Although they had two drydocks, the largest was only 470ft x 64ft, and battleships were typically 75ft broad. Armstrong also sent new battleships to Chatham, for example Yashima in 1897 and Hatsuse in 1900.[25] This expensive diversion on top of the £1500 or so drydocking cost prompted them to support Tyneside shipbuilder and locomotive builder R Stephenson & Co Ltd, who proposed to build a 700ft x 90ft drydock next to their shipyard at Hebburn, by investing £30,000 in shares in the reconstituted company.[26] Following the opening of the dock in 1904, Armstrong made regular use of the facility for its ships. It became part of Palmers Shipbuilding when they took over Stephenson's bankrupt yard in 1911. After Palmers closed in 1933, the dock passed to a new company, Palmers Hebburn Co Ltd, soon to become a subsidiary of Vickers-Armstrongs, and was much used during the Second World War, proving of great value in repairing cruisers, even if no longer large enough for battleships.

On the Clyde, the largest drydock was the Clyde Navigation Trust's No 3 at Govan, opened in 1898. At 880ft x 83ft, it was used for battleships built on the west coast, such as Dominion from Barrow, until they became too wide for it. Thereafter battleships had to be drydocked elsewhere prior to completion, including Devonport (New Zealand, Monarch,

Princess Royal, Sultan Osman I/Agincourt) and Cammell Laird (*Inflexible, Barham*), with Liverpool's Canada Dock (*Vanguard* and *Sao Paulo* from Barrow) and later Gladstone Dock used after it opened in 1913 at 1050ft x 120ft (*Erin, Revenge* and *Ramillies*) and *Kongo* at Belfast. Other builders nominated drydocks at Portsmouth and Southampton, although a Royal Dockyard was more popular as the Admiralty would then provide a navigating crew from the shipyard.[27]

Cammell Laird was the only battleship builder to have its own battleship size drydocks. Two had been completed in 1907 as part of the Tranmere Bay scheme, No 6 at 709ft x 88ft and No 7 at 862ft x 102ft, both still in use today.[28] These docks were regularly used by Grand Fleet battleships and battlecruisers for overhauls during the First World War. With a shortage of battleship drydocks on the East Coast, the Admiralty ordered two new 32,000-ton lift floating docks in 1910. Two 150-ton floating cranes were also ordered to service them – the docks were moored some distance from

Dockyard heavy lifting appliances. Initially based in the Medway and at Portsmouth, soon after the outbreak of war, they were moved to the Tyne and Invergordon respectively. The former was managed by ship repairers Smiths Dock, and was much used for battleship drydocking, including US Navy ships in 1918.

With their more generous provision of drydocks, the Dockyards could afford to use them not just for final work on the hull before trials but for lengthy periods of fitting out, e.g. *Dreadnought* in No.15 Dock at Portsmouth. At Devonport *Collingwood* had her side armour fitted while in drydock – the 30-ton travelling crane and an immobile ship allowing the 15–23-ton plates to be fitted more quickly than afloat under a sheerlegs.

All five *King George V* class battleships were drydocked at Rosyth in 1940–2, spending their last two months or so there before completion. *Vanguard* was drydocked in the Gladstone Dock in May 1946 before returning to the Clyde for her speed trials. In service she used No.10 Dock at Devonport, which is still in use today.

Below: *Kashima* in drydock at Hebburn before her trials in April 1906. Armstrong Whitworth had a share in Robert Stephenson, the owners of the 700 x 90ft dock. A Brown crane gantry at its shipyard is seen at left, similar to those at Vickers and Harland & Wolff. (*Newcastle University Marine Technology Special Collection*)

7: POWERING

THE ESTABLISHMENT OF THE MARINE ENGINE BUILDERS

Battleships, in view of their size and speed, needed the highest-powered machinery. As such, marine engine builders were required to develop ever more powerful and efficient propulsion machinery. From the earliest days of steam propulsion in the 1820s the Admiralty had relied on commercial engine builders to power their vessels, even though hulls might be built in the Royal Dockyards. The Admiralty did, however, set up 'steam factories', the first at Woolwich Dockyard in 1840, but these were intended for the overhaul of steam machinery, not its construction. But in conjunction with the experience of its seagoing engineers, the Admiralty was enabled to become an 'informed customer' when specifying machinery for its ships and supervising its construction and installation.

For the first decades of steam propulsion, the Admiralty tended to favour engine builders in the south of England, such as Maudslay in London, but eventually recognised the merits

of well-established builders in the north like Robert Napier on the Clyde. The early engine builders also built machinery for general engineering and land use, so an inland site such as occupied by Boulton & Watt in Birmingham or John Penn at Greenwich half a mile from the river was no particular handicap. From about 1850 steam began to replace sail for seagoing ships, with propellers replacing paddles and iron replacing wood. Marine engineering became a more specialised industry with new companies setting up, especially on the Tyne and Clyde. These companies wisely chose (or a few existing ones moved to) riverside locations, often near to a heavy quayside crane for installing machinery in a newly launched hull, which could be towed to the works by the now ubiquitous steam paddle tugs. Some of these works were set up by existing iron shipbuilders such as Laird, who laid out extensive new premises at Birkenhead from 1854. But other engineers set up their own shipyards, which enabled them to supply a complete vessel: for example, Napier and Elder and Thomson in Glasgow.

The working pressure of boilers was relatively low by comparison with that which was to follow, engines expanding steam in a single cylinder, so fuel efficiency was low. As better and stronger boilers such as the cylindrical 'Scotch' boiler were developed in the 1860s permitting pressures up to about 50lb/sq in, compounding was adopted with steam expanding through a high and a low pressure cylinder into a condenser with exhaust pressure below atmospheric. By the 1880s triple expansion was introduced with higher pressure boilers built of steel. More engine building facilities were developed, either as part of an existing shipyard, like Harland & Wolff at Belfast in 1881, or an independent works like Wallsend Slipway & Engineering on

Below: *Dreadnought* was fitted with eighteen Babcock & Wilcox boilers producing saturated steam at 250 lb/sq in. They were installed at Portsmouth Dockyard after launch, lifted in by sheerlegs. *(Babcock & Wilcox)*

Tyneside, which expanded from being a repair yard to building machinery from 1875. Such facilities were often built on reclaimed waterfront land, with their own quays and sheerlegs capable of lifting engines and boilers up to about 100 tons.

By the time the substantial battleship building programme started in the 1890s, there were some fifteen marine engineers capable of supplying the requisite machinery. The 'independents' could supply not only the Royal Dockyards but those shipbuilders such as Armstrong without their own engine works. Although the Dockyards did build a handful of low-powered steam reciprocating engines for minor war vessels around 1900, they never equipped themselves with the extensive shops and plant required to build high powered machinery with their numerous boilers. The Admiralty were heavily reliant on private industry to develop new designs of machinery. Warship design requirements were different from most merchant ships, requiring boilers and machinery able to respond rapidly to changing speed and power demands, and a low physical profile and centre of gravity in order to fit below protective decks. There was a continual demand for ever more powerful machinery but lighter and with lower fuel consumption, which allowed the weight saved to be converted into more powerful armament and protection and longer endurance.

Nine prime contractors survived to the end of battleship building, with the table on pp.133-5 recording the installations completed from *Majestic* to *Vanguard*; 111 were for new British-built battleships, but there were also four complete installations exported up to 1915 plus five re-enginings in the 1930s.

Before the turbine era of *Dreadnought*, a typical installation consisted of twin screw vertical triple expansion engines each with three or four cylinders (two low pressure) of around 12,000–18,000 ihp.[1] The *Majestic* class had eight Scotch boilers with a working pressure of 155lb/sq in. Such installations were designed to operate on forced draught for maximum power, whereby additional air was blown under pressure into the boilers to increase the rate of combustion, usually using the system developed by James Howden of Glasgow in the 1880s; for cruising speeds, 'natural draught' was used, with a power level around 75 per cent of maximum. But such 'firetube' boilers were heavy, as the large cylindrical boiler was full of water, through which

were passed hot gases in tubes from the coal-fired furnaces. With such a mass of water, it was difficult to produce more steam quickly, and they were also unreliable at high powers. The solution was to adopt the lighter watertube boiler, where the boiler shell contained the hot gases to circulate round the many tubes containing the water, with the steam collecting in a drum at the top of the boiler. This could be designed for much higher steam pressures and increased rates of evaporation, so could respond more quickly to changes in demand. Many different designs such as Belleville were tried from the mid-1890s with varying degrees of success. The *Canopus* class battleships were the first to use watertube boilers at 300lb/sq in (20 Belleville), where weight saving allowed speed to be increased by 1.5 knots. However, by 1902 the two most successful designs had emerged and were used in all pre-war dreadnoughts. These were the Yarrow, designed by the builder of destroyers and torpedo boats, and the American Babcock & Wilcox, whose British subsidiary set up a big new factory at Renfrew on the Clyde in 1895. Each design had its advantages and disadvantages, so the Admiralty specified both, hoping that competition would keep prices down. By 1914 B&W had supplied 144 boilers to pre-dreadnoughts and 397 to later battleships and battlecruisers.

THE PROCUREMENT OF MACHINERY

When a shipbuilding programme was agreed, the Director of Naval Construction prepared the overall ship design and the Engineer-in-Chief (E-in-C) prepared the corresponding machinery specification, estimating weight and

Above: All the pre-dreadnoughts were powered by steam reciprocating engines. The last were *Agamemnon* and *Lord Nelson*, whose twin screw engines developed a total of 16,750 ihp at 120 rpm. Illustrated is one set for the former ordered in 1904 from Hawthorn Leslie in Newcastle as Contract 2602 for her Beardmore hull, whose new engine works was not yet completed. Although working on the triple expansion principle, there were four cylinders, two 60in low pressure cylinders, plus a high pressure of 32.75in and an intermediate of 52in. Four cylinders were better balanced than three and kept the diameter of the LP cylinder down. Stroke of 48in with steam pressure 275lb/sq in. (*Hawthorn Leslie*)

space requirements for machinery and fuel. After the allocation of hull orders to the Royal Dockyards, tenders would be sought for the hull and machinery of the battleships to be built by private shipyards. The companies would be sent the specifications, contract schedules and outline drawings of hull and machinery spaces. A separate list of auxiliary machinery such as steering gear, distilling machinery and generators allowed the Admiralty to choose a preferred sub-contractor from tenderers, which permitted interchange-ability between ships of the same class. Similar tenders were also sought for machinery for the Dockyard-built hulls, depending upon when during the financial year orders were to be placed. Because of annual funding through the Navy Estimates, bunching of orders and expen-diture was undesirable, so Dockyard ships were usually started a few months before the private shipyards. Prices and delivery dates and any qualifying conditions would be reviewed by the DNC and E-in-C, together with previous experience of each builder. A preliminary deci-sion was usually communicated to the builder as soon as possible, to enable planning to start, even though a formal contract from the Director of Contracts would not be signed until some weeks later. While it was normal for those shipyards with integral engine works to receive contracts for both, occasionally the machinery contract would be placed elsewhere. In the case of *Agamemnon*, Beardmore's new

shipyard at Dalmuir was ready in 1905 before the engine works, so that contract was placed with Hawthorn Leslie on Tyneside. In the case of Palmers' *Queen Mary*, John Brown won the machinery contract, probably on account of a more competitive bid stemming from its greater experience building steam turbines (see p.280).

The Admiralty would typically invite about a dozen engine builders to tender. As well as quoting on the basic design and specification, the firms were encouraged to put forward alternative designs. In the case of *St Vincent* and *Collingwood*, the firms invited to tender on 20 October 1907 were: John Brown, Fairfield, Vickers, Palmers, Scotts, Humphrys & Tennant, Hawthorn Leslie, Wallsend Slipway, Harland & Wolff, Denny, London & Glasgow, Beardmore and Thames Iron Works. They were not given much time to prepare their tenders; in the case of *Temeraire*, invitation was on 22 November 1906, tenders to be in by 18 December, accepted on 15 January (Hawthorn Leslie).[2] The wide range of prices tendered to the Admiralty suggest that the market for warship machinery (and hulls) was very competitive, unlike armour or armament.

In the case of merchant ships not engined by the shipbuilder, the hull would be towed to the contractor's engine works, usually nearby. But in the case of Dockyard-built battleships, the engine builder had to ship a large number of machinery components to the Dockyard, where he had his own resident staff for installa-tion. So 'freight' costs had to be added to the manufacturing cost, usually via a chartered coaster. John Brown transported *Indefatigable*'s machinery to Devonport two months after her launch, using the 1228-grt coaster *Elterwater* (built in 1907) for two voyages in December 1909. The engine builder's staff would conduct the machinery trials, with Admiralty inspectors in attendance, although the Admiralty would often provide both stokers and navigating crew. Typically progressive measured mile trials would be run at various power levels and speeds, including an 8-hour full power and a 30-hour endurance trial. Since the Admiralty specified the hull form and horsepower to be installed, the shipbuilder was not required to guarantee a certain speed (apart from destroyers where the shipbuilder had a freer hand in design), but did have to demonstrate that the required power had been attained. In the case of contract deficiencies, financial penalties (liquidated damages) could be imposed: for

Below: Hawthorn Leslie received orders for early dreadnought four-shaft steam turbine machinery, including Dockyard-built *Temeraire* and *Collingwood*. Illustrated is the cruising (left) and low pressure turbine developing about 6000 shp at 325rpm, which were directly coupled to one of the inner propeller shafts. When gearing was used from 1915, effi-ciency increased with higher rpm turbines and lower rpm propellers, reducing the size of the turbines. *(Hawthorn Leslie)*

example, late delivery might incur a penalty of £100 per day, as was the case with *St Vincent,* but if the Admiralty were late with their supply (e.g. of gun mountings) or there were strikes, *force majeure* could be claimed, offsetting some of the delay.

The machinery contract specified payment in fifty-two instalments (forty-four for steam reciprocating machinery) paid at defined 'milestones' each triggering a payment of between 1 and 5 per cent of the total. This worked well for the builder, who could match this cash flow closely to his outgoings, rarely needing to finance much work in progress himself – unlike merchant ship machinery where there might only be four such instalments. In addition to these contractual payments, there were nearly always 'extras and credits' where the Admiralty wanted items added or removed. The final price paid therefore reflected such costs, which might not be settled until long after the ship had been delivered. The guarantee period was typically twelve months, during which the contractor was required to rectify any deficiencies.

The contract specified the particular machinery trials to be undertaken, but typically included:

- Basin trial: moored alongside to check machinery systems.
- Preliminary trial when first at sea, up to full power.
- 30hr endurance trial at cruising power to check fuel consumption.
- Measured mile trial, at various powers up to maximum.
- 8hr full power trial to test overall performance.
- Acceptance trial, full power at handover from shipbuilder to Admiralty.

These could extend over three or more months. Other trials included astern running and tests of auxiliary machinery. Until all such were completed satisfactorily, the contractor remained responsible, and only then did the Admiralty pay the final 5 per cent instalment.

THE ADOPTION OF THE STEAM TURBINE

When Charles Parsons developed his reaction steam turbine in the 1890s, the potential for warship propulsion was clear. It offered much higher power more compactly than the steam reciprocating engine, it was lighter, its fewer moving parts offered better reliability, its

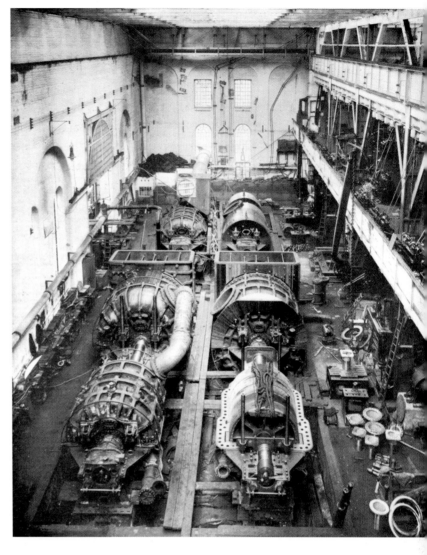

balanced rotating components resulted in less vibration, and it required less headroom. It had some drawbacks though: its higher revolutions with the turbine directly coupled to the propeller shaft meant smaller diameter less efficient propellers, and its efficiency was lower at cruising powers, somewhat compensated when cruising turbines were fitted for use at low powers. On the other hand, steam turbines were slightly more efficient at maximum power, and as it was that power which determined boiler capacity, so fewer boilers and stokers were needed. Machinery weight was slightly reduced although coal capacity was based on cruising endurance. Although the turbine-driven destroyers *Viper* and *Cobra* were early casualties (not due to their machinery), the success of the cruiser *Amethyst* with 10,000shp[3] gave the Admiralty confidence to specify Parsons steam turbines for *Dreadnought*

Above: The Fairfield erecting shop with battleship turbine machinery lined up, probably for the two inner shafts of *Bellerophon.* Nearest the camera, one set with casings removed, the cruising turbine, then low pressure, then LP astern. *(Author's collection)*

in 1905. Cunard had already taken a similar bold decision in 1904 with its Atlantic liners *Carmania, Mauretania* and *Lusitania*. With four shafts in place of the normal two, and power 25 per cent higher than pre-dreadnoughts, *Dreadnought* was two knots faster. Parsons had set up his own Marine Steam Turbine Company at Wallsend in 1897 and built her turbines, although Vickers at Barrow was the machinery prime contractor.

The turbine was the final nail in the coffin of the Thames engine builders, who had engined twenty-eight of the sixty-four battleships completed from 1890 to *Dreadnought*. These firms carried the burden of higher wage and material costs sited so far from their main suppliers in the north, and were now faced with new capital investment if they were to continue engining high-powered warships – they were already uncompetitive for merchant ship machinery. Humphrys, Tennant & Co at Greenwich had tendered successfully for the battlecruiser *Invincible*'s machinery. But her 25 knots required 41,000 shp, nearly double that of *Dreadnought*, when ordered from Armstrong Whitworth early in 1906. Humphrys had to buy her turbines from John Brown, who had already invested in new manufacturing facilities

for *Carmania*, so had a Parsons licence (for 15 years from 1905) and some experience. That and the expense of installing such powerful machinery 300 miles away from their main works only added to the final cost; they went into liquidation in 1909 when *Invincible* was completed. Thames Iron Works, who had taken over Penn in 1899, struggled on, re-equipping the shipyard to handle *Thunderer*'s bigger hull ordered in 1910, but having to sub-contract her turbines to Parsons. But she too bankrupted the company, faced with higher wages and costs, and investment in new facilities that would never pay off – see p.128.

From then on, only the northern engine builders were competitive for larger warships, though there were many other builders who concentrated on merchant ships. On the strength of their success with *Mauretania*'s 70,000-shp machinery, Wallsend Slipway with its extended facilities started to bid for larger warship contracts. Early in 1907 they received the order for *Superb*'s machinery building at nearby Armstrong, and from then until the 1960s were rarely without a warship machinery contract. They bid successfully for Dockyard contracts, getting first of class orders for both *Orion* and *Queen Elizabeth*.

Right: The large machine shop at Wallsend Slipway showing two battleship direct drive turbine units under construction, probably early in 1914. The large unit at the left in the boring machine is the port ahead LP turbine for *Queen Elizabeth* (Contract 730), nearly ready for shipment to Portsmouth Dockyard. In the centre is part of an LP casing for *Malaya* (Contract 731) at an earlier stage in the machining process. In the left foreground is a casting for *Malaya*, possibly a changeover valve housing. The overhead cranes are of 65 tons capacity, installed for the construction of *Mauretania*'s machinery a few years before. *(Brian Newman)*

Left: The boiler uptakes for *Queen Elizabeth* erected alongside the boiler shop at Wallsend Slipway. The group in the foreground serve the after twelve Babcock & Wilcox boilers using the after funnel (aft end nearest), with the group for the forward twelve boilers behind. In the distance can be seen the inner casing of one funnel (nearest) and the outer casing. *(Brian Newman)*

Another Tyneside engine builder, Hawthorn Leslie, was well experienced with warship machinery, from the days of the merger between the Leslie shipyard at Hebburn on Tyne and the Hawthorn engine works in Newcastle in 1885. The latter had started at Forth Banks near Newcastle central railway station, building mainly locomotives, but with an increasing number of marine engines from 1852. But the site was inconvenient for marine work, so in 1871 a new factory was established at St Peters on the north bank two miles down-stream of the bridges. Their first dreadnought contract was *Temeraire* building at Devonport, with an Admiralty letter dated 15 January 1907 confirming their tender price of £110,000 for eighteen Yarrow boilers and £135,000 for main machinery, with £19,449 added for auxiliary machinery.[4] Parts were to be interchangeable as far as possible with sisters *Bellerophon* and *Superb*. Drawing office work was to be shared with the contractors for those two vessels: Fairfield for turbines and shafting, Wallsend Slipway for boiler rooms and Hawthorn Leslie for pipe arrangements. All their five other Dockyard contracts (the last *Royal Oak*) were also for Devonport built hulls. They probably had their own workshop and resident staff there as they could maintain continuity. On the Tyne, they had a floating workshop which could be berthed alongside the hull being engined. However, as shown in Chapter 11, these

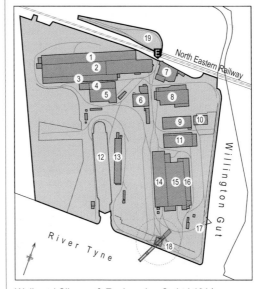

Wallsend Slipway & Engineering Co Ltd 1914

1. Erecting shop
2. Machine shop
3. Tool shop
4. Plumbers shop
5. Blacksmiths shop
6. Store
7. Offices
8. Foundry
9. Joiners and pattern shop
10. Wood shed
11. Brass foundry and coppersmiths shop
12. Graving dock 540 x 66ft
13. Dock platers shed
14. Boiler erecting shop
15. Boiler machine shop
16. Light platework shed
17. 80-ton sheerlegs
18. 150-ton giant cantilever crane
19. Sidings

Wallsend Slipway started in 1871 as a modest ship repair facility, with two patent slipways to the east of the 1895 drydock. After adding 'Engineering' to its title, it developed into one of the largest British marine engine building works under the dynamic leadership of Andrew Laing. The works were continually extended, becoming capable of producing the highest powered steam turbine machinery. After closure in the 1980s, the site was used for offshore construction, the main machine shop still visible at 54-59-26N 01-30-30W, and the drydock entrance.

contracts were not particularly profitable, but they did result in high prestige which also helped them win other high class merchant ship orders at their shipyard, even though that was too small to build battleships.

Parsons was the other Tyneside machinery contractor, but concentrated on building the turbines (and later the gearing), buying in boilers and other parts from outside suppliers. Although invited to tender for complete installations, their only successes pre-war were for *King George V* (Contract No.61) in October 1910 and *Royal Sovereign* (No.95) in 1913, both at Portsmouth. However they profited from their turbine designs fitted in the majority of pre-war RN warships, receiving a royalty of typically 1s 10½d per shp,[5] i.e. £2344 on a 25,000 shp set or about 1 per cent of machinery contract value, which enabled them to maintain research and development.

As Naval Construction & Armaments, Vickers Sons & Maxim had started building battleship steam reciprocating machinery at Barrow with *Majestic* in 1894. Although prime contractor for her machinery, they bought *Dreadnought*'s turbines from Parsons, the Admiralty having requested that her turbines came from one of Parsons, John Brown or Wallsend Slipway, the only engine builders with large turbine experience to date. The Admiralty were clearly satisfied with Vickers' contribution to the success of the new ship, writing to them on 26 December 1906, 'The Lords Commissioners recognise

with great pleasure that the work performed by your firm has materially contributed to the early completion of the ship. Please therefore accept their Lordships cordial appreciation of the efforts which have helped to achieve this satisfactory result.'[6] This applied to both her machinery and gun mountings. Although Vickers had taken out a Parsons licence in 1905, their first turbine machinery was not completed until 1908, for the Isle of Man steamer *Ben-My-Chree*. From then on, they built machinery not only for their own dreadnought hulls (*Vanguard* onwards) but for the Dockyards, e.g. *Lion* and for Armstrong (*Rio de Janeiro/Agincourt*) and also exported complete sets – *Hiei* to Japan and *España* to Spain.

John Brown was the most successful battleship/cruiser engine builder, due to its early lead with turbines and to the supply of cheaper materials such as forgings from within the group – materials made up about 60 per cent of a machinery contract. They engined five of the eleven battlecruisers completed before the First World War. They built turbines for other machinery contractors, including Harland & Wolff for *Neptune* as well as their *Olympic* and *Titanic*'s low pressure turbines. They built two complete installations for Russian battleships in 1914. Their lead was reinforced when in 1908 they took out a licence to build the American Curtis impulse turbine and engineered it into the Brown-Curtis type. The Admiralty was keen to have an alternative turbine design to Parsons, and the Curtis turbine was lighter and more compact and more economical at lower cruising powers. However, Brown had to pay royalties both to Curtis (initially 1s per hp) and to Parsons, as the latter's licence covered all turbines made at Clydebank. The first battlecruiser so fitted was *Tiger*, ordered in 1912. By 1919 over 250 Brown-Curtis sets had been installed in warships, including eight battleships/cruisers culminating in the mighty *Hood* with 144,000 shp in 1919.[7] Not all were built by John Brown; they had granted sub-licences to most of the builders such as Fairfield, Yarrow and Thornycroft. Every time a Brown-Curtis turbine was manufactured in the UK, a royalty was paid to rival turbine maker Parsons as well as Curtis. When Charles Curtis questioned why this should be the case, Thomas Bell wrote to him:

As regards paying royalties to Parsons, I would tell you, for your private information, that people in very high positions in the British

Below: The engine and boiler shops erected in 1904 by Arrol for Beardmore at Dalmuir were on a grand scale. This view of No.2 Bay, one of the smaller bays, is where components for engines and boilers were made. Although large machines were individually powered by electric motors, note the line shafting fitted to the columns at the left to drive smaller machines. See page 145 for a sectional drawing of these shops. *(Author's collection)*

Navy were so impressed with the wonderful additional tactical advantages obtained in ships fitted with turbines and oil fired boilers that they felt a big debt of gratitude to Sir Charles Parsons, and I was given to understand that, if we agreed to pay Parsons' turbine royalty during the continuance of our licence whether the turbines were his or other types, all opposition would be withdrawn to the introduction of your turbine into the British Navy. In view of this, and also in view of the fact that our Company was not prepared to carry out a wearisome and expensive law suit with the Parsons Company over the matter, we thought it well to agree, and I am sure that you will not be the losers by this.'[8]

The other three important Clyde dreadnought engine builders were Fairfield, Scotts and Beardmore. Each built largely for their own hulls, though the first two did engine one Dockyard battleship each (*Bellerophon* and *St Vincent* respectively). Harland & Wolff was the other major British engine builder, but built mainly for its own hulls, especially the large passenger vessels in which it specialised before the First World War. It had built four steam reciprocating sets for Dockyard-built pre-dreadnoughts, the last being *Hibernia* in 1906. Its only battleship/cruiser was *Glorious*, with four sets of Parsons single reduction geared turbines, based on doubling up a 'C' class cruiser twin screw installation. At 90,000 shp this was far above their previous installation powers, so with the Admiralty wartime secrecy requirements, it allocated three contract numbers (482-4) to give the impression to sub-contractors and others that there was more than one ship. For the same reason, Parsons allocated both 115 and 116 to its contract for *Courageous*, and Wallsend Slipway 763 and 764 to *Furious*.

OIL FUEL

All of the early battleships had been coal-fired, but with the increasing availability of oil, battleships from about 1906 onwards had their boilers modified to burn oil as well. The big advantage of oil was that it had a higher calorific value than coal (about 18,500 BTU/lb vs. 12,500 BTU/lb) so needing a lesser weight of bunkers for a given steam output. Being a liquid, it could be stowed in awkward spaces such as double bottom tanks, whereas coal bunkers had not only to be reasonably close to the boilers, but required more elaborate arrangements for bunkering with numerous

coal loading hatches and chutes and large gangs of men to handle sacks of coal from a collier alongside, as well as ash removal systems. Oil required only pumps and piping and a refuelling tanker, dramatically reducing the time and manpower to refuel. However, these advantages were only fully realised when the first battleships to be solely oil-fuelled were ordered, the *Queen Elizabeth* class of 1912. Fewer stokers were required compared with those needed to shovel coal to the boilers, so engineering complement roughly halved, and less accommodation space was required. Higher power could be maintained indefinitely as stoker exhaustion was no longer a factor, while the steam turbine lent itself to overloading if boilers were forced. Thus although the engine power of *Queen Elizabeth* was normally rated at 56,000 shp, they could easily maintain their overload 75,000 shp, for which boilers and propellers were sized. Special oil burning sprayers were needed for the boilers, but companies such as Wallsend Slipway had already developed such oil burning equipment, which the Admiralty developed further at their Haslar test station from 1902.[9] The problems of incomplete combustion and excessive smoke were eventually overcome. From the 1903 new construction programme, large warships had supplementary oil firing (bunkers in *Dreadnought* 2977 tons coal, 1120 tons oil). While both the price per ton and price per BTU were higher for oil, the advantages for

Below: *Nelson's* steam turbine machinery was the first battleship machinery installation completed by Wallsend Slipway & Engineering for a decade (Contract 851), albeit at a loss. One set of her twin screw Brown-Curtis geared turbines developing 45,000 shp total are seen here in the erecting shop in 1925. The casings from the port HP (nearest) and LP turbines have been removed to show the blading. *(Author's collection)*

Below: As John Brown had resident photographers, they were able to capture interesting stages of construction, while those shipbuilders who used commercial photographers hired for the event normally only recorded launches and trials. On 27 December 1939, one of *Duke of York's* eight boilers is lifted into the hull while still on the berth, using temporary sheerlegs. The timber backing for the side armour can be seen, as well as an eyeplate for attaching one of the launch drag chains. *(Upper Clyde Shipbuilders)*

Below, right: *Duke of York's* forward funnel was shipped in May 1941, long after all her machinery and uptakes had been installed. *(Upper Clyde Shipbuilders)*

high powered warships such as battleships and destroyers far outweighed the disadvantages. In the 1914–15 Navy Estimates, the Admiralty budgeted for buying 442,000 tons of oil at 70s 3d per ton (£1.552 million) and 1,226,400 tons of coal in the UK at 20s 9d per ton (£1.270 million) – the Admiralty preferred more expensive Welsh coal with its good burning properties and high calorific value. There were concerns about security of oil supplies from foreign countries compared with UK mined coal, but the Government purchased a majority holding in the Anglo-Persian Oil Co (later BP) in 1914 to reduce that risk. The 1913 *Royal Sovereign* class were redesigned from dual coal/oil firing to oil only and from then onwards all British battleships/cruisers were oil fuelled, using heavy fuel oil, rather than the distillate that early diesel engines required.

AFTER THE FIRST WORLD WAR

After *Hood's* completion, the battleship engine builders had to concentrate on merchant ship orders. Although *Nelson* and *Rodney* were ordered late in 1922 with modest 45,000 shp twin screw machinery, the competition was

fierce, and both engine builders made losses on their contracts (Wallsend Slipway and Cammell Laird respectively – see p.245). Although no more new battleships were ordered until 1936, the engine builders benefited from re-engining contracts in the 1930s. The first such was the Chilean *Almirante Latorre* (ex *Canada*) which received new Parsons geared turbine machinery (previously Brown-Curtis direct drive) built by Vickers-Armstrongs at Barrow costing £162,000, which was fitted at Devonport Dockyard in 1930.[10] The Admiralty was keen to modernise some First World War battleships, starting with *Warspite* in 1933. Progress in marine engineering with the introduction of gearing which improved both turbine and propeller efficiency, and the development of smaller lighter higher-pressure boilers, resulted in considerable weight savings which could be put into thicker deck armour. Her 15in main armament was modified to give longer range with 30° elevation in place of 20° and a stronger anti-aircraft armament fitted. In 1934 Parsons' bid of £440,000 for the 80,000 shp machinery was successful, with Vickers-Armstrongs having bid £472,000.[11] The work was completed at Portsmouth Dockyard in

1937. Three more vessels followed, with Cammell Laird receiving the contract for *Renown*'s 120,000 shp machinery in 1935; it was worth £726,000 but the company barely made a profit on it. Both *Valiant* and *Queen Elizabeth*'s re-engining was not completed until 1939–40. Fairfield made a profit of about £34,000 on the latter's contract worth £690,000. Some interesting statistics on her conversion show how successfully new wine was put into old bottles:[12]

Queen Elizabeth	1915	1940
Shaft horsepower	75,000	80,000
Boilers	24	8
Steam pressure (lb/sq in)	235 saturated	400 superheated
Machinery weight (tons)	3080	1570
Steam consumption at full power (lb/shp-hr)	12.8	9.4
Endurance at 10 knots (n miles)	4400	13,500
Maximum service speed (knots)	24	23.5
Generator capacity (kW)	700	2400

But the steam conditions were not as advanced as contemporary US Navy ships, due more to conservatism by the Admiralty than by the British marine engineering industry – Yarrow built destroyers for Portugal in the 1930s with higher steam conditions than the RN.

When the five *King George V* class battleships were ordered in 1936–7, their machinery contracts were effectively placed with their shipbuilders. *Anson*'s contract went to Wallsend Slipway, but since 1903 that company had been a subsidiary of Swan, Hunter & Wigham Richardson who received the hull contract. While Vickers-Armstrongs' Naval Yard on the Tyne received the hull contract for *King George V*, the machinery was manufactured at their Barrow works. Fairfield and John Brown received both hull and machinery contracts for *Howe* and *Duke of York*, as did the latter for *Vanguard*. This was the seventeenth complete battleship installation from Clydebank since 1895, in addition to the turbine sets for other builders.

Auxiliary Machinery

While the machinery contractor manufactured the main propulsion machinery and boilers, he also procured and installed the auxiliary machinery bought in from specialist manufac-

Above: *Vanguard* receives her port inner HP turbine at Clyde-bank on 12 January 1945, deck openings having to be left. The cruiser being refitted across the basin is *Bermuda. (Upper Clyde Shipbuilders)*

turers. The key to an efficient steam propulsion system was high-purity fresh water which was converted into high-pressure steam by burning the fuel in the boiler, expanded though the engine to below atmospheric pressure in the condenser, where it was cooled back into water to be fed back to the boiler. An evaporator (distiller) converted seawater into fresh water, a feed pump passed it into the boiler under pressure, which had fans to supply combustion air. The steam generated was passed through pipes, controlled by valves, into the cylinders (steam reciprocating engine) or rotors (turbine). It was then exhausted into the condenser, where an air pump created a near vacuum. A circulating pump passed seawater outside the condenser tubes to cool the steam back to fresh water. After making up any steam losses, and passing through various tanks, e.g. to remove air bubbles, the water was returned to the boiler. Separate pumps were needed to pump lubricating oil to items of machinery and for transferring oil fuel between tanks. Coal-fired ships needed ash hoists or expellers to dump such overboard underwater. Bilge pumps were needed for flooding magazines and draining compartments of seawater, which could also be used to provide fire-fighting water. Pumps were also needed for domestic fresh water, hot and cold. Such auxiliaries could amount to a significant cost: the pumps ordered in 1911 from G & J Weir of Glasgow for *Queen Mary* amounted to £24,240, or 5 per cent of her machinery contract.[13]

The increasing use of electricity in warships from the 1880s, initially for searchlights and lighting, rapidly extended to other uses from signalling to powering electric motors all over the ship. Direct current was used in all RN battleships, increased to 220 volts in designs from 1905, when the ring main distribution system was introduced. It was generated initially from steam reciprocating engines of modest power connected to a dynamo – a typical generator was around 36–100 kW, needing an engine of 50–150 hp. Steam turbines were also used to power generators (turbo-generator) from 1912, after extensive development in power stations ashore. Most dreadnoughts had in addition diesel powered generators for use in harbour and to provide an alternative supply in case of loss of steam. *Superb*'s two steam generators (Brotherhood engine, Siemens dynamo) cost £2899 and two diesels (Mirrlees, Watson engine, Siemens dynamo) £7550, totalling 600 kW.

In early steam ships, many of the auxiliaries were driven directly off the main engine, but it was more convenient for each to have their own source of power, which gave better control. This could be by steam from the main boilers, but for engines outside the machinery spaces such meant long runs of hot and potentially leaking pipes. Hydraulic power using distilled water was particularly useful for operating ordnance machinery, but needed separate steam-powered hydraulic pumps, typically three 500 hp ones for a dreadnought, plus associated piping. But electricity with its easy-to-run cables increasingly became the power supply for auxiliary machinery, even in the machinery spaces. So electric generating capacity steadily increased:

Majestic 3 x 48 kW steam reciprocator driven generators 80V dc. Total 144 kW.
Dreadnought 4 x 100 kW generators at 100V dc (2 steam, 2 diesel, later 3 + 1) Total 400 kW.
Queen Elizabeth 2 x 200kW turbo-generators, 2 x 150kW diesel at 220V dc. Total 700 kW.
King George V (WW2) 8 x 300kW generators at 220V dc (6 turbo, 2 diesel). Total 2400kW.

Deck machinery such as anchor capstans and steering gear were initially hand-powered but as ships grew in size, mechanical power was soon applied. Initially this was steam, but electric power was much more convenient, even if it had to be converted into hydraulic power at, for example, the steering gear. Air compressors were needed to charge torpedoes and clear the guns and in machinery spaces. Refrigerating machinery was needed for food stores and for magazine cooling. Boat hoists (or derricks and winches) were needed to handle the heavier boats. Hoists were needed both for embarking ammunition and for moving it to the secondary armament; the main armament used hydraulic power. When steam driven, all this machinery needed about 100 auxiliary engines totalling about 6000 hp in a dreadnought, about one quarter of the main engine power – and that excludes electrically driven machinery.[14] A 'modern' capital ship such as *Nelson* had about 400 electric drive motors totalling 2300 hp, ranging from the boat hoist of 195 hp to 2 hp pump motors, plus 300 miles of cable.[15]

A large number of specialist sub-contractors supplied such machinery, with some of the most important on the approved Admiralty list shown opposite.

Weir and Allen were both highly regarded by the Admiralty for the range and quality of their equipment, and for nearly a century they were never without orders from them. Allen even produced main propulsion machinery in the First World War: diesels for submarines, steam turbine machinery for patrol boats and steam reciprocating engines for minesweepers and trawlers. They provided ten sets of 1750 hp steam turbine drives and condensers for the *King George V* class VSG hydraulic pumps to

Right: Auxiliary machinery manufacturers were keen to illustrate the range of equipment they supplied. Allen of Bedford featured generators, pumps and electrical equipment. *(Shipbuilding & Shipping Record)*

ADMIRALTY AUXILIARY MACHINERY CONTRACTORS

G & J Weir Ltd, Glasgow	Boiler feed pumps, air pumps, circulating pumps, oil fuel pumps, evaporators and distillers, air compressors, de-aerating plant, feed water systems.
Drysdale & Co, Glasgow (Weir subsidiary from 1919)	Fire & bilge pumps, circulating pumps, lubricating oil pumps, oil fuel pumps, fresh & salt water pumps, salvage pumps.
Belliss & Morcom Ltd, Birmingham	High-speed steam engines for boats and generators, forced draught fans, air compressors.
W H Allen Sons & Co Ltd, Bedford	Forced draught fans, steam driven generator sets, dynamos, circulating pumps, drydock pumps, salvage pumps, motor generators, gearing. After WW1: diesel generator sets, turbo-generators, electric motors for winches etc.
J Howden & Co Ltd, Glasgow	Forced draught fans and engines, oil burning system (with Wallsend Slipway), engines for generators.
Ruston, Proctor & Co Ltd, Lincoln	Steam and diesel engines for generators.
Richard Hornsby & Sons Ltd, Grantham. (Ruston and Hornsby merged in 1918 to form Ruston & Hornsby Ltd)	Diesel engines for generators.
Laurence, Scott & Co Ltd, Norwich	Electric motors, dynamos, motor generators, ammunition hoists, lifts, winches, control gear.
J Kirkcaldy, London	Distilling machinery.
Caird & Rayner, London	Distilling machinery.
C A Parsons & Co, Newcastle	Turbo-generators
Brush Electrical Engineering Co, Loughborough	Turbo-generators.
Willans & Robinson Ltd, Rugby (Part of English Electric from 1919)	Steam and turbo-generators.
British Westinghouse Electrical & Manufacturing Co Ltd, Manchester (Metropolitan-Vickers from 1919)	Turbo-generators, boat hoists, winches, fans.
British Thomson Houston Co Ltd, Rugby (AEI subsidiary from 1928)	Turbo-generators, motor generators, electric lamps.
General Engine & Boiler Co, London	Air compressors, pumps.
Pulsometer Engineering Co Ltd, London & Reading	Refrigerating machinery, pumps, sirens.
Peter Brotherhood, Peterborough	Air compressors, steam and diesel generators, torpedo engines.
Mirrlees, Watson Co Ltd, Glasgow (1907 Mirrlees, Bickerton & Day, Stockport)	Diesel engines for generators.
John I Thornycroft & Co Ltd, Basingstoke	Diesel engines for generators.
Worthington Pumping Engine Co (later Worthington-Simpson Ltd, Newark)	Pumps.
Gwynne's Pumps Ltd, London	Pumps.
Crompton & Co Ltd, London	Steam generators, searchlights, ash hoists, ammunition hoists, motor generators.
Siemens Brothers & Co Ltd, London	Dynamos, cables, motor generators, telegraphs, ammunition hoists, torsionmeters, wireless systems.
Electric & Ordnance Accessories Co Ltd, Birmingham (a Vickers subsidiary)	Boat and ammunition hoists, motor generators, winches.

Left: *Nelson*'s single reduction gears reduced the turbine rpm of about 1500 to 160 at the propeller. A 4 cylinder Sulzer diesel for cargo ship *Enton* is seen in the background in 1925 – a new line of production. *(Tyne & Wear Archives)*

lutions per minute. That was transmitted down a shaft to a propeller where the torque was converted into thrust to drive the ship forward. The dreadnought era saw significant changes in this process. In direct drive engines (steam reciprocating and early turbines) most of the propeller thrust was taken by a multiple collar thrust block just abaft the coupling between engine and shaft. But as powers increased, a better design was needed, in the form of the Michell thrust block, using a single collar and a thin oil film with tilting plates, manufactured in Newcastle from about 1905. This could take much higher thrusts and has continued in use to this day, with the Michell Bearings company now part of the Rolls-Royce group.

Parsons introduced gearing between turbine and shaft in 1910. The Admiralty was quick to adopt such single reduction gearing in destroyers from 1913, soon to be followed by cruisers. With both turbine and propeller now operating at near optimum revolutions, propulsive efficiency increased by about 20 per cent.[17] When *Courageous* and *Glorious* received effectively two sets of the cruiser *Champion*'s twin screw geared machinery, they became the first British capital ships to be fitted with gearing when completed in 1916. Thereafter all such ships were fitted with single reduction gearing. Parsons manufactured both the turbines and gearing for *Courageous*, while the principal

Above: *Vanguard* receives her starboard outer single reduction gearbox on 26 December 1944, four weeks after launch. (*Upper Clyde Shipbuilders*)

power their 14in mountings.[16] Weir remains an important engineering company to this day, although for the offshore and onshore industries rather than ships.

POWER TRANSMISSION AND PROPELLERS

Main propulsion machinery produced torque (twisting power) at a certain number of revo-

Right: *Nelson*'s two 3-bladed propellers were 16.5ft in diameter, seen here in the shop at Wallsend. To reduce weight, the shafting was hollow forged. (*Tyne & Wear Archives*)

warship engine builders such as John Brown and Fairfield set up their own gear manufacturing shops, although others such as Scotts initially bought their gearing from Parsons. Gearing was also produced by specialist manufacturers such as David Brown of Huddersfield, still in business today.

Shafting and propellers were shipped before launch, allowing the lower hull to be closed up watertight. The main engines, boilers and auxiliary machinery were mostly shipped after launch, through temporary openings left in the decks. The hull could be manoeuvred under a heavy fitting out crane for the work; a direct drive LP turbine could weigh up to 100 tons. Battleship propulsion shafting was forged hollow to save weight. Typical suppliers were:

Orion, Malaya and *Nelson.* Armstrong Whitworth, Openshaw.
Queen Elizabeth, Hood and *Furious* inner. Thomas Firth, Sheffield.
Furious outer. W Somers, Halesowen.
Anson (17.4in outside diameter, 11.5in inside). Firth-Brown, Sheffield.

Propeller design and manufacture had been undertaken by engine builders from the earliest days, normally using cast iron to their own design. But with increasing powers in battleships and passenger ships, a better material was needed and specialist makers emerged. In 1876 Percival Parsons (no relation of Charles) developed a new manganese bronze alloy. Manganese Bronze and Brass Co Ltd established a foundry at Deptford in London in 1882, later moving to Millwall. J Stone & Co Ltd also of Deptford had started making copper fastenings for the Navy's wooden walls fifty years earlier. Both companies started using manganese bronze in the mid-1880s. Although difficult to cast at first, the Admiralty fitted some ships with such propellers at that time. This tougher metal permitted thinner more efficient blades, as well as being more resistant to corrosion and erosion from cavitation, the latter resulting from reduced pressure over parts of highly-loaded propeller blades. Initially such blades were bolted to a cast iron boss, but it was not long before the entire propeller could be cast in the new material. The larger British warships had propellers made by both companies from the late 1890s.

With steam reciprocating machinery, propellers were of large diameter with low

> ## Stone's Order for *Anson's* Propellers
> J Stone & Co. Order Z.6131. Design 9.7.37.
> Ordered 28.4.38 by Wallsend Slipway for HMS *Jellicoe*
> Two right handed and two left handed 3 bladed propellers.
> 14' 6" diameter, 15' 0" pitch, 112 sq ft blade area.
> To absorb 27,500 shp at 236 rpm.
> To Admiralty inspection standards.
> Delivery to Wallsend Slipway works July–September 1939.
> Estimated weight 14 tons.
> Price 1s 6¾d per lb. Approx £2600 each including cone.
> Cast 3 May to 6 June 1939.

revolutions, with modest thrust loading on their blades. But with faster-running steam turbines, propeller revolutions had to be increased, resulting in reduced diameter and blade area, so efficiency was reduced and they became more susceptible to cavitation with high thrust loading on the blades. While the *Duncan* class had two 17ft diameter 4-bladed propellers with 18.5ft pitch and 82 sq ft blade area for 9000 ihp each (say 7500 shp) at 120 rpm per shaft, *Dreadnought* had initially four 8.83ft diameter 3-bladed, 8.37ft pitch, 33 sq ft for 5750 shp at 320 rpm.[18] In later ships, gearing improved this situation, allowing larger diameter slower running more efficient propellers. Stone's introduced a new alloy, Turbiston, and set up a new works at Charlton on the Thames in 1916. The two manufacturers continued to be the main Admiralty suppliers of both new and replacement propellers for higher-powered ships, as well as for some overseas navies. Improved alloys and designs were introduced in the 1930s. With wartime bombing in London, Manganese Bronze moved to a new factory at Birkenhead in 1941. The two companies merged to form Stone Manganese Marine in 1963. The panel above shows details of Stone's order for *Anson's* propellers.

In 1919 Stone's claimed to have supplied 3350 tons of bronze propellers to the wartime British Fleet, transmitting 10 million hp, including those for *Queen Elizabeth* and *Lion.* At a price of around £100 per ton, that amounted to about £330,000. In the Second World War they claimed to have made 22,000 propellers absorbing 20 million hp, including nine for battleships, twenty-nine for aircraft carriers and eighty for cruisers, the majority being for smaller vessels such as motor torpedo boats, tank landing craft and motor minesweepers.

8: ARMAMENT

MAKING THE GUNS

The builder of a battleship for the Royal Navy supplied the hull and machinery, but the Admiralty supplied the armament and armour for the builder to install – although for export orders, the builder usually supplied everything, including the ammunition. The procurement process was thus different for guns and mountings, and was paid for under different Votes in the annual Navy Estimates. Indeed until about 1904, the shipbuilder usually delivered an unarmed vessel for one of the Royal Dockyards to install the armament.

The Royal Gun Factory (RGF) at Woolwich Arsenal had long been the main supplier of the Navy's guns, although run by the War Office. But with the development of large breech-loading guns from the 1860s, the Admiralty increasingly turned to private ordnance manufacturers to both design and construct some of its guns.[1] This was accentuated when guns became too large for hand-working, so

hydraulic machinery was introduced, a speciality of William Armstrong's company at Elswick west of Newcastle. In the 1890s improved 'smokeless' propellants such as Cordite increased pressure in the gun barrel, requiring greater radial strength and longer guns. The resulting higher muzzle velocity increased range and penetrating capability. The previous technique of shrinking on as many as seven hoops of steel onto the inner A tube (liner) was replaced by wire-winding, where several miles of high-tensile steel wire were wrapped around the A tube. Larger steel forgings plus hydraulic presses made it possible to produce longer and thicker barrel components, requiring ever more extensive and specialised equipment such as wire-winding machines and longer machining lathes to cut the bore and rifling and finish the outer profiles. The barrel components also needed heat treatment as well as later reheating to allow the outer jackets to be fitted over the (colder) inner tubes, so deep

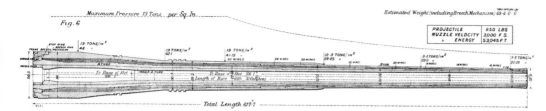

Fig. 6

heating pits were needed with high overhead clearance to handle the components vertically. See plan on p.170 for Beardmore gun shop layout.

All British battleship main guns from 1893 (12in Mark VIII) to 1927 (16in Mark I) were wire-wound. Winding steel wire (actually strip 0.25 x 0.06in in section) around the inner tubes provided radial strength against the pressure of the expanding gases from the propellant (which could reach 18 tons/sq in) in a more uniform and controllable way than shrinking on successive tubes. The basic construction by a private manufacturer of a 12in gun[2] as shown above comprised: inner A tube (a replaceable rifled liner); full length outer A tube; wire winding (usually from breech to muzzle); B tube over about 55 per cent of length from muzzle as part of the outer sleeve; jacket about 55 per cent of length from breech to form the rest of the outer sleeve, so slightly overlapping the B tube; breech ring, a short large diameter tube that supported the breech mechanism.[3]

Manufacture of such guns fell into two main stages: producing the steel forgings making up each of the tubes, and forming and machining those into a complete gun. Firms such as Vickers Sons & Maxim (Sheffield), Armstrong Whitworth (Newcastle) and Beardmore (Glasgow) could undertake the complete operation, while RGF and Coventry Ordnance Works (COW) had to buy in forgings, the latter from firms within the group such as John Brown or Cammell Laird. A 12in gun of 50 tons finished weight (e.g. Mark IX in the *Formidable* class) required 60 tons of forgings plus 13 tons of wire. The latter was high tensile steel with a breaking strength of around 100 tons/sq in (compared with 26 tons/sq in for mild steel) costing around £28–£35 per ton (compared with about £6 for mild steel). Gun steel forgings were typically of nickel steel of 34–44 tons/sq in ultimate tensile strength, formed from octagonal cast steel ingots up to 15ft long weighing up to 40 tons. A hole was trepanned through the centre to form a tube, which also removed some weaker material. After reheating, a hydraulic forging press

capable of exerting a force of 3000–5000 tons was used to squeeze and elongate the tube to the required length and internal and external diameter. Supported by a water cooled mandrel through the middle, it remained hot enough to work for the next two to four hours.

The resulting tube was annealed by reheating and allowed to cool slowly to release the stresses induced in the forging operation. If necessary it was straightened in the press before being rough machined inside and outside. It was then hardened and tempered by heating to around 1500°F before being lowered vertically into a tank about 50ft deep containing rape oil to cool it over a period of six to twelve hours. A second annealing required heating to about 1000°F and then slow cooling over twenty-four hours. Test pieces were then cut from each end. If satisfactory, the inner A tube would be bored to within about 0.25in of the final diameter, and turned on the outside to the required profile. Massive specially-designed machine tools such as lathes 90ft long were used, in which the tube revolved around the cutting tool. For the bore, the tool was pulled through rather than pushed, which gave better control and less likelihood of bending the tube. The other tubes were made in a similar manner, but

Left: The Vickers H Design 12in 50cal gun for the Spanish *España* class battleships. Typical British wire-wound construction with Inner A tube, A tube, wire winding (fifty-two layers at rear), B tube forward, jacket rear, total weight 69.3 tons including breech mechanism. *(Engineering)*

Below: Two of the three companies who owned Coventry Ordnance Works made forgings for guns in Sheffield, John Brown and Cammell Laird. At the latter's Grimesthorpe works, three forgings for a 13.5in Mark V gun are posed in front of the Davy Bros Ltd (of Sheffield) hammer. The lower 40-ton forging is for the 52ft long A tube (liner), above it is the 20-ton 31ft long B tube and furthest the 55-ton 33ft long jacket. The finished gun weight excluding breech mechanism was 74 tons. *(Author's collection)*

were finished close to their final profile. Gauges were used to check dimensions and straightness. The outer A tube had a slight taper on its inside to match that on the outside of the inner A tube (narrower at the muzzle) with the latter forced into the former using hydraulic pressure, or the former could be shrunk on hot. The combination was then taken to a special wire-winding machine, where miles of strip would be wound on to the revolving tube. A coil of wire was moved slowly down the length of the gun, paying out at up to 70ft/min. The tension was adjusted from 35 to 50 tons/sq in according to whether the layers were inner or outer. As the internal pressure on firing the gun fell off towards the muzzle, there might be only fourteen layers at the muzzle end but seventy-five at the breech end (which was about 48in in maximum diameter) in a 12in 50 cal[4] gun,

Above: Boring out gun forgings to make finished tubes was a major operation requiring very long lathes, where the cutting tool was pulled (as opposed to pushed) through. A 12in gun is in the lathe being finish bored before the rifling will be cut. A rough finished forging is suspended from the crane in the 515ft long machine shop at Parkhead. (*Author's collection*)

Gun Treating Shop
Parkhead Forge 1910

1. Vertical furnaces
2. Oil hardening tanks in water jackets
3. Shrinking pit
4. 100-ton capacity trolley
5. Tempering (annealing) furnace
6. 100-ton crane
7. 30-ton crane
8. 13.5-in A tube (50.5 feet long)
9. Office
10. Auxiliary tank
11. Chimney

section on centre line of shop

The gun treating shop was a tall building with deep pits sunk into the floor for hardening and tempering forged gun tubes and jackets which had been roughly bored and brought to near the correct dimensions. A bogie was used to take tubes into the long horizontal regenerative tempering furnace at the far end of the shop. Vertical furnaces were used for re-heating, then the overhead crane removed the forging from the furnace and dipped it into one of the hardening tanks. These cranes were especially built to operate at very high speeds to ensure minimal loss of temperature. The hardening tanks contained about 16,000 gallons of oil which was circulated continuously and were, in turn, surrounded by cooling water. Temperature control was critical in bringing the hardened steel to the correct temper. Once the tubes had been hardened and tempered, they were taken to the machine shops for final machining. After that, inner tubes were 'telescoped' or shrunk together. Two vertical furnaces for heating the tubes were situated beside the shrinking (or build up) pit. The pit, located at the other end of the shop, was fitted with water sprays and gas rings to cool or heat the tubes locally, with one forced into the other. Wire winding was then applied to the inner tubes, which were then returned to the shrinking pit for B tube and jacket to be fitted. The gun was then rifled before final checking.

Below: This stamp, both embossed and inked, was applied to Gunnery Reports produced by HMS *Excellent*. In this instance it was on documents referring to *Invincible*.

needing in total 117 miles of wire weighing 13.5 tons.

The B tube, and later the jacket and breech ring, was shrunk on by heating to a moderate temperature to expand it and then lowered from a crane into a vertical pit containing the colder inner tube.[5] After the combination had cooled, a tight shrink fit was obtained, providing longitudinal strength for the gun. The nearly-finished gun would then go to the rifling machine where the grooves (sixty in a 12in barrel) would be machined with the necessary twist (usually one turn in a length of thirty times the bore). The larger-diameter chamber to contain the propellant was also machined, the breech thread screws cut and keys formed to hold the gun body in the mounting slide. The breech mechanism was manufactured separately (at Erith for Vickers guns) and was attached to the breech ring by screws. After final examination and gauging (to ensure interchangeability) by both the manufacturer's and Admiralty inspectors, the gun was ready for despatch, initially to the proof firing range, where typically three to six rounds were fired, then ready for despatch to the gun stockyard at RGF or a Royal Dockyard, or to a private shipyard if needed for mounting in a new ship. This process now took about eleven months from order to delivery, a big improvement in manufacturing efficiency as a 12in had taken about twenty months in the mid-1890s. Vickers was able to build three such guns a month in 1910.

THE GUN MANUFACTURERS

The private manufacturers were usually the leaders in terms of developing new and larger guns, and improved manufacturing processes, partly spurred by the export market. Woolwich did adopt some of these new processes, but the annual Estimates system meant that it took several years to get such plant approved and installed. The War Office was regarded as monopolistic and reactionary, reluctant to adopt new designs with a 'not invented here' attitude. It resented the intrusion of the private firms into their long established domain, sometimes rejecting Armstrong steel samples with no sound cause.[6] Armstrong became the Admiralty's biggest supplier of heavy gun mountings from about the mid-1880s, partly based on their technical and commercial experience of hydraulic machinery. Their extensive works at Elswick produced both guns and mountings, as well as having its own shipyard

and steelworks. However, Sir Joseph Whitworth at Openshaw in Manchester offered some competition, being nearly as large a heavy gun maker as Armstrong, although falling well short in heavy gun mountings – see table of heavy gun mounting manufacturers on p.191. Concerned about this competition and to prevent control by Vickers, Armstrong merged with Whitworth in 1897 to create Sir W G Armstrong, Whitworth & Co Ltd. The new company became the world's largest supplier of warships and armaments to foreign navies, including Japan and Brazil.

Armstrong's closest rival now became Vickers at Sheffield who was a specialist steel producer, including forgings, cutting tools and some armour plate. Under the guidance of chairman Tom Vickers, they moved from being largely a steel company to a major armaments company.

Above: The inside of Beardmore's 100ft high gun treatment shop at Parkhead – probably Items 28 and 29 on the plan on p.75. The detailed shop layout is shown on the plan opposite. The photo shows an A tube (liner) just out of the heating furnace about to be lowered by the 100-ton crane into the oil hardening tank before tempering. A built-up gun is on the trolley at right about to enter (or has just left?) the furnace. *(Author's collection)*

When in the later 1880s the Admiralty was keen to extend heavy gun manufacturers from the existing three (RGF, Elswick and Whitworth), they selected Vickers with their well-equipped steel and forging plant. Vickers invested in gun-making plant, completing their first gun in 1888, merging with machine-gun maker Maxim in 1897. They turned their attention to making a wider range of guns, the bigger calibres at Sheffield, the smaller calibres

at the former Nordenfelt works at Erith in Kent and machine guns at the former Maxim works at Crayford in Kent.[7] But steel companies were keen to control more of the overall warship building process, so in 1897 Vickers, Sons & Maxim bought Naval Construction & Armaments at Barrow to provide an outlet for their guns and armour. John Brown, another Sheffield steel and armour producer, bought Clydebank Engineering & Shipbuilding in 1899 to provide an outlet for their forgings and armour.

Vickers were determined to challenge Armstrong in gun mountings to make themselves a major armaments supplier, so invested heavily in the Barrow works to include the design and manufacture of heavy gun mountings, on a scale to nearly rival Elswick. Instead of being a steel company with an interest in armaments, they became an armaments company with an interest in steel. The new shops at Barrow could also make other heavy engineering plant such as marine propulsion machinery. It was essential to win some early contracts so Vickers tendered prices appreciably below Elswick. They received their first two contracts in March 1898 for *Vengeance* and *Irresistible*'s two twin 12in mountings at a cut

Above: Beardmore made breech mechanisms as well as guns at its Parkhead works. A partially completed breech ring is side-on centre right, with an interrupted thread breech block in the foreground. Note the old-fashioned lineshaft and belt drive to machine tools on the left wall. A breech mechanism for a large gun cost about 10 per cent of the total cost. *(Author's collection)*

Right: As the private shipbuilders built more of the RN's warships, the Admiralty switched the installation of their armament from the Royal Dockyards to the shipyards. *Exmouth* was Vickers' fourth battleship gun mounting contract (No. 10G). The 90-ton turntable for her B.VII mounting is lowered into her forward barbette at Birkenhead, probably early in 1902, probably using the Mersey Docks & Harbour Board 100-ton dockside crane in the West Float. *(Published by permission of Wirral Council)*

price of £53,000 each excluding erection, guns and gunhouse armour.[8] The new shops at Barrow received extensive publicity and visits from distinguished engineers, with lengthy illustrated articles in journals such as *Engineering*.[9] However, the journal did not reveal that both sets of mountings were fourteen months late and had made a loss, not the first time that a contractor building their first set of complex equipment had underestimated production time or cost.[10] *Vengeance* herself was delivered twenty-one months late, partly due to the collapse of the dock entrance at Barrow, trapping her at her fitting out berth. But Vickers having 'bought' that experience into a potentially lucrative market, from 1902 they and Armstrong's (not merged until 1927) dominated both the British and world market for heavy naval guns and mountings, their only serious rival being Krupp of Germany. However much of the latter's output was for the German army rather than the relatively small German warship building industry.

With the armament making up about 28–34 per cent of the cost of a battleship (including gun mountings, gunhouse armour and guns but excluding ammunition), the two companies dominated the export market for large warships, since other British shipbuilders

tendering for foreign warships had little option but to buy their armament from one of the two firms, at prices higher than the firms charged internally to their own shipyards. For example, Thames Iron Works was obliged to buy the 12in guns and mountings for Japanese pre-dreadnoughts *Fuji* and *Shikishima* from Armstrongs and *Fuji*'s armour from Vickers. To break this stranglehold, two shipbuilders Cammell Laird and John Brown took over the then small Coventry Ordnance Works in 1904–05, which made some guns for the Army. Cammell Laird was another example of a merger of a steel and armour producer, Cammell of Sheffield with the shipbuilder Laird of Birkenhead in 1903. They were soon

Above: The stamp applied to completed drawings or documents at the Barrow Gun Department. Note the initials applied by a senior official, probably the chief draughtsman.

Left: Coventry Ordnance Works manufactured guns at Coventry. Here one of their 76-ton 13.5in Mark V guns is shunted on five bogies out of the works to the Midland Railway main line, before transport to the proof range. *(Author's collection)*

Left: The heavy gun shop at Coventry Ordnance Works' Coventry plant. The gun in the foreground looks like a 13.5in Mark V being finish turned on the outside, with another jacket to the right. The electrically powered lathes were on concrete foundations with brick flooring in between. *(Author's collection)*

joined by Clyde shipbuilder Fairfield, so that by 1905 the ownership of COW was 50 per cent John Brown, 25 per cent Cammell Laird and 25 per cent Fairfield. The works at Coventry was greatly extended to manufacture guns and smaller mountings, while a new works was built at Scotstoun near Glasgow to build large gun mountings, completed in 1907. But the Admiralty was reluctant to place major orders with the new company until it had proved itself, contenting itself with modest orders for smaller-calibre guns and mountings, while Armstrong and Vickers lobbied unsuccessfully against the new company. When the previous managing director H H Mulliner resigned in 1909 over a German battleship building scare (see p.20), the parent companies appointed the recent Director of Naval Ordnance (DNO), Rear-Admiral R H Bacon in his place. His inside knowledge would be invaluable, especially of the prices the Admiralty were paying for guns, mountings and ammunition, even if his commercial managerial skills were as yet unproven.[11] On 20 August 1909, before Bacon arrived at COW, the Admiralty, wanting to extend the range of armament suppliers with eight ships in that year's programme, had placed a provisional order with COW for their first battleship gun mounting contract of five twin 13.5in for *Conqueror*.

The sixth manufacturer of heavy guns prior to the First World War was forgemaster and armour plate manufacturer William Beardmore of Parkhead, Glasgow. With Vickers' help, they started making medium calibre guns in 1906 and progressed to making their first 12in gun in 1909. But as Vickers had a major shareholding in Beardmore, there were really only four companies supplying heavy guns: Armstrong Whitworth, Vickers, COW and RGF.

PROCURING THE GUNS

For centuries the Board of Ordnance[12] and the War Office had taken responsibility for procuring the Navy's guns as well as the Army's. In the days when gun carriages on board ships were little more than wooden trucks, a single source sufficed for guns, then the biggest element of armament cost. But once complex shipborne large-calibre gun mountings were needed, it was essential to integrate gun and mounting design and procurement, so the Admiralty sought to procure its own guns. Starting with DNO Captain John Fisher (later First Sea Lord) ordering 4in guns from Armstrong in 1886, the Admiralty eventually achieved procurement integration. From 1888–9, Vote 9 in the Navy Estimates included guns and ammunition previously in War Office Votes, while Vote 8 Section III included gun mountings. From 1907–10, a major dreadnought building period, average annual figures were about £800,000 (guns) and £1.7 million (mountings), with battleships taking a large proportion.[13] But it was not until 1908 that the Admiralty gained full control of specification, design, budgeting, contracting, inspection, installation and testing of shipboard ordnance. In five years, 1902–06, seventy-seven 12in guns had been completed, enough for thirteen pre-dreadnoughts with spares.[14] A typical price for a 12in gun in 1898 was £10,650 for the gun body and a further £850 for the breech mechanism. By the outbreak of the First World War, 410 guns of 12in and over were mounted in the fleet, over double the number of a decade earlier.[15]

For smaller-calibre guns, the Admiralty was content to share procurement facilities with the War Office, e.g. where guns were also used as coast defence weapons such as the 9.2in BL Mark X or 6in BL Mark VII. Woolwich manufactured many of these smaller calibres, especially for the Army, but for larger calibres, industry provided the majority. When Woolwich manufactured any of the latter's designs, no royalties were paid. The 28-ton 9.2in Mark X fitted in the *King Edward VII* class (four each) cost £4934 for the gun body plus

Below: One of the first 13.5in Mark V guns being set up on a proof mounting at Vickers about 1910 before transport to the test range at Eskmeals sixteen miles north-west of Barrow. The gun cradle has an extension housing the chain rammer for projectile and charges. *(Reproduced by kind permission of the Syndics of Cambridge University Library. Vickers 2022)*

£825 for the breech mechanism ordered in
1904. When a new design of gun was proposed,
the Admiralty and the Ordnance Committee[16]
(which had both Army and Navy members)
agreed the broad characteristics, and requested
a design sometimes from RGF or more often a
contract would be placed with one of the
armament companies to design, manufacture
and test one or more guns, e.g. Vickers with the
13.5in Mark V in the *Orion* class. Two hundred
and six such guns were made, only fifty-three
from Vickers, with fifty-eight from RGF,
forty-nine from Elswick, twenty-two from
Openshaw, fourteen from COW and ten from
Beardmore.[17] Since 1897, Vickers had a test
range for guns and armour at Eskmeals 16
miles north-west of Barrow, while Armstrong
had one at Ridsdale 25 miles north-west of
Newcastle, and another at Silloth on the
Solway Firth, while COW had theirs at
Freiston on the Wash. Woolwich shipped its
guns across the Thames to Shoeburyness near
Southend for testing, where trial projectiles
could be recovered at low tide. From 1907, the
examining and testing of heavy guns at the
maker's works was such that in emergency, guns
could go direct to their destination without
passing through Woolwich.[18]

When the Board of Admiralty and the
government of the day had decided the
number and the armament of projected ships,
an order would be placed with one or more
suppliers, after tenders had been received. A
number of spare gun bodies was also ordered,
typically two for every five mounted in ships,
but only one spare breech mechanism for every
four. Guns wore out in service; the bigger the
calibre, the faster the rate. So a 12in Mark VIII
using Cordite MD (see p.201) might have a life
of about 500 equivalent full charges (reduced
charges or practice rounds might produce only
about one-quarter of the erosion of a full
charge) while a 15in Mark I was about 330.
Guns might therefore have to be replaced
several times in a ship's life. They could then be
relined, at a typical cost of £5000 for a 15in,
often by the original manufacturer, and put
back into the reserve stock held at Woolwich or
the main home and overseas Dockyards.

Until about 1908 the technical press would
carry full reports with illustrations of new guns
and ships and their trials, including tests against
armour plate. Thereafter the Admiralty was
more security-conscious and unwilling to
provide any anticipated adversary with technical details.[19] To disguise their true calibres,

initially it designated the new 13.5in for the
Orion class in 1909 as 12inA, the 15in gun in
1912 as the 14in Experimental, and in 1915 the
18in for *Furious* as the 15inB.

This general procurement procedure served
the Admiralty before the First World War.
During the war the Admiralty tended to place
orders with manufacturers who had the
capacity to deliver quickly, without seeking
tenders. Most of the British armament manufacturing capacity was devoted to the Army
with its huge artillery demands for the Western
Front, much of it newly built for the new
Ministry of Munitions. Additional capacity was
needed at Elswick to build the 150-ton 18in
guns for *Furious*, with new shops and plant
costing £111,000 in 1916 (see Elswick plan
p.57).[20] Post-war, there was a huge drop in
armament orders. The 1921 programme for
four battlecruisers was cancelled following the
Washington Treaty. Although *Nelson* and
Rodney were built between 1922 and 1927,
their three triple 16in guns were the only heavy
ordnance built between *Hood* in 1919 and the
first of the *King George V* class ordered in 1936.

A broadly similar procurement process was
used for smaller-calibre battleship secondary
armament. In the pre-dreadnought era, such
guns could be as much as 9.2in calibre, basically
a small-scale version of the 12in gun and turret
mounting. But from *Dreadnought* onwards,
secondary armament reduced to 3in to 6in
calibre, essentially as anti-torpedo boat/
destroyer weapons. The smaller guns were

Above: Armstrong
Whitworth had their
gun and armour proof
range at Ridsdale
twenty-five miles north-
west of Newcastle. Here
what looks like a 13.5in
Mark V is about to be
tested. *(Tyne & Wear
Archives)*

Above: The *Queen Elizabeth* and *Royal Sovereign* classes were fitted with 6in secondary armament. This 7-ton Mark XIIB gun No.2838 was made by Beardmore in 1917 and installed in *Royal Sovereign* 1930-35. The P.IX (pedestal) mounting No 91 was made by Armstrong Whitworth in 1916, weighing 9½ tons including the shield (not fitted here) seen here on display at Whale Island, Portsmouth in 1991. *(Author)*

mostly QF (quick-firers) in which the propellant was contained in a brass cartridge case, while the larger were usually BL (breech-loading) where all the propellant was in silk cartridges. Up to the First World War the heavier guns were usually on single pedestal mountings behind armoured casemates, while smaller-calibre guns were usually exposed on the upper deck with light shields. Such guns were often fitted in other ships such as cruisers and destroyers, so guns and mountings were ordered by the Admiralty in batches each year, and simply allocated to battleships as construction progressed, unlike larger mountings which were 'made to order' for a specific ship. For example in 1898 Vickers received an order for twenty-seven 6in P.IV between-decks pedestal mountings at £880 each, and shortly after an order for fifty-eight 6in BL.VII guns at £1900 each[21], suitable for the *Formidable* and *Duncan* classes as well as *Cressy* class armoured cruisers. The later 6in BL.XII, fitted as secondary armament in battleships and light cruisers from about 1914 was designed by RGF, but a total of 453 were made by all the major manufacturers.[22] Such a gun cost £2100 with a further £1800 for the P.IX mounting as in the *Queen Elizabeth* class. Seventy-five of the latter were ordered for the first four ships, thirty-eight from Vickers and thirty-seven from COW, eleven being spares.

Vickers' Sheffield financial records give details of gun prices and profits from 1908–15.[23] Data is summarised in the table opposite for the principal guns fitted in battleships, but there were also other guns built for the Army and for export (e.g. Japan, Italy, Russia, Spain) from 18pdr up to 12in. Although

Kongo's 14in guns were made from 1911 they were only tested at Eskmeals from August 1912 to January 1913, when typically seven proof rounds were fired from each of her eight shipped guns Nos. 1325A–1332A.[24] The data is only for the work completed at Sheffield, so excludes the price, cost and weight of breech mechanisms which Sheffield made jointly with their Erith works, which the Admiralty ordered separately from gun bodies – a 13.5in mechanism in 1910 was priced at £1350. The cost is mainly manufacturing cost but also includes carriage and some head office costs. The figures reveal just how profitable ordnance manufacture was for the larger calibres, with prices generally yielding profits of more than 100 per cent of cost, i.e. over 50 per cent of price, broadly similar to armour – see p.216. Up until 1908, only Vickers, Armstrong Whitworth and Woolwich could build guns of 12in and over, but thereafter Beardmore and Coventry Ordnance Works were able to. With Woolwich making such guns, the Admiralty knew the cost of manufacture there and the price charged to the Government, and therefore accepted the prices being asked by the commercial makers if they were broadly similar. Since Woolwich did not make 'profits', that can only mean that manufacture there was expensive with high labour costs and overheads, if the private firms could make over 100 per cent profit on similar work. The number employed at Woolwich was generally regarded as bloated, ostensibly to provide a reserve in times of military crisis. Woolwich cost figures were published in the annual accounts for ordnance factories put before Parliament each year, so private manufacturers knew at what price to pitch for guns.[25] With more manufacturers and greater competition for smaller calibre guns however, Vickers profit rates for such were significantly lower.

The detailed annual figures reveal a 'learning curve', whereby the first production units were more expensive to manufacture than later ones, most marked with the 12in 50 cal Mark XI/XII compared with the 12in 45 cal Mark X, both Vickers designs. While guns were not sold on a 'per ton' basis, there is a general downward trend with larger guns at about £150 per ton, only about half the price per ton of smaller guns. These prices compare with a typical price of gun forgings for larger gun tubes and cradles of between £40 and £90 per ton, so give an idea of 'added value' in working the material and finishing the gun.

BREECH-LOADING GUNS (EXCLUDING BREECH MECHANISMS) BUILT BY VICKERS AT SHEFFIELD

Gun	Years covered	Number built	Av weight (tons)	Av price (£)	Av cost (£)	Av profit (£)	Profit/cost (%)	Price/ton (£)	Classes fitted in
15in Mark I	1913–15	31	96.6	14,002	6061	7941	131.0	144.9	*Queen Elizabeth, Royal Sovereign* classes, WW1 battlecruisers
14in 45 cal Type 43	1911–12	9	81.0	11,500	5154	6346	123.1	142.0	*Kongo*
13.5in Mark V	1909–12	52	73.9	11,333	4695	6638	141.4	153.4	*Orion, Lion, King George V, Iron Duke* classes
12in Mark X	1908–13	56	56.0	9088	4293	4795	111.7	162.3	*Lord Nelson, Dreadnought, Invincible, Bellerophon* classes
12in Mark XI/XII	1909–11	19	64.0	10,633	6599	4034	61.1	166.1	*St Vincent, Colossus* classes
10in	1907–08	17	31.3	6588	2626	3962	150.9	210.5	*Rurik* and other foreign
7.5in Mark V	1907–08	21	14.6	3452	1187	2265	190.8	236.4	Armoured cruisers
6in BL Mark XI	1910–12	30	8.4	1866	1059	807	76.2	222.1	Later pre–dreadnought secondary armament and cruisers
6in BL Mark XII	1913–15	56	6.7	1840	919	921	100.2	274.6	*Queen Elizabeth, Royal Sovereign* classes secondary armament and cruisers
4in BL Mark VII	1908–11	126	2.0	604	505	99	19.6	302.0	Battleship and battlecruiser secondary armament

The armaments industry contracted greatly after the First World War. Coventry Ordnance Works was taken over by English Electric in 1919, with the Coventry works going over to manufacture heavy electrical equipment and Scotstoun was sold to Harland & Wolff in 1920 to manufacture diesel engine components, deck machinery and structural steel, with the five gun pits, 36ft in diameter and 45ft deep, being filled in.[26] Vickers and Armstrongs merged most of their interests in 1927, so became the Admiralty's sole supplier of heavy gun mountings. Although both their Elswick and Barrow works remained open, capacity and employment was much reduced; Elswick's utilisation in 1928 being only about 40 per cent of capacity. Openshaw ceased gun making and filled in the four cruiser gun pits in the late 1920s.[27] Vickers-Armstrongs closed their Erith plant in 1931, Crayford taking over smaller guns and fire control equipment. The Royal Gun Factory at Woolwich retained its capacity to build guns although most designs now came from outside, while Beardmore's plant was mothballed. Vickers-Armstrongs was the only designer and builder of both heavy guns and mountings before and during the Second World War. But as re-armament started in 1936, H & W's Scotstoun works was refurbished at Admiralty expense and new shops added to the west, with some technical help from Vickers-Armstrongs, initially to build 4.7in and 5.25in HA/LA (High-Angle/Low-Angle) mountings.[28] The Armstrong Whitworth factory at Scotswood near Newcastle currently building 227 steam locomotives for the LMS Railway was acquired by the Admiralty and War Office in 1937 for £1.3 million. It was then leased to Vickers-Armstrongs for 28 years to manage, who were then asked to manufacture 4.5in, 3.7in, 25pdr and 2pdr guns and mountings.[29] The Admiralty also financed an extension to Beardmore's Glasgow gun plant at a cost of £300,000.[30] From 1936-44, the Treasury paid for £525,000 for ordnance plant extensions at Barrow (including three new pits for 14in costing £250,000 to add to the twelve) and £2.45 million for shops and plant at Elswick including one more 14in pit costing £60,000.[31]

MORE MODERN GUNS

Although both the German and US navies had adopted all-steel guns before the First World War, the Admiralty had doubts about their reliability, being dependent on forgings of the highest quality as well as more demanding manufacturing standards. Their experience of shrunk-on tubes with both modern US guns (in the First World War 14in monitors) and older 9.2in showed a tendency for the tubes to separate slightly in service and cause the barrel to droop, affecting accuracy. Despite a theoretically lower longitudinal strength, the Admiralty preferred the greater consistency of the wire-wound guns, which was used into the 1920s with *Nelson* and *Rodney*'s 16in Mark I. Of the twenty-nine 108-ton guns made (eleven spare), Elswick manufactured ten (in 1925), Vickers eight, Beardmore five and RGF six.[32] Thereafter higher quality steel forgings, and better treatment and machining facilities became available, so the 79-ton[33] 14in Mark VII for the *King George V* class used the modern auto-frettage system. Radial strength was achieved thereby by shrinking on the outer tubes (A tube and jacket) so that they remained under tension when cooled, while the inner A tube was pressurised to put it into compression, to provide a more homogeneous mass of steel. For the first three ships (mounting ten guns each) forty gun bodies and thirty-three breech mechanisms were ordered in the second quarter of 1936, eighteen and fifteen from

Right: The last (left inner) 14in gun with its counterweight above the breech is lowered onto its trunnions in *Duke of York's* A turret on 1 August 1941. After final adjustments, the 6in roof plates will be fitted. *(Upper Clyde Shipbuilders)*

Below: *Duke of York's* B turret is nearly complete at John Brown's shipyard in July 1941, as the first 14in gun is lifted in. Gunhouse A is still being erected showing trunnions for elevating the guns, and roof-supporting pillars, but only the 7in thick rear plates with their vent holes have been fitted. *(Upper Clyde Shipbuilders)*

Vickers-Armstrongs at Elswick at £20,250 each, thirteen and eleven from RGF Woolwich, and nine and seven from Beardmore, with forgings from English Steel Corporation – guns were no longer made at Sheffield.[34] The first gun (No. 60) from V-A was delivered to Shoeburyness for trials at the end of 1937. In all from 1938 to 1944, seventy-eight 14in guns were completed (including two for trials), thirty-eight by Vickers-Armstrongs, twenty-three by RGF and fifteen by Beardmore, plus two started by V-A but completed by RGF in 1947.[35] A 14in Mark VII (No. 134, the last V-A gun built in 1944) is preserved at Fort Nelson, Portsmouth (see photo opposite) and two 15in Mark I (Nos. 102 & 125) at the Imperial War Museum, London.

The gun manufacturer also designed the heavy guns' breech mechanism, although sometimes adopting a licensed design, manufactured in a specialist workshop. The Admiralty had adopted the Welin interrupted screw breech block, which achieved closure in only one-sixteenth of a turn, with an obturator pad to prevent leakage of propellant gases. In 1898,

Vickers charged a royalty on each such breech mechanism made by other producers, £500 for a 12in, £100 for a 6in. The Germans used a different system with a sliding breech block mechanism, with a brass cartridge case for the rearmost propellant charge to provide a gastight seal. Screw breech mechanisms weighed about 2.85 tons in the case of the 15in, so required hydraulic power to open and close, although in an emergency they could be closed manually.

The 15in Mark I gun was built by all six heavy gun factories to arm the *Queen Elizabeth* and *Royal Sovereign* classes of battleships plus First World War battlecruisers (including *Hood*) and monitors. One hundred and eighty-four guns were completed from 1914–19, forty-nine from Vickers, thirty-seven from Beardmore, thirty-four from Elswick, thirty-three from RGF, nineteen from COW and twelve from Openshaw.[36] This was the most successful RN heavy gun afloat for 50 years from 1915 (*Queen Elizabeth*) to 1965 (monitor *Roberts*). The price of such a gun weighing 100 tons was about £16,000 in 1915, made up as follows:[37]

Gun forgings	£6900
Gun manufacture	£7500
Breech mechanism	£1600

While a handful of high-angle (HA) guns were fitted in battleships during the First World War, much greater attention was paid to anti-aircraft armament after the war. Initially such guns had been single 2pdrs or 3pdrs, increasing to 12pdr (3in). However the triple 4in mountings designed by Armstrong Whitworth, fitted in *Renown/Courageous* classes and manufactured by Elswick and Beardmore at Dalmuir, had only 30° elevation so were of limited HA use. After the First World War 4in and 4.7in guns were fitted, while the *King George V* class had 5.25in twin HA/LA dual purpose mounts similar to *Dido* class cruisers. Generally, such lighter guns and mountings were made by all the main ordnance companies and Woolwich. V-A received an order for seventy 5.25in QF Mark I guns in 1937 worth £184,100 (£2630 each).[38] Production of naval guns built up rapidly at Elswick with deliveries in 1939: eleven 14in Mk VII, thirty-one 6in Mk XXIII, thirty-nine 5.25in Mk I, fifty-seven 4.7in Mks XI & XII, sixty-one 4.5in Mks I & III, 135 4in Mk XVI★, and 254 2pdr Mk I as well as guns for the Army, spare barrels and gun relinings.

To increase production in the Second World War, additional engineering companies were

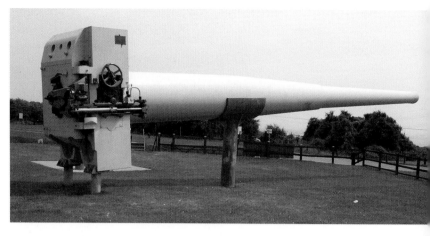

brought in, such as Marshall & Sons (Successors) Ltd of Gainsborough making twin 4in Mark XIX HA/LA mountings, widely fitted in ships from escorts to older battleships. Such were also made by V-A at Barrow pre-war. Between the wars, the 2pdr was developed by V-A into the multiple pom-pom with four or eight barrels, and fitted in all British battleships which served in the Second World War. An eight-barrel Mark VI mounting built at Barrow suitable for a battleship cost about £8000 (103 under construction in December 1937), with a further £900–£1000 per gun made at V-A's Crayford works. Openshaw (formerly owned by Armstrong Whitworth but sold to English Steel Corporation in 1929) also made 2pdr guns and it and Scotswood built four-barrel Mark VII mountings under V-A management. Openshaw later built the six-barrelled Mark VI

Above: 14in Mark VII gun No. 134, the last made by Vickers-Armstrongs at Elswick in 1944, is on display at Fort Nelson, Portsmouth. *(Author)*

Below: *Renown, Repulse, Glorious* and *Courageous* were fitted with triple 4in secondary armament on their superstructure. Beardmore built such P.1 mountings at their Dalmuir works – gun shield removed for the photograph taken in September 1916. *(Author's collection)*

40mm mountings for *Vanguard*. Her twin barrelled 40mm STAAG (Stabilised Tachymetric Anti-Aircraft Gun) mounting as well as the directors for her six-barrelled mountings were built by Rose Brothers at Gainsborough, who had been brought into Admiralty gun mounting work in 1937.[39]

GUN MOUNTINGS

Battleship gun mountings were even more impressive pieces of heavy engineering than guns. A twin 15in Mark I mounting had a revolving weight of 740–800 tons depending on gunhouse protection thickness (of which only 200 tons was the guns themselves) and took 18–24 months to build and cost in 1914 about £116,000 excluding guns (about £11.6 million in 2012 money). An armoured gunhouse protected the guns, loading and sighting mechanisms. Beneath it was the turntable which supported the guns and upon which the whole structure rotated. Below that was the working chamber with machinery to train and elevate the guns, then below that the ammunition hoists for projectiles and propellant, which reached down to the magazines and shell-rooms in the bottom of the ship, a total height of up to 60ft in superfiring mountings. See diagram on p.192. Such a complex mecha-

nism had to be first assembled in the workshop to check that all components and piping fitted and worked, before installing in the ship. Pits up to 50ft deep and 30ft in diameter were sunk below the workshop floor lined with cast iron segments like a tunnel, simulating the arrangement in a ship, served by 60- or 100-ton electric overhead travelling cranes. Bays alongside were used to assemble major components such as turntables and working chambers before erection in the pit. Trials of all the hydraulic systems and hoists would be carried out in the presence of Admiralty inspectors, before dismantling for shipment to the shipyard. Since most shipyards before the First World War could only lift up to about 150 tons at their fitting-out quays, the mountings had to be designed so that no component exceeded that weight – usually the turntable/working chamber was the heaviest item, as the gunhouse could have its heavy armour plates fitted one at a time.

The manufacture of such gun mountings involved a wide range of engineering skills. Draughtsmen produced hundreds of drawings defining all the parts, to be issued to workshops and sub-contractors. Wooden mock-ups were built to check clearances and avoid interference between moving parts, with interlocks required to prevent dangerous simultaneous movements.

Below, right: *Colossus'* A barbette ready to receive the ammunition trunk and working chamber of her twin 12in B.XI mounting at Scotts' Greenock yard on 18 August 1910. The training rack is clearly seen, but the roller path and tapered roller bearings are partially hidden under canvas. *(NRS)*

Opposite, top: *Colossus'* A mounting turntable and working chamber on the dockside at Scotts' Greenock yard on 18 August 1910. In the foreground, the 25.5-ton gun cradle with recoil cylinders for her right gun, which will elevate about the trunnion bearing holes. At right, the crane lifting hook and slings are being positioned to lift the ammunition trunk into the ship. *(NRS)*

Opposite, bottom: The turntable of *Colossus'* A mounting is now installed on 6 September 1910, with gun cradles (chain rammer in foreground), ready to receive gunhouse floor and armour, then the guns. *(NRS)*

Rough forgings received from steelworks such as for gun slides needed careful machining, requiring turners and most mechanical engineering trades in both heavy and light machine shops. Key components were machined using jigs to ensure dimensional accuracy and interchangeability of parts. Foundries cast less highly stressed components such as bearing housings and valve bodies. Hydraulic machinery was made for gun elevating, training and recoil mechanisms and ammunition hoists. The associated pipework and valves needed plumbers and coppersmiths. Boilermakers, platers, caulkers and riveters made the supporting steel structure for ammunition trunks, the cylindrical working chamber, the turntable floor, girders and sides, gun slide supports and gun shield armour supports. Gun shield plates were received from the armour makers to be erected on the gunhouse floor.

All the components were brought together in the erecting shop, assembled by fitters from the

Right: One of *Colossus'*
12in 66-ton Mark XI
guns being hoisted into
A turret on 5 October
1910, with the second
gun on the dockside,
next to the turntable
and working chamber of
P mounting. *(NRS)*

Below: *Colossus'*
midships twin 12in
turrets (P left, Q right)
fully installed by Vickers
as Contract 112G at
Scotts. *(NRS)*

bottom up in a pit, and tested almost complete apart from the gunhouse roof and minor fittings. Supporting trades included cranemen and riggers to move the components, sheet metal workers, painters, electricians and labourers. After nine to twelve months in the pit, the mounting was disassembled for transport to the shipyard and re-erected in the ship. Erection on board involved both shipyard and gun mounting contractor staff. A key feature of the shipyard work was the preparation of the turret ring bulkhead with its roller path upon which the whole weight of the mounting revolved. A special planing machine was placed in each barbette, carefully centred and levelled to machine the top surface of the roller path. This had to be absolutely parallel with all the other turrets and the director, as measured against a datum plane on the hull, so that when each rotated, they did so in exactly the same plane to point correctly at the target.

The three companies capable of building such mountings all had waterside sites, where coasters or barges could be loaded with the components for transport to the shipyard. Vickers at Barrow's Devonshire Dock had a 150-ton cantilever crane close to the gun mounting shop; Armstrong at Elswick had a 150-ton hydraulic crane on the Tyne riverside,

while COW on the Clyde had a 200ft loading dock for coasters or barges spanned by an overhead travelling crane. To minimise transport problems, gun mounting contracts for battleships being built on the east coast were usually placed with Elswick – the main Tyne shipyards were only a few miles downstream, while those on the Clyde or west coast were usually served by Barrow or Scotstoun.[40] Steam coasters with wide hatches capable of carrying outsize heavy components were used if there was an open sea voyage, but Elswick could serve the Tyne yards with barges. It was an Admiralty condition that only British ships with British crews be used. The 1735 grt coaster *Aydon* was used to transport 15in mountings from Barrow to Clydebank for *Barham* in four shipments from February to June 1915. The Second World War quadruple 14in mountings included large 40ft diameter turntables, the transport of which was usually done in Fisher's 2950 grt coaster *Sea*

Left: The maker's plate from one of *Duke of York's* forward 14in gun cradles, made at Elswick in 1941, showing the lifting weights. The same gun was fitted in the twin Mark II 14in mounting as the quadruple Mark III. (*Author*)

Below: A good view of *Barham's* quarterdeck and aftermost main armament turrets, probably in early March 1915. The last 15in gun, weighing 100 tons, is being shipped for X turret while the 6in secondary armament embrasures are still open, but it was later decided not to install guns so close to the waterline, so they were plated over. The battleship left Clydebank to run trials and join the Grand Fleet on 26 August 1915. (*Author's collection*)

The heavy gun mounting shop was the focus of an integrated ordnance works, where the entire mounting was assembled and tested before re-erection in the ship. No.24 Shop at Armstrong's Elswick works was one of three such shops there, used to erect 12in, 13.5in, 14in, 15in and 16in mountings. The drawings show the shop after modifications in 1921–2 to handle *Nelson* and *Rodney*'s triple 16in mountings, the heaviest manufactured to date, guns shown at maximum 40° elevation. The shop was 70ft high to the upper crane level, with pits extending 50ft below floor level to provide space to assemble a thousand tons or more of complex machinery.

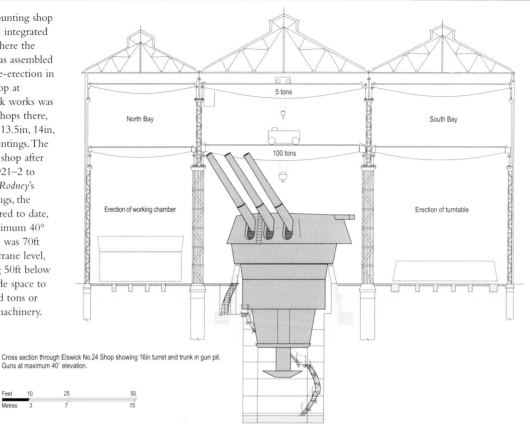

Cross section through Elswick No.24 Shop showing 16in turret and trunk in gun pit. Guns at maximum 40° elevation.

Feet	10	25		50
Metres	3	7		15

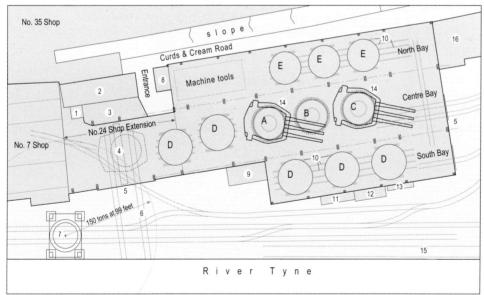

The pits, up to 35ft in diameter, were in the 60ft wide centre bay, served by 100-ton cranes, with the side bays used to machine and assemble major components such as turntables (upside down to machine the roller path). After twelve or more months in the pit, the main components were disassembled and placed on bogies to be moved out of the shop to the 150-ton crane for lifting onto a barge or coaster for transport to the shipyard. The shop was extended in 1936 to handle *King George V*'s quadruple 14in mountings. It was at 54-57-40N 01-38-31W.

Armstrong, Whitworth & Co Ltd, Elswick Works 1921 No 24 Gun Mounting Shop

Feet	125	250
Metres	37.5	75

1. Accumulator
2. Pump house for hydraulic crane
3. General store
4. 100-ton overhead crane
5. Sliding doors
6. Bogie tracks
7. 150-ton hydraulic jib crane
8. Time office
9. General store
10. Concrete beds
11. Blacksmiths shop
12. Tool room
13. Lavatory
14. 16-in triple mounting
15. Travelling crane
16. Pumping plant

A West pit
B Centre pit
C East pit
D Turntable berths
E Working chamber berths

Left: This twin 15in mounting was planned for *Furious* should her single 18in mounting prove unsuccessful. One went into the monitor *Erebus* in 1916, the other into store at Chatham Dockyard for twenty-four years. When her sister *Terror* (with the mounting from *Marshal Ney*) was lost in 1941, a new monitor was ordered at Naval Yard to take this spare mounting. It was refurbished for installation in *Abercrombie* after being upgraded to Mark I/N standard with 30° elevation, requiring a 12-ton balance weight just ahead of the breech ring. The interior of the gunhouse is revealed in an erection pit in No. 24 Shop at Vickers-Armstrongs' Elswick works on 23 December 1942. Further views of the turret components were published in Ian Buxton's *Big Gun Monitors*. On the shop floor can be seen one of the 20mm Oerlikon gun platforms to be fitted on the gunhouse roof and a 13.5in Mark V being converted to an 8in hypervelocity gun. *(Vickers Ltd)*

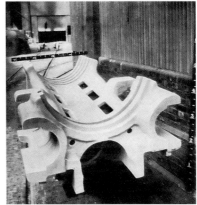

Above: Guns were supported in cast steel gun cradles which allowed the gun to recoil along a machined slide; the whole elevating together. This lower part of a 13.5in cradle cast by Cammell Laird was 10 x 4ft weighing 7 tons. *(Cammell Laird)*

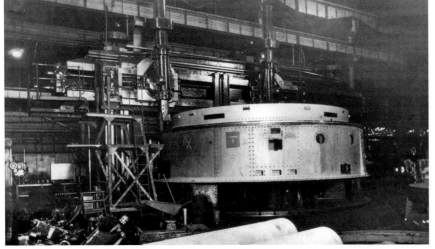

Left: The turntable of *Vanguard*'s X mounting is being machined upside down at Scotstoun. Harland & Wolff had taken over the former Coventry Ordnance Works gun mounting plant near Glasgow in 1920, which had to be redeveloped during re-armament in the 1930s, including new machine tools and shop extensions. *(Harland & Wolff)*

Above: One of *Nelson's* triple 16in turrets in Armstrong Whitworth's No 24 Shop at Elswick in early 1926. After testing its hydraulic systems, it was dismantled into the fewest number of parts that the Elswick 150-ton quayside crane could handle and loaded on to a barge. It was then transported down river to Naval Yard and re-erected by the 150-ton *Titan II* floating crane, with a slight overload as the turntable actually weighed 165 tons. (*Vickers Ltd*)

Fisher, completed in May 1940 with widened hatches, e.g. from Barrow to Birkenhead for *Prince of Wales* from June to August 1940.

It took two to three days to load the components of a large mounting, with the coaster berthed under the big crane. The battleship would already have in place her ring bulkheads to support each turret and barbette armour. When the coaster arrived at the shipyard, the receiving battleship would be moved away from their fitting out crane, allowing the crane to unload the coaster by placing the components on the dockside beneath the crane. This would take about two days; after the coaster departed, the battleship would be manoeuvred back under the crane. The components would then be lifted in sequence: long ammunition hoist trunk, the working chamber, the turntable with the gunhouse floor with trunnions and gun slides installed. The front, side and rear armour plates would then be fitted, then the guns themselves. Finally the vanadium steel

turret roof plates would be fitted to complete the mounting. Then all the piping and wiring had to be completed, and the whole assembly tested. The aftermost turrets were usually shipped first, which allowed the machinery contractors to align the propeller shafts after the heaviest weights had been placed. The last turret to be fitted was usually the forward one, but for *Nelson* with no turrets aft in the order B (superfiring, 16 March 1926), A (16 June 1926) and X (13 August 1926). To progress the six triple 16in mountings in parallel, the Admiralty had agreed to finance a third large diameter pit at Elswick for £30,000. The drawing on p.184 shows such a mounting in the pit at Elswick.

All heavy gun mounting designs were made by private industry. Gun mounting contracts for a particular ship covered the construction and testing of the mountings at the maker's works, transport to the shipyard, erection on board ship, placing the guns into the mountings and construction of any spare mountings. Progress payments were normally in six, or later ten, instalments. Spare 'mountings' were ordered one per ship, but comprised only one gun cradle, slide, trunnions, elevating gear and breech operating gear, rather than the entire revolving unit.

Armstrong Whitworth submitted a very similar quotation for *Monarch* to *Orion*, but to

FIVE TWIN 13.5IN MARK II MOUNTINGS BY VICKERS FOR *ORION* ORDERED 29 AUGUST 1909

	Estimated weight tons	Estimated price £	Price per ton
Turntable, working chamber and roller path	550	49,690	90
Training gear and rack	82	24,660	301
Gun cradles, slides, elevating gear and rammers	306	67,030	219
Hydraulic pumping engines (3) *	50	10,250	205
Piping on revolving structure	27	11,840	438
Shell room handling gear *	25	9040	362
Ammunition hoists	122	48,020	394
Piping on hull structure *	24	9300	387
Brackets, rails, covers etc	13	3320	255
Gunhouse roof (4in & 3in), floor (3in), sighting hoods etc	442	50,290	114
Gunhouse armour front, sides, rear (11in) & keys. £137.7/ton	580	79,870	138
Sub-total	2221	363,310	164
Drawings and models		930	
Spare cradle, slide and fittings		8230	
Delivery to Dockyard		4950	
Erection at Dockyard		17,000	
Total for 5 turrets		394,420	178
Average price each		78,884	
Estimated price for two 13.5in guns		25,700	
Average price per turret		104,584	
Revolving weight excluding guns and items* on hull	2122		
Average weight per turret	425		
Plus two 13.5in guns	152		169
Average revolving weight	577		181

Note that a total price was not quoted for gunhouse armour, only an agreed price per ton. Guns were not included in the contract but ordered separately by the Admiralty. Price per ton added by the authors. (*Orion* Ship's Cover)

Opposite, right: Breaking up warships often revealed parts not seen clearly before, either during construction or operation. This view of *Rodney*'s X turret at Inverkeithing in August 1949 shows the great thickness of the 16in guns, part of the gun slide and recoil cylinder (left) and the 9in thickness of the gunshield side and rear (bottom right) armour. *(Newcastle University Marine Technology Special Collection)*

Left: The 200-ton turntable supported both the gunhouse above and the hoists beneath, being shipped downriver to Vickers-Armstrongs' Naval Yard on a barge. *King George V* is moved out into the river to allow the 250-ton cantilever crane to lift the turntable off the barge on 7 June 1940. *(Vickers Ltd)*.

Above, left: The crane has lifted the turntable off the barge, ready to lower into A barbette. *(Vickers Ltd).*

Above, right: The 40-foot diameter turntable is lowered into *King George V*'s A barbette, onto the already installed roller path which will support the full 1582-ton rotating weight. In the background, the barge is being towed back to Elswick for the gunhouse components. *(Vickers Ltd)*

Right: A 13.5in Mark II twin mounting erected in a pit in No 24 Shop at Elswick, probably one of the first for *Lion*, which was ordered on 20 August 1909, followed by an order for five for *Monarch* on 10 December. *(Tyne & Wear Archives)*

Vickers design. Where the Admiralty wanted to fit a standard mounting in all ships of a class, it required the successful designer to supply drawings and manufacturing information to the other companies, upon payment. In the case of an Armstrong design of gun or mounting, the royalty was between 10 and 15 per cent, although the royalty payable by RGF was smaller. This Admiralty policy dated from about 1902:

It is pointed out that in order that interchange-ability between the parts manufactured by the respective firms might be maintained, it has been customary to make one firm responsible for the drawings, jigs and gauges in connection with the gun machinery for classes of ships – Vickers were responsible for such in the case of the 'King Edward VII' class ... the drawings and the jigs and gauges becoming the property of the Admiralty on completion of the Contract.[41]

Accounts for Armstrong's Ordnance Division reveal how profitable manufacturing heavy gun mountings was for companies who had

mastered the art – see also Chapter 11. The Admiralty had little means of checking prices, as Woolwich did not manufacture heavy mountings, while the only competitor, Vickers, regularly shared pricing information with Armstrong when bidding for overseas contracts.[42] There was some collusion on prices for the Admiralty to ensure that they remained at a profitable level, with both companies' quotations normally close, e.g. for *Tiger*'s four twin 13.5in mountings excluding gun shield armour, Elswick quoted £238,499 and Vickers £237,781.[43] It could also result in the companies sharing work, e.g. both built mountings for *Dreadnought* and *Thunderer*. Such collusion could be considered a risk reducing mechanism by each company faced with large fluctuations in orders, anxious to retain some share of the business; it also helped avoid unnecessary price cutting to secure foreign orders. The profit and loss accounts for Ordnance for the five years 1908–12 show that manufacturing profit (i.e. before overhead charges etc) averaged £340,000 a year (£187,000 net after charges and other costs): 63 per cent came from

Above: Armstrong's Elswick Ordnance Company could erect six 12in mountings simultaneously, the largest pits being 35ft deep, allowing the whole mounting and hoist machinery to be tested as if in the ship. This view of No.7 Shop in 1902 shows *Cornwallis'* two twin B.VI mountings being erected. Each weighed about 345 tons, being 28ft 6in from turret roof to bottom of hoist trunk, with a 25ft diameter turntable. *(US Library of Congress)*

SOME VICKERS HEAVY GUN MOUNTING CONTRACTS

Ship	Contract	Completed	Twin mountings Mark	Price# (£)	Av price each (£)	Cost (£)	Profit (£)	Profit/cost (%)
Vengeance	1G	5/02	2 12in B.V	63,329	31,665	99,298	-35,689	-36.1
Irresistible	2G	2/02	2 12in B.VII	64,739	32,370	84,659	-19,920	-23.5
Venerable	5G	12/02	2 12in B.VII	68,623	34,312	80,243	-11,620	-16.9
Exmouth	10G	5/02	2 12in B.VII	86,063	43,032	82,704	3359	4.1
Albemarle	11G	11/03	2 12in B.VII	86,263	43,132	70,092	16,171	23.1
Katori	80G	5/06	2 12in + 10in	269,490	–	196,150	73,340	37.4
Neptune	116G	1/11	5 12in B.XI	282,409	56,482	183,890	98,519	53.6
Colossus	117G	7/11	5 12in B.XI	294,779	58,956	186,536	108,423	58.0
Australia	121G	6/13	4 12in B.VIII*	236,494	59,123	149,092	87,402	58.6
Orion	115G	12/11	5 13.5in II	324,218	64,844	217,865	106,353	48.8
Princess Royal	119G	11/12	4 13.5in II	241,760	60,440	153,179	88,581	57.8
King George V	125G	11/12	5 13.5in II*	315,997	63,199	220,907	95,090	43.0
Audacious	129G	10/13	5 13.5in II*	316,506	63,295	218,894	87,612	44.6
Tiger	139G	10/14	4 13.5in II**	258,962	64,740	197,494	61,468	31.1
Emperor of India	135G	10/14	5 13.5in II**	325,905	65,181	250,175	75,730	30.3

Contract price plus extras, but excludes gun shield armour (from Sheffield) and guns.
Profit before deduction of head office costs. *Katori* includes 4 single 10in mountings.

Below: It took the new Coventry Ordnance Works five years to break into the heavy gun mounting market. They had to develop their own Mark III design for the 13.5in twin mounting for *Conqueror* ordered on 10 December 1909. Components were manufactured at their Coventry works and the five mountings erected at their Scotstoun works. The company's publicity made great play of this view of the first mounting, erected in 1912, with one gun at its maximum 20° elevation and one at maximum 5° depression. *(Author's collection)*

'Carriages' i.e. gun mountings, and 22 per cent from rifled ordnance i.e. guns, the two categories where naval products predominated. The remaining 15 per cent came from Shot & Shell, Hotchkiss guns, Fuses, Steel forgings, Metal borings, Royalties, Accessories and Sundries.[44]

Vickers Barrow accounts reveal large profits on battleship gun mountings after the first few years of 'learning'. The table shows profit rates of over 50 per cent of cost until orders after about 1910 by which time Coventry Ordnance Works had entered the market putting downward pressure on prices.[45]

Coventry Ordnance Works submitted their price for heavy gun mountings to their own design in September 1909, with a price about 15 per cent lower than the other two firms. Although the Admiralty formally accepted their tender on 10 December 1909 for *Conqueror*'s five turrets, they placed the order for pumping engines and associated piping elsewhere. The Admiralty insisted that the company made no arrangements with the other two companies, so were in direct competition. The requested delivery date was October 1911, but without the usual £50 per day late penalty asked of the other firms, recognising the inexperience of COW.[46] In the event, erection of the mountings at Beardmore's shipyard was not completed until well into 1912, and there were failures on initial trials on the ship, and modifications were needed. COW probably made a loss on the contract, as the company as a whole made large losses from 1910-13.[47] Its five pits limited it to making turrets for one battleship at a time. Armstrong complained about late delivery of COW's shell room gear and mountings for *Courageous*' A turret in mid-1916.[48] Beardmore considered manufacturing heavy gun mountings about 1910 but was probably discouraged by its major shareholder Vickers to avoid over-competition reducing profits, plus the high capital expenditure.[49] They did however manufacture the simpler transferable mountings up to 6in calibre at Dalmuir from about 1909; *Conqueror*'s (4in) and *Benbow*'s (6in) mountings were made there. The table opposite shows details of the 330 heavy gun mountings built from 1895.

Invincible's electrically-worked 12in mountings were not a success, and were converted to hydraulic power in 1914 at a cost of £100,000.

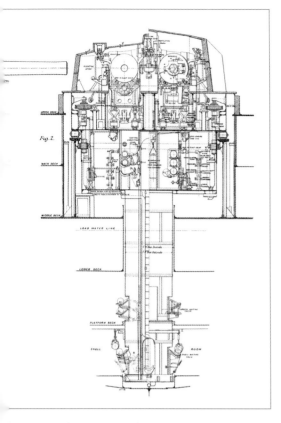

December 1914 to change *Renown* and *Repulse* from four-turret battleships to three-turret battlecruisers to be built in fifteen months had great repercussions on the procurement of 15in mountings. The eight mountings had been ordered in May 1914 with delivery due seven

Above: The first 14in 92.5-ton Mark VII gun of *Duke of York*'s B turret is lifted into place by Clydebank's 200-ton cantilever crane. *(Upper Clyde Shipbuilders)*

Left: An unusual view which few people will ever have seen live. *Duke of York*'s last 14in gun is being lifted into place on 1 August 1941, after which the 6in thick gunhouse roof plates will be fitted. She left Clydebank on 7 September for Rosyth for drydocking. *(Upper Clyde Shipbuilders)*

months before ship delivery, i.e. in February
1916. As this would be too late for the battlecruisers, six mountings had to be found from
those ordered for earlier battleships. By January
1915, the first two *Queen Elizabeth*s had
received their mountings, with the other three
due to get theirs in the next few months. It
would have been folly to divert mountings
from these powerful and strategically important
ships. But the *Royal Sovereign*s of the 1913–14
Programme were less important, and although
two had been launched, their mountings were
not due until the end of 1915, so would available in time, also to arm two monitors which
had just been ordered on the strength of
Renown and *Repulse*'s fourth turrets being
'available'.

So *Ramillies'* four turrets were re-allocated
and four replacements ordered from Vickers,
delaying the ship by over a year. *Resolution*'s two
forward turrets were diverted to *Repulse*,
delaying her completion. Details of the re-allo-
cations are shown in the table.

The final costs would have been higher than

the original contract, whose approximate values
for four turrets were:

Item	Price £
Turntables and working chambers	54,000
Gun mountings and slides	76,000
Hoists and training gear	70,000
Gun shield armour and floor	144,000
Hydraulic pumps, piping & shell room machinery	54,000
Director gear and sights	16,000
Delivery and erection	26,000
Spare cradle etc	12,000
Miscellaneous	8000
Total for four turrets excluding guns	460,000
Price each	115,000
Two 15in guns	32,000
Total per turret	147,000
Cost per ton revolving weight (760)	193.4

AFTER THE FIRST WORLD WAR

The basic procurement process was retained
until the end of battleship building in the UK,
but with only two heavy gun mounting works

RE-ALLOCATION OF R CLASS GUN MOUNTINGS

Planned Ship	Ordered	Manufacturer	Actually installed in
Ramillies	4 in July 1913	Vickers (150G)	*Marshal Ney* (Jul 1915), *Marshal Soult* (Sep 1915), 2 in *Glorious* (Aug 1916)
Ramillies	4 replacements in 1915	Vickers (154G)	*Ramillies* (Sep–Dec 1916)
Resolution	4 in July 1913	Elswick	*Resolution* X and Y (Dec 1915), *Repulse* A and B (Apr 1916)
Repulse	4 in May 1914	Elswick	*Repulse* Y (Apr 1916), *Courageous* Y (Jun 1916), *Resolution* A and B (Jul 1916)
Renown	4 in May 1914	COW	3 in *Renown* (Jun 1916), *Courageous* A (Jul 1916)

from 1920, design and manufacturing capacity was a bottleneck once re-armament started in 1936. An Admiralty paper in 1938[51] noted that gun mounting manufacture limited new construction to two and a half battleships a year, four and a half 6in or 8in cruisers, four 4.5in or 5.25in cruisers and two aircraft carriers with 4.5in. This lack of resources, especially skilled men and draughtsmen, handicapped Admiralty heavy ship construction throughout the Second World War, as the same facilities were needed to build cruiser triple 6in mountings (four each) and twin 5.25in for battleships (eight each) and cruisers (five each). Fifty-one twin 5.25in mountings for two battleships and seven cruisers were ordered from Vickers-Armstrongs in November 1936 for delivery from mid-1939 (eighteen at Barrow, thirty-three at Elswick) at an estimated cost of £43,000 each.[52] In 1937 Harland & Wolff received an order for twenty-six Mark I 80-ton battleship mountings, two being spares. Also in 1937, Scotswood was brought in with eighteen orders for cruiser mountings transferred from Elswick. Vickers-Armstrongs had kept their hand in with battleship gun mountings by converting the First World War twin 15in to Mark I/N with 30° elevation and extended range. *Warspite* was the first with work starting at Elswick and on the ship at Portsmouth

Dockyard at the end of 1934 at a cost of £150,000. Barrow built her new directors. Then followed *Renown, Valiant* and *Queen Elizabeth*.

Elswick's drawing office began work on the design of the 14in mountings for the *King George V* class in early 1936, with the first order in May. Initially three quadruple mountings were to be fitted, the first such battleship mounting in the RN. But to save weight, B turret was soon changed to a twin, which

Left: Vickers-Armstrongs' gun mounting works on the Tyne, previously Armstrong's Elswick Ordnance Works, built all three 14in turrets for *King George V* and *Anson*. Each mounting was erected in a deep pit, including the ammunition hoists, for testing before transport to the shipyard. Here the fourth gun is lifted into *King George V*'s Mark III A mounting in No 24 Shop. *(Vickers Ltd)*

Above, left: Both *Duke of York's* A and B turrets were built at Elswick, with Y coming from Vickers-Armstrongs' Barrow works, so all needed transport by sea to John Brown's Clydebank yard. Fisher's 2950 grt coaster *Sea Fisher*, built by Austin of Sunderland in 1940, had been converted to carry the turret components, including widening No 2 hatch. The quadruple turntable for A turret is was lifted in at Elswick on 5 June 1941. *(Vickers Ltd)*

Above, right: The revolving shell-ring and cordite hoist for the bottom of *Duke of York's* A turret is lifted into *Sea Fisher's* No 1 hatch in June 1941. The coaster arrived at John Brown's Clydebank shipyard on 24 June. *(Vickers Ltd)*

accentuated problems for V-A in design and tooling. With continuing shortage of skilled manpower, materials and modern machine tools, the planned completion date for *King George V's* mountings of mid-1939 could not be achieved. As much sub-contracting of components as possible was done, e.g. marine engineers Richardsons Westgarth at Hartlepool manufactured parts of the 14in ammunition hoists and twenty two 5.25in gunhouses from

1939. Sister companies George Clark at Sunderland built 5.25in ammunition trunks and North Eastern Marine at Wallsend built 5.25in gunhouses, eight for battleships, ten for cruisers, the former costing £3350 each.[53] Harland & Wolff's marine engine works in Glasgow completed eighty-four 5.25in shell hoists for £250,000.

The suspension of construction of *Howe* and *Anson* in May 1940 allowed V-A to progress

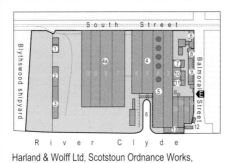

Harland & Wolff Ltd, Scotstoun Ordnance Works, Glasgow 1945

1. Decontamination station
2. Smiths shop
3. Pattern store
4. Machine shop bays. 4a added after 1938
5. No 4 Bay showing gun pits
6. Basin with large capacity overhead crane
7. Coppersmiths
8. Offices
9. Drawing offices
10. Millwrights
11. General store
12. Sentry (Home Guard)
13. Tool room

When the Coventry Ordnance Works was formed, one of the first things it did was to establish a gun mounting works close to the shipyards of the constituent companies. With John Brown holding 50 per cent of the shares and Fairfield 25 per cent, Cammell Laird had to accept that the works would be on the Clyde. In October 1906, the company purchased 20 acres of undeveloped ground on the banks of the Clyde between Mechan's Scotstoun Iron Works to the east and Yarrow's shipyard to the west. In January of the following year, the company approached the Clyde Navigation Trust for permission to construct a small dock sufficient to allow mountings to be placed on a small vessel for transportation to a shipyard. As originally completed the works extended to everything east of and including Bay 4. Bay 4 was fitted with five gun pits. It seems probable that Bays 5 and 6 were added during the First World War and certain that the remainder of the shops from Bays 7 westwards were added just before the Second World War. During that war the works reverted to ordnance manufacture under Harland & Wolff which included the refurbishment and modification of the 15in mountings destined for *Vanguard*. These works still stand owned by Albion Automotive, a division of American Axle & Manufacturing.

more urgently needed cruiser, destroyer and anti-aircraft mountings. The two Tyne-built ships, *King George V* and *Anson*, received their 14in mountings from Elswick, delivered by barge downriver. The west coast ships *Prince of Wales* and *Howe* received their mountings by coaster from Barrow, usually *Sea Fisher*, which also delivered *Duke of York*'s A turret from Elswick (B also built there) and her Y from Barrow to Clydebank in June 1941.[54] The risk of loss was significant: one of the cruiser *Trinidad*'s triple 6in turrets had been lost when *Shoal Fisher* was mined *en route* from Barrow to Devonport in February 1941.[55] *Sea Fisher* herself was mined three months later but survived; her loss would have caused further delay in completing two battleships. Coasters *Empire Gat* and *Empire Jack*, managed by Fisher, were used to ship 5.25in mountings from Scotstoun and Barrow, the latter's last such duty being *Vanguard*'s from Barrow to Clydebank in February 1946.

Every effort was made to complete *King George V*'s 14in gun mountings as early as possible, but such was the demand for new gun mountings, especially anti-aircraft, that V-A's capacity was overstretched. The new twin 5.25in mountings ordered at the same time used the same resources and took far longer to design, manufacture and test than planned, even with a prototype ordered in 1936 and fitted in *Iron Duke* for testing early in 1939. Additional capacity was established at Scotswood (Tyne) and Scotstoun (Clyde) but lacked experienced and skilled workers. The original plan required eight mountings for *King George V* from Elswick, eight for *Prince of Wales* from Barrow, with all twenty-four of the next year's programme from Harland & Wolff at Scotstoun – easy to transport to the nearby John Brown and Fairfield shipyards. But the basically similar *Dido* class cruiser mountings with five each, plus twelve planned for modernising cruisers *Frobisher* and *Hawkins* (later cancelled), proved too much for the ordnance factories. By the spring of 1940, Elswick was warning that it would be unable to complete all eight for *King George V* by September, while three *Dido* class had to complete with one mounting missing and two others with only four twin 4.5in mountings. Scotswood's 6000 workers were still struggling to complete their first 5.25in mounting, for cruiser *Naiad*. So four were switched from *Prince of Wales* to complete *King George V*, while four were switched at Scotstoun from *Duke of York* to complete *Prince*

of Wales. In turn, four planned for *Anson* were switched to *Duke of York*, to be replaced with four from Scotswood. Only *Howe*'s eight stayed as originally ordered, shipped in the second quarter of 1942.

It would have proved impossible to build the planned 1940 8in gun cruisers and 16in gun *Lion* class battleships due to lack of gun mounting capacity alone, although in the event

Above: Harland & Wolff's Scotstoun works (the former Coventry Ordnance Works) was brought back into ordnance manufacture during re-armament in the 1930s and used to build medium-calibre gun mountings. Twenty 5.25in Mark I twin mountings for battleships were delivered from 1940. A mounting for either *Prince of Wales* or *Anson* is loaded at the works' dock into a coaster. *(Harland & Wolff)*

Left: The ammunition trunk was the first turret component to be erected, that for *Vanguard*'s B turret at Clydebank late in 1945. The lettering above the loading scuttle suggests a weight of only 22 tons. The 6in NC roof plates for A turret are being completed. No hard hats in those days, not introduced until twenty years later. *(Upper Clyde Shipbuilders)*

Above: An impressive
shot of the erection
shop at Scotstoun,
showing nearest the
camera *Vanguard*'s X
turret, then A, Y and B,
probably in mid-1945.
Four of the original five
gun pits in Bay 4 were
reinstated in 1941.
(Harland & Wolff)

four 16in guns were completed for trials.[56]
Vanguard was only completed because she could
use the four twin 15in mountings removed
from the battlecruisers *Glorious* and *Courageous*
when they were converted to aircraft carriers in
the mid-1920s. But even the refurbishment of
those, including increasing the elevation from
20° to 30° and conversion to remote power
control, necessitated re-instating four of the old
filled-in gun pits at Scotstoun for their re-erection. Although Harland & Wolff carried out the
re-erection, Vickers-Armstrongs provided most
of the technical input and drawings. The
resulting cost was about £380,000, which was
only about one third of the cost of a new
installation.

After the First World War, battleship
secondary armament also became non-transferable, e.g. six twin 6in turrets (Mark XVIII) each
in *Nelson* and *Rodney* all by Vickers at Barrow,

so were 'made to order' for each ship.[57] As with
the larger mountings, the Admiralty would
request detailed changes during the long
construction period. Although the original
contract would have been agreed, there would
be many minor changes as construction
progressed, e.g. modifications to hoists for
different types of projectile, resulting in lengthy
negotiations post completion regarding the cost
of such changes. Indeed the final prices for
their Armstrong triple 16in mountings were
not agreed until 1930, three years after the ships
were completed, by which time the two manufacturers had merged to become Vickers-
Armstrongs. These extras added about
£250,000 to give a final price of about £1.65
million per ship plus about £250,000 for gun
shield armour.[58] While double the weight of a
twin 15in mounting (1150 tons excluding
guns), it was five times its (pre-war) cost –

partly due to inflation but also high development costs and many modifications.

The total value of gun mountings supplied to the RN by UK manufacturers from 1939/40 to 1945/46 was £101.8 million, and fire control equipment £20.05 million, but the battleship proportion is not given. The US and Canada supplied a further £55 million for both categories.[59] After *Vanguard's* mountings were shipped in 1945, there were no new heavy gun mounting contracts for Vickers-Armstrongs until six twin 6in were built for the cruisers *Tiger*, *Lion* and *Blake* in the 1950s, three from each works. Thereafter, the workshops at Elswick were given over to general engineering work. The Elswick shops were demolished about 1970, while the Barrow ones continued with marine engines and 4.5in gun mountings, and are now part of BAE's Global Combat Systems.

BATTLESHIP ORDNANCE FOR EXPORT

As well as building guns and mountings for the Admiralty, the two big ordnance companies also built for foreign navies. In some cases the ordnance formed part of the battleship they were building for export, e.g. Armstrong Whitworth's *Yashima* for Japan in 1897, in others the ordnance was exported to the foreign builder, e.g. to Italy's La Spezia naval Dockyard

for *Reina Margherita* in 1904. Armstrong had set up an engineering plant at Pozzuoli near Naples in 1886, building smaller guns and mountings from 1890. The Italians sought self-sufficiency in all aspects of dreadnought building, so Pozzuoli was upgraded to handle larger guns and mountings from about 1910. From 1912 it

Above: *Nelson* and *Rodney* each had six twin 6in Mark XVIII mountings. The Barrow gun mounting shop shows several in course of erection about 1926, the nearest at 60° maximum elevation, before shipment to the shipyard. *(Author's collection)*

Left: *Vanguard's* Y turret being erected at Clydebank in mid-1945. The gun cradles and the 13in front gunhouse plates are in place with a roof support in the centre. The man is standing on the 13in thick barbette armour, thinned to 11in on the centreline. X turret is nearly complete with 15in guns, with only some roof plates to be fitted. *(Author's collection courtesy of NRS)*

HEAVY GUN MOUNTINGS 12IN AND OVER BUILT FOR FOREIGN BATTLESHIPS

Mounting	Ship (builder, completion) and mounting maker (number of turrets)
Twin 12in 40 cal	*Yashima* (Armstrong 1897) EOC (2); *Fuji* (Thames Iron Works 1897) EOC (2)
Twin 12in 40 cal	*Shikishima* (Thames Iron Works 1900) EOC (2); *Asahi* (J Brown 1900) EOC (2); *Hatsuse* (Armstrong 1901) EOC (2); *Mikasa* (Vickers 1902) EOC (2)
Twin 12in 40 cal	*Regina Margherita* (La Spezia 1904) EOC (2); *Benedetto Brin* (Castellammare 1905) EOC (2)
Twin 12in 45 cal	*Kashima* (Armstrong 1906) EOC (2); *Katori* (Vickers 1906) VSM (2)
Single 12in 40 cal *	*Regina Elena* (La Spezia 1906) EOC (2); *Vittorio Emmanuele* (Castellammare 1907) EOC (2); *Roma* (La Spezia 1908) EOC (2); *Napoli* (Castellammare 1909) EOC (2)
Twin 12in 45 cal	*Minas Geraes* (Armstrong 1910) EOC (6); *Sao Paulo* (Vickers 1910) EOC (6)
Twin 12in 50 cal	*Kawachi* (Kure 1912) VSM (2); *Settsu* (Yokosuka 1912) EOC (2). Each also had 4 twin 12in 45 cal mountings built in Japan
Twin 14in 45 cal	*Kongo* (Vickers 1913) VSM (4); *Hiei* (Yokosuka 1914) VSM (4)
Triple 12in 46 cal	*Dante Alighieri* (Castellammare 1913) EOC (4); *Giulio Cesare* (Ansaldo 1914) EOC (3); *Leonardo Da Vinci* (Odero 1914) VSM (3); *Duilio* (Castellammare 1915) EOC (3); *Andrea Doria* (La Spezia 1916) VSM (3)
Twin 12in 46 cal	*Giulio Cesare* (Ansaldo 1914) EOC (2); *Leonardo Da Vinci* (Odero 1914) VSM (2); *Duilio* (Castellammare 1915) EOC (2)
Twin 12in 50 cal	*Espana* (Ferrol 1913) EOC (2), VSM (2); *Alfonso XIII* (Ferrol 1915) EOC (2), VSM (2); *Jaime I* (Ferrol 1921) EOC (2), VSM (2)

* Design and components supplied but assembly probably local.
EOC = Elswick Ordnance Co, Newcastle (Armstrong Whitworth), total 47 + 13*. VSM = Vickers, Sons & Maxim, Barrow, total 19 + 7*.

Below: Both Vickers and Armstrong shared the armament contract for the three Spanish battleships ordered from 1909. Here a 12in 50cal gun, probably for *España*, is having its breech mechanism tested at Vickers. *(Reproduced by kind permission of the Syndics of Cambridge University Library. Vickers 2022)*

was employing over 4000 (compared with 1300 in 1904), although the designs and some key components continued to supplied from Elswick; the latter received an order for 12in 46 cal guns for *Duilio* in May 1912. Vickers were encouraged to team up with Italian steel and armour manufacturer Terni to set up an ordnance company in 1905, providing expertise and designs. A new works was built at La Spezia and completed about 1911[60] but here again some key components were built at Barrow.

The Japanese government aimed at self-sufficiency a little earlier. With Armstrong's help, Kure naval yard built its first 9.2in gun in 1903, while both Armstrong and Vickers became equal partners in 1907 in Japan Steel Works (Nihon Seiko-Sho) at Muroran to build gun mountings and ordnance material. From about 1909, all Japanese heavy mountings were built in Japan, albeit with British designs and technical assistance, especially from Elswick. However, some components were built in Britain, e.g. the long 12in 50 cal guns for *Settsu* ordered in 1909, although some of her 12in 45 cal were built in Japan, also a Vickers design. Vickers' price in 1910 for one twin 14in mounting and guns for Japan was £132,000. Contracts for such orders were usually one-third payable at contract signing, one-third when half the value had been completed and one-third on completion of the work.[61] By 1911 Japan Steel Works had an order book of Y3 million (£300,000) and was employing 1700 men, at about half the average Elswick wage.[62] Some Japanese battleship secondary armament guns continued to be built in Britain, e.g. Vickers 10in 45 cal for *Katori* and 6in 50 cal for *Kongo*, while both Vickers and Armstrong supplied 6in 45 cal around 1910.

Among heavy guns built by Vickers at Sheffield for foreign navies between 1910 and 1915 were:

Bore	Calibres	Pattern	Number	For
12in	45	E	8	Japan
12in	50	F	5	Japanese *Settsu* and *Kawachi*
12in	46	G	30	Italian *Leonardo da Vinci* class
12in	50	H	12	Spanish *España* class[63]
13.5in	45	A	19	*Reshadieh*. Later British Mark VI in *Erin*
14in	52	B	4	Russian *Borodino* class[64]

The prices charged were similar to those for comparable British guns. With the high profit margins on the latter, there was no need to charge a premium price for exports.

After the war, these overseas ordnance company shareholdings frequently lost money. Armstrong Whitworth disposed of Pozzuoli in 1928, Vickers-Armstrongs of La Spezia in 1931 and Japan Steel Works in the 1930s.[65] V-A never built any more battleship mountings for export, although cruiser mountings were built as well as 15in coast defence mountings for Spain in the 1930s.

The table opposite shows which battleship mountings were built in Britain for such foreign customers. Armstrong and Vickers were able to reserve the market almost exclusively to themselves (apart from possible competition from USA or Germany) by quoting higher prices for their ordnance to other potential shipbuilders such as John Brown. Although the latter developed Coventry Ordnance Works in 1905 together with Fairfield and Cammell Laird, to counter the duopoly, they were never able to break into the battleship export market, although reasonably successful with smaller calibre and Army guns. Foreign customers were reluctant to order from suppliers who had not done similar work for the Admiralty; COW did not complete their first 12in gun until 1910 or heavy gun mounting until 1912.

AMMUNITION

The purpose of building a battleship is to enable its guns to deliver projectiles capable of sinking an enemy's ships. The development and manufacture of heavy projectiles and propellant is thus an essential component of a battleship building industry. Although the Admiralty and the War Office were the main customers of the British industry, there was a significant export trade in the period before the First World War. This could take the form of a warship's initial outfit, or continuing resupply for existing ships.

Cordite was the propellant used by British battleships from about 1895 onwards. It was a more powerful 'smokeless' propellant than previous powders – the reduced smoke allowed the gunlayers and spotters to keep the target in view better. Higher muzzle velocities became possible, around 2350ft/sec in a 12in Mark VIII with a charge of 174lb resulting in a range of about 14,000 yards at the then typical maximum gun elevation of 13½°. But Cordite made up of 58 per cent nitroglycerine, 37 per cent nitrocellulose and 5 per cent mineral jelly caused greater erosion of the gun bore and shorter life, so modified Cordite MD with proportions 30, 65, 5 per cent was introduced in 1902. Cordite was made up into quarter charges in silk bags, which not only eased handling but allowed half or three-quarter charges to be fired for shorter ranges which reduced gun erosion. Cordite was manufactured both by Government munitions factories and by commercial manufacturers such as Nobel's Explosives Co at Ardeer on the Firth of Clyde. Curtis & Harvey Ltd at Cliffe on the River Thames supplied COW with Cordite. As well as making projectiles and filling them (e.g. Armstrong's at Lemington near Newcastle) the armaments companies had their own ammunition suppliers, e.g. Armstrong's Thames Ammunition Works at Erith acquired in 1902 particularly for filling QF ammunition, and Vickers taking a 40 per cent share in 1900 in the Nobel affiliated Chilworth Gunpowder Co of Surrey.[66]

Much of the Admiralty's pre-First World War Cordite was manufactured by the long-established Royal Gunpowder Factory at Waltham Abbey north of London, producing about 70 tons a week immediately pre-war at just under 2 shillings (£0.1) per lb.[67] About double that amount was being made by the commercial manufacturers, including Chilworth and the National Explosives Co of Hayle, Cornwall. Each lot of Cordite was proved by firing five or six rounds before acceptance into service. The 1914–15 Navy Estimates included £475,970 for 5,820,000lb of Cordite 45 MD. But as the Army's huge demands for artillery and ammunition for the Western Front increased rapidly in 1915, many new facilities were built by the new Ministry of Munitions. The Admiralty had previously wished to control its own Cordite supplies, so in January 1914, Churchill authorised the construction of the 494-acre Royal Naval Cordite Factory at Holton Heath near Poole. It was opened in 1915, capable of making 150 tons a week.[68] It continued to supply much of Admiralty demand right through to the end of the Second World War. A new, more stable, longer life propellant Cordite SC (solventless carbamite, 41 per cent nitroglycerine, 50 per cent nitrocellulose, 9 per cent carbamite) was introduced in 1927, for the making of which Holton Heath was remodelled. Ardeer, now owned by ICI, continued to make Cordite, while to increase supply in the Second World War, a new Admiralty factory was built at Caerwent near Chepstow at a cost of £7.2 million which began production in 1941 of 150 tons per week.[69] By the 1960s, Royal Ordnance Factory (ROF) Bishopton near Glasgow was making all service propellants.

Unlike propellant, most heavy projectiles for the Admiralty were made by industry before and during the First World War. Armstrong made such and fuses at their Scotswood works just west of Elswick (from about 1900, heavy projectiles previously at Openshaw), also fuses at their Thames Ammunition Works.[70] Vickers made projectiles at Sheffield and Barrow. Most of the Army's demands in the First World War were met by new Ministry of Munitions factories, largely small and medium calibres. Woolwich manufactured many smaller-calibre projectiles and also filled with bursting charges the larger shell bodies manufactured mostly by industry, as well as inspecting and issuing the completed projectiles to RN ammunition depots. The latter were also used to make up Cordite into the necessary-sized charges and to fill and fuse empty projectiles. The Admiralty had long had such depots at Priddy's Hard (near Portsmouth), Upnor (Chatham), and Bull Point (Devonport) while a new depot was built in 1915 at Crombie (Rosyth).[71]

For battleships, what was required was a projectile that could penetrate the armour protecting vital spaces in a fit state to detonate its bursting charge inside the ship. Cast steel pointed projectiles had been developed in the 1880s but it was the development of stronger Harvey and Krupp armour in the 1890s that required better armour-piercing (AP) projectiles than the typical solid shot. Hardened forged steel bodies proved better at surviving initial impact, but the new Krupp cemented armour could still shatter a sharp-pointed shell body. Fitting a softer steel cap around the point

Below: Firth's advertisement from the 1912 *Jane's Fighting Ships.*

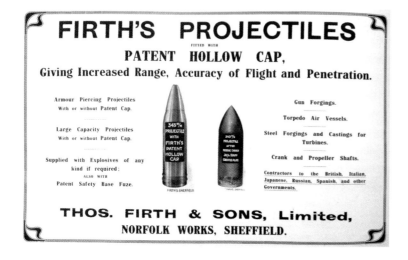

spread the load of the initial impact and pre-stressed the surface of face-hardened armour, preserving the point to allow the main body to penetrate the armour and reducing the propensity of the projectile body to break up, unfit to burst.

For pre-dreadnought RN battleships, the ammunition outfit was generally made up of some armour-piercing base-fused shell filled with black powder, but mainly of common shell with a nose fuse for use against unprotected areas of the enemy ship. The smaller calibre common shells were filled with Lyddite (picric acid) from about 1898, the heavier with black powder – black powder was better able to withstand the shock of impact than the more powerful high explosive Lyddite. AP shells with their thick walls carried bursters 2½–3 per cent of total weight. Typically eighty rounds per gun were carried (with another 110 ashore in reserve); in 1897 typically ten solid AP shot, twenty-two Palliser (obsolescent cast-iron shot no longer with a bursting charge) and forty-eight common shell. Armstrong supplied broadly similar ammunition to its export customers, including Japan who used such successfully in the Russo-Japanese War of 1905; they had also built many ships of the victorious Japanese fleet.

Better armour-piercing qualities were needed against Krupp armour, which the private manufacturers started to develop. Thomas Firth & Sons Ltd of Sheffield produced their Rendable projectile in 1903, still black-powder filled – Lyddite was considered too sensitive and might detonate before penetration or not at all. Hadfield's Steel Foundry Co Ltd, also of Sheffield (later Hadfields Ltd), brought out their Heclon APC in 1905 and their Eron CPC (common pointed capped) in 1907, using a cast chrome nickel steel body filled with black powder. Hadfield was the largest British manufacturer of shells, capable of making in 1908 up to 10,000 per week under 6in calibre plus some 2800 6in calibre and above.[72] Vickers also made APC and CPC and in July 1910 received a typical order from the Admiralty for 1200 13.5in Mark VA CPC at £3705 per 100.[73] That contract appeared to make a large loss: Vickers Sheffield accounts show 1050 13.5in projectiles produced in 1912–13 with a sales value of £40,739 (£38.8 each) but costing £70,163 to make (£66.8 each), resulting in a loss of £29,424 or 72 per cent on cost – clearly not a well-managed contract. Sheffield only

produced projectiles in modest quantities, less than 2 per cent of the works' sales. From 1907–13, 2144 12in projectiles were made there (800 tons) at an average price of £25, but barely producing a profit.[74] It is possible that some of such sales formed the ammunition outfit of Vickers export warships, where profits were earned on the rest of ship. Some forged steel bodies were made at Sheffield, but machined and finished at Barrow and tested at Eskmeals. They also made small calibre projectiles at Erith and cartridges at Dartford. Before acceptance into service, a number of rounds from each 'lot' was proof fired against armour plate; for heavy projectiles a lot was typically 400.

Both Vickers and Armstrong shared technical information with each other as well as with Nobel and Krupp. The latter had developed robust fuses, with manufacture licensed to Vickers in 1902. Fuses were also made at the Royal Laboratories, Woolwich, while Firth developed one for their AP. A total of 8800 No.44 fuses for HE projectiles were ordered in 1914 at a cost of £2200 (5 shillings each).

With the Admiralty taking increasing control of its ordnance needs from the War Office, hastened by Fisher's appointment as First Sea Lord in 1904 – a former Director of Naval Ordnance – the Naval Ordnance Department expanded its responsibilities. DNO was seen as a key appointment for a promising RN gunnery officer, e.g. Jellicoe as a Captain in 1905. Among developments was the introduction from 1907 of a new longer range more pointed projectile of 4 calibres radius of head

Above: Thomas Firth of Sheffield was a major manufacturer of projectiles, with their publicity photo showing a selection. Several have been fired at test armour plates, with driving bands missing – the 15in at front right says '15 INCH ARMOUR PIERCING FIRTH'S PATENT HOLLOW CAPPED SHELL AFTER PERFORATING 15 INCH K.C. PLATE, FIRED 9.7.15'. What seems to be its windcap is on the ground beside it. Other shells include 16in RML, 305mm AP, 9.2in, 8in, 6in, 5in, 4.7in plus nineteenth-century cannonballs. *(Firth-Brown Ltd)*

(crh).[75] Dreadnoughts with 12in guns were equipped with armour-piercing, capped (APC), common pointed, capped (CPC) and high explosive (HE, which superseded common shell), the first two filled with black powder, the latter with the somewhat unreliable Lyddite, manufactured by industry. The 13.5in APC was Lyddite-filled. It was recognised that TNT would be a more stable burster, but there was limited manufacturing capacity and it would need a new design of base fuse to detonate successfully, which the Admiralty did not pursue pre-war. The anticipation was that battleships would fire CPC at longer ranges to destroy the upperworks of an enemy ship, and then close to shorter range to deliver the coups de grace with APC at near normal (90°) impact to the main armour belt. So performance and testing at oblique impact was not a requirement.[76]

In the 1913–14 Navy Estimates 3000 15in APC were ordered at a cost of £195,000 (£65 each unfilled), 3200 15in CPC at £208,000 (£65 each) and 400 15in shrapnel at £14,000

Below: In both World Wars, ordnance companies had to greatly expand production of ammunition. This view of one of Vickers-Armstrongs' shops at Elswick shows a variety of heavy shell bodies awaiting finishing in 1944. *(Vickers Ltd)*

(£35 each), enough to supply eight ships. The following year 4000 15in APC and 3600 CPC were ordered. With wartime demands, Vickers greatly increased its production of projectiles at Sheffield, sales increasing fivefold between 1913 and 1915, including 1267 15in worth £85,525, although yielding only a modest profit of £1316.[77] By now the preferred outfit for 13.5in and heavier gun ships was 60 per cent APC, 20 per cent CPC and 20 per cent HE, for the older 12in ships 40 per cent, 30 per cent, 30 per cent, now with 100 rounds per gun stowed. By 1915 some 12in APC had been refilled with Lyddite bursters.

But early actions at sea and then at Jutland in 1916 revealed the shortcomings of such tactics and the deficiencies of British projectiles. At oblique impact typical of hits at longer range with steeper angles of descent, projectiles would break up rather than penetrate armour fully, the base fuse having insufficient delay to allow penetration before bursting and a black powder filling lacking the explosive power of TNT, while a Lyddite filling might not deto-

Left: 15in 6crh projectiles being turned on a lathe at Vickers-Armstrongs' Elswick works in 1941, probably nose-fused HE, a new product for the works. *(Vickers Ltd)*

nate at all. German projectiles were greatly superior in all such respects, so German hits at Jutland were much more damaging than British hits.[78]

A Projectile Committee was set up by the Admiralty shortly after Jutland to determine the causes of such failures and propose remedies. But it was not until Captain F C Dreyer was appointed DNO in March 1917 that real progress was made. Dreyer was a distinguished gunnery officer who had developed the fire control table bearing his name (see p.208) as well as being CO of Jellicoe's flagship *Iron Duke* at Jutland. Dreyer became President of a new Shell Committee to develop, test and introduce a more effective armour piercing projectile, without which the Grand Fleet was reluctant to face another head-on encounter with the High Seas Fleet. This required a stronger body

to withstand oblique impact, a new harder cap, a more powerful and stable burster and a more reliable delay action base fuse. Elswick developed the 16D base fuse based on a German design. With TNT in short supply, the burster was made of Shellite (60 per cent picric acid and 40 per cent dinitrophenol).

In 1917, the five main manufacturers of heavy projectiles were asked to provide new designs of APC for each calibre of 12in and over to meet these requirements. A total of 672 rounds were fired to test the designs up to 1 May 1919, when the Shell Committee submitted its final report, some at Shoeburyness, some at Eskmeals, some at Ridsdale. Elswick and Firth forged steel ingots into shell bodies, while Hadfield and Vickers cast theirs, then extruding them in a punching press to create the burster cavity; the burster formed

NEW APC PROJECTILES ACCEPTED BY 1 MAY 1919[79]

Maker	Mark	Weight (lb)	Hadfield	Elswick	Firth	Vickers	Cammell Laird	Total
15in	IIA	1920	4800	0	0	2000	0	6800
14in (*Canada*)	IIA	1586	0	800	0	0	0	800
13.5in heavy	IIA	1410	1000	800	2800	1200	0	5800
13.5in light (*Orion* and *Lion* classes)	IIIA	1257	800	0	3600	0	0	4400
12in	VIIA	854	4400	5600	0	2000	100	12,100
Total			11,000	7200	6400	5200	100	29,900

The A in the Mark number signified 4 crh.

about 2.3 per cent of total weight. Shell bodies were then hardened, heat treated, tempered and annealed, providing a gradation of hardness from highest at head and shoulders to lowest at the lower walls and base. Normally the shell bodies were left out in the open for three months to reveal any flaws, but with the need for haste, a rapid heating and cooling test in water was used to reveal any cracks. Shells that passed were then machined to precise dimensions, grooved to take the copper driving band, and prepared for fitting the cap. The caps were cast or forged from ingots and hardened and treated like the shell bodies, before being attached and the streamlined nose added. The projectiles were then sent for filling with burster, before having the fuse fitted and sent to the Fleet.[80]

Once satisfactory new projectiles from each manufacturer had been designed and tested, a major production effort was needed to replace the stocks in the main vessels of the Grand Fleet. The initial aim was first to provide the battlecruisers with the new APC to 30 per cent of their outfit, then 30 per cent for the battleships by August 1918, around 250–400 for each ship. By the summer of 1918, good progress was being made with 1796 being issued in June of the new green-painted 'Greenboy' APC projectiles. 15,335 had been issued by December 1918: 3365 15in, 613 14in (for *Canada*), 13.5in heavy 3578, 13.5in light 2807, 12in 4972.[81]

These new projectiles were also tested against *Monarch* as a target in 1925; slight changes were made including changing the Shellite proportions to 70/30.

Below: The Explosion! Museum at Priddy's Hard, Gosport, has a good display of ordnance and ammunition. Projectiles from left to right, 18in, 16in, three 15in, two 12in, one 15in. 6in and smaller calibres are lined up behind. *(Author)*

Hadfield received an order in 1916 for 500 18in Heclon APC and 500 Eron CPC of the older design for *Furious*, but none was fired in anger by her. Her only 18in gun (fitted aft) was removed for her seaplane carrier role and with the two others (one spare) allocated to monitors for shore bombardment in 1918. *General Wolfe* and *Lord Clive* used up about eighty-five of the stock, although new HE were being made.[82] New 18in guns and shells were designed after the First World War for possible new battleships but none were made.

Apart from new 16in for *Nelson* and *Rodney*, the stocks of heavy projectiles from 1919 sufficed the RN until the 1930s when improved designs were needed. Increasing 15in gun elevation to 30° in modernised battleships such as *Warspite* required longer ranging projectiles, so a more pointed 6 crh was introduced, along with improved metallurgy and an improved fuse. ROF Cardonald near Glasgow (completed in 1916 and managed by Beardmore) developed the 15in APC Mark XXIIB with a 48.5lb Shellite burster, reckoned to be one of the best Second World War APC. The private manufacturers apart from Hadfield had given up manufacture of heavy shells, but Vickers-Armstrongs continued to make smaller calibres for the Admiralty and the export market. HE nose and base fuzed projectiles were developed as shore bombardment became a prime role for battleships, e.g. 15in Mark VIIIB, now with a 130lb TNT burster.[83] The front-line battleships used the improved shells, leaving the second-line vessels such as the *Royal Sovereign* class to use up the old 4 crh and CPC stocks. But usage of heavy ordnance like the new 14in was modest during the Second World War. As the table shows, even in the two biggest user ships, the total only amounted to little more than one magazine outfit (10 guns at 100 rounds each).[84]

Ship	Rounds	Actions
King George V	1181	13
Duke of York	1265	14
Anson	509	10
Howe	602	4
Total	3557	41

A few such projectiles remain on display in Britain including 14in, 15in and 18in at the Imperial War Museum, London and 12in, 15in, 16in and 18in at Explosion! The Museum of Naval Firepower, Gosport.

Fire Control Equipment

When naval actions were fought at close range, visual estimation of range was sufficient to determine the elevation to put on the gun so that the projectile would strike the target with its near horizontal trajectory. As improved guns offered greater range, a more accurate means of estimating range was needed. Range Tables were prepared for each Mark of gun, projectile and charge, which showed the necessary gun elevation to achieve a particular range, which was then put on the gun sight. Corrections were needed for bore wear, propellant temperature, wind and drift. Angle of descent and time of flight were also given, which could be 30 to 60 seconds at long range. The fire control problem for longer ranges and faster ships thus evolved into predicting the future position of the target ship at which to aim the gun, relative to own ship. While own ship course and speed were known, that of the target ship had to be estimated in order to calculate the necessary angles of gun elevation and training (deflection). It was thus necessary to estimate the rate of change of range (the rate for two ships on approaching courses each at 20 knots was 1350 yards/minute) and rate of change of bearing to adjust the gun sights, allowing for the time delay before the shell arrived at the target. Spotting the shell splashes around the target allowed corrections to be made.

These demands sparked an ever-increasing pace of development of instruments to address different parts of the fire control problem. Thus an industrial company would propose a possible piece of equipment, offer it to the Admiralty for trials and hope to secure large orders, preferably as sole supplier. One of the first was the partnership of two professors Archibald Barr and William Stroud, who developed an optical rangefinder. A mirror and lens was mounted at each end of the rangefinder tube, with the two images being aligned by adjusting the position of a sliding prism, to which a range scale was attached. Barr & Stroud's rangefinder proved effective in Admiralty trials in 1892, this 4½ft FA model being produced in their workshop in Glasgow. It was able to estimate range to about 3000 yards with 3 per cent accuracy and was fitted in all pre-dreadnoughts. Successive development resulted in the 9ft FQ2 in 1906, costing £325 each, generally fitted in the spotting top high up on the mast and on top of the conning tower in an armoured hood. The successful company built a new factory at Anniesland in Glasgow in 1904, and became virtually the sole supplier of rangefinders to the Admiralty, although a few other companies had offered designs. They held this position right to the end of the optical rangefinder era, developing the 15ft FT24 in 1913 fitted or retrofitted in most First World War battleships (with 1 per cent accuracy up to 20,000 yards).[85] One 41ft FX3 was fitted in each *Nelson* and *Rodney* turret. The *King George V* class had not only a rangefinder fitted on the two main directors, 22ft (forward) and a 15ft (aft), but also a 42ft one in A and Y turrets and a 30ft one in B, plus a 15ft one in each of the four HA/LA directors.[86] Barr & Stroud also supplied the British Army and overseas navies, especially the Japanese.

An instrument was also required to solve the geometrical problem of converting own and target ship speeds and courses and bearing into rate of change of range and of bearing. Gunnery officer John Dumaresq developed such a mechanical instrument in 1904, named after himself, which was refined to become the Mark VI fitted from about 1911. Dumaresqs (pronounced 'dumarreks') were manufactured by precision engineers Elliott Brothers of Lewisham, London. By 1913 they had made 1042 with a value of £9539.[87] The resulting rate of change of range associated with the current actual range could be converted into predicted range, either manually or by the Vickers range 'clock', and so into the necessary gun elevation. The latter instrument was manufactured by Vickers, Sons & Maxim from 1906 at their Erith works in Kent.

The advent of *Dreadnought* with ten large guns instead of four accentuated the fire control problem. It was desirable to concentrate the fire of these guns by salvo firing, whereby one gun in each turret was fired at the same time, rather than firing independently. This not only increased the chances of a shell hitting the target but made spotting easier, as time of flight was known. Such ships had a spotting top with a rangefinder and Dumaresq and supplied data to the transmitting station below the waterline, which transmitted calculated gun range and deflection electrically to each turret where gunlayers and trainer 'followed the pointer' on their receivers, after the sightsetter had applied the correction for each gun.

To predict range and deflection, it was necessary to determine target course and speed as accurately as possible. To this end, two men began to develop fire control tables independently. Arthur Pollen was managing director of the British Linotype Corporation of

Broadheath, Manchester, making newspaper printing machinery, who had good contacts at the Admiralty. From about 1905 he developed the Argo clock and course plotting table, partly financed by the Admiralty. Six Argo Clocks Mark IV (which predicted both range and bearing) were ordered in 1912.[88] Pollen used T Cooke & Sons of York to manufacture them, which was taken over by Vickers in 1915, later becoming Cooke, Troughton & Simms.[89] Lieutenant Frederic C Dreyer, with help from his brother John, a Captain in the Royal Artillery, developed his own ideas when attached to DNO Department from 1906. He advocated plotting range and bearing against time on a moving roll of paper and, from the best line through the plotted points, finding the mean range, range-rate and bearing-rate. Dreyer patented his ideas in 1910–11 with Admiralty approval. The detailed design and manufacture of the tables was undertaken by Elliott Brothers. As well as the plotting table, a Dumaresq and range clock was fitted. After various experimental tables, five Mark III Dreyer Tables (which also had bearing clocks) were ordered in 1912, the first being fitted in *Monarch*. After trials in 1913, the Admiralty decided to order the £635 Dreyer table rather than the £2133 Argo Clock for the battle fleet. The improved Dreyer Table Mark IV capable of handling ranges up to 20,000 yards went into production in 1914, the first in *Iron Duke*.

At the same period, Rear-Admiral Percy Scott had been developing his idea of a central director, leading on from his work on improving RN gunnery as Inspector of Target Practice. Sited close to the spotting top, the director harmonised the control and firing of all the main guns. Information on the target ship was passed to the transmitting station, where the new gyro compass and speed log also had read-outs. From the fire control table, predicted gun range and deflection were passed back to the director. The master sight was aimed accordingly and elevation and bearing settings passed electrically to the guns. When the guns were ready, they could all be fired from the director. After successful trials in *Neptune* in 1911 and *Thunderer* in 1912, twenty-nine directors were ordered in October 1913 from Vickers at their Erith works, and fitted in both old and new battleships in 1914–15. Vickers also received an order from the Admiralty on 18 February 1915 for fire control gear for the *Queen Elizabeth* class.[90] Thus by Jutland, most of the ships of the Grand Fleet had a potentially effective fire control system centred around the director and the Dreyer table. British gunnery at Jutland has been the subject of many books and papers, the general conclusion being 'should have done better', particularly for Beatty's battlecruisers.

Elliott Brothers also built under licence the German Anschutz gyro compass (replaced by

Right: Precision engineers Elliott Brothers were important contractors to the Admiralty for fire control equipment. Staff in the Admiralty Assembly Shop at their Century Works in Lewisham, London are seen here in the mid 1920s making equipment for *Nelson* and *Rodney* and cruisers.

the American Sperry design from 1915), Forbes speed logs, and Robinson wind speed anemometers, which all provided inputs to the fire control table. Post-war, Elliott Brothers, with assistance from ex-Argo engineers, were contracted by the Admiralty to develop the new Admiralty Fire Control Table. This retained the principles of the Dreyer tables but took account of wartime experience. The more automated Mark I was fitted in *Nelson* and *Rodney* costing £45,000 each, the Mark VII[91] in the battleships modernised from 1936, the Mark IX in the *King George V* class and the Mark X in *Vanguard*, all supplied by Elliott Brothers. High angle fire control tables were also fitted in battleships and smaller ships, for example HACS Mark IV in the *King George V* class, built by V-A at their Crayford works at £10,000 each. The total cost of all fire control equipment on a *King George V* battleship was roughly £160,000, a twentyfold increase on the cost of a pre-First World War battleship.[92]

In the late 1920s control was centred in the Director Control Tower, sited above the bridge, fitted with the main rangefinder, director sight and spotting gear.[93] In battleships, one was fitted forward, one aft, plus smaller directors for secondary armament. The main directors were built by Vickers-Armstrongs at their Barrow works, each costing around £15,000–£20,000. They were also fitted in cruisers and exported. The four directors per ship for the 5.25in, Mark IV in *King George V* and *Prince of Wales* and Mark V in the other three, were built by English Electric at Bradford, a factory that normally built electrical equipment for trams.[94] *Vanguard*'s four US Mark 37 directors for her 5.25in guns were made in America but assembled and tested at Metropolitan–Vickers.[95] Crabtree built 2pdr pom-pom directors. When radar became available, Type 274 was fitted on top of the forward director to provide more accurate ranges from 1941. This was developed into the Type 284 in 1944 which could also spot shell splashes. By the end of the battleship era, electro-mechanical fire control equipment had served the RN well, contributing to *Duke of York* crippling *Scharnhorst* in complete darkness in December 1943.

TORPEDOES

Although torpedoes are not normally regarded as a battleship weapon, every British battleship and battlecruiser from the 1890s to 1927 was fitted with torpedo tubes, usually submerged. They were considered potentially useful at the anticipated short battle ranges before the First World War. Typical installations were:

Canopus to *Ocean* classes	4 broadside submerged 18in tubes
Dreadnought, Invincible & *Lord Nelson* classes	4 broadside, 1 stern, submerged 18in
Colossus & *Orion* classes	2 broadside, 1 stern, submerged 21in
Queen Elizabeth & *Royal Sovereign* classes	4 broadside, submerged 21in
Nelson & *Rodney*	2 broadside, submerged 24.5in.

Although the Dockyards made submerged tubes, others were manufactured at Elswick by Armstrong Whitworth: 142 18in and thirty-two 21in up to early 1913.[96] Vickers tried to break into this market offering an 18in submerged tube for £4400 in 1902.[97] As well as the launching tubes, watertight shutters were required on the hull, with extending guide rails to protect the torpedo when being discharged underway. Typically five torpedoes were carried per tube, costing about £595 each for 18in or £830 for 21in.

Robert Whitehead had pioneered the ship-borne locomotive torpedo in the late 1860s exporting from his works in Fiume in Austro-Hungary (now Rijeka). He had set up a British factory at Weymouth in 1890, but about that time, the British Government determined to produce its own torpedoes, also at Woolwich. Initially at the Royal Laboratories, work was transferred to the Royal Gun Factory in 1893, so leaving Weymouth largely geared to exports. Greenwood & Batley had a torpedo factory at Leeds from about 1886 which manufactured 14in and 18in torpedoes but had ceased by 1909.[98] The following year, a new Royal Naval Torpedo Factory was opened at Greenock on the Clyde, with key Woolwich staff transferring there. The factory was close to Loch Long which was used as a torpedo testing range up to 7000 yards, fired from Arrochar. Previously torpedoes had been tested at an artificial lake on Horsea Island in Portsmouth Harbour, but this only allowed runs up to 1000 yards.

Following Whitehead's death in 1905, Armstrong Whitworth and Vickers were together encouraged by the Admiralty to take a 50.1 per cent shareholding in the Whitehead company of Fiume, costing each of them £200,272.[99] A new company, Whitehead Torpedo Works (Weymouth) Ltd was formed in 1907.[100] Torpedo export orders in 1907

Right: Submerged torpedo tubes were fitted in all British dreadnoughts before the First World War. Armstrong Whitworth designed their own submerged torpedo tube, capable of being fired at ship speeds up to 21 knots. What looks like an 18in torpedo is being weight tested to see that the extending underwater structure will withstand the water pressure. They had supplied 174 submerged torpedo tubes of 18in and 21in diameter up to 1913. *(Reproduced by kind permission of the Syndics of Cambridge University Library. Vickers 2000)*

included fifty for the USA, seventy-one 45cm for Sweden and twenty 45cm for Brazil. In September 1911 it was employing 756 with an order book of £471,000 representing over 500 torpedoes.[101] An order for torpedoes for *Sultan Osman I* (later *Agincourt*) was received in March 1914. This factory shared Admiralty production with Greenock, especially after demand rose on the outbreak of war. Production was also increased by the Government, in conjunction with Armstrong Whitworth and Vickers, by taking over an old factory at Caton near Lancaster in 1915. This made mainly 18in submarine torpedoes but it closed in 1919. The RN had introduced 21in torpedoes in 1908 (the RGF Mark I) which were used in surface ships from 1911. The RGF-designed 21in Mark II was developed about 1909 and supplied to most battleships, some made at Weymouth. This was later replaced by the Mark IV which remained in service into the Second World War. Those battleships with 18in tubes generally used the Mark V developed by RGF in 1898, and manufactured by RGF, Weymouth and Leeds, 496 being ordered in 1903–04.[102] The 18in Mark VII was developed in 1908. But few battleship torpedoes were fired in the First World War; the thirty-seven battleships and battlecruisers at Jutland only launching thirteen torpedoes between them, compared with about 4480 shells of 12in or greater calibre.[103]

With the drop in demand for torpedoes after the war, Weymouth works were shut down in 1921, although Armstrong Whitworth and Vickers retained the facility, later buying out the remaining Whitehead shareholders, and forming the new Whitehead Torpedo Co Ltd in 1923.[104] The factory was re-opened after Vickers-Armstrongs was formed, receiving an order from the Admiralty in 1932 for fourteen 21in torpedoes worth £37,230 (£2560 each).[105] By 1938 the works were employing 1400 with torpedoes being made for the Admiralty, Netherlands, Poland, Romania and China, with annual profits averaging £150,000. By the Second World War, most submerged torpedo tubes had been removed from British capital ships, although *Hood* retained her four 21in above-water tubes, and *Nelson* and *Rodney* their two submerged 24.5in until 1942–3. But only twelve such torpedoes were launched in the Second World War.[106]

With re-armament, the Admiralty needed additional torpedo manufacturing facilities. It took over the defunct Argyll Motor Company's works at Alexandria near Dumbarton in 1936 and re-equipped it to expand RNTF Greenock's output.[107] The works eventually took over all the latter's production, which then became a R&D establishment. Both facilities closed post-war, as torpedo design and production was transferred to industry.

9: ARMOUR

MAKING ARMOUR PLATE

While Britain had clad its battleships in armour from 1860 with *Warrior*'s 4.5in wrought iron, it was not until the 1890s that armour technology and its manufacturing industry really developed. *Warrior*'s plates had been made from hammered iron, built up by rolling strips of wrought iron and welding layers together at red heat under a steam hammer. Such plates were made on the Thames, then still a major shipbuilding area, either from scrap iron or new iron made further north in Staffordshire or Yorkshire. At the same time, naval ordnance was developing rapidly, with William Armstrong making more powerful breech-loading guns at Elswick near Newcastle. Armour plating had to increase in thickness and resistivity to withstand such attack. But it was the Sheffield ironmasters who proved best able to produce such material. By 1863, John Brown at the Atlas Works and Charles Cammell at the Cyclops Works were rolling armour plate. A red-hot mass of iron was compressed to the required thickness between plate rolls, as opposed to hammering. By the late 1860s, these two companies dominated armour production and were able to command high prices and make large profits. Thickness up to 9in could be produced with individual plates weighing over 10 tons.

With the development of larger-bore rifled guns offering greater accuracy, there was continuing pressure to develop stronger armour, not just by ever-increasing its thickness but by improved metallurgy whereby a harder face could be obtained which would break up a projectile before penetration, that is, shatter the projectile nose like a ceramic cup dropped onto a tile floor, usually resulting in the entire projectile breaking apart. In the late 1870s, John Brown produced compound armour where a hard but brittle steel face about one-third the total thickness was married to a softer but tougher wrought-iron back. This back would soak up impact shock energy transmitted through the face, reducing the fracture of the face layer, as well as holding the plate together after impact. Cammell also produced compound armour but by a different process. The limitations of compound armour were that two-thirds of the plate was still soft, relatively weak wrought iron, and that the joint between the steel face and the wrought-iron back was a sharp line, resulting in splitting apart of the two materials during impact, weakening the plate compared to a solid plate with no such lamination.

At the same time, steel began to be produced in larger quantities of consistent quality at lower prices using the new Siemens-Martin open hearth furnace method. The way was now open to make all-steel armour which was stronger than compound armour by eliminating the limitations mentioned above, as shown by full scale tests. With a significant export market for armour plate as well as guns, countries such as Italy conducted tests on plates from rival manufacturers including France. The Admiralty also conducted tests, not only onshore as at the Shoeburyness range in 1888 and 1891, but also aboard trials vessels such as the ex-wooden wall *Nettle*.

As high-quality armour was essential for the protection of battleships, successful manufacturers could charge high prices, typically about £75 per ton, over ten times the price for the mild steel plates used for hull and boiler construction. This attracted newcomers to the market, including the Vickers brothers (Tom and Albert) who had long been producing special steels at Sheffield. They developed a new all steel armour plate in 1888 which did well in tests. Accordingly they expanded their River Don Works in Sheffield to produce up to 10,000 tons a year. William Beardmore also developed armour plate at his Parkhead Works in Glasgow in 1889. John Brown developed a hardening process involving high pressure sprays of water, for which Cammell and Vickers took out licences.

At the same time H A Harvey in the United States had been developing a new hardening process for nickel steel plates, whereby the face was cemented (carburised) with charcoal for two or three weeks, resulting in a thin (0.5–1.5in) layer of extremely high carbon content, and then chilled (cooled very rapidly using water sprayed on the plate face), giving a very hard face, approaching the hardness of machining tool tips or the edges of swords, to break up attacking projectiles. 'Harveyized' armour of 7in thickness was shown in tests starting in 1891 to be equivalent to 10.5in of compound armour. It was also the equivalent of 14in of wrought iron, hence half the weight for similar protection. The improvement due to the hard face was greatest for thin plates where the face layer made up the greatest portion of the plate (up to a third to a half of the plate in 3in Harveyized armour, about the thinnest made), dropping off slowly but steadily as plate thickness increased. It depended on the weakness of the projectile nose to sudden, short-lived impact shock, so improved hardened-steel projectiles could degrade its effectiveness. The main British armour producers took out Harvey licences, including John Brown. The Admiralty specified 9in Harvey armour for the belt of the new *Majestic* class battleships, ordered in 1893. But the new thinner armour offered the opportunity to divert the weight saved into extending the protected area for battleships, e.g. deeper and/or longer belt, or for cruisers into more powerful machinery and faster ships.

The 1890s saw not only a massive growth in the production of highly profitable armour from the naval building programmes, but also the expansion of its producers 'downstream' into shipbuilding with its potentially lucrative orders for export warships. In 1894, just as the armour producers were installing more powerful rolls and presses for shaping ingots and bending plates, Krupp of Essen produced their new hard faced nickel-chromium steel armour with a thicker face (both 'decrementally [deep] hardened' and surface cemented) of about one-third of the total plate thickness for all plates, regardless of thickness, and a tougher back than Harveyized armour. It had greater resistance to punching through by projectiles

than any previous naval armour, it was much better than Harveyized armour at causing projectile nose shatter, further degrading penetration through the plate, by prolonging the high resistance to projectile motion during the initial impact, and it was less prone to cracking, so that the plate resistance continued at the maximum extent for a longer time. Krupp was prepared to licence British producers, so when the Admiralty specified Krupp Cemented (KC) armour for the *Canopus* class ordered in late 1896 with a 6in belt (their other armour mostly Harveyized), companies such as Vickers prepared to make it. KC had a 'figure of merit' of about 2.3–2.8, depending on thickness, compared with about 2 for Harveyized armour, relative to a wrought iron resistivity of 1 – this proportional relationship was for the rather thick armour used on battleship sides. That meant that Krupp armour could be about 40 per cent of the thickness of wrought iron for the same protection. Krupp Non-Cemented (KNC) armour was of a similar composition but without the hardened face so was homogeneous (the same all the way through), tougher and more ductile than KC. It was used for thinner protective material and for more horizontal or sloped locations where highly oblique impacts were expected – face-hardened armour did not work well under highly oblique impact because it inhibited the ricochet of broken projectiles and could crack through and throw large armour pieces out its back even if the projectile bounced off. KC was used for thicker vertical protection, typically 4in and over. Protective plating (typically of two thicknesses of 0.75 to 1in) was used in decks, since at the then expected short fighting ranges, projectiles would have a small angle of descent, striking the (vertical) side armour nearly 'normally' i.e. at 90°. In fact, the angle of descent was so low at this time that many warships did not use any 'armour' material for decks to save money and weight, but merely built up extra layers of high-tensile-strength construction steel for protection against grazing projectiles, armour splinters, and shell fragments only, both for protective decks and internal splinter screens behind the main side armour.

The process was described in contemporary works.[1] Steel was produced by the Siemens-Martin process, being a low-carbon steel (0.2–0.4 per cent) alloyed with nickel (2–2.5 per cent) and chromium (1.5–2 per cent). An ingot weighing up to 50 tons and up to 45in thick was then cast in a mould from the output

1: The first stage in making an armour plate was to cast a steel ingot weighing about 50 tons. In this picture, a 12,000-ton hydraulic forging press is reducing the red-hot metal down to a rectangular slab about 26in thick; this one is at Beardmore's Parkhead works. *(Author's collection)*

3: An armour plate being bent hot under the 12,000-ton press in Beardmore's forge shop. *(Author's collection)*

2: After reheating in a gas-fired furnace, the slab was ready to be rolled to near-final thickness, up to 14ft wide, then trimmed to size. The rolls at Armstrong Whitworth's Openshaw works were driven by a marine type triple expansion steam engine of 10,000 hp. *(Reproduced by kind permission of the Syndics of Cambridge University Library. Vickers 2000)*

4: The plate was then machined on its surface and edges to final dimensions. It was then ready for hardening by heat treatment and cementation, the thicker plates by the Krupp process. The bank of planing machines in Beardmore's D Shop were built by Thomas Shanks & Co of Johnstone. *(Author's collection)*

of several furnaces. The upper and lower ends of the ingot would be cut off since they would be most contaminated by various unmixed alloying elements, rust, and undesirable chemicals, both from the original iron ore or used to help clean it during smelting. The red hot ingot was squeezed down to between 6in and 18in in a 10,000-ton hydraulic press, needing three reheats. The resulting slab went to the rolling mill about 12ft wide driven by a steam engine of 12,000 hp which, in a number of passes, would reduce it to just above its final thickness. After scale (rusty flakes on the surface) had been removed by pneumatic tools, the edges were trimmed and the face planed flat, and the plate cleaned by shot-blasting, ready for cementation. Two plates were placed in a special gas-fired furnace, their faces separated by a powdered charcoal mixture to be carburised, sealed within the furnace at a uniform high temperature for around 10–14 days. This increased the carbon content of the outer 0.75–1.5in of the plate from about 0.3 per cent to over 1 per cent. The plates would then be bent to shape by a 5000- or 8000-ton press if so required, e.g. for circular barbette armour. For curved side armour plates, the shipyard would supply wooden templates of the required shape. The plate was then passed to the machine shop for edge planing and slotting, e.g. to make a groove to interlock with adjacent plates. Places where large holes needed to be cut or drilled later through the entire plate (vision slits, etc) were covered with thick asbestos pads to prevent hardening. Final hardening would then be completed after reheating (the face hotter than the back), by being cooled for up to three hours (depending on plate thickness) by water jets at a high pressure ('quenching') which prevented the formation of insulating steam on the plate surface. An alternative method used in thinner plates involved horizontally dipping the plate face in a tank full of cottonseed-oil. The plate was then examined and test pieces taken for quality control; its weight now only about one-third that of the original ingot. Holes in the softer back for armour mounting bolts would then be marked, drilled and tapped. Larger holes in the face that had been protected by the asbestos pads were also now made. It then went to the erecting shop to be fitted against adjoining plates, as if on board ship. This shop would have a floor of cast iron slabs, with typically a 50-ton overhead crane. As the hard face could not be machined using standard metalworking tools,

any further finishing had to be done by electric grinding tools. If smaller holes had to be made for discharge pipes etc, a small area was softened by electric annealing to allow such to be drilled.

The finished plate now had a glass-hard, rather brittle face of roughly one-third of the plate thickness for the original KC armour, though this varied considerably from manufacturer to manufacturer and from time to time over the years, harder than tool steel on its surface – 650–700 on the Brinell Hardness Scale for the original KC armour. This was expected to break up the attacking projectile, but a softer and resilient thick back (only 200–240 Brinell) absorbing energy from the impact shock wave moving from the face to the back, drastically reducing face cracking and increasing its resistance dramatically, so as to withstand the overall impact. Plates were then despatched by rail to the shipyard if for hull armour or the gun mounting manufacturer if for a gunhouse. The whole process took around five to nine months from order to delivery.

By far the largest British naval ordnance producer, Armstrong, had already acquired Charles Mitchell's shipyard at Walker on Tyne near Newcastle in 1882, to form Sir W G Armstrong, Mitchell & Co Ltd. They then laid out a new warship building yard at its engineering and ordnance works upriver at Elswick. By this means, it could sell both ships and ordnance to the Admiralty and to overseas navies. But although it then started to produce its own steel to make gun forgings, it could not produce armour, and had to pay high prices. In 1896 it explored a possible takeover of the Naval Construction & Armaments Co Ltd at Barrow, where it proposed to build a new armour plant close to an existing steelworks.[2] However, it did not need to increase its shipbuilding capacity so dropped the idea, leaving the way open for their rivals Vickers to bid for the NCA, and so enter the shipbuilding market. A successful bid was made in 1897, the company becoming part of Vickers, Sons & Maxim Ltd. The Barrow site was substantially extended including a new facility for building gun mountings – previously Vickers had only produced guns, at its Sheffield works. Soon the company could proudly boast that they could produce steel, armour, guns, mountings, hulls and machinery, as demonstrated by the completion of *Vengeance* in 1902. They commissioned a sumptuous publicity volume that same year to extol their prowess, describing in detail all their

Left: A battery of armour machine tools at Armstrong's Openshaw works, mostly electrically driven and built by the company. Top left, planing the surface of a plate up to 25ft x 12ft prior to cementation. Top right, slotting plate sides (tongue and groove) and cutting holes on a machine weighing 100 tons. Bottom left, machining plate edges. Bottom right, drilling holes to take armour bolts and lifting plates. *(Reproduced by kind permission of the Syndics of Cambridge University Library. Vickers 2000)*

works.[3] However, it was not mentioned that construction was delayed by late delivery of armour plate and gun mountings made by the company.[4]

Armstrong had faced this threat from a major rival by merging with their former competitor, Sir Joseph Whitworth & Co Ltd at Openshaw near Manchester, who were the only other producer of heavy hydraulic gun mountings at the time – Woolwich and other producers could only make the smaller gun mountings and carriages. After the merger in early 1897 to form Sir W G Armstrong, Whitworth & Co Ltd, gun mounting construction was concentrated at Elswick, while Openshaw continued to make guns and mounting components. In April 1897, the new Board decided to manufacture armour – after 'a somewhat prolonged discussion'.[5] Work started in 1898 on a new armour making plant on the north-eastern part of the less congested Openshaw site – see plan on p.58. It was opened in 1900 at a cost of £491,000, financed from a new £750,000 debenture stock and by cutting the dividend.[6] A Krupp licence had been taken out in 1899 when the company joined the international armour cartel. The first ship for which they supplied all the armour was the armoured cruiser *Lancaster* with deliveries (of 4in bulkhead plates) starting at the end of 1901. Now

the company could produce all of the main components of a battleship except the propulsion machinery. However they and the other armour manufacturers greatly underestimated the time to bring such new facilities on stream and to achieve acceptable quality standards, quoting unrealistic delivery dates to the Admiralty. The Parliamentary Committee appointed to investigate such matters reported that John Brown delivered plates for *Irresistible* between four and nine months late, while for *Implacable* Vickers were nine months late with the conning tower and Beardmore thirteen months late with barbette armour.[7]

By 1901 there were now five British armour manufacturers: Armstrong Whitworth, Vickers, John Brown of Sheffield, Cammell of Sheffield and Beardmore of Parkhead in Glasgow. Vickers had taken a 50 per cent stake in Beardmore in 1902, partly to get greater control of armour manufacture after Armstrong entered the market, Beardmore acquiring a Krupp licence soon after. But Vickers were ambivalent about having another armour producer; they wrote to Admiralty on 19 November 1902 pointing out that they had only been awarded contracts for 2833 tons of armour (for *Dominion*) out of 14,667 tons ordered that year, 'placing us considerably below other makers', although with four other makers now, that was actually their proportionate share.[8] Together the firms could produce over 30,000 tons of armour a year, sufficient for six to eight battleships, although armoured cruisers now formed an additional market.

Face-hardened armour manufacture was an 'art' rather than a science and most manufacturers made their plates using theories that varied considerably and led to many variations in this kind of armour, some of high quality and some less so. It took quite a bit of trial and error to meet the specifications of the navy for which they were making the armour and, as competitors improved their products, so did the major producers, who did not want to be beaten during bidding or comparative tests. Even Krupp, who had a monopoly for KC armour in Germany and who did not change their 1894 KC armour manufacturing techniques through to the end of the First World War, was rudely awakened to the fact that others had improved on their armour when the British post-war testing showed that the average British KC-type plate was better than Krupp-made KC by a noticeable amount – indeed, much of the non-Krupp KC plate made anywhere else was better than Krupp KC plate by 1918.[9]

Armour was used not only for hull protection but also for gunhouses making up 30–40 per cent of their revolving weight – the sides of a twin 12in turret were about 9in thick. The industry also served the export market, both for armour and for complete warships, e.g. to Japan. At this time, a typical pre-dreadnought would have about 3500–4500 tons of armour protection amounting to about 24–28 per cent of its displacement of about 14,000–16,000 tons. For battleships built from 1908 to 1915 this percentage went up to 28–32 per cent, which included the thinner and cheaper protective plating but under Admiralty weight definitions 'protection' excluded gunhouse armour, which was part of 'armament'. For the higher-powered battlecruisers, that percentage fell to about 20. Such 'protection' amounted to about 20 per cent of a battleship's cost but if gunhouse armour was included that pushed it to over 25 per cent.

The makers could also produce thinner 'protective plating' used in decks and splinter protection, a high tensile steel with an expensive nickel content costing about one-third that of armour plate, with a less elaborate manufacturing process. Conning towers were made from cast steel because of their complex shape.

From 1908 Hadfield of Sheffield could produce them in their Era nickel-chrome steel, which was also used for communication tubes, rangefinder hoods and heavily curved parts of gun shields, as well as for projectiles.

ARMOUR PRICES

The armour-making market was hugely profitable, especially as an 'armour ring' of manufacturers had developed to maintain high prices. The Admiralty connived in this to some extent, accepting the makers' claims that they had high capital investment in specialised plant and machine tools with no commercial market, with high R&D and trial costs, a highly trained workforce, a commitment to provide adequate industrial capacity, a reserve of productive power, an ability to serve export markets, and the requirement for expensive alloying metals such as nickel and chromium. Only a handful of senior staff at each armour company would have been aware of the high prices and low costs resulting in the big profit margins. Financial records in companies were closely guarded, with individual ledgers having lockable clasps, while annual accounts only showed aggregate profit across all company divisions. Letters from the companies to Their Lordships at the Admiralty protested at any proposed price reductions, before grudgingly offering a modest percentage off the previous list prices. However, the Admiralty refused to pay extra for any plates whose weight was over that specified; thickness tolerances were typically zero over, ⅛in under, which meant that plates could be expected to be slightly thinner than specified. It also reduced the price by a few pounds per ton if any slight deficiency was revealed on test in resisting the specified striking projectile velocity.[10]

Openshaw was the most profitable division of Armstrong Whitworth, producing an average annual profit from 1901–12 of £381,000 or 43 per cent of the average annual company profit of £880,000 over the 11½ years, yet with only 27 per cent of the average total capital employed of £4.8 million.[11] Armour was by far the biggest contributor to Openshaw profits, although needing a further £450,000 spent on armour plant in later years to expand output. Further detail is revealed in some Armstrong accounts preserved in the Rendel papers[12] – the full version prepared for the directors, not the sanitised version for shareholders. The profit and loss accounts for Openshaw for the years 1907–12 show that armour profit alone averaged £302,000 a year. This formed 73 per cent of the division's profits before charges, the remainder being the former Whitworth company's products of steel, guns, machine tools and general engineering products, merely classed as 'Sundries'. However, out of the profits, commission (or royalty) payments of about £110,000 a year (largely from the Krupp patent) had to be made to the armour makers' pool operated by the Harvey United Steel Co Ltd. When the Krupp patents expired on 26 April 1909, these payments ceased, so there was a further boost to profits, although prices to the Admiralty had to be reduced. Well could the company afford to pay the three senior Openshaw managers commission of 4 per cent of net profits, or about £19,000 a year, probably about quadruple their regular salaries at a time when £1000–£1500 a year was a good salary for a senior manager.[13] Half went to H S Carington, the Armstrong director (formerly of Whitworth) responsible for the Openshaw works, whose regular salary in 1910 was £2500.[14] The Elswick shipyard managers received no such commission – there was less need to keep their mouths shut about excessive profits which were modest in shipbuilding (see p.240). But armour profits were less a result of managerial efficiency than of rigged market prices – indeed the high scrap rate suggests

poor quality control. But even the Armstrong Board, generously minded where their own remuneration was concerned, became alarmed at the huge bonuses accruing to the armour plant senior staff, due more to the booming order book for battleships with orders for Openshaw pouring in at over £1.5 million a year, rather than their own endeavours. There was apparently a high wastage rate – Armstrong Whitworth discussed in 1913 what to do with 13,000 tons of scrap armour at Openshaw,[15] a very expensive manufacturing overhead of around £40 a ton even if unfinished. Concerned also at delays supplying the armour plates for the Brazilian and Chilean battleships in 1913, the Board resolved to consolidate salary and commission into a single salary figure, but still as high as £12,000 in the case of Carington, and £7000 for manager J M Gledhill and £5500 for R Matthews. Those latter figures were still many times the salary of senior staff at Elswick, who not being on the main Board, were not aware of the rewards their Openshaw colleagues were enjoying.

The accounts for Vickers' Sheffield works reveal a similarly high level of profit for armour. For some years, information was helpfully collated into an annual volume entitled Costs, Prices and Profits.[16] Over the early years of dreadnought building 1907–11, its armour

Left: The armour erecting shop at Openshaw about 1903. Top left, 160lb (4in) non-cemented gun shield for a twin 6in mounting for the armoured cruiser *Lancaster*. Top right, gunhouse armour for twin 10in mounting on *Swiftsure*, made up of 8in and 9in cemented plates weighing 120 tons. Bottom left, half of the forward barbette for *New Zealand* (later *Zealandia*), made up of 480lb (12in) cemented plates weighing 140 tons. Bottom right, 200lb (5in) cemented armour for upper 6in gun casemate (No.1 port) for 1894 *Repulse* being refitted in 1904; 17 tons. *(Reproduced by kind permission of the Syndics of Cambridge University Library. Vickers 2000)*

VICKERS' ANNUAL AVERAGE ARMOUR PRODUCTION 1907–11

	Tons	Sales (£)	Price/ton	Cost (£)	Cost/ton	Profit (£)	Profit/ton	Profit/cost (%)
Armour plates	2368	237,159	100.15	112,032	47.31	125,127	52.84	111.7
Gun shields	1838	235,012	127.86	93,683	50.97	141,329	76.89	150.9
Foreign armour	1062	102,855	96.85	50,443	47.50	52,412	49.35	103.9
Average 1907–11	5268	575,026	109.15	256,158	48.63	318,868	60.53	124.5

output varied from a low of 2692 tons in 1909 to a high of 7377 tons in 1911. It increased to 11,027 tons in 1915 when armour for the *Royal Sovereign* class and the new battlecruisers was being rolled. The annual average figures for 1907–11 are shown above.

Foreign armour included sales to Italy, Japan, Russia and Spain. Average profit at £60.5 per ton was 55 per cent of average price of £109.1, or a massive 124 per cent of cost. Gun shield armour yielded the highest profit, forming part of the gun mounting contracts at Barrow, priced at standard rates agreed with the Admiralty. For the years 1913–15, armour output increased, with annual average profit of £764,000, or 56.6 per cent of Sheffield gross profits.[17] However, before such profits were incorporated into the overall company profit and loss account, head office costs, commissions, depreciation and interest were deducted, which took up around one-third of the profits made by the three divisions, Sheffield, Barrow and Maxim.

Some figures from Cammell Laird confirm how valuable the business was. An order for battlecruiser *Lion*'s armour was placed in March 1910 for:

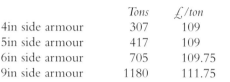

	Tons	£/ton
4in side armour	307	109
5in side armour	417	109
6in side armour	705	109.75
9in side armour	1180	111.75

This single contract including 25 tons of armour bolts came to 2634 tons worth £262,851 after a discount, 13 per cent of the ship's cost.[18] Warren shows that for 1913 and 1914 their armour sales amounted to 12,043 tons worth £1.117 million, with profits of £514,000, or 85 per cent on cost.[19] Given such a lucrative market, incredibly the company falsified test pieces for armour plate and gun forgings at its Grimesthorpe works in 1906 (Cyclops works finished the plates), allowing sub-standard work to be delivered to the Admiralty and Woolwich. When Government inspectors discovered the failings, Cammell Laird were struck off the Admiralty list. Not only did they lose valuable government contracts, but overseas customers deserted them. Only after the Chairman, J M Laird, had resigned, replaced by Francis Elgar, former Director of Dockyards, and managers and foremen at Sheffield had been removed, was the company reinstated in March 1908.[20] No dividend was paid on the ordinary shares from 1908–12 inclusive. Partly in response to this quality problem and partly due to the Admiralty taking over testing of all its ordnance materials from the War Office on 1 April 1908, the Admiralty allocated £10,000 to building a test house at Sheffield, where the armour manufacturers also made gun forgings[21] – previously test pieces had to be sent to Woolwich.

The Admiralty received a proposal in November 1912 from the American E Marshall Fox to supply 4000–6000 tons of armour a year at an appreciably lower price than the existing manufacturers, if the Admiralty would guarantee him orders. Fox was a director of Harvey United Steel Co Ltd based in London, which had just gone into liquidation. This company had been receiving royalties from armour makers using both Harvey and Krupp licences in the UK, USA, France, Germany and Italy.

Below: After armour plates had been shaped and heat treated, they were then too hard for normal machining. Any final adjustment to the edges and joints had to be done by electric grinding tools. Some of *Bellerophon*'s plates are shown in Cammell Laird's Cyclops Works at Sheffield, probably in 1907. *(Author's collection)*

He had been Harvey's European agent for twenty years, so knew of the very high profit margin, and wished to continue to benefit from such, as royalty income had virtually ceased as the patents expired. Falkner of Armstrong Whitworth had noted in 1903 that without 'the Convention' controlling supply and international prices at an average £115 per ton, a competitive selling price would be about £40.[22] Fox had yet to build a plant, but had in mind using the recently closed Thames Iron Works, and he would not quote a firm price. The Admiralty was still unaware of the high profit margins; Director of Contracts F W Black minuting in February 1914: 'The evidence in our possession, so far as it goes, indicates that the firms are not making excessive profits, and most of the statements regarding the unduly high prices paid by the British Admiralty are based on insufficient or inaccurate information.'[23] However, the Admiralty declined Fox's proposal, as they doubted his ability to supply the requisite quantity and quality from an as yet un-built plant. Appendix 2 discusses the Admiralty's guarded response to the 1913 Parliamentary Select Committee's questions on armour plate prices, where Black gave evidence.

In the battleship building frenzy leading up to the First World War, the armour producers were in full swing, not only for ships for the Admiralty but for Japan, Brazil, Turkey, Russia, Spain, Holland and Norway. Export orders were placed by the shipbuilder or a foreign government directly with the armour manufacturer. With Armstrong Whitworth building three South American battleships at Elswick each needing about 5100 tons of armour (*Rio de Janeiro*, *Almirante Latorre* and *Almirante Cochrane*), 700 tons per month had to be supplied by Openshaw in 1913–14.[24] Even more powerful plant was installed with presses capable of handling plates up to 15in thick – Openshaw had installed a second press of 5000 tons in 1904 costing £12,000. Seven years later, with their maximum output limited to 15,000 tons a year, they had been struggling to meet demand. In 1911 six new heat treatment furnaces costing £25,000 were installed there, with a 7000-ton forging press and three 150-ton cranes costing £39,200 in 1912. Beardmore installed a new press in 1911.

In 1909 the Admiralty issued instructions that its preferred maximum armour plate size was about 20 x 9.5ft with a maximum area of 180 sq ft.[25] Railway loading gauges limited the

ORION ARMOUR ORDERS

Location	Manufacturer	Ordered	Delivery	Price per ton (£)
Lower barbettes	Brown	20 Oct 1909	Feb 1910	104–152
Bulkheads	Beardmore	20 Oct 1909	Feb 1910	108.5
Upper barbettes	Brown	9 Mar 1910	Jul 1910	110.5–133
Side belt	Beardmore	9 Mar 1910	Jul 1910	92–119.5

size of plates readily handled. The Krupp patent expired in 1909 – the Admiralty had been paying a royalty of around £4–£5 per ton.[26] But by this time, British producers had developed better armour, typically with 4 per cent nickel, 2 per cent chromium and 0.5 per cent carbon for belt plates, e.g. Vickers Standard Quality, 5–10 per cent better than normal Krupp, and less susceptible to hairline cracks on the face.[27]

When a financial year's programme of armoured ship construction was being planned, the Admiralty sought an agreement with the five British armour manufacturers. The firms negotiated as a group (ring) and agreed a price at which all would supply, delivered to the shipyard. The Admiralty spread the orders for the hull armour for the four *Orion* class battleships across all the main armour manufacturers except Vickers, who were making most of the gun shield armour. Armour for the lead ship *Orion* (launched at Portsmouth Dockyard on 20 August 1910) was ordered three months ahead of the other ships, whose hull contracts were placed later; details above. Price depended on thickness, taper and shape. Further orders for the three building by industry were placed

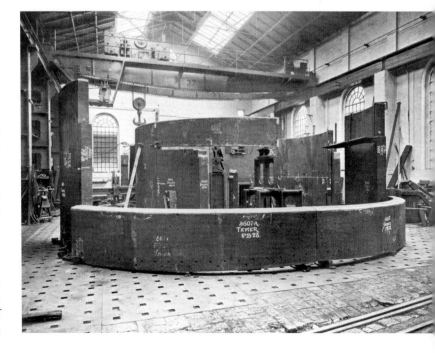

Below: The armour erecting shop at Cyclops Works was floored with cast iron slabs to give a level surface on which plates could be erected. Individual plates would be joined together and adjusted as necessary to get a tight fit. These 360lb (9in) plates were for the barbettes on *Temeraire* and *Bellerophon*, ordered in November 1906 at about £120 per ton. The 40-ton electric overhead travelling crane was by Vaughan & Son of Manchester. *(Author's collection)*

OTHER *ORION* CLASS ARMOUR CONTRACTORS

Location	Monarch	Conqueror	Thunderer
Lower barbette and bulkheads	Armstrong	Beardmore	Brown
Upper barbettes	Cammell	Cammell	Cammell
Side belt	Armstrong	Cammell & Beardmore	Brown

in January and June 1910 at similar prices, as shown above.

The following year, a new price list was agreed for armour ordered from 16 June 1910 and for the 1911–12 Programme. A selection of the prices per ton delivered by rail included:[28]

Location	Thickness (in)	£
Belt	10–12	96
Belt	4–6	93
Belt	3	85
Bulkhead	4–12	92
Barbette	10–12	97
Barbette	5–6	93
Conning tower	8–12	98
Gun shield sides	7–12	130
Gun shield roof	NA	112

Extras were charged for armour bolts and holes, which were typically 3in to 4in diameter, one per 7 sq ft. The Admiralty were pleased to find these prices about 15 per cent less than for the *Orion* class, partly reflecting the end of royalty payments. Such prices were kept confidential to a handful of senior men in the Admiralty; even the Admiralty staff at Dockyards and private shipyards building the battleships were not aware of the figures.[29]

The Admiralty reckoned that the only way they could check if the armour prices were reasonable was either by building a plant of their own, or by buying from abroad. They were reluctant to go down the latter route, both for security of supply and doubts over quality. It was known that there was also an armour ring in the US, where the three manufacturers colluded to fix prices.[30] Bethlehem, Carnegie and Midvale, all based in Pennsylvania, were the only US producers, Midvale starting in 1903. Misa shows US Navy armour prices of around $400–$450 a ton 1903–15 (about £90), which yielded high profits allowing Bethlehem to take over companies such as Fore River Shipbuilding near Boston in 1913.[31] In 1904, the French had built an armour plant at Guérigny, north west of Lyon – this state-owned factory normally made items such as anchors. The Admiralty found information that French armour prices in 1910 were around 2.3–3.0 francs per kg, or about £90–£120 per

ton, similar to British prices.[32] Schneider was also making armour at Le Creusot. But the Admiralty were reluctant to incur the capital expenditure on a new plant and lacked the experience to operate one.

ARMOUR AFTER THE FIRST WORLD WAR

Although some battlecruisers were ordered during the First World War, there were no more British battleships, so orders for armour plate fell off as the war progressed, although some light armour was produced for tanks.[33] The armour makers could see that after the war the market would be even more limited, as did the ordnance producers, often the same company, with overcapacity of at least 50 per cent. The high hopes engendered with the order for the four G3 battlecruisers in 1921 were soon dashed when they were cancelled following the Washington Treaty. Subsequent orders for *Nelson* and *Rodney* provided an element of relief with some 9400 tons each, shared roughly equally between the five manufacturers but additionally gun shields to Vickers (who did not build any of the 16in mountings), with armour belt up to 14in and deck 6.25in.[34] Gun shield armour prices were a generous £240 per ton for front, sides and rear, and £205 for the 570 tons per ship of 6in roof. After Jutland, with longer range plunging shellfire and the increased threat from aerial attack, deck protection thickness was increased and made of NC armour rather than HT steel. Export orders for battleships had disappeared after Washington.

The five armour firms requested a meeting with the Admiralty to discuss policy regarding future armour orders. At that meeting on 15 July 1925, the newly appointed Controller, Rear-Admiral A E M Chatfield,[35] stated that they anticipated orders of only 2000–3000 tons a year if the cruiser programme went ahead, but that if new battleships were ordered in the early 1930s, an average of 18,000 tons a year might be needed. As the firms' annual capacity was about 45,000 tons a year, this would be sufficient for at most three firms. The Admiralty wished to keep Vickers and Armstrong Whitworth because not only were they the two largest manufacturers but they alone could produce heavy gun mountings; they reckoned it was best to place gun shield armour orders with them also. Representatives of the other three firms (Beardmore, John Brown and Cammell Laird) requested compensation if two of them had to close their plants, or a contribu-

Below: The stamp applied to a report on castings made in Sheffield for *Rodney* and *Nelson* by the Armour & Material Overseer.

tion towards the high overhead costs of retaining under-utilised plant and specialist staff available for possible future orders. They also expressed concern that the Admiralty had brought in an additional armour manufacturer, namely D Colville & Co Ltd of Motherwell to make 3in NC armour (assisted by Beardmore at the end of the First World War), who was able to quote an undercutting price of £109 per ton owing to much lower overheads. The Admiralty then investigated the books of the five armour firms and estimated annual plant maintenance costs at £204,715. While they would not agree to pay such an annual subsidy, they did agree to pay higher prices for the first 2500 tons of armour ordered on 15 January 1926 for the four *London* class cruisers, which provided some compensation for the higher overheads per ton associated with low throughput.[36] The rates agreed with the 'ring' firms were £190 per ton for C and £160 for NC, which would reduce to £136 and £104 respectively for any orders over 2500 tons. The orders for hull armour were spread between the five firms, with Vickers and Armstrong Whitworth also receiving the orders for gun shield armour.[37]

But rationalisation was inevitable. Vickers and Armstrong merged their warship building and ordnance interests in 1927. In December 1928 the English Steel Corporation was formed from those two companies' steel making interests, together with those of Cammell Laird. The latter's armour plants at Cyclops and Grimesthorpe in Sheffield were closed together with that at Openshaw, leaving the former Vickers' River Don works as the main plant. With armour orders now mainly for cruisers amounting to only about 2000 tons a year, a 'pool' was formed in 1932, with orders shared between ESC (50 per cent), Beardmore (25 per cent) and Firth-Brown (25 per cent),[38] the latter a formal amalgamation of the two companies in 1930. Although the companies also had other markets for steel products such as forgings and railway material, they all made losses during the early 1930s slump. Beardmore was forced to close its Dalmuir shipyard, but Parkhead survived with help from the banks, fortunately retaining its armour-making plant, which had been profitable before 1928.[39]

After the Admiralty introduced better armour-piercing projectiles following the failures at Jutland to penetrate at oblique angles of attack, the armour makers realised that they would need to develop better armour to resist such attack. Molybdenum was introduced in 1926, which gave a more consistent quality steel. Post-1930 British cemented armour used a thinner face layer than most foreign competitors, 25–30 per cent, which turned out to be the optimum against the larger AP projectiles, since a thick, hard, brittle face tended to degrade resistance in thicker plates used against such projectiles more than in thin plates used to stop cruiser-size AP projectiles. This noticeably improved the resistance of cemented armour compared to most foreign competitors in ballistic tests. Later, improved face hardening was used, to a depth of 30 per cent of even 15in plate thickness. In 1936 the Admiralty invited the armour makers to put forward proposals for thicker homogeneous deck armour better able to withstand air attack. ESC's 3 per cent chromium-molybdenum Mykro steel proved better than Firth-Brown's or Beardmore's for NC armour, less brittle with greater tensile strength and toughness, while electric arc furnaces could produce higher quality steel. Such steel was also used for tank armour, although with the Director of Naval Construction claiming to be the 'owner' of the term 'armour', it was preferred to use the term 'bullet proof plating' for non-ship use.[40]

With re-armament beginning in 1936, the Admiralty was anxious to revitalise the industry, as a new battleship building programme would require armour production over double the existing annual capability of 9000 tons (ESC), 4500 tons (Firth-Brown) and 4500 tons (Beardmore). By this time the

Below: *Duke of York's* heavy side armour was fitted after launch, partly to reduce launch weight, but also because it was more convenient for the heavy fitting-out cranes to lift them. This 30-ton 600lb (15in) plate from the middle strake of her belt is suspended from the 150-ton derrick crane at Clydebank on 29 March 1940. The plate is tongued at the top and grooved at the bottom to mate with adjacent plates, but planed flat with keys at the butt edges. Once hard up against the timber support strips, armour bolts will be fitted through the shell plating into holes tapped into the softer back of the plate. The broad white diagonal line on the plate is a shaft of sunlight. *(Upper Clyde Shipbuilders)*

Above: *Duke of York's* twin 14in B barbette armour was fitted in May 1940, three months after launch. The curved 520lb (13in) plate is 20ft long and 10ft wide, extending down to the main deck (below the upper) weighing 44.3 tons. The roller path has already been machined to take the gunhouse turntable, so the planing machine is being dismantled. The ships fitting out across the basin are the destroyer *Noble* and the destroyer depot ship *Hecla*. (*Upper Clyde Shipbuilders*)

Treasury was well aware of the threat from Germany and Japan and was able to sanction significant expenditure on creating new industrial capacity (including aircraft manufacture) – unlike the early 1930s. The new *King George V* battleships would each require about 6500 tons of C and 6500 tons of NC armour, worth around £1.4 million.[41] These figures excluded D quality and protective plating but included gun shield armour: a 14in quadruple turret needed 87 tons of C (13in front and 9in front side) and 340 tons of NC (7in rear side and rear, and 6in roof) out of a revolving weight of 1550 tons. Analysis of these vessels' armour plate during the breaking-up of the ships in 1958 showed that C plates from main belt, barbettes and 14in turret fronts had typically 3.9 per cent nickel, 2.2 per cent chromium and 0.3 per cent molybdenum, while NC from decks and turret sides and rear had 0.2 per cent nickel, 3.4 per cent chromium, 0.5 per cent molybdenum, both with 0.4 per cent manganese.[42] Pressed by the Controller, Vice-Admiral R Henderson, the Treasury financed

extensions of £1.056 million for ESC and helped Beardmore restart production in new facilities both at Parkhead and Dalmuir (the latter now Government owned) costing £759,000.[43] Firth-Brown extensions cost £435,000. With the Admiralty placing orders for no less than 34,361 tons of armour in 1936, these extensions came none too soon. In 1938, regular steelmakers Colville were brought back to produce up to 7000 tons a year of NC armour up to 4in thick, rolled at Motherwell and finished at Mossend.[44] Even this was not enough: 12,500 tons of non-cemented armour from 1.5in to 4.5in thickness, including 3in plates for aircraft carrier flight decks was ordered in 1938 from Witkowitzer Bergbau-und Hüttengewerkschaft – British cemented armour was considered superior to foreign made. This company with works at Vitkovice in Czechoslovakia was owned by the Rothschilds at this time, and was one of the largest steel manufacturers in Europe; it had made the best KC-type armour used by anyone through to the end of the First World War. However, only

10,000 tons had been delivered by the outbreak of war, delaying *Victorious*.[45] NC plates were also required for cruiser turret protection, e.g. a triple 6in required 53 tons 1–2in thick; seventy-three such turrets were manufactured between 1939 and 1945.

These capacity extensions were completed just in time, not only for the battleship building programme but for the increasing volume of tank orders. After 1941 Admiralty demands for armour fell off, with about 16,500 tons a year being allocated to them. Pre-war prices were similar to pre-First World War prices, at around £123 per ton for C, £107 for NC armour. But during the war, the Admiralty exercised greater control over prices, their accountants reviewing companies' actual costs and allowing a 10 per cent rate of return on the firm's capital, but only 2 per cent if the plant had been paid for by the Admiralty. As a result, lower prices were retrospectively agreed in 1943 for 74,500 tons at £97.5 per ton for C (£146.25 if tapered plates, £111.75 if curved barbette plates) and £75.75 per ton if NC over 4.5in thick, £80 if under.[46] Allowing for inflation, such prices were well below the hugely profitable levels of before the First World War – mild steel prices had doubled in that time. At long last, the Admiralty was now paying prices based on actual manufacturing costs and a reasonable profit margin, rather than cartel prices.

Britain's last battleship *Vanguard* required about 14,000 tons excluding protective plating – most of the armour for her 15in gunhouses already existed. The three makers split the orders between them, with ESC the largest supplier. Side armour plates were typically 19ft long by 7.5ft high and 13 or 14in thick, with the top and bottom joints of the three strakes tongued and grooved, end butts flat but keyed together with a diamond shaped key. The whole starboard side was made by ESC, port side forward by Beardmore, aft by Firth-Brown – see plan on p.225. Main deck plates were about 25ft long by 13ft wide and 5in thick over machinery spaces or 6in over magazines, tongued and grooved at edges, but plain butts. The heaviest armour plate was one weighing 48 tons. Cruisers and aircraft carriers only required cemented plates up to 4.5in thick, with some 2in or 3in NC, while Landing Craft, Gun also used NC over their magazines. Some armour had been ordered for *Lion* and *Temeraire*, but with construction suspended, the plates were sent to Shoeburyness in 1943 for proof testing of projectiles.[47] From 1936 to 1946 ESC produced 174,098 tons of armour, 54 per cent for tanks, with output in peak years of about 25,000 tons.[48] Firth-Brown's Atlas works produced over 60,000 tons in the Second World War.[49]

After the Second World War, demand for armour fell off sharply, with few warships needing more than protective plating, although there was still demand for tank armour. Beardmore closed their armour and gun manufacturing plant at Parkhead in 1957,[50] leaving ESC soon to merge into Firth-Brown. By the 1960s, the River Don armour plant was the only one left in the UK, finally closing in 1972. So after just over a century, the British armour making industry ceased to exist. It had peaked in the highly profitable years before the First World War and had fulfilled all the demands placed upon it, but became of limited value in years of peace.

STEEL FOR BATTLESHIPS

While armour plate represented the most expensive and complex battleship product of the steel industry, ordinary steel comprised a much greater weight, whether structural material such as plates and stiffeners or components such as shafts, gun forgings, boilers and sternframe castings. Siemens-Martin open hearth mild steel was introduced into shipbuilding in the late 1870s. It was of a more consistent quality than the previous Bessemer steel, and it could produce larger forgings. It had a higher strength-weight ratio than wrought iron, so structural weight could be reduced by about 15 per cent, allowing more weight to be put into machinery (higher speed), heavier arma-

Below: *Anson* at Faslane in May 1958 reveals her port side armour, with 240lb (6in) at main deck level and the hexagonal bolts securing the 600lb (15in) side armour to the riveted shell plating. The deck plating is marked NC (non-cemented); samples were taken of the battleship armour to show the nickel and other alloys content which affected the scrap price paid. *(T W Ferrers-Walker)*

ment and/or thicker protection. It was more
ductile, so deformed rather than cracked under
load, while plates could be made much larger
so reducing the work content from a reduced
riveted joint length. With increasing production, it became as cheap as iron per ton by the
1890s. Thus all RN battleships from
Edinburgh/Colossus (launched in 1882) onwards
had mild steel hulls.

While the makers of special steels and armour
tended to concentrate in Sheffield, the makers of
shipbuilding steel were concentrated in the two
big shipbuilding areas – the Clyde and north-
east of England, with each tending to serve their
local market, and with access to local supplies of
coal and iron ore. But apart from higher tensile
steel for protective decks, steel for battleship
hulls was part of a normal steelworks production, calling for no special facilities – albeit sold
at a slightly higher price as the Admiralty
demanded more stringent quality tests than
merchant ship builders. While the shipbuilding
industry was one of the largest users of steel at
around 15 per cent of annual output – others
included railways, engineering, mining, bridges
and construction – the proportion that went
into battleships was under 1 per cent of the 5
million–7 million tons produced in Britain each
year before the First World War, much of it for
export.

The specialist steelmakers such as Vickers and
John Brown did not attempt to produce 'run of
the mill' products – not only were they some
distance from the shipyards, but mild steel
prices were very competitive and profit
margins slim. They did of course make raw
steel, but this was to feed into their specialist
products. When a private shipbuilder received
an order for a battleship, he simply ordered the
necessary quantities as and when required, with
the price buried in the agreed hull contract
price. But with many battleships being built in
the Royal Dockyards, the Admiralty requested
tenders to supply bulk orders of steel. For
example tenders were submitted on 10
September 1907 by Guest, Keen & Nettlefolds
Ltd (with works in Cardiff and Newport) for
3800 tons of mild steel plates between ¼in and
1in thick for *Collingwood* building at Devonport
at £6 16s 6d per ton if delivered by steamer, or
£7 2s 0d if by rail, to be delivered at a rate of
250 tons per week. Steamers of 200ft length
drawing 13ft could be accepted at Devonport.
Plates would normally be up to about 30 x 6ft.
A similar tender was submitted by GKN for *St
Vincent* at Portsmouth. For higher tensile nickel

steel ½in to 1½in thick, the Steel Company of
Scotland Ltd (with works at Blochairn near
Glasgow) submitted a tender on 7 October
1907 for 2000 tons for *St Vincent* at £18 0s 0d
per ton by steamer or £18 10s 0d by rail at 150
tons per week, plates normally up to about 30
x 8ft, 36–40 tons/sq in ultimate tensile
strength. John Spencer & Sons Ltd of
Newcastle submitted a similar tender for
Collingwood.[51] Other regular suppliers of ship-
building steel included Consett Iron Co Ltd
south-west of Newcastle; Bolckow, Vaughan &
Co, Dorman, Long & Co Ltd, South Durham
Steel & Iron Co Ltd and Cargo Fleet Iron Co
Ltd, all on Teesside; Parkgate Iron & Steel Co
Ltd, Rotherham; Barrow Hematite Steel Co
Ltd, David Colville & Sons Ltd at Motherwell,
Clydebridge Steel Co Ltd at Cambuslang,
Lanarkshire Steel Co Ltd at Motherwell,
Mossend Iron & Steel Co (taken over by
Beardmore in 1905) and Glasgow Iron & Steel
Co Ltd at Wishaw. Rivets and fasteners were
supplied by specialist companies such as the
Rivet Bolt & Nut Co of Glasgow or the Patent
Shaft & Axletree Co of Wednesbury.

A typical dreadnought would require around
6000 tons of structural steel (excluding nickel
steel), although about 15 per cent less would be
worked into the ship after allowing for 'green'
(oversize) material for trimming, holes and non-
rectangular plates. About two-thirds was in the
form of plates, the rest as stiffeners, sections such
as angle bars, channels or zed bars (each with a
flange for riveting to the plate). Normal 26–30
tons/sq in mild steel satisfied the Admiralty. Thus
providing the necessary steel for the battleship
building programmes pre-war was straightforward, the industry supplying whatever was
required. But during the First World War, steel
production had to be increased at government
controlled prices to supply munitions, especially
shells, but this had little impact on the modest
wartime battlecruiser building programme.

The importance of steel in battleship production is underlined by the detailed weight breakdown that Vickers compiled for each completed
warship. Some 12,000 tons was itemised for
Vanguard excluding a further 1200 tons or so of
scrap, as summarised on p.226. With over 80 per
cent of the armament and machinery also
consisting of different types of steel, over 16,000
tons was built into the ship with an 'equipped'
weight (i.e. light or empty) of 17,466 tons.[52]

In the short-lived shipbuilding boom of
1919–20, British shipbuilders became
concerned about availability of steel with its

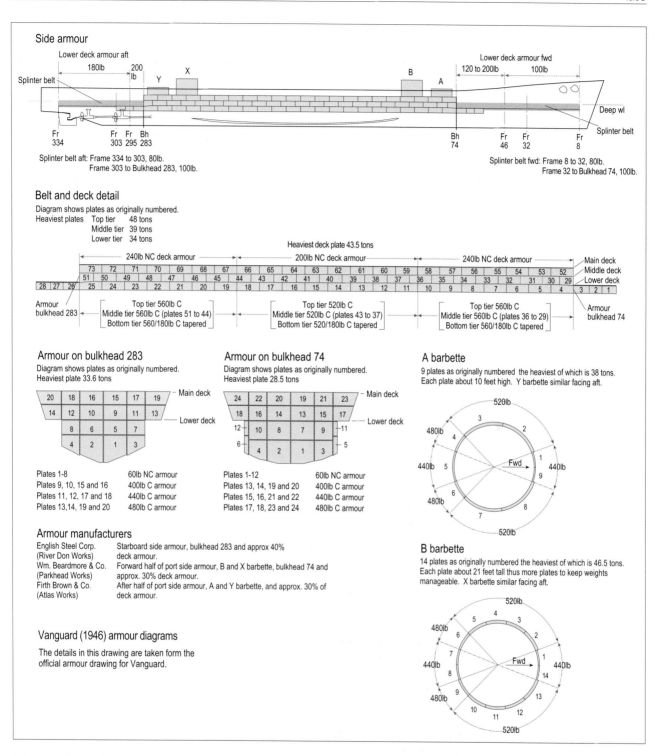

Side armour

Lower deck armour aft
180lb 200lb

Splinter belt

Y X B A

Lower deck armour fwd
120 to 200lb 100lb

Deep wl

Splinter belt

Fr 334 Fr 303 Fr 295 Bh 283

Bh 74 Fr 46 Fr 32 Fr 8

Splinter belt aft: Frame 334 to 303, 80lb.
Frame 303 to Bulkhead 283, 100lb.

Splinter belt fwd: Frame 8 to 32, 80lb.
Frame 32 to Bulkhead 74, 100lb.

Belt and deck detail

Diagram shows plates as originally numbered.
Heaviest plates   Top tier   48 tons
Middle tier   39 tons
Lower tier   34 tons

Heaviest deck plate 43.5 tons

240lb NC deck armour — 200lb NC deck armour — 240lb NC deck armour — Main deck / Middle deck / Lower deck

Armour bulkhead 283

Top tier 560lb C
Middle tier 560lb C (plates 51 to 44)
Bottom tier 560/180lb C tapered

Top tier 520lb C
Middle tier 520lb C (plates 43 to 37)
Bottom tier 520/180lb C tapered

Top tier 560lb C
Middle tier 560lb C (plates 36 to 29)
Bottom tier 560/180lb C tapered

Armour bulkhead 74

Armour on bulkhead 283

Diagram shows plates as originally numbered.
Heaviest plate 33.6 tons

Plates 1-8 — 60lb NC armour
Plates 9, 10, 15 and 16 — 400lb C armour
Plates 11, 12, 17 and 18 — 440lb C armour
Plates 13,14, 19 and 20 — 480lb C armour

Armour on bulkhead 74

Diagram shows plates as originally numbered.
Heaviest plate 28.5 tons

Plates 1-12 — 60lb NC armour
Plates 13, 14, 19 and 20 — 400lb C armour
Plates 15, 16, 21 and 22 — 440lb C armour
Plates 17, 18, 23 and 24 — 480lb C armour

A barbette

9 plates as originally numbered the heaviest of which is 38 tons.
Each plate about 10 feet high. Y barbette similar facing aft.

B barbette

14 plates as originally numbered the heaviest of which is 46.5 tons.
Each plate about 21 feet tall thus more plates to keep weights manageable. X barbette similar facing aft.

Armour manufacturers

English Steel Corp. (River Don Works) — Starboard side armour, bulkhead 283 and approx 40% deck armour.
Wm. Beardmore & Co. (Parkhead Works) — Forward half of port side armour, B and X barbette, bulkhead 74 and approx. 30% deck armour.
Firth Brown & Co. (Atlas Works) — After half of port side armour, A and Y barbette, and approx. 30% of deck armour.

Vanguard (1946) armour diagrams

The details in this drawing are taken form the official armour drawing for Vanguard.

inflated price to fulfil the expected demand for merchant ships following wartime losses. Harland & Wolff at Belfast took control of Colville, the Scottish steelmaker, with a small John Brown shareholding, through a share exchange. Swan Hunter & Wigham Richardson and Beardmore took over Glasgow Iron & Steel Co in 1920, while a consortium of Clyde ship-builders including Stephen, Scotts and Yarrow took over the Steel Company of Scotland (itself taken over by Colville about 1936). But the boom soon ended and the British steel industry found itself with excess capacity, while facing increased competition from countries such as Germany. Many proposals for rationalisation, mergers and import tariffs were discussed, but unlike the armour plate industry, the Admiralty had no particular concerns. As well as the merger that produced English Steel Corporation, other steel takeovers included Dorman Long of Bolckow Vaughan on Teesside in 1929, and Colville of Dunlop on the Clyde in 1930. South Durham and Cargo Fleet merged in 1928, in turn amalgamating with Dorman Long in 1933. With some financial support from the banks, the major steel producers were able to survive the depression until demand picked up from 1935 with world trade reviving, the start of re-armament and a more competitive exchange rate. Efficiency, management and quality (e.g. more electric arc furnaces) were improved under competitive pressures. Some plant extensions were built in the late 1930s, so that the British steel industry was able to supply much of Second World War demand, albeit with some US imports. The Ministry of Supply controlled steel allocations and prices, so that essential needs including warship construction were generally satisfied by the regular steel makers. The Admiralty used about 180,000 tons of steel on warship hull construction in 1941.[53] In a few specialist categories, there was shortage of capacity in the war, e.g. some hull forgings and castings were fabricated out of welded steel, such as shaft brackets. Of the 86 million tons of steel supplied during the Second World War (14 million tons

VANGUARD IRON AND STEEL (1910)

	Tons
Mild steel plates over 10lb (0.25in)	3127
Mild steel 10lb and under and chequered plate	598
Mild steel sections: angles, bulbs, zeds etc	1686
Nickel steel plates: decks, wing & magazine bulkheads	2135
High tensile steel sections	36
Iron plates and packing	85
Rivets	386
Structural steel castings & forgings, sternframe, shaft brackets etc	89
Total main structure	8142
Armour belt 80–400lb (2–10in)	1728
Armour bulkheads 160–320lb (4–8in)	201
Armour for five barbettes	1210
Conning and signal towers	90
Communication tubes	42
Armour bolts and fastenings	45
Armour backing (timber)	51
Total armour excluding gun shields	3367
Other iron & steel castings	76
Sheet steel	125
Smithwork, pillars, davits etc	160
Anchors and cables	127
Total	**11,997**

imported), 60 per cent went to munitions.[54]

When Swan Hunter & Wigham Richardson submitted a tender for *Anson* on 15 February 1937, they estimated that they would need to buy 14,103 tons of structural steel averaging £15.81 per ton, or £223,044, 10 per cent of the £2.283 million hull price quoted (although only 3 per cent of the total cost including machinery, armament and armour).

The Admiralty introduced a new high tensile silicon-manganese steel in the 1920s, D quality with 37–43 tons/sq in ultimate tensile strength, 6500 tons each being used in *Nelson* and *Rodney*.[55] With decks now armoured instead of HT steel, this was used in highly stressed areas of the hull, e.g. around large openings, and also for weight-saving given the new limits on standard displacement. But as well as steel for hull structures, steel was required for many other items of a battleship's machinery and equipment. Most of its armament was built of steel, forgings for gun barrels and slides, gun shield armour, castings for hoists, plate for turntables. Similarly most of the machinery was made of steel – forgings and castings, boiler plates and tubes, turbine rotors, gearbox housings and wheels, and shafting, while every type of auxiliary machinery such as generators and pumps (and their seats) required steel. Many items of deck equipment, e.g. anchor hawsepipe castings, hatch covers and accommodation fittings, all included some steel.

Below: The Steel Company of Scotland Ltd with works at Blochairn east of Glasgow was a major supplier of steel plate to Clyde shipyards. In this view of the melting shop in the 1920s, the steam crane is about to load scrap from the wagon into the open hearth furnaces at right. Pig iron was also used in the charge. After various alloying elements had been added, the furnaces were then tapped to produce steel ingots, then rolled into slabs which were subsequently rolled in a plate mill to make plate of various sizes and thicknesses. (*Author's collection*)

10: EXPORTING BATTLESHIPS

EVER SINCE THE INTRODUCTION of iron hulls and steam propulsion, Britain had dominated the export market of both merchant ships and warships. Initially the Thames shipyards had a large share of the warship market from the 1860s but by 1900 were no longer competitive with the northern shipyards. Armstrong on the Tyne had built up its overseas reputation with cruisers and ordnance supplied from its Elswick works. Navies who could not build warships themselves sought most of them from those British shipbuilders who also built for the Admiralty. Armstrong prided themselves on having built many of the Japanese warships victorious in the Russo-Japanese War, although the latter's battleships *Yashima* and *Hatsuse* were lost to Russian mines. Such builders received many requests for designs and prices. The notebooks of Owens Thurston of Vickers in the National

Maritime Museum are full of such designs, although many are for alternative configurations for a basic requirement. Between October 1909 and June 1913 no fewer than seventy-four battleship/battlecruiser designs were produced in their London office. This amounted to nearly half of all the warship designs they prepared. While many were probably no more than sketch designs and price indications, it gives some idea of the intensity of battleship inquiries. Few resulted in actual orders – the selection of John Brown tenders in Appendix 1 gives some idea of potential customers – but some British designed ships were built abroad, e.g. the Spanish *España* class, see p.230.

Between 1906 and 1914, a total of thirteen battleship contracts were signed on the international armaments market all of which, with the exception of four, either went to Armstrong or Vickers.

Such ship contracts were generally more profitable than Admiralty orders, as the complete ship was supplied, unlike RN ships where armament, armour and ammunition contracts were placed separately by the Admiralty. If the shipbuilder was able to supply the latter items – as was the case with both Armstrongs and Vickers after 1900 – the likelihood of successfully competing and the scope for profit was much higher. Shipbuilders without such supply had to buy at higher prices from the duopoly than the latter charged themselves. While there was a degree of competition from countries like France, Germany and USA, Armstrong and Vickers received the majority of battleship orders from 1898 to 1914. John Brown, Fairfield and Cammell Laird attempted to challenge this dominance by setting up the Coventry Ordnance Works in 1905 (see p.76).

INTERNATIONAL BATTLESHIP EXPORTS 1906–14

Country	Ship	Order Year	Builder	Comments
Argentina	*Rivadavia*	1910	Fore River	–
	Moreno	1910	New York SB	–
Brazil	*Minas Geraes*	1907	Armstrong	–
	Sao Paulo	1907	Vickers	–
	Rio de Janeiro	1911	Armstrong	Later *Sultan Osman 1*, *Agincourt*
	Riachuelo	1914	Armstrong	Yard No. 879. Later cancelled.
Chile	*Almirante Latorre*	1911	Armstrong	Later British *Canada*
	Almirante Cochrane	1912	Armstrong	Later British *Eagle*
Greece	*Salamis*	1913	AG Vulcan	Launched 1914 but broken up incomplete in 1932.
	Basileus Konstantinos	1914	Penhoet	Ordered but stopped soon after
Japan	*Kongo*	1910	Vickers	–
Turkey*	*Reshadieh*	1911	Vickers	Later British *Erin*.
	Fatih	1914	Vickers	Laid down but subsequently cancelled.

*The Turkish ships had been tendered for by a consortium of Armstrong, John Brown and Vickers. As John Brown had no berth available to lay down *Fatih*, the hull was allocated to Vickers (Yard No.460). The armament and armour was to have been divided among the partners.

Right: Two early dreadnoughts fitting out at Vickers Sons & Maxim's new fitting out wharf at Buccleuch Dock, Barrow, about May 1909 under the newly built 150-ton cantilever crane. Inboard is *Vanguard*, outboard the Brazilian *Sao Paulo* with a more pronounced ram. *(World Ship Society D K Brown Collection)*

Below: Armstrong Whitworth produced elaborate launch programmes, especially for foreign ships, with the cover of that for *Minas Geraes*. *(Tyne & Wear Archives)*

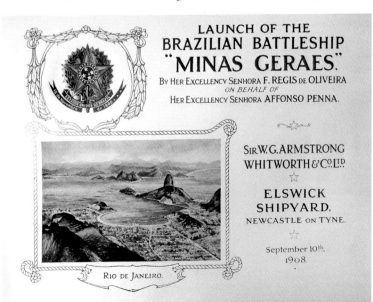

Although tendering for battleships, e.g. for Argentina see p.275, they were only able to obtain orders for smaller vessels like cruisers and destroyers, e.g. Greece in 1914.

Initially Armstrong resented Vickers intruding into this lucrative market after the latter acquired the Barrow shipyard and started to make heavy gun mountings there – it already made guns and armour at its Sheffield works. While Vickers received the order for the Japanese pre-dreadnought *Mikasa* in 1898, they were disappointed when her armament was ordered from Armstrong. The Japanese had had many warships built and armed by Armstrong, so were probably reluctant to order gun mountings from Vickers before they had even

completed their first one for the Admiralty (in 1902). But the two companies soon came to an accommodation to share out orders wherever possible. For the Chilean battleships ordered in 1902, Armstrong built *Constitucion* (but completed as *Swiftsure*), and Vickers *Libertad* (*Triumph*). Similarly in 1906, *Kashima* was ordered from Armstrong and *Katori* from Vickers. All four ships had their armament manufactured and installed to their builder's design.

Foreign navies frequently changed their minds, both as improved designs emerged, as rivalries developed and as budgets permitted. Brazil initially ordered three 13,000-ton battleships from Armstrong in July 1906, negotiated by director J M Falkner in Rio de Janeiro. But then the first ship (Armstrong No. 791) was changed in 1907 to 19,000 tons becoming *Minas Geraes*, plus two scout cruisers. John Brown seem not to have tendered. Vickers received the order for sister *Sao Paulo* at the same time. Vickers built the machinery for both ships; there was evidently some agreement between the two builders to share contract value and/or profits, as their accounts show transfer payments. Armstrong had paid Vickers for the Brazilian orders sums of £65,000 in 1908 and £66,000 in 1909.[1] Elswick was ready to lay down the second battleship (No. 792 of 32,000 tons with twelve 14in guns) in November 1910, but the Brazilians then wanted a battleship with 12in guns. So d'Eyncourt (Armstrong's naval architect) was sent out to Rio in April 1911 having to face competition from Germany before clinching the order, which became the 27,000-ton *Rio de Janeiro* with fourteen 12in guns, later *Agincourt*. A further £178,672 was paid by Armstrong to Vickers for *Rio de Janeiro* in December 1914, on top of the machinery contract.[2]

Such arrangements between Armstrong and Vickers were formalised in 1910. The two companies agreed to divide such work equally and to avoid unnecessary price-cutting beyond that needed to counter foreign competition. For any Brazilian orders, the successful bidder would pay the other firm 3 per cent of the hull price, 12.5 per cent of the armament price, £10 per ton on hull armour and £15 per ton on gun shields, but nothing on machinery. For Chile, the figures would be 3 per cent, 12.5 per cent, £6.50 and £15, and for Greece, 2 per cent, 10 per cent, £6.50 and £15. For Japan's order for battlecruiser *Kongo*, Vickers would pay Armstrong 3 per cent on hull, 3.5 per cent on machinery, 12.5 per cent on armament, £10 per ton on hull armour and £15 per ton on gun shields. For Turkey, John Brown was included in the group. Vickers would build the hull and machinery at an agreed price, Armstrong and Vickers dividing the armament, Armstrong and Brown dividing the shafting and forgings and all three dividing the armour. For Spain, all three firms were shareholders in the new Spanish shipbuilder La Sociedad Española de Construccion Naval. They would divide the armour equally, but armament would be divided between Armstrong and Vickers, each paying 5 per cent to Brown. For Italy, inquiries from the government were considered to be no more than price checks on local companies, in which both Vickers (Terni) and Armstrong (Pozzuoli) already had an interest.[3] In the case of *Reshadieh* (later *Erin*) ordered in July 1911, the design was from Armstrong, as were the three forward twin 13.5in gun mountings, the hull and machinery was from Vickers at Barrow as well as her two after gun mountings, while John Brown and Cammell Laird shared in the armour and Coventry in the gun orders. As a result, Vickers received over 50 per cent of the value of the work but had to pay commissions to other partners.[4]

It has been suggested that Armstrong and Vickers financed their overseas customers in buying armaments, but this seems not to have been the case for warships – their balance sheets show no such large loans. While Armstrong did finance the occasional building of a stock cargo ship (on 'spec' or speculation) in the period before the First World War, this was to tide their

Low Walker shipyard over a slack period. It was one thing for the company to use its funds for a £50,000 ship to be sold as soon as the market improved, but quite another for a £2 million battleship with repayment over perhaps a decade – it would have needed its banker's support. In practice, they used their good offices with merchant banks like Rothschild (who had extensive interests in Brazil) either to raise a loan for the foreign government or to issue bonds on its behalf, when that country needed money for a new construction programme, e.g. Chile issuing 4½ per cent bonds for *Almirante Cochrane*, later *Eagle*. However, Vickers did grant deferred or extended progress payments, which improved the cash flow and affordability of instalments to customers like Turkey.[5] But this only meant a slight increase in working capital, where instalments lagged the cost of work in progress in the shipyard. The first instalment for *Almirante Cochrane* amounted to 5 per cent of the total contract price of £2.425 million.[6]

Trebilcock collated foreign payments received at Vickers' Barrow works from 1903 to 1916.[7] This probably includes gun mountings as well as ships and machinery, but excludes guns and armour (Sheffield).

	£	%
Japan	2,432,119	36.2
Brazil	1,646,161	24.5
Russia	1,129,972	16.8
Peru	518,394	7.7
Chile	405,850	6.0
China	292,762	4.4
Italy	140,791	2.1
Canada	71,905	1.1
Spain	40,454	0.6
Argentina	31,733	0.5
Total	6,710,141	

Above: Foreign-based companies as well as British ones advertised in *Jane's Fighting Ships*.

While Armstrong and Vickers won overseas contracts to build battleships in Britain, they and other British firms acted as technical advisors on ships, armament, armour and shipyards to foreign governments which wanted to manufacture in their own countries. Although not as large or as profitable as constructing ships in British yards, these contracts nevertheless demonstrate the high regard with which British knowledge and expertise was held. Moreover, they continued to supply some specialised items like guns and steam turbines.

SPANISH CONTRACTS

In 1908 the Spanish Government passed a law sanctioning a major reorganisation of the Spanish Navy including the construction of new ships in the wake of the disastrous war with the United States in 1898. From the outset it was recognised that foreign assistance would be required in constructing the proposed battleships and thus Armstrong, John Brown and Vickers together took a 40 per cent

holding in a new company called La Sociedad Española de Construccion Naval. The Dockyards at Ferrol, Cartagena, Matagorda, Sestao and Santander were taken over and re-equipped. New plant was laid down for the manufacture of gun mountings and shells at Cadiz and engine works at Ferrol and Cartagena. At Ferrol, three small *España* class battleships, *España*, *Alfonso XIII* and *Jaime I*, were constructed from 1909 onwards under British management with numerous British technical personnel. The partners also supplied guns, mountings, armour and some machinery.

RUSSIAN CONTRACTS

After defeat by the Japanese at the Battle of Tsushima in 1905, Russia was reduced in importance as a naval power from third position to sixth. Surviving records from John Brown throw some light on the progress of contracts developed with Russian naval authorities.

Initially unwilling to spend large sums on what was regarded as a defeated force, a major

Below: British companies also supplied shipyard equipment to foreign navies. Vickers built the 22,000-ton lift floating dock *Affonso Penna* for Brazil (named after the President). The dock was ordered in October 1909, costing £190,000. It is seen here at Rio de Janeiro docking *Minas Geraes* on 23 December 1910. *(The Dock Museum, Barrow)*

programme of new construction was put before the Duma together with plans for capital investment in Russian shipyards. It was recognised that technical assistance, together with the supply of components, especially machinery, would have to come from abroad. In May 1906, it became known that an agency with a large British shipbuilding yard was sought to assist in the rebuilding of the Russian fleet, following the raising of a new Government loan.

It is a preconceived opinion here in the best informed circles, that a large part of the orders for new men of war will have to go to England, as the only country which is able to complete such orders within a short time. Germany, which would have counted as a serious competitor a month ago, is not favourably looked upon now after the failure of German bankers to take part in the recent loan. The friendly feeling towards England is now on the increase here, and the time is coming when England will rank equally with France in the distribution of Russian Government orders.[8]

In 1907, construction of the *Gangut* class battleships was authorised by the Russian Government. Initially, the contract was to be given to Vickers who were already building the large armoured cruiser *Rurik* for the Russians at Barrow. However, Vickers had fallen out of favour with the Ministry of Marine, the Russian equivalent of the British Admiralty, and the design for the ships was put out to international competition. Specifications and an outline of the ships to be built were prepared by Russian naval architects and given to no fewer than twenty-three competing shipyards. When the various designs were examined, two were selected, Blohm & Voss and John Brown, the latter in collaboration with the St Petersburg-based Baltic Works with the intention that the ships would be built in St Petersburg under the technical supervision of John Brown. Although Blohm & Voss's armament solution was preferred, the contract was awarded to the John Brown/Baltic Works combination and the German yard was paid 200,000 roubles (about £21,000) for its design, which was never used.[9]

On 30 January 1908, the collaboration between John Brown and the Baltic Works began with the signing of a technical agreement for the construction of the four ships which were to be laid down in the following year. This was followed by another technical agreement signed on 27 January 1909, between John Brown, the Baltic Works and also the neighbouring Admiralty Yard, for the design and supervision during construction, of four battleships, *Petropavlovsk* and *Sevastopol* at the Baltic Works and *Gangut* and *Poltava*, at the Admiralty yard. Under this agreement, John Brown also supplied designs and calculations for the Parsons turbines. Payment was calculated at three roubles for every displacement ton worked and eight roubles for each unit of horsepower developed by the turbines. In the same month, model testing in the experiment tank to determine hull characteristics was in progress at Clydebank, the results of which were sent to St Petersburg in the form of a lines plan. There was some disagreement over the general design of the vessels however, which prompted the managing director of the Baltic Works, Peter F Vershsortzoff (modern Veshkurtsev), to visit Clydebank in May. He was a Lieutenant General in the Naval Constructor Corps, also responsible for Kronstadt. At the same time, aware of potential sensitivities surrounding the sale of 'know-how' abroad, John Brown informed the British Admiralty of their activities with the Russian Government. Differences of opinion soon arose between technical staff at St Petersburg and Clydebank and when Russian engineers wanted to remove 21 tons of steelwork from turbine seatings, Thomas Bell, Clydebank's managing director, insisted that John Brown be relieved of responsibility for the outcome as this would depart 'from known and tried scantlings'. By December 1909, calculations and drawings of the launching arrangements had been sent to St Petersburg.

In 1911, with work underway on the four battleships at St Petersburg under the supervision of John Brown personnel, discussions were opened with the Russian Shipbuilding Company (Russud) concerning a technical collaboration at their yard at Nikolaev on the Black Sea, which had been selected to participate in the construction of the *Imperatritsa Mariya* class battleships for the Black Sea Fleet. This agreement, similar to the one in operation with the Baltic Works, was signed on 27 November 1911. Clydebank personnel were then transferred from the Baltic Works at St Petersburg to Nikolaev. The contract included the construction of Brown-Curtis machinery at Clydebank for two of the battleships, *Imperatritsa Mariya* and *Imperator Alexander III*.

The contract was signed on 14 September 1911 at a price of £96,000 for each set of machinery.

By the time the machinery for *Imperator Aleksander III* was ready to be transported from Clydebank to Nikolaev in 1916, the war prevented shipment by the normal route. Stage one of what would be an extraordinary journey was made by the Russian cruiser *Askold* which took the 560-ton load from Clydebank to Archangel from where it was transferred to a number of barges and taken by river, lake and canal to the village of Sarepta near Tsaritsyn. Here, the machinery was loaded on to railway wagons for carriage to Rostov-on-Don where the final leg, by ship across the Sea of Azov and the Black Sea to Nikolaev, was made – a journey of 5400 miles.

John Brown personnel working in Nikolaev in early 1918 became embroiled in the dying stages of the war and the Russian Revolution, part of which saw the workers taking control of the shipyard. Starting in February, it took the men five months to return to Clydebank in another epic journey via Moscow, Vladivostok, Kobe and Vancouver! John Brown was paid £142,000 for technical assistance on the Black Sea battleships and a further £101,000 for assistance with cruisers.

THE JAPANESE NAVAL SCANDAL

As shown in some of the John Brown tenders (see Appendix 1), costs for foreign warships usually included the item 'Commission'. Normally this was a legitimate business expense for agents in overseas countries who were middlemen acting as the point of contact between the shipbuilder and the Navy

Below: The newly-launched Japanese battlecruiser *Kongo* ready to receive her machinery at Vickers' fitting out wharf at Barrow in the summer of 1912. *Princess Royal* outboard already has her 13.5in turrets installed. *(World Ship Society D K Brown Collection)*

Department concerned, for example Armstrong used Takata Shokai in Japan and Walter Brothers in Brazil. But in a few cases, it might also be a cover for bribes. The most notorious case of bribery was that of Rear-Admiral Terugoro Fujii, when the Japanese battlecruiser *Kongo* was ordered from Vickers, Sons & Maxim in 1910 at a price of £2,367,100 including commission.[10] Fujii had succeeded Kaza Matsumoto as Director of the 4th Section of the Naval Stores Department in December that year. As an Engineer Captain he had been dealing with Vickers for many years on gun mounting and machinery contracts, so was well known to them, being particularly friendly with Barrow manager James McKechnie. He visited England in mid-1910 to discuss among other things the plans for *Kongo*, reporting to Matsumoto in August. Only Vickers and Armstrong Whitworth had been invited to tender, each submitting their own design and price. Of course, whichever company got the contract, the other would receive their agreed percentages, but the prestige of getting such an order was great. Matsumoto favoured the Vickers design, ostensibly on account of a better specification and price, although the Japanese were already forming the opinion that Vickers' quality generally was at least as good as Armstrong's if not better, including armour. He was in a position to recommend acceptance of the Vickers' design and was in contact with retired naval constructor Tsurutaro Matsuo, Mitsui's technical adviser. Mitsui Bussan Kaisha was Vickers' Japanese agent so would normally receive commission of 2½ per cent on Japanese naval orders placed with their principals, but Matsuo asked for this to be increased to 5 per cent for 'his friends', so it was the customer who initiated the 'commission' process, not the arms supplier. But it was Fujii who was central to the decision in favour of Vickers when the contract was signed on 17 November 1910. A further 2½ per cent commission also would go to Japan Steel Works, an agreement Vickers and Armstrong had with the ordnance company in which they both had a 25 per cent share, also providing technical information. Such commission may have been to provide such things as 'after sales' service but was also a sweetener to help the new company establish itself. In the event they never received the cash as they were already owing Vickers substantial sums, so the commission was simply used to pay down those debts.

Mitsui began to receive its 5 per cent commission as contract instalments were paid, typically in 5 per cent stages as construction progressed, in total about £118,000 or Y1.2 million. Matsuo was the conduit through which Matsumoto and Fujii were paid, the latter receiving it through the bank account of the sister of his elder brother's wife. But by the time the ship had arrived at Yokosuka in November 1913, rumours started to circulate about the commissions, so the authorities began to make inquiries. Fujii faced a naval court martial in Tokyo in May 1914, accused of corruption and receiving bribes of £35,270 between January 1911 and September 1912, while Matsumoto was accused of receiving some Y400,000 (about £40,000). Fujii was also accused of taking a smaller bribe of Y48,000 when *Hiei's* turbines were ordered from Vickers in March 1911 at a price of £132,000. He claimed that these payments were 'remuneration for technical advice' but the court did not accept this. Matsuo and other Mitsui staff were accused in a civil court of various acts of complicity, trying to cover up the payments, booked initially as 'secret service expenses'. In September 1914 Fujii was sentenced to 4½ years imprisonment plus repayment of Y300,000, but committed suicide not long after. Matsumoto was sentenced to three years and repayment of Y410,000. Most of the Mitsui staff received various prison sentences, later suspended, e.g. Matsuo two years. The cases received much publicity at the time including regular reports in the *Japan Weekly Chronicle*. It was also suggested that other British companies including Yarrow, Weir and Arrol had paid more modest bribes in Japan, but such charges were not proven.[11]

The case was later cited in the 1936 report of the Royal Commission on the Private Manufacture of and Trading in Arms.[12] The Fujii case was one of the few documented examples of bribery of which the armaments manufacturers were often accused. Vickers Ltd provided the Royal Commission with a large amount of evidence, including detailed newspaper and other reports of the case in 1914, but were unable to find documentary evidence that bribes had been agreed, other than that commission had indeed been paid to their agents. But it was McKechnie who authorised those contracted payments in 1911-12, requested by the Japanese. Such were included in the cost estimate leading up to Vickers' tender price quotation, albeit buried under the

heading 'Commission'. He must have had some authorisation for the increased sums, but there is no mention in the Board Minutes. It seems likely that there was informal agreement with the other directors most concerned, Trevor Dawson (group managing director), Vincent Caillard (finance), Francis Barker (overseas sales). All had died by 1935 so were unable to give evidence to the Royal Commission; the other Vickers' directors still alive denied all knowledge. But the bulky Vickers' files on the case offer a further twist. Vickers' principal foreign arms salesman, Sir Basil Zaharoff, may well have also had a hand, with his extensive contacts and private bank accounts – there are large payments to Zaharoff in the Vickers' accounts. Zaharoff was a shadowy figure who had worked for Vickers between 1897 and 1927, previously for Nordenfelt. His extraordinary career of which arms sales was but one aspect of his activities made him a very wealthy and well-connected man. Vickers' 1911 Central

Above: John Brown manufactured Brown-Curtis turbines for the Russian battleships *Imperatritsa Mariya* and *Imperator Alexander III* under construction at Nikolaev. Here, in this photograph taken on 16 May 1916, a turbine casing is being prepared for lifting on to the Russian cruiser *Askold* which transported the machinery from Clydebank to Archangel, the first leg of a 5400-mile journey to the Black Sea. Note the Scotch boilers in the background built for other vessels.
(Author's collection)

Balance Sheet (head office) includes a massive £73,660 (over £7 million in today's money) to him for 'Sundry Commissions', the year after *Kongo* was ordered.[13] Some may have been as a result of his standard commission and profit sharing agreements, but he also received some £31,000 for 'Japanese business' in 1911–12. Despite numerous allegations of corruption throughout his career, he was highly effective in winning orders for Vickers and was awarded a knighthood after the First World War for services to the Allied cause!

The Royal Commission had been set up partly in response to claims that the private manufacture of arms fomented war scares, bribed public officials, influenced public opinion, organised rings (cartels), prolonged wars by supplying arms to both sides and endangered world peace. This point of view was encapsulated in a 1934 book entitled *The Merchants of Death* by H C Engelbrecht and F C Hanighen. There was an element of truth in some of these accusations, while a large number of organisations submitted evidence, not all of it well informed. The Royal Commission's report published in October 1936 reviewed some of examples cited such as the Fujii case. However their conclusions rejected the main demand that private manufacture be banned. Their main points are summarised:

– The most effective means of minimising the objections was by limitation of arms by international agreement.
– State monopoly of manufacture was impracticable and undesirable to meet the needs of imperial defence, with the disadvantages outweighing the advantages. (Amongst the latter, the private manufacturers provided a reserve of productive capacity and staff, their exports widened experience and employment and they could cross-fertilise between civilian and military applications, e.g. aircraft.)
– Public officials, e.g. retired, should not accept appointments with armament firms without ministerial approval.
– The Government should assume responsibility for the UK arms industry and regulate collaboration with it.
– Their profits in peacetime should be restricted to reasonable remuneration.
– There should be greater control of export licences.
– The complete cessation of the private export of surplus and second-hand arms and munitions.

While the arms manufacturers sometimes used questionable methods, especially prior to the First World War and in countries where ethical standards were different such as South America and Russia, they themselves could not generate a demand for arms where none existed. There needed to be a perceived threat or international rivalry before a foreign government would sanction expenditure on arms. But in reacting to this demand, the arms suppliers might be able to persuade their customers that they needed bigger or better or more weapons than was strictly necessary, especially if they offered a battle-changing technology like torpedoes or machine guns. A century later, these issues still resonate, but in the export of arms, the modern equivalents to battleships are military aircraft or submarines.

11: MONEY

THE COST OF BATTLESHIPS

In the battleship building era, defence expenditure made up about half of the British Government's budget,[1] varying from 38.4 per cent in 1893–4 to 68.6 per cent in 1900–01 during the Boer War. Defence expenditure itself split roughly half and half between the Navy and Army, the former ranging from a low of 27 per cent in 1901–02 (Boer War) to a high of 62 per cent in 1912–13. The table below derived from Sumida summarises three eight-year periods.[2]

Below: The pre-dreadnought *Mars* fitting out in Birkenhead docks in 1896 – Laird Brothers did not then have a fitting-out basin of their own. *(Published by permission of Wirral Council)*

The absolute amount spent on the Navy trebled over the period, increasing from £15.6 million in 1889–90 to £52.9 million in 1913–14 – this was a real increase as there was little inflation. Much of the increase was due to the extensive battleship building programme from the 1890s and its associated costs of manpower, ammunition and fuel. On top of the Navy Estimate figures was further funding under the Naval Works Act used for expansion of the Dockyards, of around £1 million to £3 million a year 1895 to 1908. Compared with 2012, the purchasing value of a pound then was about one hundred times greater.

From 1909 when the naval building programme expanded significantly to meet the German fleet expansion, new construction made up about 30 per cent of the Admiralty's budget.[3] Battleships and battlecruisers made up two-thirds of that total, although the longer term average from 1895 was about half. Hence battleship building was the largest element of British Government expenditure up to the start of the First World War, and commanded great political and public interest, in much the same way that health service expenditure does today in the UK. Britain's financial system was robust enough to be able to sustain such levels of defence expenditure, on the strength of its ability to raise tax revenues (e.g. income tax) and to borrow on reasonable terms. For rivals Germany, France and Russia, their economies were less able to finance such a large navy, especially as their armies took a greater share of their defence budgets than Britain.

A Parliamentary return summarised in *Engineering* (25 September 1914) showed naval expenditure of the eight great naval powers from 1905–06. The table overleaf shows the annual averages from 1910–11 to 1913–14, the period when dreadnought construction was well under way.

BRITISH DEFENCE EXPENDITURE 1889–1912

	1889–96	1897–1904	1905–12
Gross expenditure on Navy (£M)	149.278	263.195	314.955
Annual average	18.660	32.899	39.369
Gross expenditure on Army (£M)	147.688	415.192	224.584
Annual average	18.461	51.899	28.073
Navy as % of Defence expenditure	50.27	38.80	58.37
Defence as % of State expenditure	40.2	54.8	42.4

GREAT POWERS NAVAL EXPENDITURE 1910–14

1910–11 to 1913–14	Annual average naval expenditure (£M)	% of UK	% of eight powers	Annual average new construction (£M)	% of UK	% of eight powers	Annual average of tonnage launched*	% of UK	% of eight powers
Great Britain	40.883	100.00	26.90	15.730	100.00	28.44	165,666	100.00	30.83
Germany	22.575	55.22	14.85	11.401	72.48	20.61	108,556	65.53	20.20
USA	27.451	67.15	18.06	5.930	37.70	10.72	63,857	38.55	11.88
France	18.796	45.98	12.37	6.716	42.70	12.14	52,269	31.55	9.73
Russia	16.649	40.72	10.95	5.905	37.54	10.68	32,663	19.72	6.08
Japan	9.016	22.05	5.93	3.147	20.01	5.69	50,345	30.39	9.37
Italy	10.641	26.03	7.00	3.205	20.38	5.79	40,977	24.73	7.63
Austria-Hungary	5.975	14.61	3.93	3.278	20.84	5.93	23,052	13.91	4.29
Total	151.986	371.76	100.00	55.312	351.63	100.00	537,385	324.38	100.00

* German tonnage excludes submarines

For new construction, Britain averaged about 29 per cent of the total, with Germany about 20 per cent, i.e. about 45 per cent superiority. On this measure, no longer was there a Two Power Standard, but not even a 60 per cent one.

The Navy Estimates were published annually in March to gain Parliamentary approval for expenditure during the financial year starting on 1 April; from these it is possible to gain an accurate picture of spending. They were broken down into Votes, and the subsequent Appropriation Accounts compared the actual expenditure with estimated. The annual Dockyard Expense Accounts published great detail of expenditure on new construction and

repairs. Before the First World War, it included a useful appendix showing the first cost and accumulated maintenance cost of every vessel in the active fleet right down to torpedo boats. It is therefore possible to draw up aggregate figures for new construction cost by ship type based on the 1913–14 return, the last such table published, early in the First World War.[4] As ships which had been lost prior to 1913 were excluded, the figures for *Montagu* and cruisers *Bedford*, *Gladiator* and *Pandora* have been added back, but not for smaller vessels. 'Incidental' costs (essentially Admiralty and Dockyard overheads) which are listed separately have been added in but the cost of guns is excluded, coming under a different Vote; gun mountings are however included. But as battleship guns formed a larger percentage of total ship cost than smaller vessels (at around 8 per cent compared with 2 per cent for a destroyer), the figures slightly underestimate the battleship true proportion of the total. The split over the 19 years from 1895–6 to 1913–14 was battleships and battlecruisers 54 per cent, cruisers 31 per cent, destroyers 10 per cent, submarines and torpedo boats 4 per cent and minor vessels 1 per cent.

The traditional Vote headings were:

Vote A	Manpower numbers	135,000
Vote 1	Wages of officers and men	17.11
Vote 2	Victualling and clothing	5.93
Vote 3	Medical establishments	0.61
Vote 4	Martial law	0.01
Vote 5	Educational services	0.34
Vote 6	Scientific services	0.16
Vote 7	Royal Naval Reserve	0.92
Vote 8:I	Shipbuilding, repairs & maintenance: Personnel	7.95
Vote 8:II	Materiel	11.34
Vote 8:III	Contract work	30.99

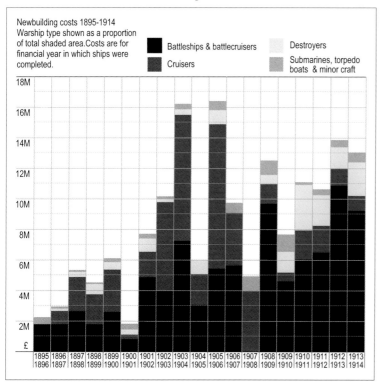

Newbuilding costs 1895-1914
Warship type shown as a proportion of total shaded area. Costs are for financial year in which ships were completed.

Battleships & battlecruisers
Cruisers
Destroyers
Submarines, torpedo boats & minor craft

Vote 9	Naval armaments	8.63
Vote 10	Works, buildings & repairs	7.44
Vote 11	Miscellaneous effective services	1.21
Vote 12	Admiralty office	0.94
Vote 13	Half pay and retired pay	2.12
Vote 14	Naval and Marine pensions	3.38
Vote 15	Civil pensions.	0.92

Percentages have been added of total estimated average annual expenditure for 1911–12 and 1912–13 of £44.238 million after appropriations in aid (i.e. income from sales).

The large Vote 8 making up half the total was broken down further into Section I Personnel, i.e. Dockyard staff, Section II Materiel, i.e. steel, timber, fuel etc, and Section III Contract work, which included ship hulls, machinery, gun mountings, armour etc. Vote 9 included ordnance establishment staff, guns and ammunition. It is not possible to work out costs of new construction from the above figures which also include repairs, but fortunately the Navy Estimates gave not only an aggregate figure for

new construction but also figures for each major ship showing costs to date and those estimated for the coming year.

From these and Dockyard Expense Accounts, it is possible to show a cost breakdown for typical ships. For Dockyard-built ships, hull labour and materials are shown separately, but both were lumped into contract work for privately-built ships, which also included armour. A large figure for Contract work on Dockyard hulls usually represented armour. As the Dockyards did not build battleship machinery, that figure is nearly all contract work, with small amounts of Dockyard input at installation. For private shipyard ships ordered before 1903, a Dockyard installed Admiralty equipment such as boats and smaller guns. Guns (barrels) and incidentals were listed separately but have been added to give the total cost figures below.

In 1913 a Parliamentary Select Committee also quizzed the Admiralty officials on how 'incidental charges' were made up. It was

BATTLESHIP COST BREAKDOWN

Dockyard Built	Victorious	King Edward VII	Dreadnought	Centurion
Hull builder	Chatham	Devonport	Portsmouth	Devonport
Machinery builder	Hawthorn Leslie	Harland & Wolff	Parsons and Vickers	Hawthorn Leslie
Gun mounting builder	Armstrong	Vickers	Armstrong and Vickers	Armstrong
Completed	Jun 1897	Feb 1905	Dec 1906	Jun 1913
Hull, fittings & equipment: labour (£)	215,436	244,051	198,513	307,859
Hull, fittings & equipment: materials (£)	441,726	564,432	535,914	217,059
Hull: contract work (£)	5400	6961	110,357	471,980
Propelling and other machinery: Dockyard work (£)	0	0	8750	11,040
Propelling and other machinery: contract work (£)	89,493	240,512	310,835	247,657
Gun mountings, torpedo tubes etc: Dockyard work (£)	7293	6737	7940	5696
Gun mountings, torpedo tubes etc: contract work (£)	69,338	214,492	382,205	427,987
Incidental charges (£)	62,997	105,490	117,969	105,011
Guns (£)	70,100	89,400	113,200	144,500
Total	961,783	1,472,075	1,785,683	1,938,789
Private Built	Mars	Cornwallis	Indomitable	Vanguard
Hull builder	Laird	Thames IW	Fairfield	Vickers
Machinery builder	Laird	Thames IW	Fairfield	Vickers
Gun mounting builder	Armstrong	Armstrong	Armstrong	Vickers
Completed	Jun 1897	Feb 1904	Jun 1908	Feb 1910
Hull, fittings & equipment: Dockyard work (£)	33,133	44,845	1674	10,346
Hull, fittings & equipment: contract work (£)	679,168	690,257	807,212	740,786
Propelling and other machinery: Dockyard work (£)	0	0	-870	-928
Propelling and other machinery: contract work (£)	91,674	174,168	476,539	250,987
Gun mountings, torpedo tubes etc: Dockyard work (£)	7111	7671	7713	4164
Gun mountings, torpedo tubes etc: contract work (£)	69,086	88,785	336,140	426,589
Incidental charges (£)	22,459	24,576	33,929	32,086
Guns (£)	61,950	65,750	90,000	142,400
Total	964,581	1,096,052	1,752,337	1,606,430

explained that these covered a proportion of Admiralty central costs, for example DNC's design work; Dockyard establishment charges such as senior staff salaries, drawing office work, yard machinery and maintenance, buildings and dock maintenance, stores facilities, police, holidays and pensions; and inspection costs for hulls, machinery, gun mountings and armour. How they were calculated was shown in detail with examples from Portsmouth Dockyard.[5] What they amounted to is shown in the table below for *Orion* and *Monarch*, 5.3 per cent for the former Dockyard-built ship total costs, and 1.8 per cent for the latter contract built.

Dockyard costs for *Monarch* were for fitting of Admiralty equipment and finishing work. Gun mounting costs for her were slightly cheaper than *Orion* as they were erected alongside the Elswick works. Inspection costs were higher as the Admiralty did not inspect Dockyard-built hulls. 'Battleship payload' items

of armour, guns and mountings amounted to 55 per cent of final cost.

When giving evidence to the Select Committee, the Director of Dockyards, Sir James Marshall, claimed that the Dockyards built as cheaply as private yards, which was broadly true. He also claimed that repairs were cheaper in the Dockyards. It is possible to compare the cost to the Admiralty of Dockyard-built battleships with those built in private yards. In several classes, there were two or three ships in each category, so it is possible to usefully average the two groups. The biggest difference was in Dockyard-built ships of the *Canopus* class, where three Dockyard ships averaged £872,120 each or 3.2 per cent more than three from private yards at £845,392 (including incidentals but excluding guns). For other classes pre-war, the Dockyard figures ranged from +1.3 per cent (*Iron Duke* class) to -2.8 per cent (*King Edward VII* class).[6] However, as armour and gun mountings would be of similar cost for all ships in the class, those percentages would roughly double when applied to hull and machinery.

From Dockyard Expense Accounts and various Navy Estimates, it is possible to show the cost to the Admiralty of each battleship including guns; see table opposite. Where possible, these are the final figures presented, as figures reported in different Admiralty accounts in different years could vary by some thousands of pounds, presumably as final contract adjustments were made, especially for ships completed during the First World War.

Wartime inflation pushed up the cost of ships completed after 1915, particularly *Ramillies* which also had bulges added. From *Nelson* and *Rodney* onwards standard displacement, i.e. full load minus fuel and reserve feed water, replaced Navy List displacement which included a nominal amount of fuel (about 1000 tons) so was around 5 per cent higher than standard.

FIRST COST BREAKDOWN FOR *ORION* AND *MONARCH*

	Orion	Portsmouth Dockyard 1909–12			*Monarch*	Armstrong 1909–12		
Financial Year	1909–10	1910–11	1911–12	Total (£)	1909–10	1910–11	1911–12	Total (£)
Dockyard labour, hull	27,992	147,881	96,880	272,753	287	2521	1011	3819
Dockyard materials, hull	71,679	73,199	53,497	198,375	843	3771	7289	11,903
Establishment charges & incidentals	10,823	35,275	25,076	71,174	117	694	406	1217
Armour	42,439	402,396	3315	448,150	22,261	390,533	25,987	438,781
Gun mountings	94,304	118,219	221,933	434,456	61,436	126,141	241,580	429,157
Machinery & other items (+ *Monarch* hull)	41,606	144,094	77,295	262,995	58,773	416,315	329,014	804,102
Incidentals (Admiralty inspection)	3363	11,136	5423	19,922	2686	15,631	10,692	29,009
Total	292,206	932,200	483,419	1,707,825	146,403	955,606	615,979	1,717,988

Total excludes guns & final price adjustments

BRITISH BATTLESHIP COSTS INCLUDING GUNS 1895–1946

	Cost (£)	Displacement (tons)	£/ton		Cost (£)	Displacement (tons)	£/ton
Magnificent	979,889	14,900	65.76	Vanguard	1,606,430	19,250	83.45
Majestic	986,482	14,900	66.21	Indefatigable	1,528,591	18,750	81.52
Prince George	965,604	14,900	64.81	Neptune	1,668,916	19,900	83.87
Victorious	955,312	14,900	64.11	Hercules	1,661,240	20,000	83.06
Mars	964,352	14,900	64.72	Colossus	1,672,103	20,000	83.61
Jupiter	976,651	14,900	65.55	Lion	2,088,915	26,350	79.28
Caesar	936,894	14,900	62.88	Orion	1,855,952	22,500	82.49
Hannibal	964,159	14,900	64.71	Monarch	1,888,916	22,500	83.95
Illustrious	952,159	14,900	63.90	Thunderer	1,892,960	22,500	84.13
Canopus	921,316	12,950	71.14	Conqueror	1,896,169	22,500	84.27
Ocean	936,578	12,950	72.32	New Zealand	1,795,068	18,800	95.48
Goliath	920,806	12,950	71.10	Australia	1,783,190	18,800	94.85
Glory	895,814	12,950	69.17	King George V	1,922,633	23,000	83.59
Albion	913,545	12,950	70.54	Centurion	1,939,348	23,000	84.32
Vengeance	891,217	12,950	68.82	Audacious	1,961,315	23,000	85.45
Formidable	1,097,245	15,000	73.15	Ajax	1,941,445	23,000	84.41
Implacable	1,063,515	15,000	70.90	Princess Royal	2,088,227	26,350	79.25
Venerable	1,159,853	15,000	77.32	Queen Mary	2,092,214	27,000	77.49
Irresistible	1,122,636	15,000	74.84	Iron Duke	2,080,918	25,000	83.24
Bulwark	1,065,816	15,000	71.05	Marlborough	2,086,914	25,000	83.48
London	1,103,493	15,000	73.57	Benbow	2,092,748	25,000	83.71
Duncan	1,088,897	14,000	77.78	Emperor of India	2,103,563	25,000	84.14
Russell	1,104,051	14,000	78.86	Erin *	2,400,000	23,000	104.35
Exmouth	1,098,159	14,000	78.44	Agincourt *	2,725,000	27,500	99.09
Cornwallis	1,096,052	14,000	78.29	Tiger **	2,215,491	28,500	77.74
Montagu	1,046,992	14,000	74.79	Queen Elizabeth **	2,633,103	27,500	95.75
Albemarle	1,078,395	14,000	77.03	Warspite **	2,684,148	27,500	97.61
Queen	1,146,669	15,000	76.44	Barham **	2,630,113	27,500	95.64
Prince of Wales	1,185,749	15,000	79.05	Malaya **	3,105,709	27,500	112.93
Triumph	957,520	11,985	79.89	Valiant **	2,697,037	27,500	98.07
Swiftsure	956,596	11,800	81.07	Canada *	2,500,000	28,000	89.29
King Edward VII	1,472,075	16,350	90.04	Royal Sovereign **	2,730,501	25,750	106.04
Commonwealth	1,471,527	16,350	90.00	Revenge **	2,566,368	25,750	99.66
Dominion	1,453,718	16,350	88.91	Royal Oak **	2,628,269	25,750	102.07
New Zealand	1,424,643	16,350	87.13	Resolution **	2,609,680	25,750	101.35
Hindustan	1,450,652	16,350	88.72	Ramillies **	3,455,810	25,750	134.21
Africa	1,420,520	16,350	86.88	Renown **	3,237,204	26,500	122.16
Britannia	1,408,533	16,350	86.15	Repulse **	2,949,087	26,500	111.29
Hibernia	1,439,170	16,350	88.02	Courageous **	1,890,121	18,600	101.62
Agamemnon	1,652,347	16,500	100.14	Glorious **	2,205,066	18,600	118.55
Lord Nelson	1,651,339	16,500	100.08	Furious **	2,465,020	19,513	126.33
Dreadnought	1,785,683	17,900	99.76	Hood	5,843,039	41,200	141.82
Indomitable	1,752,337	17,250	101.58	Nelson	6,410,071	33,950	188.81
Inflexible	1,720,739	17,250	99.75	Rodney	6,414,653	33,900	189.22
Invincible	1,767,515	17,250	102.46	King George V	7,391,000	35,000	211.17
Bellerophon	1,763,491	18,600	94.81	Prince of Wales	7,426,000	35,000	212.17
Temeraire	1,744,287	18,600	93.78	Duke of York	7,287,000	35,000	208.20
Superb	1,659,114	18,600	89.20	Anson	7,380,000	35,000	210.86
St Vincent	1,722,370	19,250	89.47	Howe	7,333,000	35,000	209.51
Collingwood	1,678,288	19,250	87.18	Vanguard	11,697,000	44,500	262.85

* Approximate.

** Navy Estimate cost probably excludes guns so their estimated cost has been added,
  e.g. £160,000 for Queen Elizabeth and Royal Sovereign classes.

Hence their costs per ton should reduced by about 5 per cent for comparability, before making an adjustment for inflation, which might roughly halve 1940s costs to 1910s.

THE PROFITABILITY OF BUILDING BATTLESHIPS

Although battleship building was a high profile and a high cost activity, it did not necessarily result in high profits for the builders. When the order for the contract-built vessel of the *St Vincent* class was awarded to Vickers, the authoritative journal *The Shipbuilder* noted:

> There was great competition for this vessel [*Vanguard*], as also for the last similar ship, which fell to the lot of Armstrong, Whitworth & Co, [*Superb*] at what was regarded as a very low price; and now the Barrow firm has followed the same example, and quoted much below other firms who tendered for the ship. It is only great concerns like those of Elswick and Barrow that can do this sort of thing, and that by reason of the great resources they possess in the many departments outside of shipbuilding proper, because while they may possibly lose money in the actual construction of a warship they are in a position to make it in other branches of their ramification.[7]

This was an accurate assessment for *Superb*, although *Vanguard* actually made a modest profit on hull and machinery – see table below. Armstrong's private detailed Profit & Loss account for Elswick shipyard in 1909 shows a loss on *Superb* of £124,606[8] and its Cost Book a hull and machinery cost of £812,178.[9] Their contract was for both hull and machinery, but none of that loss seems attributable to the machinery builders Wallsend Slipway & Engineering as the price Armstrong paid them for Contract 640 (£277,298) looks higher than their cost (£263,593). Figures from different sources at different times are not always consistent, as there are often minor changes made post completion, but these figures do not suggest that 'the Slipway' quoted a loss-making price. The Dockyard Expense Accounts for 1910–11 reveal the cost of *Superb* to the Admiralty included £804,241 for hull and £284,312 for main and auxiliary machinery, which both included small amounts for labour and materials at the Royal Dockyards. The corresponding figures for her sisters *Bellerophon* were £834,098 and £321,774 and for *Temeraire* £836,399 and £305,246. To get to a compa-

rable basis, it is necessary to deduct the cost of armour, which was shown under hull costs but as a contract item, i.e. bought in. As the armour was the same for all the class as was the price per ton, a sum of about £400,000 can reasonably be subtracted from each hull cost. The figures of what the Admiralty paid then become:

	Hull & Fittings	Machinery	Total £
Superb	404,241	284,312	688,553
Bellerophon	434,098	321,774	755,872
Temeraire	436,399	305,246	741,645

The building cost of a Dockyard-built ship was the same as the price paid by the Admiralty, as there was no profit margin, unlike contract built ships, where the contract price would normally include a profit margin on top of building cost. *Temeraire*'s hull cost seems to be a little higher than the estimate given to the Admiralty in 1907 (£425,000, see p.255) which would have resulted in a modest loss had it been a commercial fixed-price contract. But that was much less than Armstrong's hull cost of £534,880 (£812,178 – £277,298). As Armstrong had recent experience of battleship construction, it is unlikely that they underestimated their building costs when tendering for *Superb*; the inescapable conclusion is that they bid a very low price to secure the job. Page 269 shows that Armstrong's tender was £676,444 compared with an average of the other seven shipyards of about £764,000. But the profits on her armament and armour gave the company an overall profit from the ship, plus the prestige of the first dreadnought ordered from a private yard. And the Admiralty got the cheapest ship of her class by about £100,000 – see total cost table above.

Profit and loss figures exist for only some of the battleship contracts ordered before the First World War, but these indicate that building battleship/cruiser hulls and machinery was not as profitable as might have been supposed.[10]

Ship	Builder	Profit/loss (£)	% of cost
Vengeance	Vickers	-19,475	-4.2
Dominion	Vickers	111,564	21.0
Agamemnon	Beardmore	-25,163	-6.0
Invincible	Armstrong	29,686	2.9
Inflexible	John Brown	124,684	11.1
Superb	Armstrong	-124,606	-15.3
Vanguard	Vickers	30,914	4.9
Colossus	Scotts	27,986	4.0
Australia	John Brown	32,040	2.4

Ajax	Scotts	40,367	5.0
Audacious	Cammell Laird	-46,487	-5.1
Conqueror	Beardmore	44,148	5.3
New Zealand	Fairfield	50,454	6.0
Princess Royal	Vickers	122,574	11.2
Benbow	Beardmore	-54,556	-5.7
Emperor of India	Vickers	12,048	1.4
Tiger	John Brown	56,504	4.8
Valiant	Fairfield	-78,836	-5.6

Those eighteen ships average only 2.1 per cent, clear evidence of a highly competitive market. Given that machinery profits were typically 5–10 per cent of cost (see p.244-5) that suggests that building hulls was on average barely profitable. It is also known that *Exmouth* made a loss for Laird in 1902. The Palmer company made a loss of £31,580 in the year to June 1912 when *Hercules* was completed, and only a small profit of £2267 (after interest) the next year when *Queen Mary* was largely completed. Some of the losses were due to the company's steelworks but no details have survived other than brief company annual accounts.[11] The contract for *Thunderer* bankrupted Thames Iron Works in 1911, while *Albion* had been built at a loss by them in 1901, not helped when the machinery contractor Maudslay went into liquidation after her launch. The conclusion must be that battleship building could easily result in losses, whether from deliberate underpricing to win a contract, poor cost estimating when tendering or unexpected price rises during building. But

the prestige of being on the Admiralty list for building such ships was enormous, and enabled the builders to quote for export contracts, a condition of which was that the company tendering had built similar ships for the Admiralty, in essence a 'loss leader'. For Armstrong Whitworth and Vickers Sons & Maxim, there was the compensation of big profits from both ordnance and armour manufacture (see also Chapters 8 and 9) and for John Brown, Beardmore and Cammell Laird profits from armour and forgings. The 'independents' such as Palmers, Scotts, Fairfield[12] and Thames Iron Works had no such cushion and could only make a profit from lower cost production, a demanding task, as prices were very competitive. But all John Brown's eleven battleships from *Jupiter* to *Vanguard* yielded profits, due not only to efficient construction but also to buying materials cheaply within the group.

The profitability of five major warship builders from 1889 to 1914 was analysed by Arnold,[13] namely Armstrong, Vickers, John Brown, Fairfield and Palmers. For Armstrong, the figures relate to the Elswick shipyard so are largely for warship building, but for the other four shipyards include merchant ships. For Palmers, only the published accounts were available, rather than company archives, so included their other divisions such as steelmaking; these show only a miserly return on capital of 4.2 per cent over the period. Arnold's analysis reaches the broad conclusion that

Below: Like most of the shipbuilders described here with the exception of the Royal Dockyards, Fairfield built ships of all types specialising in intermediate-sized passenger liners and vessels with a high level of fitting-out. There are at least six other vessels sharing the fitting-out basin in this photograph probably taken in August 1907. Left, *Indomitable* (with the Canadian *Stanley* being rebuilt alongside) with at right the sister passenger liners *Heliopolis* and *Cairo* (nearest) for the Egyptian Mail SS Co, Canadian *Keewatin* and *Assiniboia* furthest. *Indomitable*'s main armament and armour has already been fitted although not much of her superstructure is in place. This sequence of events was to allow the alignment of main machinery and shafting in a hull after the greatest weights were already in place. *(Author's collection)*

COST AND PRICE OF *AUDACIOUS*

Audacious	Hull	Engines	Boilers	Total (£)
Labour	278,938	47,905	27,519	354,362
Materials	243,443	124,901	32,913	401,257
Establishment charges	121,190	29,148	11,930	162,268
Total costs	643,571	201,954	72,362	917,887
Contract price & extras	605,376	197,319	68,705	871,400
Loss	-38,195	-4635	-3657	-46,487
In percentage terms:				
Labour	30.39	5.22	3.00	38.61
Materials	26.52	13.61	3.59	43.72
Establishment charges	13.20	3.18	1.30	17.68
Total costs	70.11	22.00	7.88	100.00
Contract price & extras	65.95	21.50	7.49	94.94
Loss	-4.16	-0.50	-0.40	-5.06

warship building was generally more profitable than merchant ships but that excessive returns were not made. Battleship building was not separated out for the companies, but as these constituted a significant proportion of turnover, his overall figures do confirm the suggestion that the building of battleship hulls and machinery was not particularly profitable. He also confirms that the period 1910–14 was less profitable than 1900–09, indeed noting that John Brown's return was negative in the 1910–14 period at -0.4 per cent.

Some of Arnold's figures include:

Vickers' profit margin as a proportion of turnover:

Admiralty vessels 1901–07	15.7 per cent
Admiralty vessels 1908–14	6.3 per cent
Foreign naval vessels 1901–14	10.8 per cent
Merchant ships 1901–14	9.1 per cent

Return as a percentage on divisional capital, based on profit before tax, interest and dividends:

Shipbuilder	1889 –99	1900 –09	1910 –14
Armstrong, Elswick shipyard	–	14.1	8.8
John Brown, Clydebank	11.1	7.4	-0.4
Vickers, Barrow	3.8	14.2	18.9
Fairfield	5.0	9.4	3.0

The Vickers figures reflect the capital investment made after 1900 and corresponding increased output as well as highly profitable submarine construction. The average across the five companies for the whole period was 7.4 per cent, which Arnold concludes was 'unspectacular'. The return on equity (shareholder's)

capital, i.e. after excluding preference and debenture capital, was slightly higher at 9.1 per cent. Neither measure was particularly generous nor was it out of line with other industries. However that was not true of armour (owing to cartel prices) or heavy ordnance (largely two collaborating companies) as shown in Chapters 9 and 8.

Audacious is the only pre-war battleship where a clear final cost, price and profit/loss breakdown has been found – see left.[14]

Hull, engines and boilers all made losses amounting in total to 5 per cent of cost – armour and armament were not included being Admiralty Supply Items (ASIs). Normally a shipbuilder would aim for a profit margin of 5 to 10 per cent on cost. The shipyard contract was only 44.4 per cent of the £1,961,315 that the complete ship cost the Admiralty, which included £581,411 of guns, mountings and torpedo tubes, the rest (£508,504) being armour and miscellaneous costs.

While *Audacious*' labour content was not recorded, it is possible to estimate such by assuming average wages of £80 per year and 53 hours per week typical for the period (see p.257). Spread over 31 months from keel laying to delivery (the period from contract signing to keel laying was largely white collar labour on design and material ordering) suggests an average labour force of 1350 men in the shipyard totalling about 9.2 million man-hours and 370 men in the engine works (2.5 million man-hours), probably about one-third of the Birkenhead labour force, which included merchant ships and ship repair. The smaller pre-dreadnought *Vengeance* at Barrow required 4.29 million man-hours for hull (69.1 per cent before launch) and 1.65 million for machinery (only 2.5 per cent before launch) for a launch weight of 7460 tons and 10,140 tons finished weight, i.e. light displacement.[15]

Once war broke out, the Admiralty was willing to pay whatever was necessary for labour and materials to get the ships delivered, with 'acceleration' payments including overtime. Between the wars however, only two battleships were built, for which there was great competition. Builders had to quote a loss making price with at best partial recovery of establishment charges to have any chance of an order – p.292 shows the bids from the nine shipbuilders. On *Rodney*, Cammell Laird made a loss of £172,604 on a hull contract price of £1,252,825 and a loss of £107,532 on a machinery price of £507,424, an overall loss

Money

243

rate on cost of 13.7 per cent.[16] But this low
hull and machinery price was only 28 per cent
of the total cost to the Admiralty of £6.4
million which included also armament (£2.8
million), armour (£1.4 million) and Admiralty
miscellaneous (£0.4 million) but excluded
ammunition.

By the start of re-armament in 1936, potential battleship building shipyards had been
reduced to seven, including Swan Hunter &
Wigham Richardson and Harland & Wolff.
Portsmouth and Devonport Dockyards and
Scotts could now only build cruiser-size
warships, while Thames Iron Works, Palmers
and Beardmore had closed down. The
remaining warship builders had been operating
a minimum price arrangement in the 1930s
through the Warshipbuilders Committee of
their trade association, the Shipbuilding
Conference. This group of fifteen companies
coordinated bids for hulls and machinery,
ensuring that only tenders offering a reasonable profit margin were submitted to the
Admiralty to avoid ruinous undercutting of
prices, plus a degree of sharing out over time of
orders to all in the group.[17] They saw this
partially as compensating for losses on
merchant ship contracts where prices were
very competitive. The Admiralty connived at
this to ensure the survival of core warship

building facilities and skilled manpower across
the shipbuilding districts, a policy which was
vindicated in the Second World War when the
warship building yards were fully utilised.
However, it was not aware until later of just
how high some profit margins were, e.g. over
70 per cent on submarines.[18] Although they
knew the cost of constructing such vessels in a
Royal Dockyard, they were not aware of how
much lower were the costs in private yards.[19]
Thus when tenders were submitted for King
George V class battleships in 1937, the prices
included a significant profit margin. When
Swan Hunter submitted its tender for the hull
of Jellicoe (later Anson) of £2,508,600 on 15
February 1937 (accepted on 28 April), it
included an estimated profit of £274,965, or
12.3 per cent on cost.[20] Although there were
extras requested by the Admiralty during the
build period, such was the profit margin that
Swan Hunter accepted these within the original contract price.[21] When the Admiralty
investigated such contracts during the Second
World War, they found the profit margin on
Prince of Wales' hull and electrical 25.0 per cent
and machinery 14.7 per cent, and Duke of York
20.4 per cent/8.3 per cent.[22] By this time, the
purchasing power of the pound was about fifty
times the 2012 figure, or about half that of
before 1914.

Left: *Duke of York* in John Brown's fitting out basin in June 1941. Her port aft pair of 5.25in mountings have been fitted but not the forward pair, which will be installed by the 200-ton cantilever crane. *(Upper Clyde Shipbuilders)*

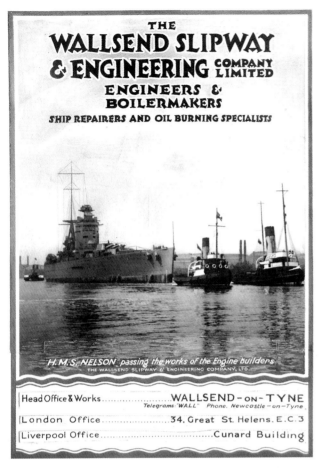

H.M.S. NELSON passing the works of the Engine builders.

VANGUARD COST AND PRICE

	Hull	Electrical	Machinery	Total (£)
Cost	3,514,665	522,998	1,385,958	5,423,621
Price	3,760,362	559,559	1,482,825	5,802,746
Profit	245,697	36,561	96,867	379,125

WALLSEND SLIPWAY FINANCES

	1908–12	1913–17
Number of new machinery installations	65	76
Total indicated hp	324,913	1,169,790
Average ihp per ship	4999	15,392
Average ihp per year	64,980	233,960
Sales of new machinery (£)	2,052,018	5,538,761
Average annual sales (£)	410,400	1,107,700
Average price per ship (£)	31,570	72,880
Average price per ihp (£)	6.31	4.73
Profit on new machinery sales (£)	129,106	485,719
Profit rate on cost (%)	6.7	9.6
Admiralty sales (included above) (£)	NA	4,195,474
As a % of total	NA	75.7
Profit on Admiralty sales (£)	NA	381,461
Profit rate on cost (%)	NA	10.0
Total sales all departments (£)	2,573,072	6,455,142
Net profit all departments after charges (£)	203,941	804,900
Overall profit rate on cost (%)	8.6	14.2
Average number employed	1942	2886
Average annual wage (£)	75.9	109.4
Average ihp per man per year	33.5	81.1
Average dividend on ordinary shares (%)	6.2	12.5

Above: Wallsend Slipway advertisement featured *Nelson*, passing the works on her way down the Tyne from Armstrong's Naval Yard. *(Tyne & Wear Archives)*

Vanguard was subject to the pricing arrangements introduced by the Admiralty on hull and machinery contracts after 1941.[23] Gone were tenders and fixed prices, in came orders wherever there was capacity and 'cost-plus' contracts, i.e. payment of the actual cost of labour, materials and agreed overheads plus a fixed percentage for profit, generally 7.5 per cent. In the case of *Vanguard*, the Admiralty accountants took until May 1949 to agree a final price with John Brown, as above.[24]

The profit margin was 7 per cent and the shipbuilder price only half the cost of the finished ship of £11.7 million which included armament and armour and ASIs such as radar, directors, cranes, hoists and in the *King George V* class aircraft equipment. The split between hull plus electrical/machinery was 70/30 with overall labour and materials each a similar percentage at 43.5, the 13 per cent balance being establishment charges. Assuming typical wage rates and weekly hours suggests about 20 million man-hours for hull and electrical and 5 million for machinery, spread over 65 months, i.e. double the amount for a pre-war dreadnought – but which was only half the displacement. The chart on p.52 shows the significant proportion of Clydebank's labour force employed on their two battleships.

Building battleship machinery seems not to have been much more profitable than building hulls pre-war, judging from some figures for the few ships available. Hawthorn Leslie's shipyard at Hebburn could not build battleships, but their engine works at St Peters installed machinery in seven battleships building in Royal Dockyards or at Armstrong Whitworth between 1908 (*Temeraire*) and 1915 (*Royal Oak*), totalling 249,500 shp. Thirty-nine sets of machinery were built over those eight years, all but six (low powered merchant ships) being steam turbines for naval vessels – their last set of steam reciprocating machinery installed in a battleship was for *Agamemnon* in 1907. Clarke shows a graph of profits at St Peters averaging £30,000 a year between 1908 and 1914 – the engine works was usually more profitable than the shipyard or the locomotive building works at Forth Banks, Newcastle.[25] Although battleship machinery made up only one-third of the total horsepower, the more complex battleship installation, compared with destroyers, meant that they represented about half of estimated annual sales of about £550,000. The corresponding profit rate on cost was thus about 5.8 per cent [30/(550-30)]. Vickers' Barrow accounts only separate out profits on machinery for hulls built elsewhere. For *Dreadnought*, *Minas Geraes*, *Lion* and *Agincourt*, the profit rate averaged 7 per cent.[26]

Wallsend Slipway & Engineering down river from St Peters produced five sets of battleship type steam turbine machinery between 1908 (*Superb*) and 1917 (*Furious*), totalling 290,000 shp. Their detailed accounts record invoiced sales and profit by department, but only separate Admiralty contracts from merchant ships in 1913.[27] Before that date, most of their work was for merchant ships, and included new boilers, repair work, oil burning installations and general spares – see table opposite.

Everything including dividends roughly doubled with increasing levels of wartime work and Admiralty business. Wallsend engined one of the two battleships built between the wars. Their cost record for *Nelson* illustrated shows that they made a loss of £60,246, even after clawing back £25,000 for delays. However, their actual building cost of £505,908 was much less than Cammell Laird's *Rodney* of £614,956, which made a bigger loss despite a higher price, due largely to higher material costs.

THE PROFITABILITY OF ARMSTRONG WHITWORTH

So if building battleship hulls and machinery was not particularly profitable, how does that compare with the other half of battleship construction cost, namely armour and armament? Chapters 8 and 9 show the high prices charged for such items, which resulted in high profits. Fortunately some figures for typical pre-war years exist for Armstrong Whitworth in Lord Stuart Rendel's private papers (a major shareholder, director and from 1907 Vice Chairman) and in Armstrong's financial balance books, summarised here, right.[28]

The 5½-year period from July 1901 to December 1906 (Armstrong changed their financial year end from June to December in 1906) covered the pre-dreadnought period and the Boer War, while 1907–12 covered the early years of dreadnought building. Generally the former period was more profitable, both in absolute terms and in return on capital – though the latter percentages are higher than would be assessed today, as depreciation was not

Left: Wallsend Slipway's cost record for *Nelson*. (*Author's collection*)

deducted from divisional profits and the value of the Elswick site was not divided between the four divisions operating there (ordnance, engine works, steelworks and Elswick shipyard) so are not included in their capital. This was reflected in the average dividend paid on the Ordinary shares: 14.6 per cent for the earlier

ARMSTRONG WHITWORTH DIVISIONAL PROFITS

Divisions	Average annual profit 1901–02 to 1906 (£)	Average annual profit 1907 to 1912 (£)	% of profits 1901–12
Ordnance	284,781	190,873	26.96
Openshaw	373,957	386,953	43.54
Elswick Shipyard	78,075	25,193	5.77
Walker Shipyard	24,555	9101	1.89
Engine works	61,758	36,211	5.54
Steelworks	73,949	125,348	11.52
Motor cars	−1371	−8765	−0.60
Dividends	32,834	60,154	5.38
Total	928,537	825,067	100.00

ARMSTRONG WHITWORTH PROFIT AND CAPITAL

Divisions	Average capital 1901–06 (£k)	Profit/capital (%)	Average capital 1907–12 (£k)	Profit/capital (%)
Ordnance	1240	23.0	1402	13.6
Openshaw	1310	28.5	1403	27.6
Elswick Shipyard	123	63.5	299	8.4
Walker Shipyard	105	23.3	167	5.4
Engine works	171	36.2	176	20.6
Steelworks	292	25.3	295	42.5

Profit and capital derived from various sources.[29]

period, 11.7 per cent for the later. Peebles noted the major Clyde warship builders also found the period after 1910 less profitable, partly from fewer Admiralty orders but also from more competition and rising costs.[30]

Although there is limited information on Armstrong sales, data in Armstrong Board Minutes shows an average order intake for the Ordnance division (excluding Pozzuoli) at a healthy annual average of £2.638 million from 1906–11, but the corresponding annual average profit for 1907–12 was only £191,000, i.e. a modest rate on cost of only 7.8 per cent, far below that of Openshaw with its armour.[31] That the profit rate was declining is supported by comparing the Ordnance division's crude profit rate, assuming that the bulk of its output was battleship guns and mountings. Twenty-nine twin turrets were completed from 1901 to 1906, a 'profit' of about £54,000 'each', whereas the fifty completed in 1907–12 produced only £23,000 each – though this simplification neglects all the smaller ordnance.[32]

The shipyards were broadly less profitable than the other Armstrong divisions, although Elswick did produce high returns from the earlier period when seven warships for foreign navies were completed. Elswick generally built warships and Walker merchant ships. While there are no figures allowing the Elswick profit rate on output to be calculated, the Walker shipyard averaged seven ships a year from 1907–12 totalling 30,000 grt sold for £379,000, producing an average annual profit of only £9100, a miserly 2.5 per cent on costs – and for three of those years, losses were reported.[33] Competition for most merchant ships was more severe than for warships, partly due to there being many more competing shipyards. However, Walker did turn in a record profit of £90,000 in 1914 building tankers, one of its specialities.

The later period saw more pressure on prices from additional suppliers to the British Government such as Coventry Ordnance Works, and competition from foreign companies for export orders. But with the armour

Below: Engine builders as well as shipbuilders took publicity photographs of ships they had engined. Wallsend Slipway & Engineering made the machinery for *Orion* built at Portsmouth Dockyard, as their Contract 680. *(Wallsend Slipway)*

ring still operating (see Chapter 9) both profits and profitability from Openshaw remained steady, with a return on capital of about 28 per cent. With a few figures for depreciation and land value at Openshaw, it is possible to estimate the return after depreciation (about £65,000 a year) on capital including land value (about £110,000),[34] which brings the figure down to about 21 per cent – a healthy figure nonetheless. With the exception of the shipyards after 1907, divisions achieved average rates of return of around 15 to 30 per cent. No wonder other engineering companies tried to get into the armaments business in the 1900s.

The 1912 profit figures confirm the low armour production costs noted in Chapter 9. Armstrong's claimed nearly 11,000 tons of finished armour produced in 1912.[35] The Openshaw division's profit that year was £563,378, armour making up 71.5 per cent of manufacturing profit.[36] This suggests an overall profit of £37 per ton (0.715 x 563,378/10,900). Typical selling price was about £96 per ton, implying a manufacturing cost of about £59 per ton, or profit about 61 per cent of cost. Cammell Laird armour profit was even higher at £43 per ton in 1913–14 while for Vickers it was about £60 in 1907–11 (see p.218).

Dividends were also received from associated companies such as Whitehead Torpedo, Thames Ammunition and Pozzuoli. The steelworks at Elswick produced both the open hearth steel and the forgings used for guns and mountings for Armstrong and Woolwich and components such as hollow shafting, the bulk of which was for warships and the military. (The steel for armour plates was produced at Openshaw.) It appears that Armstrong used transfer prices between divisions that reflected external prices, so allowing profits from making, say, gun barrels to be correctly allocated between the steelworks and the ordnance works. The engine works did not produce marine engines but hydraulic machinery such as cranes and dock equipment largely for civilian use. Openshaw's main product was armour plate. Weighting these suggests that a good 80 per cent of Armstrong's profits were derived from armaments from 1901–12, nearly 70 per cent from ordnance and armour alone. The four works on the Elswick site produced 50 per cent of the company profits.

No further detailed Armstrong Whitworth figures have been found after 1912. Indeed the expansion of war output and complex Government munitions payment mechanisms so overwhelmed their accounts department that the company was unable to produce the normal annual profit and loss account and balance sheet until 1919, belatedly producing an aggregated account for the previous four years. Vickers also only produced aggregate accounts covering the years 1916–19. While these were indeed years of high profits, the British Government clawed some back in the form of Excess Profits Duty. This was introduced in 1915 and was levied on profits above the best two of three pre-war years, at rates from 40 to 80 per cent.[37]

What did the company do with its large pre First World War profits? It paid healthy dividends of around 12.5 per cent, so shareholders benefited. In addition to dividends on their shares, the executive directors paid themselves handsomely. From 1907 to 1909 which were years of below average annual profits at £627,400, Sir Andrew Noble as chairman took an annual salary of £8000 and a total of £20,888 in commission (2 per cent of profits), his sons John and Saxton Noble each took £5000 a year in salary plus commission (0.6 per cent) while J M Falkner took £8000 (0.9 per cent); these figures excluding directors' fees.[38] £8000 was about 100 times the average workman's annual wage, a ratio not dissimilar to some generously-rewarded senior executives today, with the important differences that personal tax rates were far lower at that time, and such figures were not disclosed in the company's annual report. As today, the beneficiaries often bought large country estates and yachts.[39] The Vickers directors paid themselves even more handsomely while making slightly less profit – see below. But the profits also helped finance the new High Walker Naval Yard built from 1911–14 (together with an issue of new shares), an essential resource during the First and Second World Wars – see p.139. After the First World War, Armstrong Whitworth invested in new ventures as it tried to beat swords into ploughshares, including its ill-fated Newfoundland forestry and newsprint project which so weakened the company as to force it into a merger with Vickers in 1927.

THE PROFITS OF VICKERS BEFORE THE FIRST WORLD WAR

Although a complete run of the Vickers company and all its divisional accounts have not been located, enough have been found to compile profit data for its three divisions –

Sheffield (steel, armour and large guns), Barrow (hulls, machinery and gun mountings) and Maxim (smaller guns and ammunition) for 1901–14.[40] The table below shows that Sheffield was the most profitable division, averaging 64 per cent of the divisional total, largely due to armour, which made up 80 per cent of its profits 1907–11, followed by Barrow with 31 per cent. Maxim produced only 5 per cent, having made losses in five of the fourteen years, probably due to greater competition and lower prices in its markets. Vickers Central Office received dividends from associated companies, but also had to pay 9.25 per cent of profits as bonuses to the directors, as well as general head office costs and generous commission on foreign sales and profits to Sir Basil Zaharoff. The three managing directors received most of the bonus: 33 per cent to chairman Tom Vickers, 27 per cent to his brother Albert and 20 per cent to Tom's son Douglas, the balance to other directors. The total shared by the three ranged from £81,400 in high profit year 1906 to £16,950 in low profit year 1909, the year Tom retired. Albert, who then became

Chairman, received an annual average of £19,850 in 1906–08, over 200 times the average worker's wage. In addition, he received a director's salary but as the total for all directors only came to £12,000 a year, the bulk of their remuneration came from the bonuses. His bonus in 1914 was no less than £33,577.

The annual average profits of Vickers Sons & Maxim were about 70 per cent of those of Armstrong Whitworth over comparable periods. However some of this may have been due to different treatment of items such as depreciation in their Profit & Loss Account. Like Armstrong, the period 1907–12 was less profitable than the earlier period:

	Av 1901–06	Av 1907–12
Vickers	670,576	582,967
Armstrong	928,537	825,067

As Vickers' capital was comparable with or slightly more than Armstrong's over the period, that suggests a lower return on capital.

More detailed figures for Barrow exist for 1900–02 (bottom left), showing the predominance of government work, which included work for the War Office (Army) as well as the Admiralty. As Barrow became more experienced, losses in early years after the Vickers takeover changed to profit. In subsequent years, submarines became a major profit earner, even though about half of those profits had to be paid to Electric Boat in the USA.

Some financial figures have survived for contracts completed during each year at Barrow 1902–14.[41] Hulls and machinery, including merchant ships, made up 65 per cent of sales compared with 28 per cent for gun mountings, which included work for the War Office, with other divisions 7 per cent, comprising sundry ordnance, shells, repairs, airships (later) and miscellaneous. Contribution to operating profits, i.e. before depreciation, interest, share of submarine profits to Electric Boat etc, were 51 per cent, 45 per cent, 4 per cent. Gun mounting work was highly profitable at an average of 35 per cent of cost, compared with 15 per cent for hulls and machinery, which included submarines whose profit rate ranged from 16 per cent to 70 per cent.

Trebilcock confirms the high proportion of military work at Barrow, averaging 80.5 per cent for 1907–09 (total turnover average £1.869 million) and 88.5 per cent for 1912–14 (£3.809 million). Turnover nearly trebled to £10.686 million in 1916, with shell and field

VICKERS PROFITS 1901–14

Profit to 31 Dec	Sheffield division	Barrow division	Maxim division	Sub total	Company after bonuses & head office costs & dividends received
1901	718,933	-121,162	146,640	744,411	571,322
1902	567,596	58,874	87,855	714,325	541,434
1903	438,637	189,143	-23,222	604,558	556,121
1904	551,504	302,058	-35,543	818,019	686,895
1905	514,237	383,822	107,002	1,005,061	787,778
1906	431,253	506,784	233,057	1,171,094	879,905
1907	466,063	465,703	53,805	985,571	768,525
1908	404,416	188,574	-67,691	525,299	416,846
1909	207,704	246,364	-95,280	358,788	288,044
1910	369,314	370,535	584	740,433	510,668
1911	515,287	257,513	81,516	854,316	641,686
1912	654,305	322,827	-25,011	952,121	872,033
1913	819,097	118,310	30,300	967,707	911,996
1914	824,600	301,849	74,011	1,200,460	1,019,035
Average	534,496	256,514	40,573	831,583	675,163
% Divisions	64.27	30.85	4.88	100	

VICKERS BARROW ANNUAL TURNOVER 1900–02

	1900	1901	1902	Total (£)	%
Government work ships	767,653	676,144	677,110	2,120,907	60.07
Government work gun mountings	240,759	380,620	290,310	911,689	25.82
Mercantile work	6653	98,477	141,096	246,226	6.97
Repairs & sundries	26,147	34,637	26,272	87,056	2.47
Charges & miscellaneous	13,314	66,917	84,334	164,565	4.66
Total turnover	1,054,526	1,256,795	1,219,122	3,530,443	100.00
Profit	-86,144	-121,162	58,874	-148,432	

VICKERS BARROW COMPLETED SALES AND PROFITS 1902–14

Year	Hulls & machinery sales (£)	Hulls & machinery profit	Gun mounting sales (£)	Gun mountings profit	Other divisions sales (£)	Other divisions profits	Total sales (£)	Operating profit (£)
1902	2,264,458	234,201	249,447	-51,743	53,293	-1534	2,567,198	180,924
1903	1,914,011	200,014	749,162	121,645	104,983	4364	2,768,156	326,023
1904	1,612,517	182,663	557,984	245,622	113,632	-2377	2,284,133	425,908
1905	1,007,097	390,861	564,295	234,130	135,173	21,852	1,706,565	646,843
1906	2,351,573	555,463	635,382	222,674	199,566	38,154	3,186,521	816,291
1907	1,588,310	361,750	1,239,125	410,083	115,915	12,202	2,943,350	784,035
1908	835,952	35,247	1,050,247	219,612	165,888	26,902	2,052,087	281,761
1909	2,011,844	334,063	366,251	138,341	127,126	19,345	2,505,221	491,749
1910	1,886,361	339,220	603,911	195,097	176,827	15,343	2,667,099	549,660
1911	1,347,979	147,747	967,516	295,035	199,506	6854	2,515,001	449,636
1912	2,109,915	178,005	1,273,750	338,915	243,606	24,764	3,627,271	541,684
1913	3,047,261	118,998	1,034,988	210,985	438,295	36,959	4,520,544	366,942
1914	3,587,093	219,903	1,648,546	287,874	553,314	51,208	5,788,953	558,985
Total	25,564,371	3,298,135	10,940,604	2,868,270	2,627,124	254,036	39,132,099	6,420,441
Average annual	1,966,490	253,703	841,585	220,636	202,086	19,541	3,010,161	493,880
% sales	65.33		27.96		6.71		100.00	
% profits		51.37		44.67		3.96		100.00

artillery production rapidly expanding. Trebilcock also gives work in hand by class of product at year end from 1908–15 confirming that in 1912–14 hulls and machinery were over 70 per cent of Barrow's business in peacetime, despite the new additions of airships and field artillery.[42]

Barrow Work in Hand	Average 1912–14	%
Hulls and machinery	2,059,265	72.53
Gun mountings	538,519	18.97
Sundry ordnance contracts & spares	56,641	1.99
Shell manufacture	89,722	3.16
Airships	69,019	2.43
Field artillery	147,039	5.18
Total	2,839,172	100.00

THE PROFITS OF VICKERS-ARMSTRONGS

With the merger of the armaments and warship building interests of Vickers Ltd (so renamed in 1911) and Sir W G Armstrong, Whitworth & Co Ltd, there was from 1928 effectively only one company capable of producing a battle-ship's armament – Woolwich and Beardmore could only make guns and smaller mountings. Despite the scarcity of naval armament orders, British and foreign, Vickers-Armstrongs Ltd (V-A) retained both Barrow and Elswick works in the expectation that battleship ordering would recommence in the 1930s, although numbers employed fell as workloads reduced. The former Armstrong Naval Yard was again put on care and maintenance after completion of *Monarch of Bermuda* in 1931, although Barrow continued to build both hulls and machinery, including its speciality submarines.

Although orders were slim with defence cutbacks worldwide, there was virtually no competition for naval armaments, so prices could be maintained at profitable levels. Indeed the Admiralty was anxious to maintain core skills and plant for when warship demand would revive. Similarly, the warship builders were able to maintain minimum prices for Admiralty orders, so the few contracts available from 1930 were at least generating some profit. This ensured the survival of most of the warship yards, whereas in merchant ship-building, both national and international competition for the few orders had usually to be taken at loss-making prices, resulting in the closure of many shipyards without the financial resources to withstand such losses.

After re-opening in 1934 to build the cruiser *Newcastle*, the Naval Yard saw a steady recovery, with number employed rising from about 200 to about 4000 at the outbreak of the Second World War – see table on p.261. From then until the end of the war, Naval Yard's entire order book consisted only of naval vessels, including the battleship *King George V* ordered in 1936. The V-A accounts record sales of completed ships at healthy profits of around 10–25 per cent on costs. Naval Yard sales were only about one-third of Barrow shipbuilding, which not only included machinery but also the highly profitable submarines. Shipbuilding

VICKERS-ARMSTRONGS SHIPYARDS SALES AND PROFITS

Year to 31 December	Sales (£k)	Naval Yard, Newcastle		Barrow Shipyard		
		Profit (£k)	% on costs	Sales (£k)	Profit (£k)	% on costs
1935	8	1	14.3	3513	466	15.3
1936	893	123	16.0	2175	273	14.4
1937	703	151	27.4	3438	163	5.0
1938	547	73	15.4	3290	429	15.0
1939	339	56	19.8	2860	603	26.7
1940	4175	727	21.1	6733	1884	38.9
1941	3549	454	14.7	7140	1835	34.6
1942	2890	139	5.1	9611	1057	12.4
Total	13,104	1724		38,760	6710	
Average 1936–42	1871	246	15.1	5035	892	20.9

represented around 55 per cent of Barrow sales, with naval armament about 25 per cent, the balance being land armament and general engineering.[43]

While naval armament production continued to be concentrated at Barrow and Elswick, rearmament saw Scotswood brought in to produce medium calibre mountings, especially anti-aircraft, both Army and Navy, managed by V-A. Later Manchester (Openshaw) was brought in to manufacture close-range automatic guns such as the 2pdr, and later on mountings. The table opposite shows the range of naval armament items on order at Barrow, Elswick and Scotswood in December 1939,

with work well under way on battleship 14in and 5.25in guns and mountings ordered from 1936. At £30 million this represented over two years' work. With shipbuilding orders at £26.9 million, those two divisions made up 60 per cent of V-A's order book, the rest being land and air armaments, aircraft and general engineering. In the case of Elswick, naval armament made up only about one-third of the total workload, the rest being land armament, tanks and general engineering; at Scotswood only about one-sixth.[44]

The figures reflected the declining proportion of export sales, as orders for the British Government took priority. Barrow's naval armament sales were on average about 10 per cent less than Elswick (they did not make large guns), but profitability was higher at 16 per cent on costs compared with 12 per cent – the Admiralty could compare prices for more Elswick products with Woolwich and other factories, than it could for Barrow.[45] After 1942, V-A battleship work had largely finished.

THE CENSUS OF PRODUCTION 1907

The first ever UK Census of Production was taken for the year 1907. Its survey of the output of companies and employers covered manufac-

Below: *King George V* ready for departure to Rosyth is dwarfed by the 250-ton cantilever crane at Walker Naval Yard in October 1940. *(Author's collection)*

turing industries, excluding agriculture, transport and services. The main contributors to the British battleship building industry were included under several of the thirteen main industrial group headings, with sub-sections such as shipbuilding, marine engine building, ordnance and steel manufacture. While such were not always identified as warship construction, there is sufficient detail in the massive 938-page compilation to provide some interesting statistics.[46]

The Census covered work carried out during the calendar year 1907 for private firms, but financial year to 31 March 1908 for government departments such as the Royal Dockyards. Output was recorded for all ships under construction during that year, whether or not launched or completed. Indeed since a battleship or battlecruiser typically took nearly three years to build, only about one-third of the work on any one such ship would be included, so data included vessels completed from 1907 to 1909.

Shipbuilding was included together with Marine Engineering and Shiprepairing as a sub-group within 'Iron and Steel, Engineering and Shipbuilding Trades'. Survey forms were sent out to individual firms in England, Scotland, Wales and Ireland, but aggregated in such a way as to prevent identification of individual companies. The Census shows 'War Vessels' as a separate category, divided between private firms and Dockyards. The private firms' output for 1907 is shown as 63,000 displacement tons with a value of £3,512,000, i.e. an average of £55.7 per ton.[47] As this is under the average price of a warship, it probably excludes armament and armour. Of this, 6600 tons worth £555,000 were for export (16 per cent). However with an average value of £84.1 per ton, it probably includes most if not all of the ship value, the largest vessel completed in 1907 being the 3200-ton Peruvian cruiser *Coronel Bolognesi*. During 1907, these yards were working on *Lord Nelson*, *Agamemnon*, *Invincible*, *Inflexible*, *Indomitable* and *Superb* plus three armoured cruisers with an average construction time of 2.9 years. With a number of smaller vessels such as destroyers under construction during the year, this recorded output probably represents about 40 per cent of the aggregate tonnage being worked on during the year.

For the Dockyards, output for the year to 31 March 1908 was recorded as 37,300 tons worth £3,355,481,[48] an average of £89.9 per ton, so

VICKERS–ARMSTRONGS NAVAL ARMAMENT ORDERS IN HAND 31 DECEMBER 1939

	Barrow	Elswick	Scotswood	Total (£k)
Naval guns over 6in		746		746
Naval guns 6in and under		1166		1166
Hydraulic gun mountings 6in and over	4568	7226		11,794
Transferable gun mountings 5.25in and under	428	1167	4671	6266
Machine guns and mountings incl 2pdr*	985			2935
Breech mechanisms		426		426
Directors and fire control gear*	535			3531
Empty shell*		24		134
Cartridge cases*		297		298
Fuses, primers and tracer*		556		700
Torpedo work excl Weymouth		102		102
Mines, paravanes and depth charges	58			58
Miscellaneous*	253	22		401
Argentinian naval armament	374			374
Brazilian naval armament	644			644
Turkish naval armament	427			427
Total orders*	8272	11,732	4671	30,002
Percentage	27.6	39.1	15.6	
Expenditure in 1939	4063	4688	1342	12,012

* Total includes Crayford and other V-A works

VICKERS–ARMSTRONGS NAVAL ARMAMENT DIVISIONS

	Barrow			Elswick		
Year to 31st December	Sales (£k)	Profit (£k)	% on costs	Sales (£k)	Profit (£k)	% on costs
1935	917	254	38.3	795	181	29.5
1936	1119	256	29.7	1186	210	21.5
1937	1314	316	31.7	1574	260	19.8
1938	1581	236	17.5	1403	234	20.0
1939	2497	471	23.2	2901	475	19.6
1940	1507	128	9.3	2364	385	19.5
1941	3527	239	7.3	4731	66	1.4
1942	4109	385	10.3	3775	202	5.7
Total	16,571	2285		18,729	2013	
Annual average	2071	286	16.0	2341	252	12.0

Excludes Scotswood, Crayford etc

probably includes armour as well as hull and machinery. Two battleships were under construction during the year, *Bellerophon* and *Temeraire*, plus three armoured cruisers and some smaller vessels. The average construction time for the five large vessels was just under three years, suggesting that this annual figure represented about 35 per cent of the total tonnage under construction. War vessel construction amounted to 57 per cent of the total Dockyard output of £5,907,402 which included ship repair and work for other government departments. Employment at the Dockyards (Portsmouth, Devonport, Chatham, Pembroke, Sheerness in the Medway and Haulbowline near Cork) averaged 23,359, of which 3.4 per cent were salaried, 6.1 per cent under 18 and 0.2 per cent female.[49] This figure excluded the 2010 in Dockyard workshops making naval stores such as ropes and castings. Dockyards were also shown as having installed machinery for powering workshops and electric dynamos of 61,998 hp, of which 32 per cent was used to generate electricity. In the private yards, the figures were higher at 114,546 hp and 46 per cent.[50]

The output for private yards was broken down into:[51]

	£k
War vessels of 63,000 tons	3512
Steamships, iron or steel, hull & fittings, of 1,585,000 grt	19,162
Steamships, iron or steel, machinery	4437
Wooden steam ships, hull & fittings, of 13,000 grt	226
Wooden steam ships, machinery	103
Sailing ships, of 16,000 grt	255
Boats and barges	512
Ship repair	8473
Miscellaneous non-ship products	557
Total	37,237

540,000 grt of steamship hulls were exported worth £6.586 million (34 per cent of total). Imports were a mere 695 grt worth £27,000.

All such output figures were classed as 'gross output', so there was some duplication with other industries' output. Thus output of steel was separately measured, but also formed an input to shipbuilding. The Census allowed for such by recording figures for (bought in) material costs, which when deducted from gross gave 'net output' or value added. This comprised mainly labour and establishment charges (overheads). For the private yards, net output was valued at £18.534 million, which worked out at £98 per employee. Employment averaged over four dates in the year was 188,312, 9802 being salaried (5.2 per cent), 21,523 under 18 (11.4 per cent) and 1217 female (0.6 per cent).[52] The Census estimated the value of all types of ship, machinery and repairs at £40 million–£41 million, plus £5.8 million of Dockyard output.[53] The total for new 'war vessels' was £6.867 million of 100,300 tons, or about 15 per cent of the total. The Census also recorded output for other

warship related material from different industries. 18,000 tons of armour plate was manufactured worth £1.771 million, or £98.4 per ton, but only £70,000 was exported.[54] Steel plate ⅛in thick and over amounted to 1,227,000 tons worth £8.505 million averaging £6.95 per ton. Royal Ordnance Factory output was £3,359,810, with guns making up £433,113, mountings and carriages £452,703, torpedoes and mines £265,943, ammunition, shot, shell, propellant and explosives £1,469,891.[55] While no breakdown was given, the majority was for the Army rather than the Navy. Employees totalled 14,533. The Naval Ordnance Department was shown separately, the output of whose establishments was £83,074, mainly for repairs to guns and torpedoes and shell filling; employees 1118.

Under 'Engineering' private manufacture of ordnance was recorded as £2,763,000 (all in England), and ammunition and components £753,000.[56] Separately shown under 'Explosives, Ammunition and Fireworks' but excluding Government factories, was £2,175,000 for explosives and propellants, £1,435,000 for ammunition of all types including torpedoes, fuses and rockets. The latter figure excluded £962,000 for ammunition recorded elsewhere, resulting in a total of £2,397,000.[57] Exports of ammunition amounted to £898,000, or 37 per cent, while no less than 63 per cent of explosives and propellant was exported. Employment of 12,744 included 44 per cent females.

To put all these figures into context, the Census calculated the value of UK gross output at £1765 million and net output £712 million, with 7.087 million employees in the survey.[58] The shipbuilding and directly associated industries constituted about 3.0 per cent of the national total. Although 'war vessels' accounted for only 15 per cent of this latter, when armament and armour is added, that figure nearly doubles. By making some assumptions about the proportion of naval work in such as ammunition and ordnance manufacture, the authors estimate that the whole warship related business was worth about £13 million or around ¾ per cent of UK industrial output in 1907, a smaller figure than might have been expected given the industry's high profile.

12: MANPOWER

SHIPBUILDING AND ENGINEERING LABOUR AND WAGES

Shipbuilders and engineers divide their costs into three major categories: labour, materials and overheads, the latter covering 'establishment charges' not attributable to any particular contract, such as senior management, plant maintenance, utilities and rent. 'Materials' includes both semi-fabricated material such as steel plate and pipe and timber, to be worked into their final form, and equipment bought in for installation such as steering gear and pumps. 'Labour' includes direct costs, mainly wages of the men employed, usually paid weekly in cash in the dreadnought era. Holiday pay was usually paid only to foremen grades, while there were no deductions until later in the twentieth century for income tax or social security.

At that time, shipyards only recorded labour costs as money figures for each trade, without including the corresponding man-hours as they do today. Indeed when the squad system operated as in private shipyards, the shipyard would not know the detailed labour input for all their work. A group of men would offer to bend a number of frames for a lump sum, so the squad leader would decide how many men he needed and what to pay each. Hence when it came to estimating the labour cost for a new contract, all the shipbuilder had to go on was the wage total for previous ships for trades such as platers, shipwrights, painters etc. Thus few detailed figures for work content in the battleship era exist, but it is possible to make estimates based on average wage rates and hours, as below.

Past cost records are always important for estimating labour and material costs when tendering for new ships, often based on the nearest comparable previous ship. The Admiralty would invite tenders from selected shipbuilders, accompanied by Hull and Machinery Specifications, Contract Conditions and guidance plans. If the shipbuilder also had an engine works, such as John Brown or Cammell Laird, tenders would be submitted for hull and machinery. Yards without an engine works such as Armstrong Whitworth would usually tender for the hull to the Admiralty, but accompany that with tenders from suitable engine builders such as Wallsend Slipway. The latter companies also tendered separately for battleships built in the Royal Dockyards, which had no engine works. All the companies tendering would make their own estimate of labour and material costs, although the Admiralty would supply estimated weights of major items such as steel. They then added establishment charges, usually as a percentage of direct labour, typically 25–40 per cent for hulls, 40–55 per cent for machinery. Finally a profit margin would be added to give a tender price, the exact figure depending on the anticipated competition and state of the market, typically

Below: Workers stream out of the John Brown shipyard gate onto Glasgow Road with its tramlines and overhead wires. Clocking-on gates are to the right, then a row of shops, with tenements above (modest apartment blocks with rows of coal-fire chimneys), backing on to the high engine works shops, whose entrance was at the extreme right. The London & North Eastern Railway advertisement dates it to after 1923. (*Author's collection*)

around 5 to 10 per cent. But if the shipbuilder underestimated the costs, whether from not including everything required or from an unexpected rise in wages or material costs over the period of the contract, that profit could turn into a loss, as the contracts outside wartime were on a fixed price basis. Indeed when Laird Brothers found they were making a loss on *Exmouth* in 1902, they pleaded to the Admiralty for an increase in price. 'Owing to the wish of the Admiralty that orders then to be given out should be to some extent distributed over the various parts of the country, it has been decided to offer us the order for a battleship at the reduced price of £546,000. The cost of the machinery has made this contract particularly unfortunate and if the original price at which we tendered were allowed to us [£572,807], the difference would hardly recoup us for the loss thereon.' But the Admiralty were unsympathetic, in effect saying, you knew the lower price when you accepted the contract.[1]

For merchant ships, hull and machinery normally constituted the entire ship, but for battleships only about half of the final cost, as the expensive armour and armament had to be added. Manufacturers of the latter two would generally tender separately to the Admiralty, who would then direct the resulting order to the appropriate shipyard as Admiralty supply items. Depending on the power of the machinery, its cost made up about 30 per cent of the total price for higher powered ships. In the case of export contracts, the shipbuilder would tender for the entire ship (and the armament would usually include some ammunition) so providing more scope for a higher profit margin. There was less competition as few shipbuilders could supply the complete ship, while armour and heavy ordnance were not only high cost but also high profit items – see Chapters 8 and 9. 'Hull' consisted both of structure and of outfitting and equipment outside the machinery spaces. For a battleship, this made up only about a quarter of final cost.

DOCKYARD LABOUR AND COSTS

Few detailed figures have survived in private shipyard archives, but for Dockyard-built ships, the Dockyard provided the Admiralty with a breakdown of its estimated costs. A summarised example from *Temeraire*, signed off by the Admiral Superintendent and his senior officers

TEMERAIRE HULL COSTS

	Tons	Materials (£)	Wages (£)	Total (£)	Material (£/ton)	Wages (£/ton)
Forgings and castings	86	3600	727	4327	41.86	8.45
Structural iron and steel	6480	82,500	79,660	162,160	12.73	12.29
Armour, wood backing & installation	3590	4900	6738	11,638	1.36	1.88
Draughtsmen		100	8647	8747		
Galvanising		500		500		
Shipwrights, smiths & caulkers and timber	539	21,500	20,150	41,650	39.89	37.38
Joiners and furnishings	80	5000	6882	11,882	62.50	86.03
Painters	170	2900	7503	10,403	17.06	44.14
Launching and docking		3200	5255	8455		
General labour		1300	10,392	11,692		
Tools and consumable stores		3900	3897	7797		
Armament, fitting	120	17,300	21,785	39,085	144.17	181.54
Torpedo equipment	20	3300	3990	7290	165.00	199.50
Electric lighting	100	10,100	5422	15,522	101.00	54.22
Pumping, drainage, fresh & salt water systems	105	6100	8729	14,829	58.10	83.13
Ventilation	130	4200	9000	13,200	32.31	69.23
Watertight doors and hatches	90	4100	4660	8760	45.56	51.78
Steering gear	30	1700	2697	4397	56.67	89.90
Anchors & cables	90	1200	1285	2485	13.33	14.28
Masts, rigging & derricks	133	4800	3580	8380	36.09	26.92
Machinery & coaling fittings	60	4700	7396	12,096	78.33	123.27
First fitting stores	163	5200	635	5835	31.90	3.90
General shop expenditure		7900	5970	13,870		
Total	11,986	200,000	225,000	425,000	16.69	18.77
Includes						
Electric light engines		3500				
Capstan engine		4200				
Refrigerating installation		900				
Excludes						
Transferable 4in gun mountings (16)		12,586		12,586		
Boats		6460		6460		
Armour plate						
Total				444,046		

at Devonport on 28 September 1907 (after the ship had been launched), is shown above.[2]

No profit margin was included; any higher costs were simply charged to the Admiralty, via the Dockyard accounts. The last two columns have been added by the authors.

Such estimates could be compared with tenders from private shipyards. In practice, the two Dockyards with a dreadnought-size slipway (Portsmouth and Devonport) were allocated one battleship or battlecruiser a year up to 1914. As well as totals, the Dockyards had to break anticipated expenditure down by financial year, as the annual Navy Estimates allocated money on that basis. That system usually required orders to private shipyards to be placed later in the financial year to avoid bunching of expenditure, similarly armour orders were spread over the year. Each year, the Dockyard Expense Accounts compared esti-

mated with actual expenditure by ship, while the Appropriation Accounts explained significant differences. The accounts also recorded total expenditure in Dockyards, including the total of wages on new construction. Over the period 1905–06 to 1913–14, newbuilding labour at Portsmouth ranged from £196,747 to £364,366 a year, with Devonport £188,736 to £403,651. As a proportion of total Dockyard labour, that varied from 34 per cent to 47 per cent. Most of the rest was spent on ships under repair. Men could be taken off newbuilding work when urgent repairs were needed to maintain ships in commission. Labour costs as a proportion of total Dockyard costs including materials and establishment charges was around 40 per cent of the annual total for each of the two yards of around £1.5 million to £2.5 million – a higher proportion than a private shipyard.

DOCKYARD EMPLOYMENT 1905–14

| | Portsmouth | | | | Devonport | | | |
	Dockyard officers	Men	Wages (£)	Av £/man	Dockyard officers	Men	Wages (£)	Av £/man
1905–06	333	9000	632,091	70.23	296	7916	556,528	70.30
1906–07	327	8000	550,699	68.84	291	7000	481,306	68.76
1907–08	361	8000	583,158	72.89	320	7000	521,165	74.45
1908–09	360	9050	698,976	77.23	321	7790	595,956	76.50
1909–10	366	9510	735,884	77.38	316	8300	639,565	77.06
1910–11	365	10,450	831,796	79.60	318	9440	746,643	79.09
1911–12	389	10,900	853,477	78.30	344	9634	768,310	79.75
1912–13	400	11,000	865,343	78.67	356	9540	755,207	79.16
1913–14	414	11,750	1,003,049	85.37	375	11,450	971,020	84.81

For all the detail in the 160 pages of the annual Dockyard Expense Accounts, the number employed at each Dockyard during the financial year is not given. It is necessary to extract figures from the Navy Estimates for each year, where Vote 8 Section 1 gives the average number and total wages for the preceding year – see above.[3]

With those figures and the amounts spent on new construction wages from annual Dockyard Expense Accounts, and assuming wage rates were the same as the Dockyard average, it is possible to come up with some estimated production statistics for battleship building, since Portsmouth (unlike Devonport) was only building battleships over the period (part of *Britannia* to *Dreadnought* to part of *Queen Elizabeth*) – see table below.

This suggests that productivity (e.g. tons per man-year) improved by over 10 per cent over the period, although much of the 'tons' was bought in complete, e.g. armour, rather than

PORTSMOUTH DOCKYARD NEW CONSTRUCTION STATISTICS

	1905–06 to 1909–10	1910–11 to 1913–14
Number of years	5	4
Equivalent number of battleships built	4	4
Displacement tons built, Navy List	74,000	95,000
Average tons per year	14,800	23,750
Average tons per ship	18,500	23,750
Total new construction wages (£k)	1030	1270
Average wage cost per ton (£)	13.92	13.37
Average wages per battleship (£)	257,500	317,500
Average annual total wages (£k)	206	317.5
Average annual wages £/man	73.3	80.5
Average number on new construction	2810	3944
Average tons per man per year	5.27	6.02
Average man-years per battleship	3513	3944
Av man-hours if 50 weeks/yr and 48h/wk	8,431,105	9,465,839
Average man-hours per ton	456	399
Average years keel lay to completion	2.1	2.1
Average men per ship over build period	1673	1878

produced in the Dockyard. With wages rising though, wage cost per ton was little reduced. The 9 million man-hours per ship about 1910 can be compared with the 1982 aircraft carrier *Illustrious* with a similar displacement of about 17,000 tons (Navy List) requiring about 22 million man-hours – but for a vessel with much lighter structure and no armour and much more outfitting, taking six years to build, i.e. about 2000 men on average, about the same as a dreadnought.

Brassey reported a figure of 5.49 million man-hours for an early dreadnought, for 'ship' only (presumably hull, excluding machinery), and an estimated 7.2 million for an *Iron Duke* class, the latter equating to about 2800 men for two years.[4] However, the latter ships actually averaged 28 months keel to delivery, which would represent about 2400 men. This was for a private yard, probably Vickers. Johnston shows a graph of number of men working on *Repulse*'s hull in 1915–16, averaging about 1050 steelworkers over 18 months (peak about 1800), an average of 900 fitting out trades (peak about 1500), a total on average of about 1950 (peak 2700) which probably equates to about 8.5 million man-hours.[5] If the Dockyard estimate of 9 million man-hours is correct, this suggests that they were less productive than private yards.

EARNINGS AND HOURS IN 1906

A very detailed study by the Board of Trade was published in 1911 of earnings and hours in 1906. Section VI covered the Metal, Engineering and Shipbuilding Trades.[6] The survey covered 109,285 workers in shipbuilding and shiprepairing, estimated at 78 per cent of the total. Marine engineering was included under Engineering, but only formed a small proportion of that 368,552 total. Average weekly earnings for adult men working full time in the last week of September 1906 were

35s 11d (£1.79) in shipbuilding. Lads and apprentices averaged 11s 10d, while the few women averaged 14s 8d. The overall average, including those working other than full time was 30s 7d. But there was a wide range for the men: 5.1 per cent earned under 20s (£1), while 5.5 per cent earned over 80s (£4). For engineering and boilermaking, the average for men full time was 32s 5d. Annual earnings were estimated at £70.5 in shipbuilding and £69 in engineering. While the survey did not cover the Royal Dockyards, their annual earnings were very similar in 1906, as the table opposite shows.

The survey also recorded average hours per week at 52.9 for shipbuilding and 53.1 for engineering, i.e. a six-day week. There was a slight difference between the two main battleship building regions, Tyne, Wear and Tees at 53.4 and Clyde at 54.0. The vast majority worked between 48 and 56 hours. Annual holidays were also recorded at 13.8 days in shipbuilding and 13.7 in engineering – but usually without pay. A further breakdown for shipbuilding noted that only 48.3 per cent worked the full week, the rest working either more (overtime) or less, as casual employment and absenteeism was common in the less skilled trades. The best paid were the platers (who prepared and shaped the plates and stiffeners) at 71s 3d, riveters (who joined the plates and stiffeners) at 55s 7d and caulkers (who made seams watertight and cut holes) at 51s 8d. All these were when paid on piecework, time rates being very much less at 42s 5d, 34s 9d and 32s 11d respectively. Piecework was paid where it was relatively easy to measure a worker's output, e.g. Tyne & Wear riveters were paid 12s 6d for 100 1in rivets on the bottom shell in 1915.[7] Time workers who made up 66 per cent of the workforce were generally paid less than pieceworkers, shipwrights (who prepared the building berths and helped erect the hull and worked the heavier timber) at 36s 4d and ship joiners (who made the interior wooden fittings) at 37s 0d. Foremen's average wages at 49s 11d were less than many of the pieceworkers. Among the lowest paid were rivet heaters at 23s 1d and general labourers at 21s 1d. Platers were the best paid, 18 per cent of those working a full week earning over 100s (£5), three times the typical wage. No wonder the boilermakers trade union to whom skilled steelworkers belonged tried to restrict membership to limit supply and force up wages.

The survey also reported figures for the main shipbuilding regions, showing averages for full time men for the two main battleship building areas of:

Trade	Tyne, Wear & Tees	Clyde
Foremen	54s 0d	50s 5d
Platers (piecework)	82s 0d	63s 1d
Riveters (piecework)	58s 1d	54s 4d
Caulkers (piecework)	61s 4d	49s 10d
Fitters (time)	36s 11d	36s 6d
Shipwrights (time)	39s 11d	37s 3d
Ship joiners (time)	38s 4d	37s 5d
Plumbers (time)	38s 0d	40s 9d
Painters (time)	33s 11d	40s 6d
Labourers (time)	22s 5d	20s 0d
Apprentices (time)	8s 11d	10s 7d
Rivet boys (time)	7s 2d	9s 0d

The north-east was generally higher than the Clyde. While the survey does not distinguish between those working on warship building from those on merchant ships, it is likely that the former normally received slightly higher wages owing to the higher skills demanded – except when a prestigious passenger liner was being built – in 1906 Cunard's *Mauretania* was being built on the Tyne and *Lusitania* on the Clyde.

The Dockyards had a shorter working week. The 1907-08 Navy Estimates reported that whereas 50 hours had normally been worked in summer and 41.25 in winter, that had been standardised at 48 now that electric lighting was widespread. The hours on Monday to Thursday were 8½, Friday 9 and Saturday 5 – the latter enabling the men to attend football matches in the afternoon.

EMPLOYMENT AT BATTLESHIP BUILDERS

The armament companies and shipbuilders were among Britain's largest employers in 1907. Excluding the railway companies, the Royal Dockyards were third with 25,580 after the General Post Office and Fine Cotton Spinners & Doublers, Armstrong Whitworth fourth with 25,000, Vickers fifth with 22,500, John Brown eleventh with 20,000, and Royal Ordnance Factories sixteenth with 15,651.[8] They were often the largest employers in their district, e.g. Barrow. Armstrong's Elswick works excluding the shipyard was recorded as employing an average of 12,066 in 1909, with a wage bill of £848,565, i.e. ordnance, steel and

ARMSTRONG WHITWORTH EMPLOYMENT 1902–15

January	Ordnance	Elswick Shipyard	Low Walker Shipyard	Openshaw	Steel Works	Engine Works	Naval Yard	UK total
1902	10,935	2219	1876	3261	1246	1381		20,918
1903	9213	2506	1111	3321	1080	1369		18,600
1904	9573	3230	1577	3388	1115	1560		20,443
1905	12,568	3326	1097	3966	1200	1874		24,031
1906	11,884	2428	1888	4156	1188	1919		23,463
1907	11,183	3343	1746	4757	1104	1596		23,729
1908	8720	4998	2455	3991	1109	1217		22,490
1909	8873	5182	828	3707	913	1231		20,734
1910	9113	2565	1065	3959	1023	1368		19,093
1911	8768	3112	1420	4137	1174	1325		19,936
1912	9272	2654	1791	4432	1218	1454		20,821
1913	10,253	2896	1976	5139	1260	1913		23,437
1914	10,386	5330	1876	5940	1066	1992	600	27,190
1915	19,128	4705	1587	6497	1237	1905	2648	37,707

Opposite: Although not on a battleship, this photograph taken in 1918 in Harland & Wolff's Govan shipyard, is a typical scene depicting various skilled and non-skilled persons on the deck of a ship. Women workers were recruited into the shipyards and factories under the dilution scheme, part of the Munitions of War Act of 1915. This allowed women to undertake certain tasks, usually semi-skilled or non-skilled as in this photograph, thereby replacing men who had joined the forces. In the foreground two rivet fires are being maintained by 'rivet boys', members of a riveting squad. When heated to the correct temperature as determined by eye, rivets will be passed to the nearby riveters. *(IWM)*

engine works.[9] At an average wage of £70.3 per year, this was similar to the shipbuilding and engineering wages shown above for 1906, but slightly under the Dockyard figures for 1909. Employment figures for Armstrong's various divisions were regularly reported to the Board from 1902 as shown in the table, but data for other companies is fragmented. Elswick shipyard employed 3100 in September 1897 but Openshaw only 1831 in 1894 in Whitworth days.[10] Warren gives 26,651 in November 1913 (20,669 on the Tyne) which had increased to 47,583 (40,835 Tyne) by July 1915 and about 78,000 (21,000 female) by November 1918, the great bulk probably on ordnance related work.[11] The labour force at Elswick warship building yard fluctuated appreciably with the workload, but averaged about 3500 between 1897 and 1913, see above.[12] Just getting into its stride, the new High Walker (Naval Yard) employed 3437 in May 1915, with its first ship *Malaya* just launched.

Only isolated labour figures for Vickers have been found. With the company investing heavily in its new acquisition from 1899 onwards, it was reported as employing 10,300 in total at Barrow in 1901 with a weekly wage bill of £10,500 (average £1.02 a week).[13] Sheffield employed about 5000 in 1905, Erith about 4000 in 1902. The Barrow shipyard itself expanded from 2723 in March 1906 to 4590 in May 1912, excluding apprentices – an unhelpful omission since apprentices formed a significant proportion of every shipbuilder's labour force.[14] From about 15,500 in mid-1913, Barrow more than doubled to 35,000 by mid-1917, which included all the works there, including airship construction. The Vickers

company peak during the First World War was reported as 107,000 (37,500 female)[15] with total wartime wages of £46.23 million, many at Sheffield.[16]

Shipbuilding labour statistics were patchy for many years. Surveys did not include all firms, e.g. Harland & Wolff was not a member of the Shipbuilding Employers Federation (SEF), while companies such as Cammell Laird carried out newbuilding, ship repair and engine building on the same site, making it difficult to obtain consistent figures for those activities which were often lumped together, and employment in the Royal Dockyards was usually not included. A SEF survey for March 1906 gave a total of 72,358 (possibly for shipbuilding and repair) while one for March 1914 gave 171,748 including engine works.[17] Peebles gives some figures for Clyde shipyards and engine works when all had at least one battleship/cruiser under construction: Scotts 5657 (2000 in engine works) in 1913, Beardmore 5854 in 1914, John Brown 9715 in January 1913.[18] Fairfield employed 5866 staff in the shipyard and 2566 in the engine works in 1913. Parsons employed about 1200 in 1914. Clarke shows a graph of employees at Hawthorn Leslie's St Peters engine works averaging about 2100 during the First World War.[19]

A paper on 'Shipbuilding in the War' gave the following table for shipyards and engine works in September 1918:[20]

New naval work	146,000
Naval repair	53,000
New merchant work	116,000
Merchant repair	66,000
Total	381,000

This total was compared with 250,000 at the outbreak of war. However, by 1918 battleship building was down to a single ship, *Hood*, her sister-ships being suspended. Some other Admiralty statistics suggest that the hull/machinery split was about 60/40.

EMPLOYMENT AND EARNINGS TO THE SECOND WORLD WAR

A variety of sources emanating mainly from Tyne shipbuilders shows how wage rates agreed with the trade unions rose in shipbuilding after about 1910, having remained little changed for some thirty years.[21] Standard weekly hours dropped from 54 in 1893 (the nine-hour day) to 47 in 1919 to 44 in 1947 – a five-day week. Some time rates in shillings and pence per hour for years representative of when battleships were being built are shown overleaf.

With wages and steel prices doubling between the start of the First and the Second World Wars, it is not surprising that battleship cost per ton also doubled – see table on p.239.

Re-armament and the Second World War saw a large rise in employment in the armaments industries. Harland & Wolff at Scotstoun making mainly naval gun mountings went from

VOLUME VI, 1924

Left: The armaments companies that had expanded before and during the First World War were organisations with very large workforces and multiple sites. One way of keeping employees informed about company activities was through a works journal. Beardmore began producing them during the war and all featured cover art illustrating products or in this instance the suggestion of man's heroic mastery over material. *(Author's collection)*

eleven staff and eighty-five workmen in 1936 to 187 and 1593 in 1942.[22] Cammell Laird employed an average of 10,438 in 1938 in the shipyard, engine works and repair department,

SHIPYARD TIME WEEKLY WAGE RATES

Year	Platers	Riveters	Shipwrights	Joiners	Painters
1893	34/-	31/-	36/-	35/-	31/-
1906	36/6	34/-	39/-	38/-	34/-
1910	35/-	33/-	37/6	37/-	33/-
1913	39/-	37/-	41/6	41/-	38/-
1916	46/-	44/-	48/6	48/-	45/-
1924	53/-	51/-	55/6	58/-	52/-
1939	70/-	70/-	70/-	70/-	70/-
1944	93/6	93/6	93/6	93/6	93/6

when *Prince of Wales*, cruiser *Dido* and three submarines were under construction, which was over three times higher than in the depression in 1932–3. Wages in 1938 totalled £1,788,872, or an average of £171 a year, split about 52 per cent, 28 per cent and 20 per cent between the three departments.

Good employment figures exist for Vickers-Armstrongs companies from the date of the merger in 1928, reported by each general manager in his quarterly reports to the Board.[23] From 1936 battleship armament was a key activity, while the group built one of the five *King George V*s. The table shows how employment and wages steadily increased from the depth of the depression (when Naval Yard was on care and maintenance) until the end of the group's main involvement in battleship construction in 1942. While *Vanguard* was still under construction after 1942, V-A involvement was mainly her secondary armament, directors etc. Barrow average wage rates were generally a few per cent higher than the Tyne. The level of white collar (staff) average wage above blue collar (workmen) declined from around 50 per cent to 13 per cent, although much of this may have been due to greater overtime earnings in the Second World War (which staff did not receive) – the average

weekly hours worked at Barrow were 59 in 1941.[24]

Better shipbuilding employment statistics were gathered by the Second World War. The SEF did regular surveys, while a new Central Statistical Office was set up nationally, which helped allocate labour resources more effectively during the war. The first period reported in the Statistical Digest of the War was June 1940, when five battleships were under construction. [25] After June 1942, only *Vanguard* remained.

	June 1940	June 1942
New naval shipbuilding	62,400	75,900
Naval repairs and conversions	41,500	38,400
H M Dockyards	26,400	34,900
New merchant shipbuilding	28,800	37,200
Merchant ship repair	44,000	58,500
Total	203,100	244,300

These figures exclude marine main and auxiliary machinery building which employed 85,000 in March 1942 (82 per cent on Admiralty work).[26] This suggests a total industry employment a little less than the 1918 peak. Sir Amos Ayre claimed that merchant ship productivity had increased by 50 to 75 per cent between 1917–18 and 1941–3, owing to simplification of design, technical progress including welding and better plant.[27] By 1943, women made up about 3 per cent of the labour force, with apprentices about 10 per cent. In September 1943, employment at John Brown was reported as 6101, Swan Hunter & Wigham Richardson 5201[28] and Cammell Laird 8527, although by then both the latter had completed their battleships.[29] These figures probably include repair but not engine building. The average number of workers in 1943 of the

VICKERS-ARMSTRONGS WAGES 4TH QUARTER AVERAGE

	1934		1935		1936		1937	
	Staff	Workmen	Staff	Workmen	Staff	Workmen	Staff	Workmen
Elswick engineering	1147	3535	1288	5315	1555	7711	1857	9678
Total wages for quarter £	59,145	124,296	60,730	185,158	86,664	309,620	100,820	393,025
Average annual wage £	206.26	140.65	188.60	139.35	222.93	160.61	217.17	162.44
Naval Yard	76	139	155	1194	243	2079	276	1989
Total wages £	3420	4012	7380	35,330	12,304	72,688	12,973	70,187
Average annual wage £	180.00	115.45	190.45	118.36	202.53	139.85	188.01	141.15
Barrow shipyard & engineering	2063	8567	2101	8400	2437	11,980	2645	14,118
Total wages £	109,497	307,672	105,140	312,443	140,353	473,427	167,718	623,867
Average annual wage £	212.31	143.65	200.17	148.78	230.37	158.07	219.82	164.13
Total workforce 3 works	3286	12,241	3544	14,909	4235	21,770	4778	25,785
Av wage 3 works staff £	199.52		193.08		218.61		208.33	
Av wage 3 works workmen £		133.25		135.50		152.85		155.91

battleship engine builders was: Vickers-Armstrongs Barrow 5092, Cammell Laird 3848, John Brown 3507, Wallsend Slipway 2710, Fairfield 2029.[30]

Other statistics confirm that battleship building became relatively less important as the war progressed, with more emphasis going into building escorts, and later aircraft carriers and landing vessels, dropping from around 12 per cent of naval construction to less than 4 per cent when only *Vanguard* remained.[31] While these figures also include labour on the two monitors built in the Second World War (*Roberts* and *Abercrombie*) each only took about 20 per cent of the hull and machinery resource for a battleship. However, the graph on p.262 excludes manpower on building tank landing craft at structural engineering firms, over 20,000 from 1943.

Trade Unions and Skills

One of the strengths of the British battleship building industry was its highly skilled labour force. The steel-working trades had evolved out of steam engine and boiler making in the early nineteenth century, when iron was the dominant material. The craftsmen learned their skills through serving an apprenticeship rather than formal training schemes, such experience resulting in them becoming time-served 'journeymen' by their early 20s. In top class companies such as Armstrongs and railway companies, a small number of 'premium apprentices' were taken on, the premium of several hundred pounds paid for by their parents upon entry, but they did get a more structured training scheme spread across a variety of departments and better conditions. Some rose to the highest position, for example Tennyson d'Eyncourt became Director of Naval Construction in

1912, and later a director of Armstrongs. Famously Charles Parsons was also an Elswick premium apprentice. Such was the attraction of these positions that the Armstrong Whitworth Board resolved in 1903 that directors and senior managers could enter only one son free of premium.

In the main shipbuilding districts, there were many potential employers, not just a single shipyard, so if work ran down at one yard, there were often jobs at other nearby works, so evening out fluctuations. A 'hire and fire' attitude developed which worked both for the employer who could match his labour force to the current workload, and the employee who could readily move to where wages were higher or conditions better, although the unskilled had to take what they could get.

The Dockyards had a somewhat different system. The more experienced craftsmen could become 'established' so were retained even when the workload reduced and could expect a modest pension. The other 'hired' hands had the benefit of a slightly higher wage (shipwrights 35s 6d per week in 1906 compared with 34s for established men) but less security of employment.[32] But the Treasury was concerned about the additional 'through life' costs and limited the number of established men to 6500 before the First World War.

Trade unions evolved to mitigate the worst effects of such systems, at least for the skilled men. The origins of the United Society of Boilermakers and Iron & Steel Shipbuilders went back to 1834. With their Associated Shipwrights Society, the shipwrights jealously guarded work opportunities by insisting that only they carried out certain tasks, with exclusive rights to certain tools or processes. Unions generally tried to negotiate wages and working

| 1938 | | 1939 | | 1940 | | 1941 | | 1942 | |
Staff	Workmen	Staff	Workmen	Staff	Workmen	Staff	Workmen	Staff	Workmen
1972	9641	2186	10,131	2475	12,151	2881	13,349	3295	14,865
105,609	418,288	125,317	471,099	173,441	721,830	220,277	824,544	261,534	1,029,925
214.22	173.55	229.31	186.00	280.31	237.62	305.83	247.07	317.49	277.14
287	2610	366	3795	438	5078	474	4721	409	5467
13,913	9,374	17,829	173,335	28,445	280,725	28,230	246,315	28,001	327,990
193.91	147.70	194.85	182.70	259.77	221.13	238.23	208.70	273.85	239.98
2769	12666	2981	14228	3209	15,960	3313	16,524	3703	16,487
169,140	588,295	181,883	723,383	233,024	956,540	260,646	1,110,101	294,865	1,192,866
226.88	161.02	244.06	203.37	290.46	239.73	314.69	268.72	318.51	289.41
5028	24,917	5533	28,154	6122	33,189	6668	34,594	7407	36,819
211.67		222.74		276.85		286.25		303.29	
	160.75		190.69		232.83		241.50		268.84

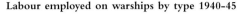

Labour employed on warships by type 1940-45

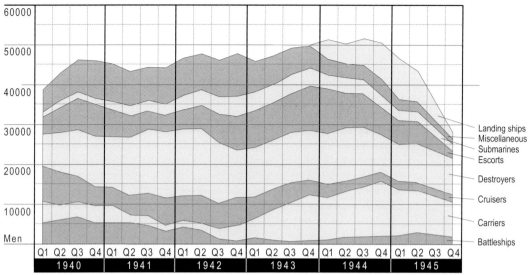

hours on a district basis, although both were subject to national trends in the industries served. Thus in times of slump, wages could fall, influenced by supply and demand. The boilermakers had a broader range of industries they could work in, as well as a wider range of shipbuilding trades – platers, angle-smiths, riveters, drillers, caulkers, and later, welders and burners – so tended to be the dominant group of shipyard employees.[33] Membership numbers reflected the fortunes of those industries: 52,000 at the beginning of 1907, of whom 5800 were unemployed.[34]

But in the Dockyards, it was the shipwrights who worked the steel. When Chatham Dockyard was allocated the first order for an iron warship – *Achilles* ordered in 1861 – boilermakers were recruited from Thames private yards to bring in the necessary skills. But when they went on strike, the Admiralty retrained the shipwrights previously used to build wooden hulls for iron shipbuilding, with the help of a few strike-breakers.[35] From then on, the shipwrights worked steel, unlike private shipyards where they remained working in wood – setting up building blocks, marking off, launching ships and laying wood decks. They could however also work in repair yards or on board ships at sea, but were forever fighting encroachment from boilermakers on hull work and joiners working on internal woodwork. There were thus many demarcation disputes, often resulting in strikes, some of which could be settled by arbitration by some acknowledged shipbuilding expert. For example, shipwrights might be allocated the work of marking off and

making templates for some part of the hull, but the boilermakers would undertake the actual fastening by rivets or bolts. It was not until 1963 (over forty years after it was first proposed) that the two unions plus the blacksmiths united to form the Amalgamated Society of Boilermakers, Shipwrights, Blacksmiths and Structural Workers with the prospect of reducing such disputes.

The shipwrights (sometimes called carpenters in Scotland) had long been fragmented geographically, sometimes starting as 'friendly' societies to provide benefits against sickness, death or unemployment. Many of these came together in 1882 to form the Associated Shipwrights Society based in Newcastle. The Society also sought to regulate the intake of apprentices, to maintain a higher proportion of men on a journeyman's wage. Some employers regarded apprentices as cheap labour, sometimes employing more of them than time-served men. In 1893 the society now with some 13,000 members negotiated an agreement of a maximum of two apprentices to seven journeymen, a period of indenture of five years (preferably with one firm) entry ages typically from 16 to 19, and a scale of wages starting at 6s per week in the first year to 12s in the fifth.

The unions also campaigned for a shorter working week, after the success of the strike of 1871 bringing in the nine-hour day (54-hour week). The Dockyards introduced a 48-hour week in 1894, a quarter century before most of private industry.[36] But even though the weekly wage rate was somewhat lower, the hourly rate for shipwrights there was not much less than a private yard. The shipwrights had always fought for time-based wages, arguing that not only was much of their work difficult to measure for piecework, but the pressure could lead to shoddy workmanship. The boilermakers however often preferred piecework, especially where it was easy to measure output in terms of number of frames worked or rivets driven, while workmanship quality could be checked. As a result boilermakers on piecework could earn 60 per cent more than those on time rates.

In many other trades, members in ship-building tended to be a minority – joiners, plumbers, painters, blacksmiths, electricians, pattern-makers or fitters and turners, the latter two likely to be members of the Amalgamated Society of Engineers. Hence employment terms tended to be settled by other industries. But all benefitted from the battleship building boom that started around 1910. Wages increased significantly, partly because of high demand, partly pressure of rising domestic prices, and partly because of legal immunities won by trade unions increasing their bargaining strength. When negotiations failed, the strike weapon was frequently used, although employers could retaliate with the lockout,

closing the whole shipyard, in the hope that the other workers would put pressure on the strikers to settle. Other benefits obtained were a move in 1906 to paying wages weekly rather than fortnightly, which reduced the pressure on workers to seek credit from shops or pawnbrokers as money ran out. Holidays with pay were introduced much later in 1938, from which date shipwrights' standard wage rose steadily throughout the war period from 68s in 1938 to 98s in 1945 – such increases have continued to this day.[37]

With each trade jealously guarding its territory to preserve work for its own skilled members, this had the adverse effect of discouraging the employers from the introduction of new labour saving building techniques or equipment – and the associated higher capital costs. By contrast, Continental or American shipyards, which came later to the business with a less experienced labour force with often only a single shipyard in a district, were more willing to invest in new methods. So the skilled labour in British shipbuilding was sometimes a blessing and sometimes a curse, especially when overseas competition intensified in the merchant shipbuilding market after the First World War.

13: CONCLUSIONS

THE ROYAL NAVY BUILT MORE battleships than any other navy. Indeed Britain had not only the world's largest navy but also the largest shipbuilding industry for most of the battleship era. The Admiralty and the supporting industries produced a wealth of new designs and features before the First World War, which larger navies sought to emulate and smaller navies sought to purchase. *Dreadnought* with her all big gun armament was truly revolutionary, both strategically and tactically with her uniform main armament and powerful new steam turbine machinery.

In the period from 1860 to the 1960s and beyond, the battleship, the Royal Navy and the shipbuilding industry shared a similar destiny rising to prominence before respectively facing extinction, rapid depletion in numbers and all but statistical irrelevance. To this should be added Britain's rise and decline as a power of the first rank.

Prior to 1860, the Admiralty relied almost exclusively for its warships on the Royal Dockyards which were well equipped to build in timber and had the necessary capacity to meet demand for hulls. The introduction of steam as a motive power and iron as a construction material from the 1830s began a process of change which saw the rise of a technological approach to the design and construction of ships. This formed the basis for a vibrant private shipbuilding industry to take hold in Britain, based initially on orders for merchant vessels.

The shipbuilding industry became engaged with naval work because it was more technically advanced than the Royal Dockyards, driven by the competing demands of shipowners who required increased cargo and passenger space and faster but more economical passages. The Admiralty's increasing reliance on private yards was evident from 1860 onwards but took a greater hold after the 1889 Naval Defence Act which saw a large increase in warship numbers, especially battleships. The additional shipbuilding capacity required was met largely by the private yards and not by the Royal Dockyards. With the prospect of profitable and prestigious Government work, private industry did not take much encouragement and large sums were invested in new plant and facilities, not simply to build the hulls but to arm and armour them, where Government owned capacity was very limited. This was a risky path however and even the shipyards that became heavily involved in building warships continued to construct merchant vessels. The notorious swings in demand that affected merchant shipbuilding were to some extent offset by warship orders. This can be gauged from the switch from the Dockyards providing the majority of the Navy's warships to the private yards. The Dockyards newbuilding share of £7.639 million out of £13.628 million (56 per cent) in 1893–5 was reduced to £13.321 million out of £42.214 million (31.5 per cent) in 1911–13. However, the abrupt decline in naval work after the First World War, combined with the start of a global recession, paralysed swathes of British industry and forced a significant contraction in shipbuilding capacity, while sections of the armaments industry also collapsed.

Nevertheless, the battleship building industry was high profile, engendering a national pride before the First World War. Books with titles like *The Boys Book of Warships* (J R Howden, 1911) encouraged youngsters to enter a thriving and glamorous industry. Premiums could be charged for apprenticeships at the most prestigious firms. Companies such as Armstrong or Vickers claimed to be able to build and arm four or five dreadnoughts a year. The warship builders and associated armaments producers employed about 100,000 people before the First World War, becoming dominant employers on Clydeside, Tyneside, Barrow and Sheffield.

Writers have often underestimated the importance of the contribution of warship building to the British shipbuilding industry, the world's largest for the best part of a century. Statistics of warship production were often patchy and measured in displacement tons, a measure of weight, while merchant ships were measured in gross registered tons, a measure of volume. Such numbers cannot meaningfully be added together, but writers who have done so have underestimated the warship proportion of output. But it is possible to apply correction factors based on average cost per 'ton' to convert displacement to gross tonnage in terms of value, at the same time allowing for the much greater complexity of warships compared with an equivalent size of merchant ship. The authors estimate that a factor of about 4 applies to warships in the early twentieth century. That is, that 1 ton displacement is approximately

equivalent to 4 gross tons in work content. Analysis from the British Shipbuilding Database for 1900–14 shows 9569 merchant ships over 100 tons completed of 21.9 million gross tons plus 646 warships of 2.35 million displacement tons, i.e. 9.4 million equivalent gross tons. Hence warships made up about 30 per cent of total output (9.4/31.3), a more realistic measure of their national importance than is normally accorded.

The placing of Government work with privately-managed companies raised some objections on moral grounds that shareholder interest came before national interest, a cry that resonated throughout the battleship era and beyond. While there is some truth in this, as evidenced by the fixing of excessive armour prices, it was overwhelmingly the case that private industry more often operated to public advantage than against. Competition between shipbuilders kept the cost of hulls and machinery down and in some cases hulls were built at break-even cost or at a loss.

Below: July 1946 and the last of a long line of British battleships and battlecruisers runs trials in the Firth of Clyde. During her trials on the measured mile off Arran, *Vanguard*'s fastest run was 31.57 knots with 136,000 shp on a displacement of 45,720 tons. With a deep displacement of 51,070 tons she made 30.379 knots developing 132,950 shp, all well in excess of her designed power. She was the first and last British battleship to make 30 knots. Pounding from the sea has taken a toll of her paintwork forward. *(Upper Clyde Shipbuilders)*

It has been claimed that battleship building was very profitable. While broadly true for export battleships, where one company supplied the entire vessel, it was an over-simplification for battleships for the Royal Navy. As the detailed chapters show, separate contracts were placed for hulls, machinery, armament and armour. Those figures show that making armour was hugely profitable (five companies in a cartel), making gun mountings was also very profitable (two, later three, companies) building machinery moderately profitable (about a dozen companies) but building hulls barely profitable on average, with a competitive market of a dozen shipyards including the Royal Dockyards. Those companies that could supply most of those components were indeed able to make healthy profits before and during the First World War.

The British battleship building industry entered the First World War in good shape, both financially and in terms of its facilities. It and the associated armaments manufacturers were able to meet most of the demands of the Admiralty in the early years, including completing *Renown* and *Repulse* in record time. Supplying the Army, however, whose demands for artillery and ammunition massively increased, required the creation of a whole new munitions manufacturing industry. As the war progressed, labour shortages limited capital ship construction as resources had to be diverted to building merchant ships and smaller naval vessels in the face of losses to U-boats. Although investment in new shipbuilding facilities had been modest, the whole armaments industry faced an uncertain future from 1919 onwards.

The shipping slumps of the 1920s and 1930s and the scarcity of warship orders from 1920–35 put Britain's military industrial potential under real threat. The most immediate outcome was the loss of employment for many thousands of highly skilled personnel. Armstrong and Beardmore collapsed. In the case of the former most of its businesses were taken over by Vickers in 1927. The survival of the resulting Vickers-Armstrongs company with its essential defence manufacturing capability and sounder finances made possible Britain's re-armament in the late 1930s. With an enlightened management, supported by a trickle of British and overseas armament orders in the early 1930s, it maintained a core of skilled manpower across its various factories. Its gun, gun mounting, fire control systems (all now including anti-aircraft), torpedo, armour and aircraft design and manufacturing capacity plus its warship building yards only just enabled Britain to withstand the German onslaught from 1939–41.

Of the battleships themselves, the Admiralty did not fully give up on design work until after 1945 when it was finally recognised that the era of the big-gun battleship was over.[1] While the industry had struggled to build six out of ten projected battleships between 1936 and 1946, fourteen fleet carriers and twenty-five light fleet carriers were projected of which seven and twenty respectively were completed by 1946 and two further fleet carriers, *Eagle* and *Ark Royal*, in the early 1950s, although these required little of the critical gun mounting and armour manufacturing capacity. In these numbers it is clear that of the shipbuilding capacity available to the Admiralty after 1939, a greater portion was correctly allocated to newer types including aircraft carriers and anti-submarine escorts, rather than to the battleship.

As it was, *Vanguard* was the last of the line. But what a line it had been. In the dreadnought era, fifty-four battleships and battlecruisers had been laid down in British yards for the Royal Navy alone up until 1920 of which fifty-one were completed. In the last phase of construction, from 1921 onwards, a further sixteen were contracted for of which eight were completed.[2] If battleships for foreign governments are added from 1906 onwards, the total built by the British naval construction industry is sixty-nine. This prodigious output is matched by an overall direct cost to the Exchequer of an estimated £175 million, with battleships and battlecruisers making up over half of the new construction budget pre First World War.

For the tens of thousands who lived beside and worked in the shipyards and factories that bore household names and whose very existence gave a sense of national security, the unthinkable happened as they too have gone the way of the battleship. The decline of British political influence after 1945 coupled to the winding up of Empire resulted in a steadily decreasing role for the Royal Navy which shrank accordingly. From the early 1960s onwards, the shipbuilding industry that might otherwise have been expected to concentrate on merchant work was subject to severe overseas competition and one by one the shipyards disappeared until today only a tiny fraction remains, with those building warships almost exclusively.

Appendix 1:

Tenders 1905 to 1945, John Brown & Co Ltd[1]

THESE NOTES ARE BASED ON TENDER BOOKS kept by John Brown & Co Ltd, eight volumes of which were consulted covering from 1905 to 1946. Each book contains approximately 250 separate tenders for vessels of all kinds. 'Tender book' is something of a misnomer as only basic ship details and financial details were recorded.

For the most part these books are hand-written and inconsistent in their presentation of data with only the last few in the series having typed details. What follows therefore is abstracted from information concerning capital ships only, often ranging from scant details in some cases to very full in others. Only a small proportion of these tenders were converted into contracts.

Most of the shipbuilding firms discussed in this book would have tendered for these contracts and to that extent this listing could equally apply to them. From 1905 onwards John Brown was part of the Coventry Syndicate which included Cammell Laird and Fairfield and information would have been shared with these firms. In a few instances there was collusion between the Coventry firms and the Armstrong and Vickers firms.

After the start of both world wars, the Admiralty no longer invited tenders from shipbuilders and instead placed orders directly with them based on the availability of a suitable berth, workload, labour and other operational factors. War built capital ships are therefore missing although John Brown was required to submit prices to the Admiralty some time after work on the ship had begun.

The Royal Dockyards did not participate in tendering and neither did they construct ships for foreign governments. As the Dockyards did not possess the means to construct main propelling machinery, the machinery for Dockyard-built ships was contracted by the Admiralty to one of the private firms as was armament and armour.

In the context of what follows, 'hull' usually means all of the structure of a ship, main hull and superstructure and outfit, while machinery is usually a reference to the main propelling machinery or engines with boilers quoted separately. Two significant elements, armament and armour were not generally included in the tender as they were contracted for separately by the Admiralty. However, in quoting for foreign battleships, all elements of the ship including armament and armour usually formed part of the tender.

The process of tendering was to ensure that all appropriate contractors were able to compete and for the Admiralty to identify the lowest price in the knowledge that each shipbuilder estimated to identical specifications. The winning tenderer would then have further discussions with the Admiralty on specifications which inevitably changed in detail over the construction period, resulting in a final price that would be different, usually more, than the original tender.

In reaching a tender price, the shipbuilder had a number of financial variables at his disposal which could be applied in addition to material costs and wages, either to make the tender very competitive where there was a high priority to win the contract or less competitive where the order book was full. The first of these variables was 'charges'. This was a means of ensuring that overheads were recovered and were often applied as a percentage of labour costs (wages). The other was 'profit' which was generally applied as a percentage to the estimated total cost to give the price. In the lists that follow, profits of between 2 per cent to 10 per cent were generally applied – some were quoted at a loss. Where a shipbuilder was desperate to win work, profits and charges would be reduced and in the worst case eliminated. Such practice was referred to as 'buying' the contract, i.e. submitting a price less than estimated cost, resulting in a loss, as in the case of *Rodney* and *Nelson*. Invariably, the actual price finally paid for a ship on completion changed; firstly because the Admiralty would negotiate with the winning shipbuilder on various refinements to the design before construction and secondly, to the numerous on-going changes made during construction.

The date of the tender submission is given first followed by the customer – usually the Admiralty. Clarifying comments added by the authors are in square brackets at the end of each entry.

12 October 1905
Admiralty
An armoured vessel to be fitted with turbines of 41,000ihp and 31 Yarrow boilers.

	Estimate	Profit (7.5%)	Price
1. Hull (complete)	478,000	35,850	513,850
2. Main machinery	383,480	28,761	412,241
3. Aux machinery	27,264		27,264
4. Inclining vessel	115	–	115
5. Armour etc.	242,925	–	242,925
6. Boats	2050		2050
Total	1,133,834	64,611	**1,198,445**

Above: The battlecruiser *Inflexible* was drydocked at Birkenhead in October 1908, shortly before delivery. The 862 x 100ft No.7 drydock had only recently been completed for Cammell Laird's Tranmere Bay development scheme. *(Williamson Gallery Birkenhead)*

If the vessel is to be fitted with Babcock & Wilcox boilers add £8660 + 1340 profit giving a total of £10,000. Delivery on the Clyde to be in 2.5 years with 6 weeks extra for the completion of drawings etc.

[The above successful tender for the battlecruiser *Inflexible* (which had Yarrow boilers) shows the manner in which the shipbuilder has broken the work down into separate elements, estimated the cost for each part and added a profit margin, in

this case 7.5 per cent, to give a final price. Unusually, a price for armour is included with no (shipbuilder) profit added but the price of the armament is not included. The final price indicated, £1,198,445, was therefore not the final price of the vessel but the amount agreed between the shipbuilder and the Admiralty if a contract resulted. John Brown would expect to supply the bulk of the armour from its Sheffield works, with its huge profit margin – see Chapter 9 – so there was no need to add a further profit margin.]

7 November 1905
Humphrys, Tennant & Co
2 LP and astern turbines as per specification with tender.

Cost	21,700	Charges	4,500
Profit (25%)	5425		
Interest on money	2625		
Total	59,500	(for two)	

Payment 75% on delivery of turbines, 25% after acceptance by Admiralty. Delivery at Clydebank in May 1907.

[These turbines are for *Invincible*. Humphrys, Tennant & Co

who was awarded the machinery contract, but as they could not manufacture turbines asked John Brown to supply them.]

9 May 1906
Argentine Government (per Rear Admiral Manuel José Garcia, Hotel Cecil, London W.C.)
Design A. Proposed battleship 410' x 76' x 41' 6". 19.5kt
Price 784,100 approximate for each of two.
Design B. Proposed battleship 435' x 75' x 41'. 20kt
Price 729,500 approximate for each of two.
[These ships were never built.]

19 June 1906
Chilean Government (per His Excellency Domingo Garcia, Chilean legation, London)
Design A. Proposed battleship 450' x 73' x 40'. 19kt

Price	**773,950**
Armament:	
By Armstrong	585,000
By Vickers	676,200
By Skoda	545,200

Design B. Proposed battleship 460' x 73'6" x 40'

Price	**797,450**
Armament:	
By Armstrong	632,000
By Vickers	656,350

[These ships were never built. Evidently no collusion by Vickers and Armstrong on armament price.]

---

1 November 1906
Chinese Government
H M Shultz & Co., Tiensin
Approximate prices for Chinese Government.
Type A. Battleship 435' x 75' x 41'. 20kt. 12 10in guns

Price	Charges
846,450	56,800

Type C. Battleship 345' x 60' x 40'. 20kt. 1 10in, 2 8in guns
Price 784,100 approximate for each of two.

[These ships were never built.]

---

18 December 1906.
Admiralty
Proposed First Class Battleship of the Dreadnought type. 490' x 82' x 43'3", turbine engines of 23,000 ihp and boilers of the Yarrow or Babcock & Wilcox type.

	Yarrow	B&W
Hull	478,600	478,600
Engines	166,785	166,785
Boilers	70,215	78,175
	715,600	723,560
Aux mach		
Hull	18,360	
Machy	9015	27,375
	742,975	**750,935**
charges	77,650	74,900

Delivery – two years from receipt of building drawings.

[This refers to prices for one *Bellerophon* class battleship which was ordered as *Superb* at Armstrong Whitworth with B&W boilers. The list below was added to the tender book after contracts were awarded and tender prices advised unofficially by the Admiralty to the various bidders. The difference in price between the lowest and highest is over £200,000 – a staggering amount and suggesting that Scotts were just keeping good faith with the Admiralty in tendering but were not really interested in the work. However, as shown on page 240, Elswick (Armstrong) had put in a loss-making bid to get the work, while most of the other builders had probably included some profit margin.]

NEW 'DREADNOUGHT'

	Hull	Machinery	Boilers	Auxiliaries	Price
Elswick	395,000	167,500	68,500 (Y)	25,944	656,944
			88,000 (B&W)		676,444
Beardmore	406,500	169,500	71,500 (Y)	27,502	675,002
			90,500 (B&W)		694,002
Vickers	403,500	188,115	82,158 (Y)	24,841	698,614
			96,059 (B&W)		712,515
Fairfield	472,050	200,285	41,275 (Y)	24,841	740,615
			55,165 (B&W)		754,505
Brown	478,600	166,785	70,215 (Y)	27,375	742,975
			78,175 (B&W)		750,935
Palmers	–	–	–	–	760,173
					772,230
Laird	–	–	–	–	776,148
					786,148
Scotts	–	–	–	–	865,447

18 December 1906
Admiralty
Main propelling and auxiliary machinery for battleship of Dreadnought type to be built at HM Dockyards Portsmouth and Devonport. Engines to be turbines of 23,000shp.
With B&W boilers

	Est Cost	Profit 5%	Price
Engines	171,035	8550	179,585
Boilers	80,925	4050	84,975
	251,960	12,600	264,560
Aux machinery	20,960		20,960
	272,920	(charges 22,000)	**285,520**

With Yarrow boilers

	Est Cost	Profit 5%	Price
Engines	171,035	8550	179,585
Boilers	72,965	3650	76,615
	24,400	12,200	256,200
Aux machinery	20,960		20,960
	264,960	(charges 24,750)	**277,160**

Devonport ship £1000 extra in each case.

[The above is for the machinery only of *Bellerophon* (Portsmouth) and *Temeraire* (Devonport)].

Wallsend Slipway	251,102 (Y)
	271,102 (B&W)
Hawthorn Leslie	266,834 (Y)
	284,834 (B&W)
Fairfield	271,040 (Y)
	285,040 (B&W)

John Brown	277,160 (Y) note these are the same as JB tender above
	285,520 (B&W)
Denny	292,000 (Y) (less 3000 for Devonport ship)
	302,500 (B&W)
Palmers	289,370 (Y)
	301,429 (B&W)
Scotts	292,985 (Y)
	305,233 (B&W)
Thames Iron Works	293,309 (Y) (1000 more for Devonport ship)
	303,609 (B&W)
Harland & Wolff	296,216 (Y)
	300,216 (B&W)
Humphrys	305,083 (Y)
	308,083 (B&W)
London & Glasgow	317,726 (Y)
	330,426 (B&W)

[The list above and to the left, added later to the tender book shows the prices of those who tendered. The three lowest prices won the contract. The machinery for *Superb* was by Wallsend Slipway (B&W boilers), *Temeraire* (Yarrow boilers) by Hawthorn Leslie and *Bellerophon* (B&W boilers) by Fairfield. Note the increased cost of fitting Babcock & Wilcox boilers, which probably included higher royalty payments to the American parent.]

Above: This train of Fairfield steam turbines (probably for *Bellerophon* before shipping to Portsmouth in 1907) shows the engines mostly for one side of the ship. From right to left, cruising turbine, HP ahead, HP ahead, LP ahead, two HP astern. *(Fairfield)*

26 November 1907
Harland & Wolff Ltd
Belfast
Turbines for battleship of *St Vincent* Class.
Similar to those proposed by us for our own tenders.

Cost of turbines	50,200
Charges at 55%	9900
	60,100
Profit at 5%	3000
	63,100

For unloading, fitting-up ready for steaming, attending trials and opening-out etc.

Materials	3000			
Wages	7000			
Charges at 55%	3850			
	13,850			

Less deduction from wages and charges 10,000 (approximate)

[Harland & Wolff had not yet installed turbine manufacturing facilities at Belfast and consequently requested prices from John Brown & Co., with whom they were associated, for turbine ship contracts they were pursuing.]

27 November 1907
Admiralty
Machinery for *St Vincent* Class battleships to be built at HM Dockyards
With Yarrow boilers.

	Cost	Profit	Price	Charges *(included in Costs)*
Engines inc. delivery of 4,470	158,920	9950	168,870	14,400
Boilers inc. delivery of 2,080	64,880	3880	68,760	9450
	223,800	13,830	237,630	23,850
Auxiliary machinery	21,566		21,566	
	245,366	13,830	**259,196**	

With B&W boilers

	Cost	Profit	Price	Charges
Engines inc. delivery of 4470	154,450	9950	168,870	14,400
Boilers inc. delivery of 2080	75,760	3880	79,640	7785
	234,680	13,830	248,510	22,185
Auxiliary machinery	21,566		21,566	
	256,246	13,830	**270,076**	

[Above: an unsuccessful tender submitted by John Brown for *St Vincent* (Portsmouth) and *Collingwood* (Devonport)
Below: machinery prices in order for the Dockyard ships:]

Builder	Price	
Hawthorn	215,000	with Yarrow boilers excluding auxiliaries
Scotts	–	price as quoted for contract built ship.
Palmers	2?4,500	excluding auxiliaries (either £224,500 or 234,500 – original not clear)
Clydebank	237,630	with Yarrow excluding auxiliaries [note same as JB quote above]
H&W	254,457	with Yarrow excluding auxiliaries

[The machinery contracts for the Dockyard ships were awarded to Scotts for *St Vincent* with turbines from Parsons and B&W boilers and Hawthorn Leslie for *Collingwood* with Yarrow boilers.]

27 November 1907
Admiralty
Proposed battleship of *St Vincent* Class. 500' x 84' x 43'6" with Yarrow boilers.

	Cost	Profit	Price	Charges *(included in Costs)*
Hull	460,000	–	410,500	49,500
Engines	154,450	3860	158,310	14,400
Boilers	62,800	1565	64,365	9450
Aux Machinery	27,353		27,353	
Inclining vessel	150		150	
Total	655,253	5425	**660,678**	23,850
With B&W boilers	73,680	1565	75,245	7785
Total	666,133	5425	**671,558**	

Delivery two years from receipt of building drawings.

[John Brown's tender price for a *St Vincent* class battleship was unsuccessful, despite a loss making hull price, with no charges or profit. The £460,000 includes the charges of £49,500 but the £655,253 total cost is based on the reduced price of £410,500. The list below subsequently added after contracts had been awarded shows the prices of all those who submitted a tender. *Vanguard* was ordered from Vickers with B&W boilers.]

Builder	Price B&W	Price Yarrow
Scotts	738,100	–
Palmers	739,500	732,500
Elswick	738,096	725,300
Fairfield	–	–
Beardmore	705,000	702,000
Clydebank	671,558	660,678
Vickers	625,050	622,050

21 November 1908
Harland & Wolff Ltd
Belfast.
Turbines for a 43,000 shp cruiser and turbines for a 25,000 shp battleship.

	[Battle] **Cruiser**		**Battleship**	
Cost of turbines completed specified in schedule A	87,000	charges 15,000	62,500	charges 11,300
Profit 5%	4500		3200	
	91,500		65,700	
Extra for supplying lifting gear and motors as specified in schedule C.				
	3500		1200	
profit	175		60	
	90,500		63,700	[Turbine cost plus extras]
Profit	4675		3260	
	95,175		**66,960**	

[This is Harland & Wolff using John Brown & Co as a sub-contractor for the turbines in their tender for the battlecruiser *Indefatigable* and battleship *Neptune*. They were successful with the battleship *Neptune*.]

21 November 1908
Scotts Shipbuilding & Engineering Co Ltd
Turbines for 43,000shp cruiser for HM Navy
Estimated cost of turbines completed as detailed in specification A and delivered at Devonport.

	85,500	
profit 5%	4500	
	90,000	
charges	15,000	
Fitting in place on board and supplying parts referred to in specification B		
	15,700	
profit 5%	800	
	16,500	
Total	101,200	[Turbine cost plus fitting]
Profit	5300	
	106,500	

[This tender for *Indefatigable* prepared for Scotts was unsuccessful. Note the increase in price over that supplied to Harland & Wolff, an associate company of John Brown, for the same specification. However, the Scotts' one included fitting on board.]

23 November 1908
Admiralty
Machinery for 43,000 shp cruiser for HM Navy. Engines, turbines of Parsons type.
Boilers B&W type (31 in number)

	Cost	Charges off	Charges on	Price
Machinery	250,215	23,850	13,920	236,295
Spare propellers	2500			2500
Boilers	114,765	12,600	7300	107,465
Sub-total	367,480	36,450	21,220	346,260
Auxiliary machinery	20,430			20,430
Total (B&W boilers)	387,910	36,450	21,220	**366,690**
Total Yarrow boilers	367,500	38,250	22,120	**345,380**

[John Brown's successful tender for the machinery of *Indefatigable* with B&W boilers. Note the reduction in charges (charges off) followed by the addition of charges of a smaller sum but no profit shown. Figures suggest a loss of £5990 was budgeted for.]

23 November 1908
Admiralty
Machinery for a battleship of 25,000 hp. Engines, turbines of Parsons type. Boilers, Yarrow type (18) WP 235lb

	Cost	Charges off	Charges on	Price
Machinery	164,320	15,750	9880	154,440
Spare propellers	1525			1525
Boilers	56,740	8775	5400	51,340
	222,585	24,525	15,280	207,305
Auxiliary machinery	16,347			16,347
Total Yarrow boilers	238,932	24,525	15,280	**223,652**
Total B&W boilers	248,157	23,310	14,660	**233,497**

[Despite budgeting for a £6035 loss, John Brown's tender for *Neptune's* machinery (which had Yarrow boilers) was unsuccessful. However, John Brown was sub-contracted by the successful bidder, Harland & Wolff, to build the turbines – see tender of 21 November above.]

....

12 January 1909
Greek Government (per CL Embericos, London)   Say 946,000 approximately
Proposed battleship 385' x 62'6" x 21' 6". 21kt. 11in guns   [This ship was never built]

....

27 February 1909
Argentine Government

	A	B	C	D	E	F	G
Length	510'	535'	510'	535'	510'	535'	510'
Speed	20.5	22	20.5	22	20.5	22	20.5
Estimated Costs							
Hull	445,000	468,100	455,000	480,000	455,000	480,000	446,000
Charges	58,500	62,400	59,000	63,000	59,000	63,000	59,000
Allowances	18,000	14,500	–	14,500	–	14,000	–
Machinery	187,000	227,375	187,000	227,375	187,000	227,375	218,875
Charges	33,000	40,125	33,000	40,125	33,000	40,125	38,625
Armour	418,500	424,500	401,150	423,750	361,600	384,200	390,000
	1,160,000	1,237,000	1,135,150	1,248,250	1,095,600	1,208,700	1,152,500
Agree Group Prices	1,160,000	1,250,000	1,150,000	1,260,000	1,110,000	1,225,000	1,169,000
" Deductions	100,000	102,000	100,000	95,000	95,000	95,000	95,000
" Hull Machy Armr	1,060,000	1,148,000	1,050,000	1,165,000	1,015,000	1,130,000	1,074,000
Armament	825,000	825,000	–	–	852,500	852,500	710,210
Ammunition	114,650	114,650	–	–	125,000	125,000	104,860
	1,999,650	**2,087,650**	–	–	**1,992,500**	**2,107,500**	**1,889,070**
Alternatives							
Less for recip. machy.	30,000	30,000	30,000	30,000	30,000	30,000	
B&W boiler Inc	14,000	19,000	14,000	19,000	14,000	19,000	18,000

Deductions for A	
1, armour and shafting	50,000
2, part of discount on armament	20,000
3, armour (additional)	20,000
4, ammunition, shells etc	10,000
Total	**100,000**

Delivery on Firth of Clyde. 24 months from delivery of drawings.

[This tender which is for the entire ship was at an early stage in a process that led to the *Rivadavia* class battleships. See revised tender of 25 October 1909. The tender is from the Coventry Syndicate of which John Brown was part. Seven designs are quoted A through to G. Fairfield proposals were for C to F inclusive. The high profit margin on armour allowed the overall price to be reduced by around £100,000, as it would have been supplied by John Brown and Cammell Laird, also members of the Coventry Syndicate.]

20 April 1909
Admiralty

Proposed battleship 510' x 85' x 43' 3". Parsons turbines of 25,000SHP. Boilers WP 235lbs.

	Est Cost	Profit	Tender	Charges
Hull	526,000	53,000	579,000	60,000
Engines	167,000	–	167,000	17,775
Spare gear not to be carried on board :				
A) propellers	1700			
B) remainder	700			
Boilers (Yarrow)	59,005	5,995	65,000	9000
Aux Machinery	20,713	–	20,713	–
Inclining vessel	150	–	150	
Total	775,268	58,995	**834,263**	86,775

As above but with Babcock & Wilcox boilers

Total	784,953	59,860	**844,813**	85,425

Delivery two years from supply of building drawings.

[Unsuccessful tender for *Colossus* (Scotts' with B&W boilers) and *Hercules* (Palmers with Yarrow boilers).]

25 August 1909
Harland & Wolff Ltd
Belfast

Turbine installation for 27,000shp battleship.

Cost of material	34,000
Parsons' royalty @ 2/6d per hp.	3375
Wages	14,500
General charges at 75%	10,875
Total	62,750
Delivery at Portsmouth and supervision given during erection, trials and opening up.	2150
	64,900
Profit	3500
	68,400

[Unsuccessful tender for part of machinery of an *Orion* class battleship.]

Above: *Colossus* departing Scotts yard at Greenock on 11 March 1911 for trials watched by some of the men who built her. *(NRS)*

30 August 1909
Admiralty
Parsons turbine machinery of 27,000 shp for battleship building at Portsmouth Dockyard.
With Yarrow boilers

Engines	170,025
Spare gear	
A	1,700
B	900
Boilers	63,310

Aux Machinery	15,434
Total	**251,369**
Total with B&W boilers	261,529

Delivery at Portsmouth

1. underwater fittings	31 May 1910
2. remainder of machinery ready for sea trials	31 May 1911
3. whole complete	31 August 1911

[John Brown's unsuccessful tender for the machinery for *Orion*.]

---

16 September 1909
Admiralty
Machinery for armoured vessel of 70,000shp with Parsons turbines and Yarrow boilers.

Machinery	382,831	charges	38,810
Spare gear:			
A	4050	charges	240
B	1300	charges	240
Boilers	140,337		

1/3 charges off	20,127
Sub-total	508,391
Charges on	23,426
Total	**531,817**
Extra for templates and jigs etc	1500
As above but with B&W boilers	
Total	**558,117**

[Unsuccessful tender for the machinery of battlecruiser *Lion* (Vickers with Yarrow boilers, Devonport hull)]

---

25 October 1909
Argentine Government
Proposed Battleship 580' x 90'

	J Brown		**Fairfield**	
Hull inc. protection	545,000	104,100 charges	598,767	110,218 charges
Machinery	287,855		283,445	
Sub-total	832,855		882,212	
Charges	104,100		110,218	
Total	936,955		992,430	
Average approx		964,470		
Basis, hull machinery and charges	950,000			
Armour	615,000		637,600	
	10,600			
Average approx		630,000		
		off 100,000		
		530,000		
Hull and Machinery		950,000		
Armour		530,000		
Final agreed price	**1,480,000** (Brown-Curtis turbines)			

With Parsons Turbines, 5 foot longer ship = +£15,000 = £965,000. Extra length requires additional armour of 40 tons. Total

Armour	534,000
	1,499,000 (Parsons)

[Unsuccessful tender for ships that became *Rivadavia* class battleships, ordered in USA, see 27 February 1909 above. Armament excluded. Note use of more compact Brown-Curtis turbines over Parsons saves 5 feet in overall length with a corresponding reduction in hull and armour costs.]

---

29 October 1909
Scotts Shipbuilding & Engineering Co Ltd.
Turbines for armoured vessel of 70,000 shp for HM Navy.
[*Princess Royal*]

Estimated cost of bare turbines, with mountings and cladding, as per our specifications sent to them. **150,600**
Charges included at 75% = 23,250

Above: Boilers took up more than half the machinery space and weight of battlecruisers. Some of *Lion*'s forty-two Yarrow 235lb/sq in watertube boilers are shown in the boiler shop at Vickers' Barrow works in 1910, prior to shipment to Devonport. The machinery contract (No. 401) was worth about £500,000, about 25 per cent of the total ship cost – John Brown's unsuccessful bid had been for £531,817. *(Author's collection)*

2 November 1909

Palmers Shipbuilding & Iron Co Ltd

Machinery (turbines of Parsons type) for an armoured vessel of 70,000 shp. [*Princess Royal*]

	Yarrow	Charges	B&W	Charges
Main Machinery 382,400 off 16,700	365,700	37,460	365,700	37,460
Spare gear not to be carried on ship.				
A) propellers	4100	90	4100	90
B) remainder	1320	45	2910	45
Boilers	130,760	19,830	163,871	19,830
Total	526,982	57,425	553,281	57,425
Aux machinery	13,855	–	13,855	–
Special trials + water measure fitgs	2845	90	2845	90
Total	**518,580**	32,323	**544,680**	32,124

Steaming twice from Newcastle to Liverpool and back, £7,500 [for drydocking]

[A tender £25,000 higher had been submitted on 30 Oct.]

2 November 1909
Wm Beardmore & Co Ltd
Machinery for armoured vessel of 70000 shp For HM Navy (Lion Class) [*Princess Royal*]

	Yarrow	**charges**	**B&W**	**charges**
Main machinery	368,220 (less 3320)	34,200	368,220 (less 3320)	34,200
Spare gear				
Boilers	134,437	details not added		
Total	**524,962**	45,058	**551,792**	45,589

---

2 November 1909
Armstrong Whitworth & Co Ltd
Total with Yarrow boilers   **526,992**
with B&W boilers   **553,092**

[John Brown & Co prepared the tenders above for the machinery for the *Lion* class battlecruiser *Princess Royal* for four shipbuilders, three of whom had their own engine works. The price quoted in each case is slightly different yet the machinery specification remains unchanged. To that extent John Brown is able to show favour. In this instance, John Brown favoured Palmers with whom it had discrete business links. Despite reduced charges and no profit margin, the machinery contract was won by Vickers with Yarrow boilers, who also won the hull contract – see below.]

---

2 November 1909
Armstrong Whitworth & Co Ltd
Machinery Parsons turbines type for a battleship of 27,000 shp
Total with Yarrow boilers   **257,745**
with B&W boilers   **267,595**

[Unsuccessful tender for machinery for an *Orion* class battleship. Armstrongs won the contract to construct *Monarch* and sub-contracted the machinery to Hawthorn Leslie with Yarrow boilers.]

---

4 November 1909
Admiralty
Proposed armoured cruiser of 660' x 88'6" x 44'. Engines Parsons type 70,000 shp. Yarrow boilers.

	Est Cost	**Profit**	**Tender price**	**Charges**
Hull	570,000	75,100	645,100	68,100
Machinery	368,220	–4440	363,780	43,200
Spare Gear	5350	70	5420	135
Boilers Yarrow type	134,437	–5537	128,900	18,950
	1,078,007	65,193	1,143,200	121,385
Aux machinery	28,117		28,117	
Inclining vessel	150		150	
	1,106,274	65,193	**1,171,467**	

[As above but with Babcock & Wilcox boilers.]

	Cost	Profit	Tender price
	1,132,573	65,994	**1,198,567**

[John Brown's unsuccessful tender for *Princess Royal* hull and machinery.]

---

4 November 1909
Admiralty
Proposed battleship for HM Navy 545' x 88'6" x 43'6".

	Est Cost	**Profit**	**Tender**	**Charges**
Hull	499,200	103,200	602,400	60,300
Machinery	160,840	7460	168,300	16,425
Spare gear not to be carried				
	2600		2600	75
Boilers	59,845	4555	64,400	9000
	722,485	115,215	837,700	85,800
Auxiliary Machinery	28,900		28,900	
Inclining etc	240		240	
Total Yarrow boilers	751,625	115,215	**866,840**	
Total for B&W boilers	761,785	115,155	**876,940**	

[Unsuccessful tender for a battleship of the *Orion* class. *Conqueror* to Beardmore with B&W boilers, *Thunderer* to Thames Iron Works with B&W boilers and *Monarch* to Armstrong Whitworth. See p.127 for *Thunderer* price.]

5 November 1909
Imperial Russian Navy (per John Sampson Esq., at
St Petersburg)
Proposed armoured cruiser [battlecruiser] of high power
(60000shp).

Total   **1,755,000**

[An early Russian battlecruiser design that did not proceed.
Excludes armament. John Sampson was a member of the
Clydebank Board charged with winning Russian work]

---

27 January 1910
Admiralty
First Class Armoured Colonial Cruisers. 18,800 tons and
44,000hp.
For delivery in 24 months

	Cost	Profit	Price
Hull	456,500	30,700	487,200
Main machinery	232,160	29,940	262,100
Spare gear not to be carried on board-			
A) spare propellers	3000	800	3800
B) remainder	1800	–	1800
Boilers	107,470	16,730	124,200
Aux Machinery	22,750	–	22,750
Inclining	150	–	150
Total	823,830	78,170	**902,000**

Delivery in 30 months

	Cost	Profit	Price
Hull	449,000	26,000	475,000
Main machinery	232,160	24,440	256,600
Spare gear not to be carried on board:			
A) spare propeller	3000	800	3800

B) remainder	1800	–	1800
Boilers	107,470	16,730	124,200
Aux Machinery	22,750	–	22,750
Inclining	150	–	150
Total	815,315	65,485	**880,800**

[the rows and columns both add up to £884,300, so a deduction of £3500 has been made somewhere.

Actual totals	816,330	67,970	884,300]

[pencil note written on above tender as follows which was for
successful tender for HMAS *Australia* with B&W boilers]
Prices finally accepted

Hull	475,015
Engines	254,632
Boilers	120,700
Aux machinery	22,650
Spares A)	3800
Spares B)	1800
Inclining	150
Total	**878,747**

---

9 March 1910
Turkish Government
Proposed war vessels for Turkey. Battleship 448' x 80' x 41'.
15,400 tons, 20 knots, 18,000 HP
Total   **891,000**

No.623 Design. Displacement 15,000 tons, shp 25,800. Speed
22.5 knots
Total   **939,000**

[These ships were never built. Armament excluded.]

---

23 March 1910
Imperial Japanese Navy
Captain T Fujii, IJN, Yokosuka Dockyard.
Price for 50,000 shp Brown-Curtis turbines. Three turbines in
total excluding shafting, propellers and condensers etc.

Price 90,200 charges 13,500

[Not built. Fujii was later charged with bribery over the
Kongo order]

---

13 July 1910
Armstrong Whitworth & Co Ltd
Machinery for quadruple screw armoured cruiser of 60,000 shp.
Engines, Brown-Curtis turbines, Boilers Yarrow or Babcock & Wilcox.
1, 40 Yarrow boilers with specified safe firing area. Cost 459,148 allowance 11,885, charges 49,725. Price 471,000
2, 40 Yarrow boilers with specified length of stokehold space. Cost 452,145, allowance 11,855, Charges 49,725. Price 464,000
3, 32 Babcock & Wilcox boilers with superheaters 100 degrees. Cost 474,145, Allowance 11,855, Charges 48,375. Price 486,000
Division of prices as stated in our letter to Elswick of 17 August 1910 –
1, Machinery 335,600. Boilers 135,400 = 471,000
2, Machinery 335,600. Boilers 128,400 = 464,000
3, Machinery 335,600. Boilers 150,400 = 486,000
Three prices quoted from 464,000 to 486,000 depending on boilers selected.

[Prices quoted to Armstrong Whitworth for battlecruiser machinery with various boiler options. It was unsuccessful. This was probably for *Kongo*, see below.]

28 July 1910
Vickers Sons & Maxim
Brown-Curtis turbines for an armoured cruiser. shp 60,000,
speed 27 knots for 8 hours.

Cost, 104,600, say	105,000	(Charges included at 17,250)
Less John Brown's royalty	−3000	
	102,000	
Commission	4000	
New machines	6600	
Profit	10,000	
	122,600	

Delivered at Barrow in Furness. For 64,000 shp extra price
would be about 4000 to 5000.

[Unsuccessful tender but note that John Brown waived their
royalty, but applied charges, a profit, commission as well as the
cost of new machines. This was probably for *Kongo*, ordered
from Vickers but with Parsons turbines and Yarrow boilers.]

29 July 1910
Turkish Government (per Charles E Ellis Esq.)
Proposed battleship 490' x 83' x 40' Parsons type turbines
23,000 shp, 16 Babcock & Wilcox boilers, speed 21 knots.
Price (hull and machinery) **670,000**

[Charles Ellis was a member of the John Brown board. These
ships were never built]

24 August 1910
Messrs Harland & Wolff Ltd, Belfast
Turbines of Parsons type for proposed Battleship 31,000 shp for
HM Navy.

Cost including royalty and delivery	55,475	charges 9375
Profit 5%	2525	
	58,000	

Delivered at Portsmouth or Devonport
For a second set, the above price would be reduced by 10,000

[Unsuccessful tender for turbines for *King George V* or
Centurion.]

29 August 1910
Admiralty
Main and auxiliary machinery for a battleship of 31,000 shp,
Parsons type turbines.
Yarrow Boilers

	Cost	**Off**	**Price**	**Charges**
Machinery	166,305	8000	158,305	15,875
Boilers	59,970	3800	56,170	8905
Total	226,275	11,800	214,475	24,780
Babcock & Wilcox Boilers				
Machinery	166,305	8000	158,305	15,875
Boilers	70,415	4425	65,990	8905
Total	236,720	12,425	224,295	24,780
Aux machinery	19,688		19,688	
Spare gear	1425		1425	
Total	257,833	12,425	**245,408**	

For Devonport ship add   Machinery 1500
                              Boilers 500

Delivery :	underwater fittings	30 August 1911
	Ready for trials	15 August 1912
	Complete	15 November 1912

[Unsuccessful tender for machinery for *King George V*
(Portsmouth) awarded to Parsons Marine with B&W boilers,
and *Centurion* (Devonport) awarded to Hawthorn Leslie with
Yarrow boilers. Note reductions in 'Off' column.]

31 October 1910
Admiralty
Proposed battleship 555' x 89' x 43'6" Parsons type turbines
31,000 shp.
Babcock & Wilcox Boilers

		Delivery 16 January 1913		Delivery 15 July 1913	
	Cost	Profit	Price	Off	Price
Hull	485,000	104,200	589,200	8000	581,200
Engines	158,910	15,890	174,800	1800	173,000
Boilers	64,915	6495	71,410	1000	70,410
	708,825	126,585	**835,410**	10,800	**824,610**

Yarrow Boilers

		Delivery 16 January 1913		Delivery 15 July 1913	
	Cost	Profit	Price	Off	Price
Hull	485,000	104,200	589,200	8000	581,200
Engines	158,910	15,890	174,800	1800	173,000
Boilers	55,470	5530	61,000	1000	60,000
	699,380	125,620	**825,000**	10,800	**814,200**

Auxiliary machinery quoted separately 30,333

[Unsuccessful tender for *King George V* class battleship. *Ajax*
awarded to Scotts' with B&W boilers, *Audacious* to Cammell
Laird with Yarrow boilers.]

9 November 1910
Imperial Chinese Government (per Edmund Backhouse)
Proposed armoured cruiser 650' x 89' x 45'. Turbines of Parsons type 70,000 shp

[Improved Lion]
Design A and B. Say 2,330,000 [armament included]
Vickers price for Japanese Lion – hull 1,080,000 plus armour at £93 per ton.

Armour, armament and ammunition costs assumed by Clydebank when tendering
Price submitted as per Backhouse letter of 21 July 1911 was **2,397,000**

[These ships were never built. Edmund Backhouse, later Sir Edmund Backhouse, was an oriental scholar who among other things acted as an agent for John Brown in China. He was later considered to be a fraudster.]

---

29 November 1910
Messrs Palmers Shipbuilding & Iron Co Ltd
Main and auxiliary machinery for armoured cruiser for HM Navy shp 75,000

	Delivery 1 March 1913	1 September 1913
Yarrow boilers		
Machinery	364,120	360,200
Boilers	129,880	128,360
Total	494,000	488,560
Babcock & Wilcox boilers	517,200	511,760

Modified figures submitted to Admiralty by Palmers:

	Delivery 1 March 1913	1 September 1913
Yarrow boilers		
Machinery	354,000	354,000

Boilers	125,800	125,800
Total	**479,800**	**479,800**
Babcock & Wilcox boilers	**502,800**	**502,800**
Auxiliary Machinery	21,327	21,327

Modified figures include £5000 for spare propellers, all of the remainder of spare gear not to be carried, and cost of lifting and fitting machinery on board estimated by Palmers at £3200. See letter of 10 December 1910 to Mr Bell.

Original estimated charges	Engines 35,000 less 10,000 =	25,000
	Boilers 14,000 less 4000 =	10,000
		35,000

[Successful machinery tender for *Queen Mary*. Hull contract to Palmers who sub-contracted the machinery to John Brown with Yarrow boilers.]

---

30 November 1910
Sir W G Armstrong Whitworth & Co Ltd
Main and auxiliary machinery for armoured cruiser for HM Navy shp 75,000

[Unsuccessful tender for *Queen Mary*. The prices are identical to the original price supplied to Palmers above plus £2,000, so more favourable to a company with links to John Brown.]

30 November 1910
Scotts Shipbuilding & Engineering Co Ltd
Turbines for armoured cruiser for H M Navy 75,000 shp.
2 HP ahead turbines, 2 HP astern turbines, 2 LP ahead and astern turbines with mountings as stated in specification sent with tender. Price £134,620. Charges 21,000

[Unsuccessful tender for *Queen Mary*]

---

5 December 1910
Admiralty
Proposed armoured cruiser 660' x 89' x 44' turbines of Parsons type 75,000hp.
Yarrow boilers
Completion by 1 March 1913

	Cost	Profit	Price	Charges
Hull	586,500	154,300	740,800	69,300
Engines	355,120	–2000	353,120	33,750
Boilers	125,880	200	126,080	18,900
	1,067,500	152,500	**1,220,000**	121,950

Completion by 1 September 1913

Hull	571,500	152,300	723,800	69,300
Engines	351,200	1920	353,120	33,750
Boilers	124,360	1720	126,080	18,900
	1,047,060	155,940	**1,203,000**	121,950

Babcock & Wilcox boilers
Completion by 1 March1913

	1,090,700	152,300	**1,243,000**	121,950

Completion by 1 September 1913

	1,070,260	155,740	**1,226,000**	121,950

[This is John Brown's unsuccessful tender for *Queen Mary*. Note that a shorter build time cost more, involving more overtime]

---

24 March 1911
Imperial Japanese Navy
Tokyo. Engineer Admiral Fujii,
Designs for Brown-Curtis turbines for large cruiser to be built

in Japan.
Price quoted 5 December 1910   £30,000
Including cost of sending representative to Japan to supervise construction and attend trials.

Amended price quoted on 24 March 1911   **£27,000**   £22,000
If order for drums, spindles and shafting for 38,000hp battleship   [Probably for battlecruiser *Haruna*]
given to us, the price for the design would be reduced by 5000.

....

5 April 1911
Chilean Government
Proposed battleship with turbine machinery

[Six designs A to F are detailed of which F appears to be the one selected]
'F' Design 610' x 91' x 44' 26,800 tons, 37,500 shp, 10 x 14" BL, 20 – 4.7"
On 28 July 1911 the following details were added for 'F' design :

	Coventry Armament		**Armstrong Armament**		**Vickers Armament**	
	1st ship	2nd ship	1st ship	2nd ship	1st ship	2nd ship
Hull	596,140	596,140	596,140	596,140	596,140	596,140
Engines	238,800	238,800	238,800	238,800	238,800	238,800
Boilers	80,700	80,700	80,700	80,700	80,700	80,700
Armour	419,050	419,050	419,050	419,050	419,050	419,050
Margin	17,310	17,310	17,310	17,310	17,310	17,310
Delivery and lift of armament	-	-	2000	2000	2000	2000
	1,352,000	1,352,000	1,354,000	1,354,000	1,354,000	1,354,000
Armament & ammunition	941,000	891,000	940,000	937,000	940,000	937,000
	2,293,000	**2,243,000**	**2,294,000**	**2,291,000**	**2,294,000**	**2,291,000**
Charges included in above						
Hull	62,400	62,400	62,400	62,400	62,400	62,400
Machinery	31,540	31,540	31,540	31,540	31,540	31,540
Total charges	93,940	93,940	93,940	93,940	93,940	93,940
Spare armam't & ammunt.	94,000	94,000	93,900	93,900	93,900	93,900

Reduction on Coventry tender only of £40,000 each if fixed angle of elevation for loading of guns is accepted. Messrs Armstrong
agree to give delivery of 2 sets of armament in 30 months.

[This is for the Chilean battleships *Almirante Latorre* and *Almirante Cochrane*. The contract was won by Armstrongs as *Almirante Latorre*
and *Almirante Cochrane*, subsequently HMS *Canada* and HMS *Eagle*. Note Vickers and Armstrongs quoting identical armament
prices, evidence of collusion. Contract for first ship signed with Armstrong for £2,335,000.]

....

11 April 1911
Palmers Shipbuilding & Iron Co Ltd
Hebburn on Tyne
14 large boilers for HMS *Queen Mary* complete with mountings fitted on board 25,445.

Additionally funnels, uptakes etc., for all boilers fitted up on
board 18,170. To be made by Palmers. [Presumably the other 28
boilers were to be built by Palmers]

....

6 May 1911
Palmers Shipbuilding & Iron Co
Proposed Portuguese Warships
First Class Battleship of 19,000 tons displacement, 500' bp x 84'
extreme x 27' mean draft. 25,000shp
Price   1,770,450

First Class Battleship of 16,500 tons displacement, 450'bp x
81'6" extreme x 27' mean draft. 21,000shp
Price   1,544,515

[Neither of these ships were built. Prices include armament
from Coventry.]

....

31 May 1911
Imperial Japanese Navy
K Matsukata, President of Kawasaki Naval Dockyard.
Working drawings for Brown-Curtis turbines of 64,000 shp for
large cruiser also calculations and other data. Price 10,000. This
price allows for facilities to be given to an Outside Manager,

Draughtsmen, Foreman and workmen from Japan to acquire
knowledge of our practice at Clydebank. (Accepted)

[For the battlecruiser *Haruna*.]

7 August 1911
Armstrong Whitworth
Machinery for Chilean battleship. 37,000 shp

	Yarrow boilers	B&W Boilers
Main & auxiliary machinery	239,700	–
profit 2%	4780	–
	244,480	244,480
Boilers	75,800	97,800
profit 2%	1500	1960
	77,300	99,760
	321,780	**344,240**

John Brown & Co., Sheffield, pay for agent and commission and 6000 towards cost of Yarrow boilers. All this from profit on forgings. Figures as adjusted between Mr Sampson and Mr Perrett as per letter of 23 April 1912. Total 332,000

[Successful machinery tender for *Almirante Latorre*, later *Canada*, with Yarrow boilers, under construction at Elswick]

11 August 1911
Imperial Japanese Navy
Tokyo.
Admiral T Fujii,
Set of Brown-Curtis turbines for battleship to be built at Kure

Dockyard **109,500**. Delivered at TOB [Tail of the Bank] Clydebank.

[Supplied by John Brown & Co for the Japanese battleship *Fuso*.]

23 September 1911
Palmers Shipbuilding & Iron Co Ltd.
Duplicate 'Inflexible' for China.
Price **1,820,030**

[This ship was never built. Price includes armament.]

10 October 1911
Portuguese Government
Battleship – 16,500 tons, 20 knots speed. Dimensions 450' x 81.5' x 27'. shp 21,000. 12 Yarrow boilers. Armament: 8 x 12" guns, 10 x 6" guns, 10 x 4" guns, 2 x 3" landing guns, 3 TT.
Price 1,670,015 and 5,010,045 for three.

[This ship was never built. Price includes armament.]

25 October 1911
Cammell Laird & Co
Fairfield Shipbuilding & Engineering Co Ltd
R&W Hawthorn Leslie & Co Ltd
London & Glasgow Engineering & Iron Shipbuilding Co Ltd
Palmers Shipbuilding & Iron Co Ltd
Scotts
Thames Ironworks

Brown-Curtis turbines for proposed battleships for HM Navy of 29,000hp.

Cost	56,475
Charges	9000
Contingencies 2.5%	1650
	67,125 delivered at Clydebank.

[Unsuccessful tender for machinery for Dockyard-built *Iron Duke* class battleships. In the event, Parsons turbines were fitted. Note Thames tendering when on the point of bankruptcy.]

25 October 1911
Harland & Wolff Ltd
Brown-Curtis turbines for proposed battleships for HM Navy of 29000hp.

Cost	57,100
Charges	9000
Contingencies 2.5%	1650
Delivered at Dockyard	500
	68,250

Parsons type

Cost	55,975
Charges	9000
Contingencies 2.5%	1650
Delivered at Dockyard	500
	67,125

[Unsuccessful tender for turbines for *Iron Duke* class battleships and slightly higher than that quoted to the other shipbuilders for same specification.]

30 October 1911
Admiralty
Proposed battleship 580' x 90' x 44'. Engines Parsons or Brown-Curtis.

	Cost	Price
Hull	474,250	
Charges 12.5%	59,500	
	553,750	
Ironworkers extras	10,000	
2.5% margin	14,000	
Engineers	6000	564,250 (less 1,000)
Engines	158,225	
Charges 7%	11,075	169,300
Boilers	52,210	
Charges 7%	3650	55,860
Auxiliary machinery		32,821

| Total with Yarrow boilers | **822,231** |
| With B&W boilers | **831,931** |

[Unsuccessful tender for an *Iron Duke* class battleship]

[In pencil:]

Beardmore	754,000	520,000 hull, 234,000 machinery
Vickers	762,000	515,000 hull, 247,000 machinery
Fairfield	810,000	–
Swan Hunter	815,000	597,000 hull, 218,000 machinery
Cammell Laird	837,000	–
Scotts	850,000	615,000 hull, 235,000 machinery
Elswick	901,000	685,000 hull, 216,000 machinery

[Pencil note says that as per telegram of 8 November 1911, that for delivery in 30 months we are offering a reduction on hull of 12,000 and on machinery 5000.

Orders for two *Iron Duke* class battleships were placed – *Benbow*, built and engined by Beardmore with B&W boilers and *Emperor of India*, built and engined by Vickers with Yarrow boilers. This appears to be Swan Hunter's first tender for a battleship.]

Above: HM King George V and Queen Mary visited industrial locations on Clydeside in July 1914 including the Fairfield and Beardmore shipyards. Having arrived in Dalmuir basin by paddle steamer, they are seen here rounding Y turret on *Benbow's* quarterdeck. *(Author's collection)*

---

30 October 1911
Admiralty
Machinery for proposed Dockyard battleship.
Engines Turbines of Parsons type or Brown–Curtis 29,000 shp. Boilers: Yarrow type.

			Cost	Profit 5%	Price
Engines	164,225	charges 7% (11,495)	175,720	8780	184,500
Boilers	54,210	charges 7% (3790)	58,000	2900	60,900
			233,720	11,680	245,400
Auxiliaries			22,941		22,941
			256,661	11,680	**268,341**

Boilers: Babcock & Wilcox type.

			Cost	Profit 5%	Price
Engines	164,225	charges 7% 11,495	175,720	8780	184,500
Boilers	64,210	charges 7% 4490	68,700	3435	72,135
			244,420	12,215	256,635
Auxiliary machinery			22,941		22,941
			267,361	12,215	**279,576**

[Unsuccessful tender. *Iron Duke* at Portsmouth with machinery by Cammell Laird with B&W boilers; *Marlborough* at Devonport with machinery by Hawthorn Leslie with Yarrow boilers.]

---

12 December 1911
Imperial Russian Navy
Russian Shipbuilding Co., St Petersburg.
Turbines for battleship building at Nicolaieff, Black Sea.
Maximum cost guaranteed not to be exceeded.
Turbines, shafting, propellers complete delivered at Clydebank but excluding Parsons royalty, freight, insurance and customs dues.
Includes 10% profit. **96,000**

Main condensers of Weir Uniflux type, including royalty of 550.	**9450**
Main air pumps (Weirs)	**4683**
Main circulating pumps (if purchased in this country and delivered at Clydebank)	**3500**

Delivery at Clydebank. Shafting and propellers – 9 months from approval of drawings.
Turbines and condensers – 9 months from approval of drawings.
For guidance – mentioned royalty payable to Parsons would be Rs12 per shp on 26,000 shp = Rs312,000. Ditto freight, insurance plus dues estimated at 4000 to 4500. Commission included in above prices: For J G Crookstone 2.5%, Mr Dimitrieff 2%.

[This was the basis of the machinery contract won by John Brown & Co for the turbine machinery installation for the Russian battleships *Imperatritsa Mariya* and *Imperator Alexander III*.]

---

19 January 1912
Palmers Shipbuilding & Iron Co
Turbines for proposed battle cruiser of 85,000 shp
2 HP ahead, 2HP astern and 2 LP ahead and astern turbines complete with all mountings and fittings as per specification.

Cost	133,150
Charges 70%	21,000
Profit	7700
	161,850

Quoted 153,880 with a further 7970 for Parsons' royalty.
Shafting complete with liners and couplings etc. 33,030

[Unsuccessful tender for turbines for *Tiger.*]

---

20 January 1912
Armstrong Whitworth & Co Ltd
Machinery for proposed battle cruiser for HM Navy. Displacement 28,200 tons and 85,000shp.
Yarrow boilers.
Price 552,268 inc. charges 48,800 (40%) and profit at 8095.
Babcock boilers.
Price 578,789 inc. charges 48,800 (40%) and profit 11,360.
Auxiliary machinery 27,777

[Unsuccessful tender for turbines for *Tiger*]

---

20 January 1912
Wm Beardmore & Co Ltd
[Identical tender to above for Armstrong and equally unsuccessful.]

---

23 January 1912
Admiralty
Proposed battlecruiser. Displacement 28,200 tons, shp 85000, 660' x 90.5' x 44.5'
B&W boilers and Brown-Curtis turbines

	Cost	Charges	Price
Hull	530,200	58,000	595,200
Preparing berth, alts to island platform	7000		
Engines	369,950	22,700	387,645
Deductions for forgings	−5000		
Boilers	124,265	5125	129,390
Total	1,026,415	85,825	**1,112,235**

Extra for superheaters 7,000 (not accepted)

The price for above but with Parsons turbines was:

Total	1,028,385	85,825	**1,114,210**

Yarrow boilers and Brown-Curtis turbines

	Cost	Charges	Price
Hull	530,200 (537,200)	58,000	595,200
Preparing berth alts to island	7000		
Engines	369,950 (364,950)	22,700	387,650
Deductions for forgings	−5000		
Boilers	107,445	5670	113,115
Total	1,009,595	86,370	**1,095,965**

Extra for superheaters 7,000 (not accepted)
The price for above but with Parsons turbines was:

                              1,011,565   86,370   **1,097,935**

[in pencil under the quote for Babcock boilers]

Hull	595,200
Engines	387,645
Boilers	129,390
Auxiliary Machinery	27,967
Inclining	190
Total	1,140,392

Vickers price 17,000 higher than JB and Fairfield higher again but latter prepared to drop price by 20000 if three months for delivery added. Delivery 24.5 months. Coal strike [lasted] 2 months.

[Successful tender for *Tiger*, with Brown-Curtis turbines and B&W boilers. Actual delivery 30 months.]

---

5 March 1912
Portuguese Government
Portuguese Naval Construction Syndicate. For Palmers Shipbuilding & Iron Co.
Battleship 510' x 84' x 43'. 21.5 knots
Clydebank price **1,907,750**   Palmers price **1,917,140**

[This ship was never built. Price includes armament.]

10 July 1912
Portuguese Government. For Palmers Shipbuilding & Iron Co
Proposed battleship 510' x 84.5' x 26.75' Engines Parsons turbines 26,000 shp. Yarrow boilers
Clydebank price **1,172,200**   Palmers price **1,177,115**

[Excludes armament of approx £797,830. This ship was never built]

---

30 July 1912
Received with L.O. [London Office] memo dated 30 July 1912
Greek Battle Cruiser

Builder	Tons	Armament	
Vulcan	13,220	Skoda	1,234,000
		Bethlehem	1,091,500
Orlando	14,000	Vickers	1,166,000
		Bethlehem	–
Krupp	14,200	Krupp	1,193,000
Palmers	14,200	Coventry	1,314,000
		Bethlehem	1,212,500
Cramp	13,500	Bethlehem	1,157,600
Vickers	13,500	Vickers	1,220,000

	14,000	Vickers	1,230,000
Beardmore	14,000	Vickers	1,226,600
Armstrong	14,950	Armstrong	1,282,500
Fairfield	14,900	Coventry	1,285,000 (less 19,500)
St Nazaire	13,800	–	1,337,000
Thames		–	1,428,000

[Prices obtained and circulated to British shipbuilders. This was probably *Salamis/Vassilefs Giorgios* launched at Vulcan Werke, Hamburg on 11 November 1914 but never completed. Her four Bethlehem twin 14in turrets were sold to the Admiralty to arm four monitors.]

---

23 September 1912
Admiralty
Machinery for battleship to be built at HM Dockyard. Parsons turbines and Yarrow boilers
For engines, boilers and auxiliaries. Price **444,833** inc. profit of 23,472 and charges at 38,760
For Parsons geared turbines add 19,500

[In pencil] Suggest for Armstrongs 2.5% profit
Parsons turbines and Babcock boilers

For engines, boilers and auxiliaries. Price **464,957** inc. profit of 24,612 and charges at 40,549
For Parsons geared turbines add 19,500

[Unsuccessful tender for machinery for a *Queen Elizabeth* class battleship. *Queen Elizabeth* (Portsmouth) machinery by Wallsend Slipway with B&W boilers, *Warspite* (Devonport) machinery by Hawthorn Leslie with Yarrow boilers. The geared drive option was not taken up, probably deemed too risky technically until more experience had been gained.]

---

17 October 1912
Armstrong Whitworth & Co. Ltd
Newcastle on Tyne
Machinery for proposed battleship of 56,000shp.
With Babcock & Wilcox boilers
Engines, boilers and auxiliaries. Price **450,564** inc. profit of 10,254 and charges of 40,649
With Yarrow boilers

Engines, boilers and auxiliaries. Price **431,105** inc profit of 9779
For Parsons geared turbines add 19,500

[Unsuccessful tender for machinery for a *Queen Elizabeth* class battleship (*Barham/Valiant*). Armstrong did win the later contract to build *Malaya* and sub-contracted the machinery to Wallsend Slipway with B&W boilers, see 2 December below.]

22 October 1912
Admiralty
Proposed battleship for HM Navy. 600' x 90'3" x 44'9" Turbines of Parsons type shp 56,000
Babcock boilers

	Cost	Profit	Price	Fairfield
Hull 564,700 charges 70,000	634,700	53,000 (8%)	687,700	673,000
Engines 271,725 charges 26,000	297,725	14,885 (5%)	312,610	348,600
Boilers 91,300 charges 8000	99,300	4965 (5%)	104,265	73,400
	1,031,725	72,850	1,104,575	1,095,000
Aux machinery	37,051		37,051	
	1,068,776	72,850	**1,141,626**	
Yarrow boilers as above but	1,055,676	72,195	**1,127,871**	1,083,000
Steering gear			2928	
Electric boat hoists			2250	
Extra for Parsons geared turbines			19,500	

Delivery 30 January 1915.
For ordinary arrangement of Brown-Curtis turbines as being fitted in HMS *Valiant* at Fairfield offered reduction of 4,500 over Parsons type. 8/2/13
[In pencil – actual prices submitted by various builders, excluding auxiliaries.]

Fairfield	1,080,000
Brown	1,090,000
Elswick	1,135,000
Beardmore	1,150,000
Cammell Laird	1,150,600
Vickers	1,164,000
Scotts	1,168,000

[Above: John Brown's successful tender for *Barham* with Brown-Curtis turbines and Yarrow boilers. The engine and boiler price of £416,875 was lower than that quoted to Armstrong, Whitworth. The pencil list at left added after the tenders were opened shows the actual prices submitted. Apparently no tenders from Palmers, Harland & Wolff or Swan Hunter. The contract for *Valiant*'s hull and machinery was awarded to Fairfield with Brown-Curtis turbines and B&W boilers.]

2 December 1912
Admiralty
Proposed battleship duplicate of HMS *Barham*.

Prices as above plus 40,000.

[This is probably for *Malaya*.]

1 May 1913
Turkish Government
Repeat Turkish battleship, displacement 23,000 tons, shp 26,500

	Armstrong	Vickers	Brown
Hull inc charges	597,000	619,220	633,750
Profit	63,000	61,922	49,250
	660,000	661,142	683,000
Machinery inc charges	254,000	260,660	255,750
Profit	25,000	26,066	20,250
	279,000	286,726	276,000
Price of hull & machinery	939,000	967,868	959,000
Armour @ 85 per ton	370,000	370,000	370,000
Armament	734,000	734,000	734,000
Add all expenses, commissions etc	75,000	75,000	75,000
Total	**2,118,000**	**2,146,868**	**2,138,000**

Final prices quoted. First ship 2,182,000. Second ship 2,109,000. Reduction for a repeat 25,000.

[The three companies were in partnership to build for the Ottoman Navy]

'Princess Royal', displacement 26,250 tons, shp 70,000

	Armstrong	Vickers	Brown
Hull inc charges	–	–	781,000
Profit 10%			79,000
	–	912,000	860,00

Machinery inc charges	–	–	537,900	
Profit 10%	–	–	53,410	
Price for hull and machinery	–	1,509,000	1,451,310	
Armour @ £85 per ton	–	324,700	324,700	
Armament	555,000	555,000	555,000	
Add for expenses and commissions	90,000	90,000	90,000	
Total	–	**2,473,700**	**2,421,000**	a mean of 2,450,000

Second ship 2,425,000

'Delhi', displacement 25,000, shp 29,000

	Armstrong	Vickers	Brown	
Hull inc charges	–	–	718,500	
Profit	63,000 (10%)	73,400 (10%)	60,500	
	–	912,000	779,000	
Machinery inc charges	–	–	257,400	
Profit	–	–	21,600	
Price for hull and machinery	1,055,000	1,095,182	1,058,000	
Armour @ 85 per ton	435,285	435,300	435,300	
Armament	713,000	713,000	713,000	
Total	2,203,285	2,243,482	2,206,300	a mean of 2,217,660
Add for expenses and commissions	–	–	35,000	
			2,291,300	

Quoted 2,300,000 for first ship and 2,275,000 for second ship.

Latest British Battleship, [i.e. *Queen Elizabeth* class] displacement 27,500 tons, shp 56,000

	Armstrong	Vickers	Brown
Hull inc charges	–	–	785,000
Profit			70,000
	–	–	855,000
Machinery inc charges	–	–	412,000
Profit	–	–	34,000
Price for hull and machinery	–	–	1,301,000
Armour @ 85 per ton	–	–	461,550
Armament	–	–	757,000
Add for expenses and commissions	–	–	80,000
Total	–	–	2,599,550

[Unsuccessful tender. Probably for 23,000-ton battleship *Fatih* ordered April 1914 at Vickers (No. 460). There was probably a work sharing agreement among the partnership, e.g. Armstrong armament, John Brown armour. Cancelled after outbreak of war.]

....

10 July 1913
Admiralty
Machinery for battleships for HM Navy to built at Portsmouth or Devonport.
Yarrow boilers and Parsons turbines.

	Cost	**Profit**	**Price**
Engines charges 40% 16,600, 193,850	210,450	10,520	220,970
Boilers charges 40% 8,120, 58,800	66,920	3350	70,270
	277,370	13,870	291,240
Auxiliary machinery			33,414
			324,654
Price with Babcock boilers was			**335,154**

Quoted 5000 extra for Brown-Curtis turbines

[Unsuccessful tender for *Royal Sovereign* class battleship machinery. *Royal Sovereign* (Portsmouth) machinery from Parsons Marine with B&W boilers, *Royal Oak* (Devonport) from Hawthorn Leslie with Yarrow boilers.]

Above: *Revenge* on trials on the Clyde in March 1916, perhaps on the new Arran measured mile. *(Vickers Ltd)*

10 July 1913
Admiralty
Proposed battleship for HM Navy of 25,750 tons and 31,000 shp, Yarrow boilers. [Original design *Royal Sovereign* class]

		Cost	Profit	Price
Hull	564,000, charges 66,625 = 630,625	630,625	63,065	693,690
Engines	187,850 charges 12,000 =199,850	199,850	10,000	209,850
Boilers	56,800 charges 5940 = 62,740	62,740	1880	64,620
		893,215	74,945	968,160
Aux machinery				40,704
				1,008,864

With Babcock boilers	903,215	75,265	978,480
			40,704
			1,019,184

Extra for Brown-Curtis turbines 5000

[In pencil, probably actual prices submitted excluding auxiliaries]

Palmers	960,000
J Brown	970,000
Vickers	1,000,000
Beardmore	1,002,000
Fairfield	1,070,000
Armstrong	1,075,000
Cammell Laird	1,039,000
Scotts	1,043,000

[Unsuccessful tender. Contracts all with Parsons turbines were awarded to Vickers for *Revenge* including machinery with B&W boilers, Palmers for *Resolution* including machinery with Yarrow boilers, and Beardmore for *Ramillies* including machinery with B&W boilers. According to the list above, John Brown should have been awarded a contract as they were second lowest, but the Admiralty probably wished to support Beardmore.]

---

20 November 1913
Imperial Japanese Navy
Kawasaki Dockyard, per J Watanabe Esq.

Cruising turbines and gearing for proposed Japanese battleship.
4 Brown-Curtis cruising turbines.
Total **13,990**

---

4 February 1914
Greek Government
Proposed battleship

Design A	Design B	Design C	
600' x 90.5' x 44.5'	580' x 88.5' x 44'	590' x 90' x 44.25'	
28,200 tons	26,000 tons	27,200 tons	
56,000 shp 24k	32,000 shp 21.5k	46,000 shp 23k	
8 x 15", 16 x 6"	8 x 15", 16 x 6"	8 x 15", 16 x 6"	[Never built.]

Hull £755,000   Hull £715,000   Hull £736,000
Machinery £445,000   Machinery £300,000   Machinery £395,000
Total £1,200,000   Total £1,015,000   Total £1,131,000

Fairfield prices for above were:
Hull £762,000   Hull £722,000   Hull £742,000
Machinery £460,000   Machinery £305,000   Machinery £400,000
Total £1,222,000   Total £1,027,000   Total £1,142,000

---

4 May 1914
Admiralty
Proposed battleship of 25,750 tons
Prices similar to 10 July 1913 quote.

Swan Hunter	962,240
Cammell Laird	965,000
Vickers	966,000
Armstrong	975,000

[In pencil]
Beardmore   943,190
Fairfield   944,000
Palmers   945,000
Scott   961,000

[For the later *Royal Sovereign* class ships, *Renown* (Fairfield) and *Repulse* (Palmers), subsequently changed to battlecruisers.]

---

18 January 1915
Admiralty.
Conditions of contract for building HMS *Repulse*.
Hull – Percentage on wages for establishment charges 46%.
Machinery – Percentage on wages for establishment charges 59%.
Percentage on total for profit 10% in both cases.

[The contract to construct *Repulse* and *Renown* was originally based on *Royal Sovereign* class battleship prices quoted in May 1914, of which there were two. When both contracts were subsequently changed to battlecruisers in January 1915, the war was in progress. This enabled the Admiralty to move quickly without issuing tenders and thus avoided a lengthy procurement process. However, the removal of this process left the Admiralty open to potential overcharging on such cost-plus contracts, subsequently addressed by excess profits legislation introduced later in the war.]

---

9 April 1915
Wallsend Slipway & Engineering Co Ltd
Wallsend on Tyne
Half-set of Brown-Curtis turbines for cruiser for HM Navy.

Materials	14,000	
Royalties	7000	
Labour	11,000	32,000
General charges 100%		11,000
		43,000
Profit		4500
		47,500
5% for contingencies		2380
		49,880

[Successful tender to construct half of the turbines for 4-shaft *Furious* which was under construction at Armstrong Whitworth. Wallsend Slipway was the main contractor, building the other two sets, the boilers and all other elements of the ship's machinery.]

---

9 June 1915
Imperial Japanese Navy
Kawasaki Dockyard, per J Watanabe.
Japanese battleship No 5
Estimated cost of two HP and two IP cruising turbines and two sets of gearing together with one spare wheel and two spare pinions for same. Wheels to have cast steel centres.

Material	7830	
Wages	4400	
Total	12,230	
Charges at 125% 5500 =		17,730
Profit at 10%		1770
Total		**19,500**

Extra for delivery at Albert Docks £100.

[Possibly for *Kaga*.]

28 December 1917

Admiralty

Estimate of cost of No 460, HMS Hood

Hull

Structural Materials	532,000	
Outfit Materials	212,500	
Dredging, light, coal etc. less scrap	63,000	808,000
Wages		800,000
Charges 38%		304,000
		1,912,000

Machinery

Materials Engines	522,000	
Materials Boilers	92,000	614,000
Wages Engines	175,000	
Wages Boilers	66,000	241,000
Charges 50%		120,500
		975,500

Hull	1,912,000
Machinery	975,500
	2,887,500
Auxiliaries	72,500
	2,960,000
Profit	288,750
Total	3,248,750

[Because the First World War was in progress, *Hood* was not tendered for in the normal way. Consequently the Admiralty selected four shipbuilders to construct the four ships of the *Hood* class. Orders were on a cost-plus basis with shipbuilders asked to quote their estimated price as soon as possible. Although *Hood* was laid down in September 1916, the major design changes made to the *Hood* class made it impossible for the shipbuilder to provide an estimate of costs until the above submitted in December 1917. As with Admiralty contracts, this excluded armament and armour.]

Above: Last of the First World War capital ships, *Hood*'s after turrets in the fitting-out basin at Clydebank in December 1919. The stern of the 'V&W' class destroyer *Veteran* can be seen at lower left. (*Author's collection courtesy of NRS*)

14 October 1919
Chilean Government
Coventry Syndicate
Battle Cruiser 'A' Design, 660' x 104' x 40'6"

	Estimate	Final
Hull and Charges	1,834,500	–
Machinery and charges	1212,500	–
	3,047,000	3,050,000
10% profit	304,700	305,000
Armour	1,032,000	1,032,000
Torpedo and mine equipment	123,000	123,000
(Armstrongs price for torpedoes 73,000)		
Armament and ammunition	1,700,000	1,700,000
Commission	100,000	100,000
Total	6,306,000	**6,310,000**

[in pencil –] Armstrong 5,965,000 (per Captain Crease)
Less 100,000 for second ship.

Battle Cruiser 'B' Design, 670' x 104' x 40'6"

Hull, Machinery and Charges	3,063,000
10% profit	306,300
Armour	984,000
Torpedo and mine equipment	123,000
Armament and ammunition	1,700,000

Commission	100,000
Total	**6,276,300**

[in pencil –] Armstrong 5,965,000 (per Captain Crease)
Less 100,000 for second ship.

Penalties – Battle Cruisers 'A' and 'B' Designs
Speed:
      28 knots, draft 26', 6 hours' trial
      Deficiency of one tenth of a knot for 1st half knot
      £10,000
      Ditto for 2nd half knot £20,000
Radius of Action:
      Commencing displacement 30,500 tons – 6000 miles.
      £50 per mile
Draft:
      26ft in normal conditions – £1500 per 1in increase.
Delivery:
      From date of approval of principal working drawings.
      1st 3.5 years – £100 per day
      2nd 3.75 years – £100 per day

[Coventry Ordnance Works was in process of disposing of its works in 1919, but if an order had resulted would no doubt have continued.]

7 October 1921
Admiralty
Proposed battlecruiser for HM Navy
Displacement 48,000 tons, 160,000 shp Brown-Curtis turbines, 20 small tube boilers 3-drum type WP 250lbs.

	Labour	Materials	
Hull	948,130	709,870	1,658,000
Electrical	96,500	159,500	256,000
	1,044,630	869,370	1,914,000
Engines	304,200	656,937	961,137
Boilers	83,000	141,000	224,000
Aux machinery			139,863
	1,325,000		
less cut of		60,000	1,265,000
Establishment charges and profit			700,000
Total			**3,879,000**

In the above tender, the following reductions were made from original estimates –
Hull.

Indirect labour from 7.5% to 5% of direct labour	20,000

Engines and Boilers
Indirect labour from 7.5% to 5% of direct labour	10,000

6% on direct labour for a further reduction
in 1922 of 6/– per week over and above the 12/5%

		19,200
£9 per ton on castings		8425

Reduction in hope of 4-turbine arrangement being adopted without a rebate

Labour 11,800, materials 28,063	39,863	
'Cut' off total price		60,000
Total machinery reduction		139,063

[This is the successful tender for a G3 battlecruiser ordered in October 1921 but cancelled in February of the following year. This was a time when previously high wartime material and labour costs were being reduced and the shipbuilder has endeavoured to show how these reductions have been included.]

15 April 1921
Spanish Government
La Sociedad Espanola de Construccion Naval. Madrid

	Design A Battleship	Design B Battleship	Design C Battlecruiser	Design D Battlecruiser
Hull. Wages and Material	2,210,000	2,055,000	2,845,000	2,645,000
Machinery. Wages and Material	500,000	500,000	1,100,000	970,000
Armour. (Excluding gun shields)	1,774,000	1,809,700	2,538,400	2,002,900
Armament. (Excluding ammunition)	–	–	–	–
Sundry expenses				

General expenses	not included
Industrial profits	not included
Cost of design	not included
Technical guarantee	not included
and other High Office expenses	

Trials etc.,	included in Hull and Machinery
Insurance	included in Hull and Machinery
Launching	included in Hull and Machinery
Docks and other similar expenses	included in Hull and Machinery

Note: No armament prices are included. Searchlight and torpedo control will be included in the armament prices, which will also include the gun shields.

With respect to the above designs, and in accordance with the requirements of the Draft Contract between La Sociedad Espanola de Construccion Naval and the Ministry of Marine, the British Firms, acting as technical guarantors to La Sociedad for the construction of the ships for the Spanish Government, hereby certify that the figures given above for the various items are the actual estimated costs of wages and materials at the present day for building the ships in British shipyards.

[Each of the above designs had an alternative which affected the prices marginally. In 1908, Armstrong Whitworth, John Brown and Vickers, Sons & Maxim entered into an agreement with the Spanish Government to provide technical assistance to them in the construction of ships under their Navy Law of 1908. See Chapter 10.]

---

23 November 1922

Armstrong Whitworth and Swan Hunter & Wigham Richardson

Main propelling and auxiliary machinery for proposed Battleship for HM Navy
Brown-Curtis turbines driving 2 shafts, shp 45,000. Boilers, 8 Yarrow type WP 250lbs.

	Material	Wages	Total
Engines	213,900	114,800	328,700
Boilers	49,325	29,160	78,485

Wages for overtime and increases etc.			12,865
Margin			2950
			423,000
Extra for delivery on NE Coast	9730	5500	15,230
			438,230

[Unsuccessful machinery tender for *Nelson*. It is possible that Armstrongs used John Brown's price as a basis for ensuring their own price was lower or for obtaining a lower price from Wallsend Slipway.]

---

25 November 1922

Admiralty

Proposed battleship for HM Navy 660' x 106' x 55'3", 35,000 tons displacement.
Engines Brown-Curtis turbines (2 shafts) Boilers, 8 Yarrow type, WP 250 lbs.

Hull	
Materials	604,000
Wages including 49,000 for wage increases	539,000
Armour	92,450
	1,235,450

SY charges 12.5% on 539,000	68,000
EW charges 18% on 156,825	28,000
Extra cost of overtime and nightshift on machinemen, erecting and boat fitters	7000
5/– increase on wages for last 12 months of contract	17,000
	108,000
Strengthening and alteration to crane	20,000
Machinery	
Materials	263,225
Wages	144,775
(machinery charges included in hull price)	
	1,771,500

[This is John Brown's unsuccessful tender for *Rodney* or *Nelson*, the orders for which went to Cammell Laird (*Rodney*) and Armstrong Whitworth (*Nelson*), the latter with machinery subcontracted to Wallsend Slipway.]

[In pencil-]
Extreme estimate without charges

Hull	1,176,000
Machinery	384,000
Total	1,560,000

[Had John Brown tendered tendered with the figures in the pencil note above, they would have replaced Cammell Laird with the second lowest price and won the order for *Nelson*, but incurred a significant loss]

	Hull	Machinery	Total
Armstrong	1,130,000	349,000	1,479,000
Cammell L	1,215,000	348,000	1,563,000
Swan H	1,267,000	349,000	1,616,000
Fairfield	1,275,000	375,000	1,650,000
Palmers	1,291,000	476,000	1,767,000
Brown	1,363,000	408,000	1,771,000

Beardmore	1,378,000	396,000	1,775,000
Vickers	1,476,000	382,000	1,858,000
Scotts	1,478,000	581,000	2,059,000

[Actual prices submitted for these ships. Armstrong and Cammell Laird tendered at a loss to win these contracts, see Chapter 11 for *Rodney*.]

Actual Machinery Estimate

Materials	263,225
Labour	156,825
Charges	28,000
	448,050

[John Brown's cost for the machinery. They tendered at £408,000 which implies the removal of all charges, so covering only direct costs.]

---

8 August 1935

Admiralty

New machinery for HMS *Renown*

120,000 shp at 275 rpm

Engines   4 sets Geared Parsons Turbines each 1 HP, 1 LP, and astern turbine and 1 set single reduction gearing

Main Boilers   8 small tube type, 350 lb WP and 230°F superheat

	Generating surface	94,560 sq ft
	Superheating surface	15,920 sq ft
	Air heating surface	25,200 sq ft.
Aux Boiler	1 small tube type, 350lb WP	
	Generating surface	2570 sq ft
	Air heating surface	700 sq ft

Admiralty supply certain of the auxiliaries, recondition and fit shafting and supply and fit new propellers.

Estimated Cost

	Material	Labour	Total
Engines	249,195	79,140	328,335
Boilers	103,615	42,175	145,790
	352,810	121,315	474,125
Power, Insurance and upkeep of Tools 12%			14,560
			488,685
Charges @ 50%			60,655
			549,340
Extra cost of delivery and erection at Dockyard			10,155
			559,495
Profit 7.8%			45,000
Increase of wages or materials			10,000
Contingencies			43,505
			658,000

[Unsuccessful tender. The contract was awarded to Cammell Laird.]

---

26 November 1936

Admiralty

New main and auxiliary machinery and boilers for HMS *Queen Elizabeth*.

Material	306,170
Delivery at Portsmouth	9,900
Labour	103,580
	419,650
Power & Insurance 12%	12,430
	432,080

Charges at 50%	51,790	
	483,870	
Profit 10%	48,387	
	532,257	
Contingencies	105,743	**638,000**

Completion of contract 15 September 1939.

[Unsuccessful tender. The 80,000shp contract was awarded to Fairfield.]

---

26 November 1936

Admiralty

New machinery for *Valiant*

Material	257,345
Delivery at Devonport	7015
Labour	78,160
P&I 12%	9380
Charges at 50%	39,080
Profit	39,098

| Contingencies | 111,922 |
| Total | **542,000** |

Completion of contract 15 September 1939.

[Unsuccessful tender. The contract was awarded to Parsons Marine. The lower material and labour figure than *Queen Elizabeth* suggests a slightly different specification plus some reduction because it was a repeat design.]

---

15 February 1937

Admiralty

Proposed battleship for HM Navy

Engines 4 set Parsons type geared turbines 100,000 shp at 230 rpm

110,000 shp at 236 rpm

Boilers 8 small tube with superheaters. 400lb WP and 250°

Fahrenheit superheat.

Hull

Material			736,550
Wages	Ironworkers	242,400	
	Increase 5%	12,100	254,500
	Remainder	385,870	
	Increase 15%	57,880	443,750

			1,434,800		
P&I	12%	75,390			
	Increase 10%	8410	83,800		
Charges	50%	314,140			
	Increase 10%	34,960	349,100	1,867,700	

Electrical

Material			118,700	
Wages		41,350		
	Increase 10%	6200	47,550	
			166,250	
P&I		4960		
	Increase 15%	765	5725	
Charges		20,675		
	Increase 15%	3100	23,775	195,750

Machinery

Material			468,900
Wages		159,000	
	Increase 15%	23,500	182,500
P&I		19,080	

		Increase 15%	2820	21,900	
Charges			79,520		
		Increase 15%	11,730	91,250	764,550
					2,828,000

Delivery – On Firth of Clyde 15 January, 1941

Hull	Basis price	1,832,300	
	Profit	183,700	
	Increased wages	150,000	
	Increase in materials	35,000	
	Contingencies	37,000	
	Yard equipment	15,000	
	Probable delay in delivery of Sub-Contracts & Admiralty supplies	30,000	2,283,000

Electrical	Basis price	190,500	
	Profit	19,000	
	Increased wages	10,000	
	Increase in materials	5000	
	Contingencies	5000	229,500

Above: *Duke of York*'s forward superstructure captured by the John Brown photographer on 6 September 1941, the day before leaving Clydebank. Anti-aircraft weapons, directors, aircraft equipment, searchlights and boats are all fitted. The destroyer at left is *Onslow*. (*Upper Clyde Shipbuilders*)

Above: *Duke of York* leaves Clydebank for Rosyth on 7 September 1941, assisted by tug/tender *Paladin*, drawing 31ft amidships, 2.5ft short of her deep draft. *(Upper Clyde Shipbuilders)*

Machinery	Basis price	787,500	
	Profit	78,700	
	Increased wages	30,000	
	Increase in materials	15,000	911,200
			3,423,700

Tender Price	Hull	2,270,000
	Electrical	233,000
	Machinery	906,000
		3,409,000
	Contribution from F	14,700

Insurance	(1) Underwriters to be liable for all claims up to £500,000. Admiralty to indemnify for any excess over that amount	23,500
	(2) As at (1) but cover to the extent of £2,000,000	25,000

[Successful tender for *Duke of York*. With more complex ships by the Second World War, cost estimators would have to go into more detail than the First World War era to get to a price, hence this and subsequent more detailed account in John Brown records.]

....

31 January 1939
Admiralty
Proposed battleship for HM Navy
740' x 105' x 52'6" Displacement 40,000 tons
Engines – 4 set Parsons type geared turbines 130,000 shp
Boilers – 8 small tube type with superheaters. 400lb WP and 250° F superheat.

	HULL	ELECTRICAL	MACHINERY
TENDER PRICE	2,835,000	288,000	1,035,000

Delivery: Firth of Clyde – 42 months from date of order.
Auxiliary machinery   86,030

[Tender total £4,158,000 for one of the first two battleships of the *Lion* class, the orders for which went to Vickers-Armstrongs (*Lion*) and Cammell Laird (*Temeraire*).]

17 July 1939

Admiralty

Proposed battleship for HM Navy, 40,000 tons Displacement

Engines – 4 set Parsons type geared turbines 130,000 shp

Boilers – 8 small tube type with superheaters. 400lb WP and 250° F superheat.

Hull

Material				826,600
Wages	Ironworkers 16,080 tons @£21.5/ton		345,720	
	Plumbers	40,000		
	Engineers	125,000		
		165,000		
	Add 7.5%	12,400	177,400	
	Other trades	310,950		
	Add 5%	15,600	326,550	
			849,670	
P&I 12%			101,950	
Charges 50%			424,830	1,376,450
				2,203,050
	Increase now estimated			8000
	To cover long term uncertainties			9000
Total hull				2,220,050

Electrical

Material			140,000	
Wages		50,000		
	Add	5000		
		55,000		
	P&I 12%	6600		
	Charges 50%	27,500	89,100	
			229,100	
	Increase now estimated	2000		231,100

Machinery

Material			551,000	
Wages		186,500		
	Add 15%	28,000		
		214,500		
P&I 12%		25,800		
Charges 50%		107,250	347,550	
			898,550	
	+3%	26,950		
		925,500		
	Increase now estimated	2000		927,500
[Total				3,378,650]

	HULL	ELECTRICAL	MACHINERY
Estimated Price	2,220,050	231,100	927,500
Basis Price	2,264,400	240,300	938,000
Profit 10%	222,300	24,000	94,000
Wages Increase	150,000	10,000	
Materials increase	50,000	5000	
Yard Equipment	15,000		
Delays in delivery of sub-Contractor & Admiralty supplies	30,000		
Contingencies	42,000	6000	
	2,773,700	285,300	1,032,000
Transferred from Machinery	4000		−4000
	2,777,700	285,300	1,028,000

Delivery: Firth of Clyde – 52 months from date of order.
Auxiliary machinery   89,030

[Total £4,180,030 including auxiliary machinery. Tender for the second two battleships of the *Lion* class, the orders for which one each was given to John Brown (*Conqueror*) and Fairfield (*Thunderer*), both later cancelled.]

---

17 October 1941
HMS *Vanguard*
Make-up of the main items for a Tender based on present-day cost of materials and on present-day rates of wages etc.

	HULL	ELECTRICAL	MACHINERY
Materials	1,090,000	182,000	748,000
Labour	1,470,000	127,000	300,000
Charges	440,000	38,000	150,000
Profit	300,000	35,000	120,000
Contingencies	145,000	25,000	30,000
TOTAL	3,445,000	407,000	1,348,000

Future increases in cost of materials and labour and increased cost which might result from air raids, air raid warnings and other dislocations due to enemy action are not provided for in the above sums.

Sent privately to Mr Jubb for purposes of instalment payments.

[This estimate for *Vanguard*, which was laid down on 2 October 1941, gives a total of £5,200,000.]

Above: *Vanguard* was laid down on Clydebank's Berth No. 3 on 2 October 1941, the same berth as *Duke of York* and *Roberts*. Progress was delayed by shortage of labour and more urgent priorities. By May 1944, her sides and bilge keels are complete, but much work has still be done on her upper deck, especially forward. The ring bulkhead to support X turret is being erected. The derricks could only lift five tons. *(Upper Clyde Shipbuilders)*

---

25 May 1945
Admiralty
J1567 – HMS *Vanguard*
(Excluding separately priced auxiliaries)
HULL

Materials	1,222,250	
Labour	1,790,000	
Charges at 27%	483,300	
	3,495,550	
Profit at 7.5%	262,165	
	3,757,715	
Levy 0.25% on above	9400	3,767,115

ELECTRICAL INSTALLATION

Materials	240,400	
Labour	210,000	
Charges at 27%	56,700	
	507,100	
Profit at 7.5%	38,030	
	545,130	
Levy 0.25% on above and on separately priced auxiliaries	1580	546,710

MACHINERY AND BOILERS

Materials	795,000	
Labour	410,000	
Charges at 39%	160,000	
	1,365,000	
Profit at 7.5%	102,375	
	1,467,375	
Levy 0.25% on above and on separately priced auxiliaries	4000	1,471,375
TOTAL		5,785,200

This vessel is being fitted for tropical service.

The foregoing prices allow for all Extras and Rebates which have been officially notified to us up to and including this date (25 May 1945) and for trials in accordance with Specification Part IB and Part IV Machinery, also opening up of machinery after trials.

Any rebates will be offered on completion of the vessel for any trials and opening up not carried out.

[Chapter 11 gives the final price as agreed post-war as £5,802,746. The levy was for Shipbuilding Conference expenses.]

Appendix 2:

Armour, the Admiralty and Parliament: Investigating Collusion and Monopoly Prices

SHORTLY AFTER THE 1913–14 NAVY ESTIMATES had been published in March 1913, the House of Commons appointed a Select Committee to examine and report on them, in effect reviewing value for money. The procurement of armour plate formed an important issue in their deliberations, the MPs suspecting that a manufacturers' ring (cartel) existed and that prices were higher than they should be. Three key witnesses were:

Dr T J Macnamara MP Parliamentary and Financial Secretary to the Admiralty (since 1908)
Sir F W Black Director of Contracts (since 1906)
Mr H W Whiting Superintendent of Contract Work (since 1912).

But the proceedings and minutes of evidence showed that the MPs could not get all the information they requested, with these three witnesses unable or unwilling to provide complete answers, especially on prices. The published report ran to over 300 pages and 4364 questions when published on 24 July 1913.[1] Some of the relevant questions (numbers in square brackets) and answers are quoted verbatim in quotation marks, with the authors' comments in italics.

Dr Macnamara was questioned first on 31 March 1913:

[32] Q: 'Is there any foundation for the assertion that the price of armour plates is forced up by means of a combination of the manufacturers pro [who] produce these things?' A: 'We have secured reductions in the cost of armour plate within recent years… There are five great firms, and we have so far laid it down that we must not be dependent on foreign supplies … and therefore not having open competition available to us, we being in this restricted competition that we get all the work done in this country under our own supervision, I daresay the price may probably be higher than it would be if we were in the open market with competitors on all sides.'

[36] Q: 'What I am suggesting is that there is an impression in existence that these armour plate manufacturers are making most exorbitant profits?' A: 'I hold no brief for them, but I do not think that can be borne out. The making of

armour plating is a very specialised industry; it requires, in the first instance, very expensive plant – expending capital in laying it down, they have many failures, and there is no finality… I do not think it would be fair … to say that they make enormous profits.'

Vickers and Armstrong certainly did with armour – see Chapter 11, page 247.

[42] Q: 'Do you mean that there are only five manufacturers of armour plating altogether in the kingdom?' A: 'Yes'. Q: 'Would it not be easy for those five to combine and keep up prices?' A: 'Yes, certainly, and we make constant representations on the question of price.'

[45] Q: 'Is there any way of comparing the prices that you pay for armour plating with the prices paid by foreign Powers?' A: 'No, I think not.' Q: 'There has never been any investigation into that?' A: 'It would be difficult for us to make such an inquiry.'

[70] Q: 'Do you ever publish in any way the prices you pay for armour plate?' A: 'There have been some figures. I think on one occasion a reply was given as to the price in general terms… I do not think there has been any precise figure given at any time showing the price per ton of various types of armour plate.' Q: 'Would there be any public injury, do you think, in your handing in such a statement, so far as you are concerned?' A: 'Let me put this to my honourable friend. Supposing I were to say that certain armour plate costs so much a ton, and then supposing it was stated that the hull of a certain ship cost so much, you would know how much armour plate she had in her. In those Estimates there are statements showing what is proposed to be spent on the hull of a ship … Then if I were to tell you the price of armour plate of a particular kind per ton, I think if you were an ingenious person (I am not suggesting that you are not) you could arrive at the amount of armour plate in a particular ship.'

That would not be possible: the hull weight and cost also include protective plating and hull structure and fittings. Armour was also used in gun shields, which came under 'Armament' weight. However a reasonable outline of the vessel and the thickness of the main parts of the armour were often published, e.g. in Brassey's, so that a better estimate of armour weight could be made by direct calculation, without knowing the price per ton – which varied significantly with shape and thickness.

[147] Q: 'Do the high profits of the contracting firms for armour plate come under the review of the Admiralty as a reason for asking for a reduction in price. For example, when one looks at the balance sheets, the dividends that accrue to contracting firms are very high?' A: 'For armour plate?' Q: 'Yes, they are very high'. A: 'I should say that they are very high; but as I have said already, when some phrase was used suggesting that they were stupendous, I said that I did not think so… I think the prices are still high, and hope to see them reduced.'

Black was next, making several appearances before the Committee from 7 April.

[600] Q: 'Do you not think that the existence of a sort of close corporation [cooperation] would tend to raise prices? … What I mean is that if a man came in and knew that there was free competition between three other firms, he would know that the prices would be cut considerably, but knowing that they had a combination to keep prices up, would he not naturally raise his prices to something approaching theirs?' A: 'As a matter of trade, that is a possibility, of course; but one can form a rough general opinion as to whether that kind of trade is particularly profitable or not, by studying the balance sheets of particular firms, and if you take some of these, which appear in the public press … you will find, I think, that the highest dividend paid by any of these big firms of recent years has been 12½ [%]; you will find that 10% is a very ordinary dividend, and you will find that some firms have not paid any dividend at all on their ordinary shares.'

Black had been questioned about gun mountings as well as armour; his first dividend comment would apply to Vickers and Armstrong, and his last to Cammell Laird and Coventry Ordnance Works.

[631] Q: 'Has there been any corresponding reduction in the price of armour plates through the [Harvey and Krupp]

Above: An example of the elaborate advertisements that shipbuilders used in the technical press.

royalties having no longer to be paid?' A: 'Yes; the whole of those royalties have ceased to be payable. I think that the last fell in three or four years ago.'

[633] Q: ' … I would like to ask what is the price per ton that the British Admiralty is paying now?' A: 'I would rather ask to be excused from giving that information…'

[905] Q: 'You will remember that we had some talk the other day about the prices paid for armour plate by Foreign Powers, and the meagre information that was available as to those prices, and also as to that fact that the Admiralty does not appear to have made any searching attempt to obtain the prices paid in other countries?' A: 'I think we cannot really get any very exact or reliable information on that point. We do get a certain amount of general information, but, as I explained at the last meeting, the price of armour plate is not merely a matter of price per ton; so that you cannot make a direct comparison of the prices in different countries. The price will vary according to the quality, shape, and the finishing of the plates, and according to the thicknesses; and what you read in the papers perhaps as the American price or the French or the German price may or may not be the basis price for a rectangular plate of a certain thickness and of a uniform standard quality.'

When the Committee came to Vote 8, which included shipbuilding and made up about half the Navy Estimates, Whiting was a an important witness. He had succeeded W E Smith in 1912 when the latter became Director of Naval Construction, a post he held only briefly before Churchill, First Lord, replaced him with d'Eyncourt. The Chairman, Sir Frederick Banbury, started off.

[1971] Q: 'We now come to Item D: "Armour for His Majesty's ships and vessels". This is a very important item, and statements have been made in public that there is a ring which is operating against the Admiralty for the price of armour plate, and I think if I remember rightly some question was raised with Dr Macnamara what, if this was correct, were the best steps that could be taken to counteract it in the interest of economy. Have you anything to say upon that point?' A: 'No, except that that particular question must necessarily, I think, be answered by some of the Board [of Admiralty], and not by myself.'

[1973] Q: 'Do you think there is such a ring?' A: 'I think there are certain things which one can see which are quite consistent with the existence of a ring. It is another thing to say that I believe in the existence of a ring, because that would mean some positive proof.' Q: 'Do you think there is any way by which the Admiralty could obtain equally good armour plate at a lower price?' A: 'I am quite sure they could not.'

The Armstrong Whitworth Board used the word 'ring' when deciding whether to enter the armour making business, so its existence was known outside the current makers themselves.

[1978] Q: 'You understand the question I put to you? I intended the question to be, Could you or could you not, if this ring was not in existence, obtain the same thing cheaper, and your answer was "No".' A: 'I did not understand you to put in the hypothetical clause.' Q: 'But it all turns upon that. The object of this Committee is, without touching upon any question of policy [outside the Committee's terms of reference], to see whether or not it can make any recommendations by which the same result would be achieved at a lower price. My question to you is, assuming, for the sake of argument, that there is a ring, could you by making any arrangements either to make armour plate yourselves or to obtain it from some other quarter obtain the same article cheaper?' A: 'I believe that there are no practical steps which can be taken at the present moment which would bring about such a result, but I should like to draw attention to the fact that this comes so nearly within the limit of questions of policy, that it is a matter upon which information should be obtained, I think, if at all, from a member of the Board.'

[1980] Q: 'This Committee is not allowed to ask questions upon matters of policy, but I do not quite see where the policy comes in. Would you explain to the Committee where the question of policy comes in?' A: 'Whether it is possible to put forward any business proposals which should have the effect of cheapening the supply of armour plating in this country is a matter which must necessarily depend upon a great deal of information which would only be accessible to members of the Board in their confidential dealings with all the matters and interests involved.' Q: 'That is rather a different point.' A: 'The people who can deal with your questions thoroughly are the members of the Board, because they alone, have full information on certain points.' Q: 'Which particular members of the Board do you allude to?' A: 'The Third Sea Lord and the Additional Civil Lord in particular.'

Whiting had passed the buck, but was dissembling in implying that the Board had any more knowledge of armour plate, its manufacturers and prices than was supplied by the professional officers such as himself (Superintendent of Contract Work), the Director of Naval Construction and the Director of Contracts. Whiting had the reputation of being a difficult man, and his stonewalling continued, parrying the Committee's questions.

[1985] Q: 'Have you nothing to do with the prices paid for armour?' A: 'I have to report on the subject.' Q: 'When a price is given to you, do you form a judgment as to whether it is a right price or a wrong price? I mean to say, do you report to the Board, "This is a fair price for the article for which we have asked"?' A: 'The whole question of the price of armour is a matter which the Board regard at the present time, and has for many years regarded, as strictly confidential; and they hold that it is against the interests of the public service that these prices should be disclosed.'

[1987] Q: 'I did not ask for any disclosure of prices; what I asked was – and I am very anxious to get an answer – when prices are quoted to you by one of the five firms, or whatever the number of firms is, do you in your own mind form a judgment as to whether it is a fair price to charge for the armour that you propose to order?' A: 'Yes, and I do form a judgment; but the question you put to me is a very difficult

one for me to answer in such a way that it shall be at once accurate and shall not at the same time be misleading. The position of things is this – Supposing that you are considering a certain price for certain armour, there is a basis price, the price, that is to say, on which the prices of all forms of armour are fixed, with which I have very little to do; that is matter which is governed by the business arrangements which have been made between the Government and the five large firms. But when you ask me whether I have to report on the price of armour, I reply that I do so as regards particular contracts for particular portions of armour; on these I have to form a judgment and to report on what is a fair price for particular orders on certain ships.'

[1989] Q: 'Have you not any means of forming a judgment as to the fairness of the general price, so to speak – what you call the base price?' A: 'That is very large question, and I should hesitate to offer a definite opinion upon the point here apart altogether from the question whether I am prohibited from doing so.' Q: 'Are you not really the expert adviser to the Board of Admiralty on this point?' A: 'I am'. Q: 'And are you not as their expert adviser in a better position to know what is a fair price to pay these makers of armour than any member of the Board is likely to be? If you cannot form a judgment, or if you hesitate to say that you can … is any individual in the world in a position to form a judgment?' A: 'I would not go so far as to say that he was not, and for the reasons I pointed out just now. There is information available to members of the Board which is not necessarily at my disposal, information with regard to the many sides of this question. I am afraid there is nothing more that I can tell you with advantage on that point.'

[1993] Q: 'Would you be able to give an estimate to the Government if they said, "Well, now, we are going to make the armour for this ship in our yard," would you tell them what the armour would cost?' A: 'I could not tell them what the armour would cost for some years to come, that is to say, until the plant was got into working order. It would be impossible for me to give an estimate now of what, say, the first 5,000 or 10,000 or 20,000 tons of armour would cost.'

[1996] Q: 'In the circumstances under which armour is ordered by the Admiralty at the present time, would it, in your judgment be an easy thing for the firms that you employ to arrange prices together?' A: 'I think it would be quite possible.' Q: 'Do you think they do arrange prices together?' A: 'That, again, is the question that I was asked to reply to just now, as to whether a ring actually exists. I am not prepared to say that it does not exist. I am not prepared to affirm that it does.'

Whiting's reply was disingenuous. He well knew that for each year's building programme, the armour makers collectively negotiated with the Admiralty a price list that all would adhere to. That required collusion on their part to agree the same price that all were willing to accept – which was far above production cost. The makers were not invited to tender separately. Previously they had asked the Admiralty to preserve the strictest secrecy on armour prices, presumably so as not attract newcomers to this lucrative business.

[2004] Q: 'Then it amounts to this – that whatever price they choose to quote you have got to pay?' A: 'No, I think not; the price is one arranged between the Admiralty and the firms, and, like other prices, is not fixed at the absolute dictation of the firms.' Q: 'Then what alternatives have the Admiralty got from possible unreasonable raising of prices by these five firms?' A: 'There are three possible alternatives; they might encourage an independent firm to set up armour making, they might undertake to make it themselves, or they might obtain it from abroad. All these matters naturally must be taken into consideration by any Government in negotiations of this magnitude, and they constitute, as far as I am aware, the principal weapon, shall I say, that the Government has in entering upon negotiations of that kind.'

[2010] Q: 'Would it be contrary to the public interest to disclose the price paid by the Government for any given thickness of armour?' A: 'Yes, I believe it would be.' Q: 'Has the Admiralty any knowledge of the price paid for armour plating in foreign shipbuilding yards?' A: 'We have some knowledge; some of it has been published. But in making any comparison between the price of armour in this country and the price of armour in other countries it is all but impossible to make that comparison a definite and an accurate one, because of specific differences in the armour itself and differences in the character of the inspection, and the character of the tests are absolutely identical, a mere offhand comparison of prices would be very misleading.'

[2019] Q: 'Have you ever attempted to form any conjecture as to the rate of profit that is being earned by the armour plate manufacturers at the present day?' A: 'I do not think that to conjecture would be of much use, but the Admiralty have taken all steps in that direction which, in my judgment, it has been possible to take.'

[2020] Q: 'We may take it from your answers, I think, that the Government have a basal contract with the five firms which are the only five firms in Great Britain capable of making armour, and we may deduct from that, may we not, that there must be a ring; because, if the Government has only got five firms to deal with, and those five firms deal collectively with the Government, [is] it not fair to deduct that there is a ring?' A: 'I think it is not an unfair deduction.' Q: 'Then we have it that in your opinion there is a ring to keep up the price of armour?' A: 'I do not wish to go further than my last answer ...'

[2031] Q: 'These five firms, then, are what I may call the survival of the fittest. Have many armour plate manufacturers gone into bankruptcy? ... A: '... So far as I know, there are no armour plate making firms who have gone into bankruptcy; but in reply to what I understand is in your mind in asking that question, I would point out that the fact that only five firms have ventured on armour plate manufacture is a very strong presumption that the obtaining of these enormous profits is not a very easy or certain process.' Q: 'Is not that chiefly because it requires a very large capital to start with?' A: 'That alone would not be a sufficient deterrent'. Q: 'But as a matter of experience I may take it, then, that

Above: Part of the armour price list agreed between the Admiralty and the five armour manufacturers – confidential information that was restricted to very few people. *(ADM116/3456)*

practically all the firms who have started armour plate making have continued and are paying, all of them, good, and some of them very high dividends?' A: 'No, that is not the case.' Q: 'Can you give me instances of any firms that have not done so?' A: 'I think it is a matter of public knowledge that some of the armour-plate making firms at this moment are not paying high dividends.'

There was some truth in Whiting's statement. Armstrong, Vickers, John Brown and Cammell Laird had either lowered or passed their dividends in 1912. Beardmore was paying only 5% after four years of no dividend in 1907–10. But Vickers and Armstrong accounts suggest that it was other activities rather than armour making that contributed to reduced profits.[2]

[2035] Q: 'Do you know whether any of those firms who have set up plant have given up armour-plate making?' A: 'No.'

It is not clear if Whiting is saying he does not know, or whether no firms had given up. The latter is true – all five firms had been in business for many decades.

[2036] Q: 'Supposing the Government decided to start an armour-plate manufactory of their own, would they not be able to obtain the armour-plate for the Navy in the end cheaper than they do at the present time?' A: 'That again is a repetition in another form of the question whether we pay a fair price for armour. I am afraid I cannot give you a definite reply to that question; but I do wish to emphasise this point ... that if you were to undertake to set up an armour-plate manufactory you would be undertaking a most difficult and highly speculative process.'

[2039] Q: ' ... Has any armour ever been bought from abroad?' A: 'No.' Q: 'Has the advisability of doing so ever been considered?' A: 'When you say considered, that is very broad expression.' Q: 'What I mean is this. The Admiralty probably have said to themselves, "We would like to get our armour-plate cheaper. One alternative would be to spend a large sum of money in setting up an Arsenal; we cannot find the money in this year's Budget." Then another alternative you pointed out was buying it abroad. Have the Admiralty ever made inquiries abroad as to whether they can get the armour that they want at a reasonable price?' A: 'The Admiralty have, I believe, made all inquiries possible with a view to obtaining armour at the lowest possible rate.' Q: 'Abroad?' A: 'Including, necessarily abroad.' Q: 'Could you tell us what establishments there are abroad where armour-plating such as we use in warships could be obtained apart from State establishments – in America for example?' A: 'There are several establishments in America, and there are also armour-plate establishments in Germany, France and Italy.'

[2046] Q: 'Could you tell us why it is against the public interest to disclose the price paid for armour?' A: 'I can only reply that that is the decision of the Board, and by that I have to abide.'

[2051] Q: 'With regard to a possible ring, have you any reason to suppose that there is a ring of armour-plate manufacturers abroad as well as in England, and if so, are they connected with those here?' A: 'I have not sufficient knowledge to answer that question. If I may merely give it as my personal opinion, I do not think there is now; but I cannot say with any confidence.'

Whiting may well have been right to suggest not 'now' but when the Harvey United Steel Company controlled the Krupp patents, there almost certainly was a ring. Every major international armour maker had a seat on its Board and royalties were paid into a pool which was distributed amongst its members in some way. However after the patents expired and the Harvey company was wound up, it is possible that there was less price fixing internationally. Whiting continued to stall further questions on whether Krupp in Germany, Creusot in France or Bethlehem in USA had ever been asked for prices.

[2062] Q: 'You told Mr Bird [one of the MPs on the Committee] that there were three alternatives to accepting the terms indicated by the armour-plate ring. I want to know whether you have adopted any of these alternatives? The first you said was that you might encourage another firm to start making armour-plate. Have you ever done it?' A: 'That again is a question to which I can only reply in the affirmative if I am prepared to give you a specific instance, and I am not prepared to give you a specific instance. I submit that that question is one which should be addressed to a member of the Board.' Q: 'Can you tell us have any of those alternatives ever been tried?' A: 'Those three alternatives are encouraging an independent firm, or we might start our own factory, or we might buy abroad. We have not started our own factory, and with regard to the other two alternatives, I wish to reply in each case that I cannot give to the Committee any definite information.' Q: 'Do you know?' A: 'Generally, in a general sense I do.' Q: 'And in a general sense, is the answer yes or no?' A: 'I think I must decline to reply to that question.'

[2087] Q: 'Orders for armour-plate are distributed over the whole year for delivery?' A: 'Very generally they are, but I repeat that that is not the only consideration. In giving an armour-plate order to a particular firm regard is always paid, amongst other things, to the condition of that particular firm as regards its manufacturing capacity at that moment.'

Apart from having a high fixed price, this also meant that firms in the ring could expect to be allocated a fair share of whatever Admiralty orders were going, without worrying if their price was competitive.

No doubt irritated by Whiting's continual prevarication, one of the Committee, John Henderson, prefaced his next question with 'I wonder whether I can penetrate this armour.'

[2090] Q: 'Have you had any practical knowledge of the cost of producing plates; have you ever had anything to do with a rolling mill, for instance?' A: 'No'. Q: 'You are not a practical man in any way?' A: 'I am not an expert in the manufacture of armour in that sense at all.' Q: 'Are you an engineer?' A: 'I am a naval constructor; I have been for many years Senior Assistant Director of Naval Construction, and I became Superintendent of Contract Work eight months ago.' Q: 'Have you had any practical experience in works like Brown's, or have you ever gone through them?' A: 'Constantly.' Q: 'I do not mean merely passing through, but have you served in them, in the draughtsmen's office or anywhere?' A: 'Never.'

[2098] Q: 'A general knowledge of what it is usually costing it might be; but the cost of production, taking the materials and the wages and the details of the operations in a rolling mill and machine shops, a man who had been through these shops, and had been through the draughtsmen's office, could always give you some very approximate idea of the cost per ton?' A: 'I venture to express the opinion that he could not, but in any case I have not got that kind of expert knowledge.'

Henderson was quite right in his supposition – any competent engineer observing the plant and operations as Whiting did on his visits should have been able to make an approximate cost estimate after finding out typical material prices and wages. He proceeded to needle Whiting:

[2101] Q: 'You were a clerk in the Admiralty, and you have gone a step up and a step up and come to your present position?' A: 'I beg your pardon; I am not an Admiralty clerk at all. I am an Engineer; I am a Naval Constructor. I have been trained as such. I am not a clerk in any sense' responded Whiting huffily… Q: 'I was suggesting an honourable position.' A: 'Quite.'

[2109] Q: 'With regard to the relations of the Admiralty with certain firms, is there any form of agreement that is entered into by the Admiralty with these five great firms?' … A: 'My answer is that there is a collective arrangement as regards the making of armour-plates.' Q: 'Of course, you do not see your way to tell us what the conditions of that agreement are?' A: 'Precisely.'

That was the nearest that Whiting got to admitting that there was a collective price list.

[2114] Q: 'I should like to ask you whether you know of any Government in the world which manufactures its own armour plate?' A: 'Directly, I think no. I am not sure that there are not Governments which have some association with armour-plate works, but I am not able to reply definitely.'

Whiting appeared not to know that the French government manufactured armour at its Guérigny plant. Brassey's 1912 reported that the price from this works was 40–50 per cent below that of private manufacturers, surely an indication worth investigating that the latter were overcharging. The recently re-equipped Russian state owned Izhorskii Works near St Petersburg was producing armour at around £70 per ton from 1911, well below the British price, trebling output to 19,000 tons in 1914. But unless the British Naval Attaché was particularly diligent in studying the Russian Naval Ministry accounts, such figures were unlikely to have been known in Britain.[3] Whiting also appeared unaware that the US Government also had concerns about high prices of armour. In the 1890s there were only two manufacturers: Bethlehem Steel Company of South Bethlehem, Pennsylvania and Carnegie Steel Company of Munhall, Pennsylvania, selling at prices of around $600 per ton (about £120). After Krupp armour became available from about 1900, prices dropped to around $410, including royalties. The entry of a third manufacturer from 1903, Midvale Steel Company of Philadelphia, initially produced a further drop to around $350 per ton. But the three firms colluded to push prices up to $420–$450 before 1914. From time to time, the US Government explored the idea of setting up its own armour manufacturing plant, reckoning it could produce for around $300. It eventually started building a new plant in 1917 at Charleston, West Virginia, to make steel ingots, forgings and castings, but it did not produce any armour until 1921, by which time demand had virtually disappeared.[4]

[2124] Q: 'Have you formed any estimate yourself as to the cost of producing a ton of armour-plate?' A: 'In existing works do you mean?' Q: 'Or similar works in this country?' A: 'I can hardly say that I have, because that would involve a very considerable amount of investigation'. Q: 'Can you say whether £60 a ton is a reasonable price.' A: 'I should think from the published figures it would be hopeless to get it at such a price.'

The questioner, Sir Alfred Mond [of the Brunner, Mond chemical company, later ICI], was evidently well informed. Vickers' actual production costs around that time were about £40–£50 per ton. At average prices of about £90–£120 per ton, the profit margin was well over 100 per cent. A price of £60–£70 per ton would still have yielded a reasonable profit, and would have saved the Admiralty over £30 per ton.[5] The resulting annual saving on the 34,000 tons produced in 1913 would have been about £1 million, which would have allowed the equivalent of ten extra destroyers to be built each year. With Admiralty inspectors in the works making a few discreet inquiries about how long operations took and how many men were involved and their wage levels and how many of the machine tools and plant were being used, a rough

estimate could have been built up with known material prices to show that the ring's prices were far above their costs. Armed with such figures, the Admiralty would have been in a far better negotiating position. Whiting's lack of technical curiosity cost the nation dear.

[2138] Q: 'With regard to the question of continuity of orders, can you tell me how many months, about in the year, the large armour-plate plants are fully engaged? A: 'For some time past they have been engaged up to the limits of their production.' ... Q: 'So that any claim that they may make that a great deal of their capital has been lying idle for a long time, would not relate to the last three years?' A: 'On the contrary some of the largest firms are increasing their plant very greatly, in order to cope with the present and future orders.' Q: 'These firms, of course, make armour-plate for the ships of other countries beside the British Admiralty?' A: 'They do.' Q: 'And that gives then an advantage in keeping their works fully employed on work other than that for the Government.' A: 'Yes'. Q: 'And they ought therefore, to be able to produce more cheaply on that account than a Government factory?' A: 'That is so.'

[2146] Q: 'Do you think they [armour prices] are still high?'. A: 'To some extent, yes.' Q: 'Not to any considerable extent?' A: 'I do not think they are so high that there is any reasonable expectation of getting a very large reduction in the immediate future'. Q: 'Is that because of the impossibility of securing them, rather than in relation to the cost of production?' A: 'I think it is largely due on the one hand to the great cost of production, secondly to the extent to which the initial outlay and other circumstances preserve them from very large competition, and thirdly to the difficulty of forecasting the demands, both in amount and character, which will be made on our manufacturers in the immediate future.' ... Q: 'Was the price not originally high because of the limited call upon their plant?' A: 'I daresay that reason has been alleged, but I do not recollect it.'

[2154] Q: 'Has there been a considerable reduction in the price of armour-plate in recent years?' A: 'Yes.' Q: 'Could you give us any idea by way of percentage, if not in actual figures, as to what that reduction has been?' A: 'I prefer to defer a reply on that point if I may'. Q: 'Shall we be able to get that information from the Third Sea Lord?' A: 'Possibly, I cannot tell, of course, but I should like to ask for instructions with regard to it.' ... Q: 'Have you made efforts recently by way of representations to these five firms to secure reductions in price?' A: 'The Admiralty has constantly endeavoured to obtain reductions.'

The prices agreed in the June 1913 price list were the same as those in the June 1910 list so any representations seem to have been ineffective. In March 1914, Black and Whiting recommended retaining the same prices for 1914–16, arguing that there were no grounds for asking for a price reduction, especially as the firms were still experimenting to improve the quality of plates.[6] The firms had evidently continued to conceal their huge profit margins, which if known would have been strong grounds for a price reduction.

[2167] Q: 'Is it ever left to the contractors who are

Above: Vickers Sons & Maxim's private Costs, Prices and Profits ledgers reveal just how profitable armour manufacture was before the First World War. In 1908 they produced 1773 tons for the Admiralty at Sheffield sold at £105 per ton but only costing £35 to make. Even after royalty payments to Harvey United Steel Co of about £4.38 a ton, the net profit was still £63 per ton, 60 per cent on sales or 150 per cent on cost. *(Sheffield Archives)*

building ships to make their own arrangements for the manufacture of armour plate?' A: 'Only in the sense that sometimes the main shipbuilding contract is made with an armour-plate firm, and in that case it is sometimes convenient for the detailed arrangements with regard to the supply and the time of supply of armour to be made as between two branches of the same firm; but that does not alter the financial or other arrangements of the Admiralty with regard to either the ship or the armour.'

[2168] Q: 'Did I rightly understand that you never get a tender for a completely-fitted ship? I do not mean with guns and gun mountings, but a whole ship fitted up with armour?' A: 'I would not go so far as to say that it has never been done but that is not the usual form of a shipbuilding and armour contract.' Q: 'May I ask you what is the objection to that?' A: 'It is rather that I think there would be no advantage in that method. The simpler method is to do as we do, undertake to supply armour under our definite agreement, and then call for tenders for the ship.'

If such were the case, those shipbuilders who were also armour manufacturers would probably lower the armour price for their own tenders and raise it for their competitors who had no such plant. While this might reduce the ship cost overall, it would concentrate battleship building in the hands of those five companies (Vickers, Armstrong Whitworth, Brown, Cammell Laird, Beardmore). With central procurement of armour (and gun mountings) there was at least a level playing field for all shipbuilders.

[2182] Q: 'Do you know the prices actually paid for armour.' A: 'I do.' Q: 'How many people in the Admiralty

know?' A: 'Very few.' Q: 'Ten?' A: 'Possibly.' Q: 'Twenty?' A: 'I should think not.'

And with that Whiting departed, leaving the Committee little the wiser on armour, but hoping they might get more out of the Third Sea Lord five days later on 5 May. Tantalisingly Rear-Admiral A G H W Moore (who was previously Director of Naval Ordnance) gave his evidence in confidence, so no record was published. But he may have been more forthcoming than Whiting, as despite the Committee's misgivings about the armour ring and the high prices, that section of their report was hardly critical. Paragraphs 17 and 18 stated: 'On the question of armour-plating and its cost, your Committee received valuable information from the Third Sea Lord, which the Admiralty asked should be treated as confidential. They desire to say that, after a careful consideration of Admiral Moore's evidence, they are satisfied that, having regard to the particular considerations which must govern the Admiralty in dealing with this matter, the money voted is efficiently administered, with a due regard to economy so far as it is compatible with considerations of fighting efficiency. Your Committee heard evidence with reference to the difficulties in obtaining competitive tenders for armour plating and gun mountings, owing to the existence of Trade Rings, and are of the opinion that it is desirable that the question should be further carefully considered by His Majesty's Government.' But this recommendation seems not to have been followed up, and once war broke out, it was production at any price that counted.

Appendix 3:

The British Battleship Breaking Industry

BRITAIN ALSO DEVELOPED A 'BATTLESHIP breaking' industry, although on a far more modest scale than the building industry. Seventy-nine British-built battleships and battlecruisers from the *Majestic* class onwards were broken up from 1919 to 1960, twenty-five were lost in action, and seven to other causes such as internal explosion. A shipbreaking industry had developed in Britain from the 1890s, by which time early iron steamships had come to the end of their lives. While wooden sailing vessels had practically no scrap value, iron and later steel could be recycled in open hearth furnaces. Thomas W Ward Ltd of Sheffield was one of the first to recognise the potential of this new

industry, starting shipbreaking yards at Preston, Barrow, Morecambe and Briton Ferry in South Wales before the First World War. Surplus naval vessels would be regularly offered for sale, especially after Fisher's clear-out of obsolete vessels from 1905, with auctions being held at naval Dockyards.

After the First World War, the Admiralty had a huge surplus of naval vessels, some only a few years old. Some were sold for conversion to commercial use, but most were sold for scrap at low prices to clear the Dockyards. Ward was a major buyer of such ships, scouring the British coastline for additional shipbreaking sites. From 1919, they set up new yards at Hayle and Lelant in Cornwall, New Holland

Above: T W Ward Ltd broke up four battleships at their main Inverkeithing yard between 1948 and 1951. In May 1949, *Rodney* is shown on the beaching ground (drying out at low tide to allow a hulk to be completely removed), *Nelson* at the main deep water berth with its 50-ton crane, with *Revenge* outboard. *(Newcastle University Marine Technology Special Collection)*

on the Humber, Grays and Rainham in Essex on the Thames, and Milford Haven. All these yards could take warships up to light cruiser size, though Milford Haven did handle the pre-dreadnought *Prince of Wales*. But they invested most in a new yard at Inverkeithing, just downstream of the Forth Bridge and close to Rosyth Dockyard, to handle the largest ships. It had a new deep water jetty built with a 50-ton crane, with some berths drying out at low tide to enable the hulks to be finished off. Its first battleship was *Dreadnought* herself, arriving on 2 January 1923. She was one of 113 surplus vessels sold by the Admiralty en bloc to Ward on 9 May 1921 at a flat rate of £2.50 per ton actual displacement, later reduced to £2.20. *Dreadnought* was assessed at 16,650 tons so cost them £36,650. Ward also handled two German battleships handed over to Britain after the First World War; *Helgoland* was lightened at Birkenhead in 1921 before being finished at Morecambe. They also took over part of Pembroke Dockyard for shipbreaking when the Admiralty closed it in 1926.

But there were so many surplus vessels that the regular British shipbreaking industry could not handle them all. Dozens of small opportunist breakers sprang up on creeks all over the country, but these were mostly short-lived amateurs who soon went out of business. The British government allowed some warships to be sold abroad, including to Holland and Germany. In the latter case, several German shipbreakers set up a subsidiary Slough Trading Co Ltd about 1921, which bought British warships including eight battleships and towed them to Germany for demolition, e.g. *Hercules* at Kiel in 1922. One of the few new yards that was professionally managed was Alloa Shipbreaking Co Ltd, who started in 1923 at Charlestown, a small harbour just west of Rosyth. By producing their own oxygen on site more cheaply than it could be brought in stored in cylinders, it could reduce cutting costs by using oxy-acetylene torches compared with the traditional 'unbuttoning' where the head

Above: *Duke of York* at Shipbreaking Industries' Faslane yard in August 1959 looking forward. The large rectangular space is Y magazine. Her four valuable manganese bronze propellers are half out of the water. The tapered lower side armour strake still stands proud on her starboard side. *(Author)*

Above: *Duke of York* at Faslane in August 1959 looking aft reveals the layout of her machinery spaces. The three open compartments abreast are the harbour machinery room (centre) and the two engine rooms driving the outer shafts. The two compartments ahead are their boiler rooms, each with two oil-fired boilers, while the two astern are the boiler rooms for her after engine rooms driving the inner shafts, directly behind. *(Author)*

of each rivet was manually cut off with hammer and chisel to separate the plates and stiffeners. They also extracted maximum resale value by separating and grading valuable non-ferrous metals like bronze and gunmetal – plentiful in warships with high-powered machinery. In 1926 they leased deepwater berths at Rosyth Dockyard, which had been put on a care and maintenance basis by the Admiralty. This enabled them to bid for battleships, their first purchase being *Ajax* at Portsmouth on 9 November 1926 for £59,287 – see photo on p.34.[1] They had to pay 10 per cent before they could remove the ship, with the balance six months later, financed partly from a Royal Bank of Scotland loan. She arrived at Rosyth in tow on 14 December, with her much cut-down hulk being moved to Charlestown on 24 February 1928 for final demolition. Over the next six years they broke up six battleships, double the rest of the British industry put together.

Alloa changed its name to Metal Industries Ltd (MI) in 1929 – it had never actually operated at Alloa further up the Forth. It also bought hulks of German battleships scuttled at Scapa Flow in 1919 and salvaged by Cox & Danks in the late 1920s. The hulks were towed south, usually floating upside down on a cushion of compressed air, where MI had temporarily leased one of the Rosyth drydocks from the Admiralty. Wooden blocks were built up to support the unevenly shaped hull, which could then be demolished in the dry. The first such vessel was the battlecruiser *Moltke* bought for £40,000, which arrived at Rosyth on 18 May 1928. MI took over Cox & Danks' plant in 1933 and then bid itself for other wrecks at Scapa. The Admiralty sold *Bayern* for only £750[2] – not knowing the true value of the hulks but glad to get rid of them. MI managed the salvage operations with better equipment much more professionally and quickly than Cox. Altogether they broke up eleven such vessels at Rosyth until the Second World War put an end to operations at Scapa and Rosyth. The ships were hugely profitable to MI yielding around £60,000 each, and enabling the company to go public in 1935, and the founders to make a good profit selling some of their shares.

With treaties requiring Britain to dispose of or demilitarise many of its battleships and battlecruisers, nine were scrapped between 1927 and 1932. In the depression of the 1930s, steel scrap prices fell to £1.50 per ton compared with £3.50 per ton in the 1920s. Breakers could only offer about £30,000 for a battleship, less than 2 per cent of cost new. But breakers also had plenty of merchant ships to keep them busy in the shipping depression of the 1930s, although many British ships were sold to Continental or Japanese buyers.

During the Second World War, shipbreaking effectively ceased, as every obsolete vessel was pressed into service, if only for harbour duties or as blockships. British shipbreakers were contracted to recover as much steel scrap as possible from wrecks around the coast, whether arising from the perils of the sea or from enemy action. After the Second World War, there was another massive warship disposal programme, both for commercial sale and for breaking up.

Above: *Anson's* hulk on the beaching ground at Faslane in May 1959. The transverse bulkhead separates the forward boiler rooms from the forward engine room. The three layer side protection scheme below the armour belt can be seen: the outermost and innermost ones empty, the inner would be filled with oil fuel or water which gave maximum protection against torpedoes. *(Author)*

All the remaining pre-war battleships, battlecruisers and those converted to aircraft carriers like *Furious* went to the breakers as soon as the yards could handle them, such was the demand for steel for post-war reconstruction. Ward at Inverkeithing received four within fifteen months, including *Nelson* and *Rodney*, resulting in some impressive pictures from the company photographer and even a publicity brochure commemorating their passing – see example on p.186. In some cases, their heavy guns had been removed by the Admiralty before demolition, e.g. 15in as spares or for test purposes. As all their steel had been made before the atomic bombs had been dropped in 1945, it was free from even the slightest radioactive contamination, so could be sold at a good price for lining test chambers.

Metal Industries had to give up most of their lease at Rosyth Dockyard in 1939 when the Dockyard was put on a war footing, but kept a small site at the north-west corner of the yard, where together with nearby Charlestown, vessels up to destroyer size could be handled after the war. They were therefore given first refusal on the lease of the emergency military port at Faslane on the Clyde. This had been built in 1942 to supplement the overloaded west coast port facilities – German air attacks had reduced the value of ports on the south and east coast. A similar facility at Cairnryan near Stranraer was leased to Arnott, Young & Co Ltd in 1948. The latter's main yard was at Dalmuir on the Clyde, using part of the former Beardmore shipyard, which could also handle battleships. As it had no beaching ground, lightened hulks were towed to their associated West of Scotland Shipbreaking Co Ltd yard at Troon, e.g. *Queen Elizabeth*, as were those from Cairnryan, e.g. *Ramillies*. Both emergency ports had rail access, long deepwater quays, but only modest capacity cargo handling cranes (although Cairnryan had a second-hand 60-ton cantilever crane). So some heavier 12-ton Scotch derrick cranes were installed at Faslane and a 60-

Faslane and a 60-ton war-built floating crane was purchased, while a beaching ground was built at the north end of the yard. Faslane saw a succession of seven British battleships/battlecruisers broken up, starting with *Iron Duke* in 1946 and finishing with *Vanguard* in 1960. They also broke up the German battlecruiser *Derfflinger* which they had salvaged at Scapa in 1939. But with no Rosyth drydock available, they had to keep her afloat upside down for seven years. In July 1946 they bought Admiralty Floating Dock No 4, which had been based in the Clyde from 1941, in order to demolish the no longer buoyant upturned hulk. MI also bought *Warspite* for scrapping at Faslane, but she broke her tow from Portsmouth in April 1947, and was driven ashore near Mounts Bay in Cornwall, where she was broken up in situ over the next ten years. They were equally unlucky with the British built Brazilian battleship *Sao Paulo* which was lost on tow from Rio de Janeiro to Faslane in November 1951. MI's shipbreaking division changed its name to Shipbreaking Industries Ltd in 1953, at which time it employed around 200 men. After the Second World War

VANGUARD'S OUTTURN

	Tons	£/ton	£
Steel scrap	22,285	12.00	267,420
Armour	13,789	18.47	254,718
Non-ferrous metals	1910	130.69	249,621
Re-usables and sundries	816	32.83	26,792
Total sales	38,800	20.58	798,551
Purchase price to BISCO			540,000
Demolition costs			216,402
Carriage, towage etc			62,343
Total costs			818,745
Loss to BISCO			-20,194

all battleships were broken up in Scotland, whose shipbreaking yards were more suited to large vessels and where there were nearby steelworks like Colvilles at Motherwell.

Most of the RN battleships broken up from 1947 were not 'sold' as described in reference books but once approved to scrap were 'handed over' by the Admiralty to the British Iron & Steel Corporation (Salvage) Ltd, usually known as BISCO. BISCO was the raw material supply organisation for the British steel industry, so provided most of the steel scrap (and iron ore) for the industry. BISCO would select a breaking yard on the basis of its suitability for a ship of those dimensions (especially depth of water), its facilities and its current workload. It contracted the yard to break up the ship, paying the direct costs of labour, gases etc plus a commission, typically £1 per ton of steel. Steel was despatched by rail to nearby steelworks cut to furnace size (about 5ft x 2ft), while valuable non-ferrous metals were recovered and re-usable equipment sold; from the latter they received a percentage of the sale value. BISCO collected the overall sale proceeds, deducted delivery, breaking costs and commission, and then returned the net proceeds to the appropriate government department, such as the Ministry of Supply (rather than the Admiralty), in effect a deferred sale price. This system remained in force until 1962, after which breakers bid for and paid for ships on their own account, whether naval or merchant. While the last battleship *Vanguard* was broken up under BISCO auspices, unusually a sale price of £540,000 was agreed in advance with the Admiralty. That price was about 4.6 per cent of her original cost, but about 2.5 per cent if inflation 1945 to 1960 is taken into account. Great publicity surrounded her last voyage, enlivened by her running aground on leaving Portsmouth harbour on 4 August 1960, which gained extensive news coverage, as did her arrival at Faslane on 9 August. The barrel of one of her 15in guns was immediately cut off for the benefit of the cameras, but it was not until June 1962 that the last dripping section of double bottom was lifted off the beaching ground. Britain's last battleship had disappeared for ever; the largest preserved British warship is now the cruiser *Belfast*. However one British-built battleship still survives: *Mikasa* preserved as a national memorial at Yokosuka in Japan, albeit without her original armament or machinery.

Above: *Vanguard* at Faslane in November 1960 with A and B turrets removed plus much of her superstructure. Cuts have been made in B barbette armour, but the side armour has yet to be started. *(Author)*

Notes

Chapter 2

1. J T Sumida, *In Defence of Naval Supremacy* (London: Routledge, 1989/93), p.13.
2. Sumida, *In Defence of Naval Supremacy*, p.191.
3. Battlecruisers were not referred to as such until 1911.
4. Quotes in this section are from *Hood*'s Ship's Cover in NMM unless otherwise stated.
5. In the Ship's Covers the ships are referred to as both the Admiral Class and the *Hood* Class.
6. Lord Aberconway was chairman of both Palmers and John Brown and it may be that he was instrumental in suggesting his 'other' company. However, with an issue of such national importance it is more likely that the berth at Clydebank was selected as a result of considered appraisal.
7. From a speech by Sir Thomas Bell made on his retirement in 1935. Bell, as Managing Director at Clydebank along with Alexander Gracie of Fairfield, was in attendance at the meeting with Fisher.
8. Quotation from an eight-page summary of the construction of *Repulse* and *Renown* in the Ship's Cover held at the National Maritime Museum.
9. UCS1/5/15, Shipyard Reports, 2 November 1916). Glasgow University Business Archives.
10. Dieter Thomaier, of the 'Groener Circle'.
11. For more information about the design of the other three ships, see Ian Sturton, 'Cancelled Sisters: The Modified *Hood* Class', *Warship 2010* (London: Conway Maritime Press, 2010).
12. *Anson* was dismantled in May 1919, with Berth No 2 cleared by 10 June, and the P&O liner *Mongolia* laid down.

Chapter 3

1. Most sources in this section are from the Ships' Covers held at the National Maritime Museum. These large volumes are broadly chronological in page order although individual pages are generally not numbered. As they contain papers, notes and drawings from many sources they are difficult to reference.
2. From *The Romance of Engineering*, published by Wm Beardmore & Co Ltd in 1926.
3. Ship's Cover, HMS *Hood*, National Maritime Museum, Curator 367.
4. For an analysis of this and its effect on warship design see John Jordan, *Warships After Washington* (Barnsley: Seaforth Publishing, 2011).
5. Standard displacement as defined at the Washington Conference refers to a ship fully equipped for sea but not including fuel or reserve feed water.
6. *Agamemnon*'s sister-ship, *Lord Nelson*, was sold

for disposal in 1920. All *King Edward VII* class pre-dreadnoughts, with the exception of *Commonwealth*, were for disposal in 1921.
7. *Shipbuilding & Shipping Record*, 8 October 1925, p.369.
8. *Shipbuilding & Shipping Record*, 1 August 1929, p.147.
9. This restriction was lifted in the Second World War to allow tank landing craft to be erected on some of the sites.
10. The sites of the Beardmore and Palmer shipyards were subsequently used for industrial and marine related purposes but no new hulls were ever built there again.
11. UCS2/1/6 Fairfield directors minute books.
12. Vickers File 164. Cambridge University Library.
13. An interesting venue given the ship had left Clydebank on 24 March for drydocking and was delivered to Cunard on 12 May after trials, sailing on her maiden voyage on the 27th.
14. The DNC's department had moved from London in September 1939.
15. V-A had continued to use this Berth 2, building smaller vessels like destroyers and submarines on either side of *Lion*'s keel.
16. UCS1/5/44, Shipyard drawing office report, 18 December 1940.
17. *Snipe* and *Sparrow* were eventually built and engined by Denny.
18. UCS1/5/49, Report, 21 March 1942.
19. Ibid.
20. UCS1/5/50, Notes on meeting dated 2 July 1942.
21. UCS1/5/55, Report, 30 March 1944.
22. For more information on these designs see the two-part article by John Roberts, 'Penultimate Battleships', *Warship* Nos 19 and 20 (London: Conway Maritime Press, 1981).

Chapter 4

1. Armstrong Whitworth Board Minutes No. 1. Tyne & Wear Archives 130/1266.
2. Rendel Papers. Tyne & Wear Archives 31/6969-7002.
3. Such coordinates can be used on Google Earth to show the present site.
4. Ian Johnston, *Ships for a Nation* (West Dumbartonshire Libraries & Museums, 2000), p.98.
5. J R Hume and M S Moss, *Beardmore: The History of a Scottish Industrial Giant* (Aldershot: Heinemann, 1979), p.78.
6. Armstrong Whitworth Board Minutes No. 3. Tyne & Wear Archives 130/1268.
7. N J M Campbell, 'British Super-Heavy Guns Part 4', *Warship* No.12 (1979).
8. See Appendix 2, Q.2168.
9. Directors' Minute Book, various refs 1908-1917. Glasgow University Business Archives.

UCS2 1/4
10. K Warren, *Steel, Ships and Men* (Liverpool: Liverpool University Press, 1998), p.149.
11. Directors' Minute Books 1908–1917. Meeting of 15 December 1915. Glasgow University Business Archives, UCS2.
12. Parsons manufactured steam turbines for electrical power stations at C A Parsons & Co Ltd with works at nearby Heaton.
13. *Shipbuilding & Shipping Record*, 15 Oct 1914, p.386.
14. *Shipbuilding & Shipping Record*, 8 Nov 1945, p.461.

Chapter 5

1. Hume and Moss, *Beardmore*, p.232.
2. *Regulations for the Government of His Majesty's Dockyards at Home* (London: HMSO, 1926), Art. 609.
3. Vickers Ltd Sheffield Balance Sheet, 1912. Sheffield Archives 1988/50/13539.
4. Statement of the First Lord Explanatory of the Navy Estimates 1903–4.
5. Select Committee on (Navy) Estimates. House of Commons Paper 231. 1913.
6. N B J Stapleton, *Steam Picket Boats* (Lavenham: Terence Dalton Ltd, 1980), p.88.
7. Elswick Shipyard Report Book No.2. Vickers File 1158. Cambridge University Library
8. *Orion* class Ship's Covers. Curator Nos 248 & 248A (ADM 138/346-7).
9. Ibid.
10. Associated Shipwrights Society Annual Report 1907.
11. *Orion* class Ships' Covers.
12. Ibid. Other shipbuilder's tender prices are given in Appendix 1.
13. A J Arnold, 'National Strategic Objectives, the Interests of the 'Armaments Ring' and the Failure of Thames Ironworks in 1912', *International Journal of Maritime History*, Vol 23, No 1 (March 2012).
14. A J Arnold, *Iron Shipbuilding on the Thames 1832-1915* (Aldershot: Ashgate, 2000), p.149.
15. Swan Hunter contract records via authors.
16. *Journal of the Iron & Steel Institute*, Vol LXVIII (1905).

Chapter 6

1. B Newman, *Plate and Section Working Machinery in British Shipbuilding 1850-1945* (Glasgow: Centre for Business History in Scotland, 1993).
2. Ian Buxton, 'The Output of Thames-side Yards from 1850-1914'. Proceedings of Fourth Symposium on 'Shipbuilding and Ships on the Thames'. London, 2012.
3. Warren, *Steel, Ships and Men*, p.163.
4. Armstrong Whitworth Directors' Minute Books Nos. 2 & 3. Tyne & Wear Archives 130/1267 and 1268. Walker Naval Yard

1908–1943. Marine Technology Special Collection, Newcastle University.

5. W E Smith, Superintendent of Contract Work, had been intended to succeed Watts but did not meet with Churchill's approval.

6. M J Bastable, *Arms and the State: Sir William Armstrong and the Remaking of British Naval Power 1854-1914* (Aldershot: Ashgate, 2004), Chapter 9 discusses the various Armstrong directors.

7. Armstrong later took over A & J Main to form Armstrong & Main Ltd.

8. Extensive description in *Engineering* in 1920: 19 March, 2, 9, 23, 30 April, 7 and 21 May.

9. *Marine Engineer* (September 1894).

10. B Newman, *A Work of Titans* (Published by the author 2012), p.21.

11. Select Committee on (Navy) Estimates. Parliamentary Paper 321, 1913.

12. B Newman, *Materials Handling in British Shipbuilding 1850-1945* (Glasgow: Centre for Business History in Scotland, 1996).

13. The merchant shipbuilding yard Furness Shipbuilding on Teesside was also an early user of such cranes (1918).

14. *Engineering* 21 July 1905.

15. B Newman, *The Genesis of the Cantilever Structure in Fitting Out Cranes*, PhD thesis, Newcastle University, 2003.

16. Newman, *The Genesis of the Cantilever Structure in Fitting Out Cranes*, p.165. Downrated to 90 tons by 1910.

17. *Engineering* 27 April 1906, p.554. Later uprated to 120 tons.

18. Cammell Laird Accounts 1913. Wirral Archives 005/0049.

19. Newman, *The Genesis of the Cantilever Structure in Fitting Out Cranes*, Chapter 9. Parkhead crane works were built for Glasgow Electric Crane & Hoist Co, a company set up by Vickers and Beardmore. Arrol acquired the works in 1911 – via Appleby.

20. *Engineering* 30 June 1911.

21 Newman, *A Work of Titans*, p.38.

22. *Titan II* Crane log-books. Marine Technology Special Collection, Newcastle University.

23. Vickers File 599. McKechnie papers. The shipyard manager recruited by Vickers after the takeover in 1897, James Dunn, was also from the Admiralty. Cambridge University Library. Fairfield Board Minutes 25 Apr 1919. UCS 2/1/5.

24. Vickers Ltd Central Department Accounts and Schedules 1914. Vickers File 1512, Cambridge University Library.

25. But Chatham's biggest drydock (No 9) was only 82ft wide (650ft long), necessitating *Lord Nelson*'s planned 12 x 9.2in armament to be reduced to 10 guns to permit using it.

26. 3000 £10 ordinary shares. Later £10,000 6 per cent debentures added.

27. In tendering for *Tiger*, the Admiralty advised that the cost of using a drydock at a Dockyard would be £30 rent per 24 hours plus about £300 for other services. They required six weeks' notice for such services. *Tiger* Ship's Cover NMM Curator No.279 (ADM 138/420).

28. Admiralty Dock Book, 1914.

Chapter 7

1. ihp = indicated horsepower, used as the measure of output of steam reciprocating engines, where an 'indicator' attached to a cylinder measured change in pressure during the stroke allowing power to be calculated.

2. *Bellerophon* Class Cover. NMM. Curator No. 222. (ADM138/250)

3. shp = shaft horsepower, used as the measure of output of steam turbines, where a torsionmeter attached to the shaft allowed torque to be measured so, in association with shaft rpm, power could be calculated. Although shaft power was not usually measured for steam reciprocators, the ratio of shp/ihp was about 80 per cent.

4. Hawthorn Leslie engine contracts. Tyne & Wear Archives. DS.HL/4/49.

5. *Audacious* contract. Cammell Laird had taken out a Parsons licence in March 1905. Cammell Laird Archive. 005/0164. Wirral Archives.

6. Vickers Correspondence Reference Book No.3. Sheffield Archives 1988/50/13033.

7. E C Smith, *A Short History of Naval and Marine Engineering* (Cambridge: Cambridge University Press, 1937), p.252.

8. Johnston, *Ships for a Nation*, p.128.

9. D K Brown gives more detail on the introduction of oil fuel in his *The Grand Fleet: Warship Design and Development 1906–1922* (London: Chatham Publishing, 1999), p.21.

10. Vickers File 157. Quarterly Reports 1930. Cambridge University Library.

11. Vickers File 173. Quarterly Reports 1934. Cambridge University Library.

12. S V Goodall, 'The Royal Navy at the Outbreak of War', *Trans Inst Naval Architects*, Vol 88 (1946).

13. W J Reader, *The Weir Group* (London: Weidenfeld & Nicholson 1971), p.42.

14. H J Oram, 'Fifty Years Changes in British Warship Machinery', *Trans Inst of Naval Architects*, Vol 53 (1911).

15. W McClelland, 'The Applications of Electricity in Warships', *Inst Electrical Engineers Journal*, Vol 65, No 369 (1927), p.829.

16. M R Lane, *The Story of Queen's Engineering Works, Bedford* (London: Unicorn Press, 1995), p.117.

17. R W C Skelton, 'Progress in Marine Engineering', 3rd Thomas Lowe Gray lecture, *Proc Inst Mechanical Engineers* (Jan 1930), p.35.

18. John Roberts, *Anatomy of the Ship: The Battleship Dreadnought* (London: Conway Maritime Press, 1992).

Chapter 8

1. Of seventy 12in Mark VIII guns made in the mid-1890s, Woolwich built thirty-nine, Armstrong eleven, Vickers ten and Whitworth ten.

2. 'Vickers, Sons & Maxim'. *Engineering* (1902).

3. *The Engineer* had a series of articles on wire-wound gun construction from 7 Jan 1898 to 6 May 1898

4. The length of a gun was measured by the number of 'calibres', i.e. its actual bore length from breech end to muzzle divided by the bore diameter, so a 12in 50 cal gun was 50ft long.

5. A new gun shrinking pit was built at Elswick in 1911 costing £20,000, capable of handling guns up to 150 tons, i.e. 18in. Armstrong Whitworth Minutes. Tyne & Wear Archives 130/1268.

6. Bastable, *Arms and the State*, p.101

7. Vickers claimed in 1902 that they could produce in a year 12 12in guns, 24 9.2in, 24 7.5in, 120 6in, 100 4.7in and 90 howitzers. 'Vickers, Sons & Maxim', *Engineering* (1902).

8. Contract Book Barrow. Vickers File 1116. Cambridge University Library. Their price was about £5000 less than Armstrong's. Palmer and Woolwich also submitted designs.

9. *Engineering* (July/August 1901). That journal also gave an extensive description in November 1897 of Vickers Sheffield works making guns and armour.

10. 'Arrears of Shipbuilding'. Cd.1055, 1902

11. Warren, *Steel, Ships and Men*, p.148. Bacon's quarterdeck manner did not endear him to his industrial colleagues. With COW producing no profits, the owning companies considered getting rid of their troublesome managing director in 1912 but backed off. They were relieved when he resigned in January 1915 to take a direct part in the war.

12. Board of Ordnance (1597–1855), Ordnance Select Committee (1855–68), Ordnance Committee (1881–1907), Ordnance Board/Committee (1908–1973).

13. Navy Estimates 1907–08 to 1910–11.

14. Navy Estimates 1901–02 to 1905–06. Over the same period 100 9.2in and 629 6in were completed.

15. H W Semark, *The Royal Naval Armament Depot of Priddy's Hard* (Hampshire County Council, 1997), p.234.

16. So renamed in 1881, reverting to Ordnance Board in 1907. About 1909 the Admiralty set up its own Gun Design Committee under DNO. N Friedman, *Naval Weapons of World War One* (Barnsley: Seaforth Publishing, 2011), p.17.

17. Ibid, p.51. Five of *Erin*'s 13.5in Mark VI were made by Vickers, five by Elswick, the two firms also sharing the gun mounting order.

18. Navy Estimates 1907–08.
19. An Official Secrets Act had been passed in 1889, and a more comprehensive one in 1911. Contractors were not allowed to admit foreign visitors without express Admiralty permission. Krupp also restricted export of its technology.
20. Armstrong Whitworth Executive Committee Minute Book 4. Tyne & Wear Archives 130/1295.
21. Register of Quotations. Vickers File 1146. Cambridge University Library.
22. Friedman, *Naval Weapons of World War One*, p.84.
23. Vickers Balance Sheets. Sheffield. Sheffield Archives 1988/50 series.
24. Record of Ballistics. Tyne & Wear Archives 1027/6320.
25. Army (Ordnance Factories) Annual Accounts for 1906–07 showed that four 12in Mark X had been built at a cost of £42,050 (average £10,512), and that excluded rent and interest and other overhead charges that a private manufacturer would incur. Some of the higher Woolwich costs may have been due to the cost of forgings bought in from companies like Vickers at prices probably higher than they charged themselves.
26. The partially-completed 15in mountings for the cancelled *Rodney* were purchased from the Admiralty for scrap. Harland & Wolff annual works reports. Public Record Office of Northern Ireland, Box 28 D.2805.
27. Naval Gun Mountings. National Archives. SUPP 3/43.
28. Vickers-Armstrongs noted in their second quarter report for Barrow in 1936 'We have offered to give all the help we can to Armstrong, Whitworth and Harland & Wolff to enable them to manufacture some of the simpler naval mountings of our design. … There is going to be great difficulty retaining foreign armament and commercial business that has been gradually been built up by hard work and at great expense…'Vickers File 181. Cambridge University Library.
29. Quarterly Reports 1937. Vickers File 186. Cambridge University Library. G A H Gordon's *British Seapower and Procurement between the Wars* (Basingstoke: Macmillan Press, 1988) discusses the negotiations over the acquisition of Scotswood.
30. Ordering of Gun Mountings 1936. National Archives. T161/93.
31. Vickers-Armstrong rate of profit. ADM1/17863. Also CAB102/526.
32. John Campbell, *Naval Weapons of World War Two* (London: Conway Maritime Press 1985).
33. Excluding the 13-ton balance weight needed to bring the gun centre of gravity in line with the trunnions.
34. Ordering of Gun Mountings 1936. T161/93.
35. Vickers-Armstrong File 1027/6320 Tyne & Wear Archives. The seventy-six operational guns were given serial numbers S.61-S.136. Numbers were allocated to a particular British gun calibre in sequence, irrespective of Mark or whether ship service (S) or land service (L).
36. A Hague, 'The 15-inch Gun in the Royal Navy', *Warships* No. 67 (World Ship Society, 1981. Woolwich production during the First World War (Aug 1914–Dec 1918) included thirty-three 15in, two 14in, eight 13.5in, four 12in, four 9.2in, nine 7.5in and 219 6in guns (not all for the Admiralty), while they repaired thirty-nine 15in, thirty-six 13.5in, 101 12in, 73 9.2in, six 7.5in and thirty-three 6in. *History of the Ministry of Munitions*, Vol.1.
37. Ian Buxton, *Big Gun Monitors* (Barnsley: Seaforth Publishing, 2008), p.218.
38. Quarterly Reports 1937. Vickers File 185. Cambridge University Library.
39. National Archives. CAB 102/526.
40. Tenders for gun mountings included separate quotations for delivery and erection. For example for *Tiger's* four turrets, EOC quoted £15,180 if at the Armstrong shipyard, £18,490 if at another Tyne shipyard, £19,360 if at a home Dockyard or £25,725 if on the Thames. *Tiger* Ship's Cover. NMM. Curator 279. (ADM138/420).
41. *Bellerophon* Class Ship's Cover. NMM. Curator 222. (ADM138/250). 21 May 1906. When COW built the four twin 15in mountings for *Royal Sovereign*, they had to pay Elswick £4000 for drawings.
42. Woolwich manufactured between 2 per cent and 10 per cent by value of naval gun mountings between 1899 and 1906. Report on … Shops and Machinery at Woolwich Arsenal. Cd.3514, 1907, p.73.
43. Armstrong and Whitworth had colluded on prices for 12in gun mountings for the Admiralty in April 1896 before the merger, seeking a 'uniformity of price'. Armstrong Whitworth Minute Book No.1, Tyne & Wear Archives 130/1266.
44. Armstrong Whitworth Balance Books. Tyne & Wear Archives 130/283.
45. Data supplied by A J Arnold derived from Barrow annual accounts.
46. *Orion* Class Battleships Ship's Cover. NMM. Curator 248 (ADM138/346).
47. Warren, *Steel, Ships and Men*, p.149.
48. Armstrong Whitworth Ordnance Committee. Tyne & Wear Archives 130/1291.
49. *Brassey's Naval Annual* (1910).
50. P Hodges, *The Big Gun* (London: Conway Maritime Press, 1981), and Friedman, *Naval Weapons of World War One*.
51. Miscellaneous Correspondence. National Archives ADM265/2.
52. Contract Papers: Gun Mountings. ADM116/5310. Final prices for 5.25in mountings were not agreed until 1944.
53. 5.25in Gun Mountings. Tyne & Wear Archives 1027/5875.
54. Ian Buxton, 'British Battleship Gun Mounting Construction in WW2', *Warships* No 155 (World Ship Society, 2007).
55. It was replaced by one removed from *Belfast* still under repair from her mining.
56. Campbell, *Naval Weapons of World War Two*, p.24.
57. Although Berry in his INA 1929 paper on *Nelson* and *Rodney* claimed that the former's 6in mountings came from Armstrong, this is not correct. Most of *Nelson's* mounting components were shipped from Barrow to the Tyne in the coaster *Sagenite* in February and March 1926.
58. *Nelson* and *Rodney* Gun Mountings. ADM116/3426.
59. War History: Electrical Engineering Items. CAB102/532.
60. J D Scott, *Vickers* (London: Weidenfeld & Nicholson 1962), p.84.
61. Vickers Guns 1902-11. Vickers File 665. Cambridge University Library.
62. Armstrong Minute Book No.3. Tyne & Wear Archives 130/1268.
63. The three ships had four twin 12in each. Armstrong built the other twelve guns, serial numbers 16573–16580, 17066–17069. *Warship International*, Vol 44 No 1 (2007), p.113.
64. Twenty-four guns were ordered from Vickers in 1913 at £12,500 each for two battlecruisers of the *Ismail* class with four triple 14in turrets each, with further guns ordered in Russia, including at a new ordnance works at Tsaritsyn (now Volgograd) in which Vickers had a 20 per cent interest. None of the ships were completed. S E Vinogradov, 'Naval Ordnance and Armor Manufacturing', *Warship International*, Vol 37 No 3 (2000), p.232.
65. K Warren, *Armstrongs of Elswick* (Basingstoke: Macmillan Press, 1989), p.213.
66. C Trebilcock, *The Vickers Brothers* (London: Europa Publications, 1977), p.97.
67. *History of the Ministry of Munitions*, Vol VIII, Part II, p.36. In FY 1906-07, 821 tons of Cordite MD had been made at a cost of 1s 7d per lb.
68. W D Cocroft, *Dangerous Energy* (English Heritage, 2000), Chapter 6.
69. Ibid, Chapter 7.
70. In the twelve months to September 1901, Armstrong Whitworth made 4684 tons of gun mountings, 700 guns, 446,306 shells, 670,000 fuses & primers and 174,000 cartridges.
71. D Evans, *Arming the Fleet* (Gosport: Explosion! Museum, 2006), p.191.
72. *Brassey's Naval Annual* (1908).
73. Register of Quotations. Vickers File 1147 Cambridge University Library. The price probably excludes filling and fuse.

74. Vickers Sons & Maxim Sheffield annual reports on Costs, Prices and Profits 1907–11 and Balance Sheets 1912–14. Sheffield Archives 1988/50 series.

75. Calibres radius of head measured the 'point-edness' of the head. It measured the radius of the ogive forming the head of the shell, i.e. a 15in 4 crh had a radius of 60in. Older shells were 2 crh.

76. A full discussion of pre-war shell trials is given in Friedman, *Naval Weapons of World War One*, Chapter 1/1.

77. Vickers Sheffield Costs, Prices & Profits 1915. Sheffield Archives 1988/50/6447.

78. I McCallum, 'The Riddle of the Shells', *Warship 2002-2003* (London: Conway Maritime Press, 2003).

79. Report of Shell Committee. ADM186/169.

80. Report of Shell Committee. ADM186/169.

81. Progress in Naval Gunnery 1914-18. ADM186/238.

82. Buxton, *Big Gun Monitors*, p.67. Hadfield were also making shells for the US in 1917.

83. Buxton, *Big Gun Monitors*, p.220.

84. *Hansard* March 1957 p.358.

85. M Moss and I Russell, *Range & Vision: The first 100 years of Barr & Stroud* (Edinburgh: Mainstream Publishing, 1988), p.79.

86. *The Rangefinder Handbook*. Admiralty 1943. MoD Naval Library.

87. J Brooks, *Dreadnought Gunnery and the Battle of Jutland* (London: Routledge, 2005), p.53.

88. Ibid, p.96.

89. Scott, *Vickers*, p.139.

90. Contracts Index 1914-17.Vickers File 1148. Cambridge University Library.

91. Other Marks in between were for cruisers. J Brooks, 'The Admiralty Fire Control Tables', *Warship 2002-2003* (London: Conway Maritime Press, 2003).

92. Production of Fire Control Equipment. CAB102/526.

93. Those in *Nelson* and *Rodney* were quite lightly protected, with 2in front and 1in sides and roof, weighing 24 tons.

94. *Anson*'s were replaced by four Mark VI at her 1945 refit costing £22,000 each, SUPP3/43.

95. National Archives CAB102/526.

96. Elswick Ordnance Co, 1913. Newcastle Central Library.

97. Vickers Guns.Vickers File 665. Cambridge University Library.

98. E N Poland, *The Torpedomen* (Kenneth Mason, 1994), p.53. Friedman, *Naval Weapons of World War One*, p.320.

99. Notes for Royal Commission.Vickers File 58, Cambridge University Library.

100.This venture was initially very profitable. Profits in 1909 amounted to £53,310 while orders in 1908 were worth £124,588. A 14 per cent dividend was paid. Armstrong Whitworth Directors Minute Book No.3, Tyne & Wear Archives 130/1268.

101.Armstrong Whitworth Directors Minute Book No.3. 26 Oct 1911. Op cit.

102.Friedman, *Naval Weapons of World War One*, p.330.

103.John Campbell, *Jutland: An Analysis of the Fighting* (London: Conway Maritime Press, 1986) pp 347 & 401.

104.E Gray, *The Devil's Device* (London: Seeley, Service, 1975), p.191.

105.Quarterly Reports 1932.Vickers File 167. Cambridge University Library.

106.Campbell, *Naval Weapons of World War Two*, p.81.

107.The Argyll factory had been used to make shells in the First World War.

Chapter 9

1. *John Brown and Co Ltd*, Publicity book 1903.

2. Warren, *Armstrongs of Elswick*, p.59.

3. *Vickers Sons & Maxim Ltd*, Publicity book 1902.

4. Report of Parliamentary Committee into Arrears of Shipbuilding. Cd.1055. 1902.

5. Armstrong, Whitworth Directors Minute Book No.1. Tyne & Wear Archives 130/1266.

6. Armstrong. Tyne & Wear Archives 130/1280.

7. Report of Parliamentary Committee into Arrears of Shipbuilding. Cd.1055. 1902.

8. Vickers Correspondence Reference Book No.3. Sheffield Archives 1988/50/13033.

9. The authors are grateful to Nathan Okun for advice on the metallurgy and performance of armour.

10. Armour Plate for Battleships 1910–1915. ADM116/3456.

11. R J Irving, 'New Industries for Old? Some Investment Decisions of Sir W G Armstrong, Whitworth & Co Ltd 1900-1914', *Business History* (July 1975). Additional calculations by author, including adding July 1905 to June 1906 omitted from Irving's Table 3. The company changed its financial year end from 30 June to 31 December in 1906.

12. Tyne & Wear Archives 31/6573-6587. Also in Balance Books 130/282-3.

13. For comparison, the industry's most senior 'customers' were the Director of Naval Construction on a scale of £1500–£1800 p.a., Superintendent of Contract Work £1200–£1500, Director of Navy Contracts £1200–£1400, Director of Dockyards £1500, Engineer-in-Chief £1500, Superintendent of the Admiralty Experiment Works at Haslar £1000.

14. Armstrong Whitworth Private Minute Book No.1. Tyne & Wear Archives 130/1278.

15. Armstrong Ordnance Committee 3 Jun 1913. Tyne & Wear Archives 130/1291. The figure is clearly written as 13,000 tons (about one year's output) but even if an error for 1300 still represents a large wastage.

16. Vickers Sons & Maxim Sheffield annual reports on Costs, Prices and Profits 1907–11. Sheffield Archives 1988/50 series.

17. Vickers Costs and Prices. Sheffield Archives 1988/50/6447.

18. *Warships* No.142. (World Ship Society, 2001) Nominal thicknesses. British armour was actually specified on a pound weight per square foot basis. 14in armour was ordered as 560lb, but as armour actually weighed 40.8lbs/sq ft, it was only 13.72in thick. Nominal thicknesses used in this book.

19. Warren, *Steel, Ships & Men*, p.174.

20. Warren, *Steel, Ships & Men*, pp 128–31. Elgar died not long after, on 17 Jan 1909. W L Hichens became the new Chairman in Sep 1910 at £3000 p.a.

21. Navy Estimates 1910–11.

22. Bastable, *Arms and the State*, p.214.

23. Armour Plate for Battleships 1910–1915. ADM116/3456.

24. Elswick Shipyard Report Book No.2. Vickers Archive, Cambridge University Library.

25. *Orion* class Ship's Cover. NMM. Curator 248. (ADM 138/346).

26. Scott, *Vickers*, p.597.

27. Armour Plate.Vickers File 755, Cambridge University Library.The Japanese viewed Vickers armour as superior.

28. Armour Plate for Battleships 1910–1915. ADM116/3456.

29. Although the annual Navy Estimates gave a value for armour ordered, no corresponding tonnage figure was given, thus hiding even the average price per ton.

30. The US government had considered building its own armour manufacturing plant in 1898 for the same reason. K Warren, *Bethlehem Steel* (University of Pittsburgh Press, 2008), p.56. The three US makers bought most of their specialised armour processing machine tools from Openshaw.

31. T J Misa, *A Nation of Steel* (Johns Hopkins University Press, 1995), Chapter 3. There was evidently similar secrecy in the US about the true costs of making armour as even Andrew Carnegie's personal papers have the unit costs clipped out (p 322).

32. G Weir, *Building the Kaiser's Navy* (Annapolis: Naval Institute Press, 1992) gives Krupp armour prices ranging from 2320 marks a ton in 1899 to 1600 marks in 1909 (about £116 to £80).

33. Navy Estimates 1919–20 showed armour supplied by contract as £3.542 million in 1914–15, £1.951 million in 1915–16 and £147,000 in 1916–17.

34. *Nelson* and *Rodney* Ship's Cover. NMM. Curator No.421. (ADM138/636)

35. Chatfield was appointed First Sea Lord in 1933. He was responsible for pushing for re-equipping armour producers during re-armament.

36. Vickers had 32 160lb plates for *London* weighing 171 tons rejected for failure at

proof in 1927, at a loss of £29,567. Vickers Sheffield Archive 1988/50/13570.

37. Armour for *London* class. ADM116/3351
38. Hume and Moss, *Beardmore*, p.231.
39. Hume and Moss, *Beardmore*, p.216.
40. Armour Plate. Vickers File 755, Cambridge University Library.
41. A Raven and J Roberts, *British Battleships of World War Two* (London: Arms & Armour Press, 1976), p.294 gives a breakdown of armour weights excluding gunhouses.
42. Shipbreaking Archive, Marine Technology Special Collection, Newcastle University.
43. G A H Gordon discusses pre-war armour procurement in greater detail in *British Seapower and Procurement between the Wars*.
44. Hume and Moss, *Beardmore*, p.249.
45. D K Brown, *Nelson to Vanguard: Warship Development 1923-1945* (London: Chatham Publishing, 2000), p.16.
46. Armour Plate Prices. ADM1/12584.
47. Ship's Cover for *Lion* class. NMM. Curator 577.
48. Armour Plate. Vickers File 755, Cambridge University Library.
49. A Grant, *Steel and Ships* (London: M Joseph, 1950), p.94.
50. Hume and Moss, *Beardmore*, p.243.
51. Ship's Cover for *St Vincent* class. NMM. Curator 237. (ADM138/265).
52. 'Net Weights War Vessels, No.1, Vickers Ltd'. National Maritime Museum.
53. CAB102/539.
54. J Vaizey, *The History of British Steel* (London: Weidenfeld & Nicholson, 1974), p.101.
55. W Berry, 'H M Battleships *Nelson & Rodney*', *Trans Inst of Naval Architects*, Vol 71 (1929).

Chapter 10

1. Armstrong Whitworth Balance Book No.3. Tyne & Wear Archives 130/283.
2. The long saga of Brazilian battleship orders is detailed in D Topliss' 'The Brazilian Dreadnoughts 1904-1914' in *Warship International*, Vol 25 No 3 (1988).
3. Vickers File 551. Cambridge University Library.
4. Vickers File 1512. Cambridge University Library.
5. C Trebilcock, *The Vickers Brothers* (London: Europa Publications, 1977), p.130.
6. Her requisitioned sister *Canada* and the three destroyer leaders *Broke*, *Botha* and *Faulknor* were sold back to Chile in April 1920 for £1.4 million.
7. Trebilcock, *The Vickers Brothers*, Appendix B. Unfortunately the detailed Barrow accounts used by Trebilcock have not been located.
8. UCS1/4/6. Letter from a Russian source sent to John Brown by H J Stockman & Co., Philpot Lane, London dated 8 May 1906.
9. Glasgow University Business Archives UCS1/21/106
10. Vickers Documents 58 and 59. Contain much evidence on the case submitted to the Royal Commission. Cambridge University Library. The *Kongo* contract gave the Japanese access to technical information and drawings, as well as allowing their technical personnel into the Vickers works during construction, which allowed them to build three sisters in Japan. H Lengerer, 'The Battlecruisers of the *Kongo* Class', *Warship 2012* (London: Conway Maritime Press, 2012).
11. Admiralty contracts had long contained a clause banning 'Corrupt gifts to persons in the Crown's service'.
12. Parliamentary paper Cmd 5292.
13. Vickers File 1506. Cambridge University Library.

Chapter 11

1. Social security was not introduced until 1908.
2. Sumida, *In Defence of Naval Supremacy*, Table 15.
3. Navy Estimates 1914–15.
4. Dockyard Expense Account 1913–14.
5. Select Committee on (Navy) Estimates. House of Commons Paper 321, 1913. Appendix 5.
6. Figures extracted from Dockyard Expense Accounts for relevant years.
7. *The Shipbuilder*, Vol II (1907–08), p.206.
8. Rendel Papers. Tyne & Wear Archives 31/6969-7002.
9. Ships Costs Book. Vickers File 1155. Cambridge University Library.
10. For Clyde yards: thesis by H B Peebles, *Warship Building on the Clyde 1889-1939* (Univ of Stirling, 1986). Vickers and Armstrong from company accounts. For *Invincible* and *Inflexible*, the shipbuilder's contract (unusually) included armour as well as hull and machinery.
11. A J Arnold, 'Dependency, Debt & Shipbuilding in "Palmer's Town"', *Northern History*, Vol XLIX:1 (2012).
12. While Fairfield later was a member of COW from 1905, that company made no profit until 1914. Warren, *Steel, Ships and Men*, p.149.
13. A J Arnold A J. 'Riches beyond the dreams of avarice?: Commercial returns on British warship construction 1889-1914', *Economic History Review*, LIV, 2 (2001), pp 267–89.
14. Cammell Laird Accounts 1913. Wirral Archives 005/0049.
15. J Dunn, 'Shipbuilding Works', *Proc Inst Mechanical Engineers* (1901). She was trapped in Barrow docks for some time by the collapse of a dock sill.
16. Cammell Laird Accounts 1927. Wirral Archives 005/0051. More detailed cost breakdown including ammunition in Brown, *The Grand Fleet*, p.182.
17. Lyon states that a price fixing arrangement existed among the battleship shipbuilders for the 1910 programme. But with *Audacious* making a loss, it cannot have been too successful. H Lyon, 'The Relations between the Admiralty and private industry …', in B Ranft (ed), *Technical Change and British Naval Policy 1860-1939* (London: Hodder & Stoughton, 1977), p.61. The 1930s price coordination is discussed in Vickers File 58, Cambridge University Library.
18. Brown, *Nelson to Vanguard*, p.186. The warship builders knew the cost of Dockyard-built submarines from the Navy Estimates, so could pitch their prices at similar levels without raising any questions.
19. The average cost per ton of warships (excluding battleships) built 1925-34 was £220.6 in the Dockyards compared with £210.4 in private yards. Vickers File 58. Cambridge University Library.
20. Swan Hunter Cost Estimate via author.
21. The same applied to 128 other ships. Navy Appropriation Account 1941, HC 1943.
22. Certified Costs. ADM 1/12161.
23. W Ashworth, *Contracts and Finance* (London: HMSO, 1953), pp 106–13.
24. Contract Settlement with Shipbuilders 1943–47. Naval Historical Branch, Ministry of Defence.
25. J F Clarke, *Power on Land & Sea. A History of Hawthorn Leslie* (Published by the company, 1979), p.65.
26. Vickers Ltd Accounts for Barrow, 1906-14. Courtesy Prof A J Arnold.
27. Wallsend Slipway & Engineering. Abstract of Balance Sheets. Tyne & Wear Archives DS.WS/46/2.
28. Detailed Balance Sheets. Tyne & Wear Archives. Rendel Papers. 31/6573-6587. Armstrong Whitworth Balance Books 130/281-283.
29. Balance Books (Tyne & Wear Archives 130/282-3) and Irving, 'New Industries for Old', . and Lyon, 'The Relations between the Admiralty and private industry…' To get figures for the entire period, the authors have had to draw on each source to make their analysis.
30. H B Peebles, *Warship Building on the Clyde* (Edinburgh: John Donald Publishing, 1987), Chapter 6.
31. Figures collated by authors from Armstrong Board Minutes and Balance Books.
32. Calculated by dividing total ordnance profit for the period by number of battleship mountings built, though this takes no account of the smaller guns and mountings, hence 'crude'.
33. Figures collated by authors from Armstrong Board Minutes and Balance Books.
34. Openshaw Profit & Loss 1911. Armstrong, Whitworth balance sheet 1907 (Rendel op cit).
35. Elswick Ordnance Company 1913. Newcastle City Library.
36. Balance Book No.3. Tyne & Wear Archives 130/283. Openshaw's other products

included machine tools and high speed steels, e.g. for drills.

37. Warren, *Steel, Ships and Men*, p.176.
38. Balance Book No.3. Tyne & Wear Archives 130/283. Warren discusses Rendel's concerns over excessive management salaries in 1910 (*Steel, Ships and Men*, Chapter 21).
39. Joseph Vavasseur bought the Kilverstone estate in Norfolk, at which Fisher was a regular visitor. At his death in 1908, the childless Vavasseur bequeathed Kilverstone to Fisher's son Cecil. Fisher himself not only lived there but took the title Baron Fisher of Kilverstone when ennobled in 1909.
40. Vickers Balance Sheets. Sheffield Archives 1988/50 series. Vickers Files 1503-1512. Cambridge University Library.
41. Figures kindly supplied by Prof A J Arnold.
42. Trebilcock, *The Vickers Brothers*, Appendix B.
43. Vickers-Armstrongs Profit & Loss Accounts. Vickers Files 1600-1615. Cambridge University Library.
44. Vickers-Armstrongs Profit & Loss Accounts. 31 Dec 1939. Vickers File 1609. Cambridge University Library.
45. Vickers-Armstrongs Profit & Loss Accounts. Vickers Files 1600-1615. Cambridge University Library.
46. Final Report of the First Census of Production of the United Kingdom (1907). Cd.6320. 1912.
47. Ibid, p.194.
48. Ibid, p.197.
49. Ibid, p.198.
50. Ibid, p.137.
51. Ibid, p.134. In the 1912 Census the figure for War Vessels had risen to £6.8 million.
52. Ibid, p.195.
53. Ibid, p.135.
54. Ibid, p.102.
55. Ibid, p.168.
56. Ibid, p.190.
57. Ibid, p.567.
58. Ibid, pp 9 and 21.

Chapter 12

1. Letter from R R Bevis 26 Apr 02. Cammell Laird 005/0197/008. Wirral Archives.
2. *Bellerophon* class Ship's Cover. NMM Curator 222. (ADM138/250). Authors have added the two final columns.
3. Data extracted from Navy Estimates 1905–06 to 1913–14.
4. *The Naval Annual* (1913), p.6.
5. Ian Johnston, 'A Shipyard at War', *Warship 2009* (London: Conway Maritime Press, 2010), p.101.
6. Report of an Enquiry by the Board of Trade into Earnings and Hours of Labour. Cd.5814. 1911.
7. Tyne & Wear Riveters' Piece Work Price List. 1915. A 77-page booklet containing over 600 rates and sketches for riveting of every part of a ship, plus the history of

previous price rises since 1884, with hand-written additions to 1936. Author's collection.
8. D J Jeremy, 'The Hundred Largest Employers in the UK', *Business History* (Jan 1991).
9. Rendel Papers. Tyne & Wear Archives. 31/6969-7002.
10. Elswick Ordnance Company 1913. Newcastle City Library.
11. Warren, *Armstrongs of Elswick*, p.190.
12. Elswick Shipyard Report Book No.2. Vickers File 1158. Cambridge University Library.
13. *Engineering* 26 July 1901.
14. Shipbuilding Employers Federation: Number of Workpeople Employed. 1906-22. File 4090(i). Marine Technology Special Collection, Newcastle University.
15. Notes for Royal Commission. Vickers Document 58. Cambridge University Library.
16. Armament Orders. Vickers File 551. Cambridge University Library.
17. Shipbuilding Employers Federation. Op cit.
18. Peebles, *Warship Building on the Clyde*, p.90.
19. J F Clarke, *Power on Land and Sea* (Hawthorn Leslie, 1979), p.75.
20. L C Money, 'The Triumph of Nationalisation', Shipbuilding Employers Federation op cit.
21. D Dougan, *The Shipwrights* (Newcastle: Frank Graham, 1975), p.335. There is a large amount of detail on standard rates across the UK in 'Standard Time Rate of Wages 1906', Cd.3245.
22. National Archives CAB102/526. Average 1101 men in 1939, paid £4101 per week.
23. Vickers-Armstrongs Works Reports. Vickers Files 175-207. Cambridge University Library.
24. Naval Yard report for the second quarter of 1941 noted that there were 152 workers from Barrow on machinery installation, but included in the latter works' figures. Overtime was regularly worked on Tuesdays, Thursdays and Saturdays but rarely on Sundays. Important visitors included A V Alexander (First Lord), S V Goodall (DNC) and C Hannaford (Director of Contract Work).
25. 'Statistical Digest of the War', HMSO, 1951. Table 21.
26. 'Naval New Construction Programmes 1935-45', Naval Historical Branch, MoD.
27. A L Ayre, 'Merchant Shipbuilding during the War', *Trans Inst of Naval Architects*, Vol 87 (1945), p.19.
28. This figure looks low, as Mr C Bentham when reviewing shipyards and engine works equipment in September 1942 reported 6000–7000 men at Wallsend yard and 1700 at Neptune yard. Report of Machine Tool Controller on the Equipment of Shipyards and Marine Engine Shops. National

Archives BT28/319.
29. National Archives CAB102/276.
30. National Archives CAB102/441.
31. Ian Buxton, *Warship Building and Repair during the Second World War* (Glasgow: Glasgow University Centre for Business History, 1997) (derived from CAB102/539).
32. Dougan, *The Shipwrights*, p.141.
33. Sheet metal workers had their own trade union.
34. J E Mortimer, *History of the Boilermakers' Society Vol. 2: 1906-1939* (London: Allen & Unwin, 1982), p.6.
35. Philip Macdougall (ed), *Chatham Dockyard 1815-1865: The Industrial Transformation* (Aldershot: Ashgate Publishing for the Navy Records Society, 2009).
36. Dougan, *The Shipwrights*, p.74.
37. Dougan, *The Shipwrights*, p.336.

Chapter 13

1. For more information on these designs see *Warship*, Numbers 19 and 20 published by Conway Maritime Press in 1981, for the two-part article 'Penultimate Battleships' by John Roberts.
2. Including the *Lions* but excluding the G3s cancelled shortly after being ordered.

Appendix 1

1. Based on the tender books of John Brown & Co Ltd. (Glasgow University Business Archives)
   UCS1/74/5 August 1905 to February 1909.
   UCS1/74/6 March 1909 to April 1913.
   UCS1/74/7 May 1913 to December 1920.
   UCS1/74/8 December 1920 to October 1923.
   UCS1/74/10 Jan 1925 to April 1927.
   UCS1/74/11 May 1927 to December 1938.

Appendix 2

1. Report from the Select Committee on Estimates. House of Commons Paper 231. 24 July 1913.
2. Hume and Moss, *Beardmore*, p.84.
3. S E Vinogradov, 'Naval Ordnance and Armor Manufacturing', *Warship International*, Vol 37 No 3 (2000).
4. Based on B F Cooling's *Gray Steel and Blue Water Navy* (Hamden USA: Archon Books, 1979).
5. Vickers Sons & Maxim Sheffield annual reports on Costs, Prices and Profits 1907-11. Sheffield Archives 1988/50 series.
6. Armour Plate for Battleships 1910-1915. ADM116/3456.

Appendix 3

1. Ian Buxton, *Metal Industries: Shipbreaking at Rosyth and Charlestown* (Kendal: World Ship Society, 1992).
2. Ibid, p.28.

Sources and Bibliography

The authors have consulted an extensive number of sources, the key ones noted below. Other sources and references are cited in the endnotes, e.g. articles in journals, while others are from the authors' personal notes and photocopies made over many decades, some from sources no longer existing.

ARCHIVES, LIBRARIES AND COMPANIES

The National Maritime Museum, especially the Admiralty collection of Ships' Covers (Director of Naval Construction's design files), ship and ordnance plans.

The National Archives, mostly Admiralty files (ADM series) on specific subjects such as armament and armour.

The Naval Library, Portsmouth, for Admiralty material on subjects such as armour, construction programmes, ship movements and disposals.

Glasgow University Business Archives, especially company records from John Brown, Beardmore and Scotts.

Tyne & Wear Archives, especially company records from Armstrong, Vickers-Armstrongs, Swan Hunter, Hawthorn Leslie and Wallsend Slipway.

Cambridge University Library, Manuscripts Department, with its extensive collection of Vickers, Armstrong and Vickers-Armstrongs material.

Wirral Archives for Cammell Laird records.

Sheffield Archives for Vickers records.

The Mitchell Library for Fairfield records.

Newcastle Central Library for Tyneside industries.

The McLean Museum and Art Gallery, Greenock.

BAE Systems, Glasgow.

COMPANY HISTORIES AND PUBLICITY MATERIAL

Allen
Lane, M R, *The Story of Queen's Engineering Works, Bedford* (London: Unicorn Press, 1995).

Armstrong
Warren, K, *Armstrongs of Elswick* (Basingstoke: Macmillan, 1989).

Babcock & Wilcox
Babcock & Wilcox, *Water-tube Marine Boilers* (1914).

Barr & Stroud
Moss, M, and Russell, I, *Range & Vision: The First 100 years of Barr & Stroud* (Edinburgh: Mainstream Publishing, 1988).

Beardmore
Hume, J R, and Moss, M S, *Beardmore: The History of a Scottish Industrial Giant* (Aldershot: Heinemann, 1979).

Johnston, Ian, *Beardmore Built: The Rise and Fall of a Clydeside Shipyard* (Clydebank Museums and Libraries, 1993).

'The Works of William Beardmore and Co Ltd', *Engineering* (1910).

Cammell Laird
Warren, K, *Steel, Ships and Men* (Liverpool: Liverpool University Press, 1998).

Coventry Ordnance Works
The Coventry Syndicate: Builders of Battleships etc (Published by the company, c1912).

Fairfield
'The Fairfield Shipbuilding and Engineering Works', *Engineering* (1909) (a full modern history has yet to be written).

Firth-Brown
Thomas Firth & John Brown Ltd, *100 Years in Steel* (1937).

Harland & Wolff
Moss, M, and Hume, J R, *Shipbuilders to the World: 125 Years of Harland & Wolff 1861-1986* (Belfast: Blackstaff Press, 1986).

Hawthorn Leslie
Clarke, J F, *Power on Land & Sea. A History of Hawthorn Leslie* (Published by the company, 1979).

John Brown
Grant, A, *Steel and Ships* (London: M Joseph, 1950).

Johnston, Ian, *Ships for a Nation* (Clydebank: West Dumbartonshire Libraries & Museums, 2000).

'John Brown and Company Limited', *Engineering* (1903).

Palmers
Dillon, M, *Some Account of the Works of Palmer's Shipbuilding & Iron Company Limited* (Newcastle: published by the company, 1904) (a full modern history has yet to be written).

Scotts
'Two Centuries of Shipbuilding by the Scotts at Greenock', *Engineering* (1920).

Swan Hunter
A full modern history has yet to be written.

Vickers
Scott, J D, *Vickers: A History* (London: Weidenfeld & Nicolson, 1963).

Trebilcock, C, *The Vickers Brothers* (London: Europa Publications, 1977).

'Vickers, Sons & Maxim', *Engineering* (1902).

Weir

Reader, W J, *The Weir Group* (London: Weidenfeld & Nicholson, 1971).

OTHER SIGNIFICANT BOOKS AND ARTICLES

Arnold, A J, *Iron Shipbuilding on the Thames 1832-1915* (Aldershot: Ashgate, 2000).

Bastable, M J, *Arms and the State: Sir William Armstrong and the Remaking of British Naval Power 1854-1914* (Aldershot: Ashgate, 2004).

Brooks, J, *Dreadnought Gunnery and the Battle of Jutland* (London: Routledge, 2005).

Brown, D K, *A Century of Naval Construction: A History of the Royal Corps of Naval Constructors* (London: Conway Maritime Press, 1983).

_____, *Warrior to Dreadnought: Warship Development 1860-1906* (London: Chatham Publishing, 1997).

_____, *The Grand Fleet: Warship Design and Development 1906-1922* (London: Chatham Publishing, 1999).

_____, *Nelson to Vanguard: Warship Design and Development 1923-1945* (London: Chatham Publishing, 2000).

Burt, R A, *British Battleships of World War One* (London: Arms and Armour Press, 1986).

_____, *British Battleships 1889-1904* (London: Arms and Armour Press, 1988).

_____, *British Battleships 1919-1939* (London: Arms and Armour Press, 1993).

Buxton, Ian, *Metal Industries: Shipbreaking at Rosyth and Charlestown* (Kendal: World Ship Society, 1992).

_____, *Warship Building and Repair during the Second World War* (Glasgow University Centre for Business History in Scotland, 1997).

_____, *Big Gun Monitors* (Barnsley: Seaforth Publishing, 2008).

Campbell, John, *Naval Weapons of World War Two* (London: Conway Maritime Press, 1985).

Dawson, A T, *The Engineering of Ordnance* (Junior Institution of Engineers, 1909).

Evans, D, *Arming the Fleet: The Development of the Royal Ordnance Yards 1770-1945* (Gosport: English Heritage, 2006).

Friedman, Norman, *Naval Firepower: Battleship Guns and Gunnery in the Dreadnought Era* (Barnsley: Seaforth Publishing, 2008).

_____, *Naval Weapons of World War One* (Barnsley: Seaforth Publishing, 2011).

Gordon, G A H, *British Seapower and Procurement between the Wars* (Basingstoke: Macmillan, 1988).

Gray, E, *The Devil's Device: The Story of the Invention of the Torpedo* (London: Seeley, Service, 1975).

Johnston, Ian, *Clydebank Battlecruisers* (Barnsley: Seaforth Publishing, 2011).

McDermaid, N J, *Shipyard Practice as applied to Warship Construction* (London: Longmans Green, 1911).

Moore, G, *Building for Victory: The Warship Building Programme of the Royal Navy 1939-1945* (Gravesend: World Ship Society, 2003).

Newman, B, *Plate and Section Working Machinery in British Shipbuilding 1850-1945* (Glasgow University Centre for Business History in Scotland, 1993).

_____, *Materials Handling in British Shipbuilding 1850-1945* (Glasgow University Centre for Business History in Scotland, 1996).

Peebles, H B, *Warship Building on the Clyde* (Edinburgh: John Donald Publishing, 1987).

Ranft, B (ed), *Technical Change and British Naval Policy 1860-1939* (London: Hodder & Stoughton, 1977).

Raven, A, and Roberts, J, *British Battleships of World War Two* (London: Arms & Armour Press, 1976).

Roberts, John, *Anatomy of the Ship: The Battleship Dreadnought* (London: Conway Maritime Press, 1992).

Roberts, John, *Battlecruisers* (London: Chatham Publishing, 1997).

Sturton, Ian, 'Cancelled Sisters: The Modified *Hood* Class', *Warship 2010* (London: Conway Maritime Press, 2010).

Sumida, J T, *In Defence of Naval Supremacy* (London: Unwin Hyman, 1989; London: Routledge, 1993).

ANNUALS AND PERIODICALS

Brassey's Naval Annual.
Warship. Quarterly 1977 to 1989, thereafter annually.
Warship International. Quarterly from 1970.
Warships. Quarterly from 1966. World Ship Society.
The Engineer (weekly, especially in years to 1914).
Engineering (weekly, especially in years to 1914).

REGULAR PARLIAMENTARY PAPERS

Navy Estimates. Annual.
Navy Appropriation Account. Annual.
Navy: Dockyard Expense Accounts. Annual.
Report from the Select Committee on Estimates. Parliamentary Paper 231. 24 July 1913.
Plus individual papers as referenced in endnotes.

Index

THE BATTLESHIP BUILDERS. The companies from after First World War to 2010. The complex histories of these

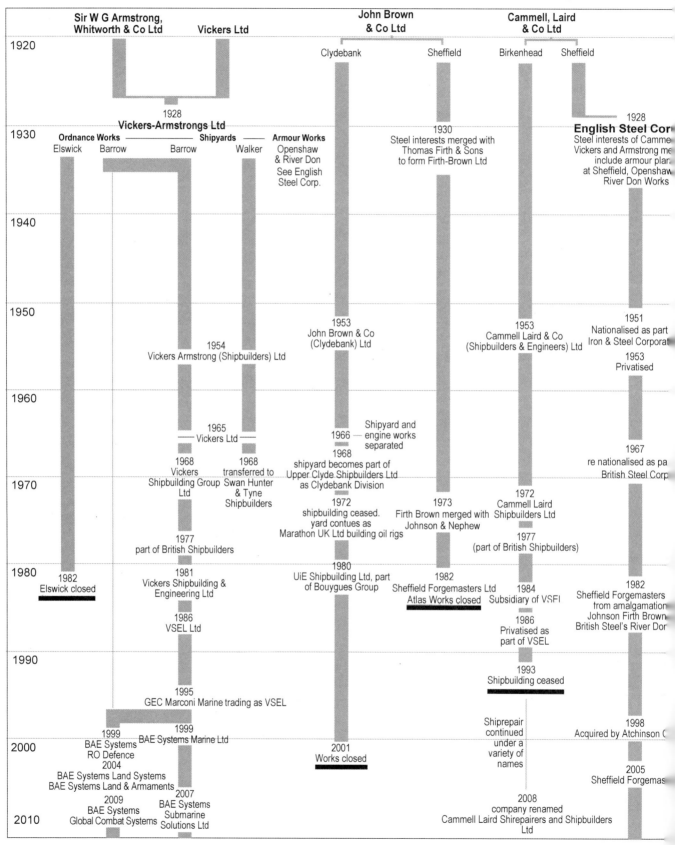

1920	Sir W G Armstrong, Whitworth & Co Ltd	Vickers Ltd		John Brown & Co Ltd		Cammell, Laird & Co Ltd	
				Clydebank	Sheffield	Birkenhead	Sheffield
	1928 Vickers-Armstrongs Ltd						1928 **English Steel Corp**
1930	Ordnance Works — Shipyards — Armour Works			1930 Steel interests merged with Thomas Firth & Sons to form Firth-Brown Ltd			Steel interests of Cammell Vickers and Armstrong me include armour plate at Sheffield, Openshaw River Don Works
	Elswick Barrow Barrow Walker Openshaw & River Don See English Steel Corp.						
1940							
1950		1954 Vickers Armstrong (Shipbuilders) Ltd		1953 John Brown & Co (Clydebank) Ltd		1953 Cammell Laird & Co (Shipbuilders & Engineers) Ltd	1951 Nationalised as part Iron & Steel Corporat 1953 Privatised
1960		1965 — Vickers Ltd —		1966 Shipyard and engine works separated			1967 re nationalised as pa British Steel Corp
1970		1968 Vickers Shipbuilding Group Ltd	1968 transferred to Swan Hunter & Tyne Shipbuilders	1968 shipyard becomes part of Upper Clyde Shipbuilders Ltd as Clydebank Division 1972 shipbuilding ceased. yard contues as Marathon UK Ltd building oil rigs	1973 Firth Brown merged with Johnson & Nephew	1972 Cammell Laird Shipbuilders Ltd	
		1977 part of British Shipbuilders				1977 (part of British Shipbuilders)	
1980	1982 Elswick closed	1981 Vickers Shipbuilding & Engineering Ltd		1980 UiE Shipbuilding Ltd, part of Bouygues Group	1982 Sheffield Forgemasters Ltd Atlas Works closed	1984 Subsidiary of VSEL	1982 Sheffield Forgemasters from amalgamation Johnson Firth Brown British Steel's River Dor
		1986 VSEL Ltd				1986 Privatised as part of VSEL	
1990						1993 Shipbuilding ceased	
		1995 GEC Marconi Marine trading as VSEL					
		1999 BAE Systems Marine Ltd			Shiprepair continued under a variety of names		1998 Acquired by Atchison C
2000	1999 BAE Systems RO Defence 2004 BAE Systems Land Systems BAE Systems Land & Armaments			2001 Works closed			
							2005 Sheffield Forgemas
2010	2009 BAE Systems Global Combat Systems	2007 BAE Systems Submarine Solutions Ltd				2008 company renamed Cammell Laird Shirepairers and Shipbuilders Ltd	